TP
248
E7.2
R3

HIGH POLYMERS

Other volumes in preparation

HIGH POLYMERS

A SERIES OF MONOGRAPHS ON THE CHEMISTRY, PHYSICS AND TECHNOLOGY OF HIGH POLYMERIC SUBSTANCES

VOLUME XI

POLYETHYLENE

R. A. V. RAFF and J. B. ALLISON

Koppers Company, Inc.,
Pittsburgh, Pennsylvania

INTERSCIENCE PUBLISHERS, INC., NEW YORK
INTERSCIENCE PUBLISHERS LTD., LONDON

LIBRARY OF CONGRESS CATALOG CARD NUMBER 56–8227

© 1956 by

INTERSCIENCE PUBLISHERS, INC.

INTERSCIENCE PUBLISHERS, INC.
250 Fifth Avenue, New York 1, N. Y.

For Great Britain and Northern Ireland:
INTERSCIENCE PUBLISHERS LTD.
88/90 Chancery Lane, London, W. C. 2

PRINTED IN THE UNITED STATES OF AMERICA BY
MACK PRINTING COMPANY, EASTON, PENNSYLVANIA

PREFACE

Over twenty years ago, one of the authors of this volume was a member of the Austrian State Patent Office. He still recalls his scientific surprise when he received for examination a patent application to Imperial Chemical Industries, Ltd., claiming that solid polymers of ethylene could be obtained by the catalytic polymerization of ethylene at high temperatures and pressures. A sample of a waxlike, colorless, semiopaque solid was subsequently submitted to illustrate and substantiate this invention. Later, it became known that polyethylene had first been obtained unintentionally when two of the inventors, Fawcett and Gibson, attempted to react ethylene with benzaldehyde at 2,000 atmospheres pressure. While repetition of the experiment resulted in an explosion, the importance of the discovery nevertheless had been recognized. Better experimental methods were developed which allowed the preparation of eight grams of the new polymer in a single experiment by the end of the year 1935. Since then, polyethylene has become one of the most important of all plastic materials.

A great discovery and invention it was, since until then, only ethylenes containing an activating atom or group in the molecule, such as styrene or vinyl chloride, had been considered capable of undergoing polymerization to solid products. Attempts to polymerize ethylene itself had, to that time, yielded only gases or low molecular weight liquids which, from their formation and structure, could not, for the most part, be considered simple polymers of ethylene.

This volume attempts to summarize the present state of the knowledge of those polymers of ethylene which, depending upon their molecular weight, range from viscous liquids, through semisolids, to tough, flexible solids suitable for use as plastics.

A book of this kind should explain facts with theories; should integrate structural observations, manufacturing conditions, properties, and suitable fields of application; and convey a deeper insight into proven or assumed relationships. This, as the authors were aware from the start, is possible in isolated instances only, since the theoretical treatment of this intricate subject is but in its beginnings. Moreover, in view of the highly competitive situation, an adequate treatment of more recent developments, that is, the new low-temperature, low-pressure processes which are beginning to operate in this and other countries, can hardly be expected.

v

For these and similar reasons, the advisability of postponing the writing of this book for one or two years was seriously discussed; but consideration of the broad scope of the subject and the large amount of important information available for critical examination decided the issue. It is a fact that the vast and expanding literature of the polyethylenes has not, to the authors' knowledge, been presented elsewhere in an organized form. This is submitted to the prospective reader as further justification for the existence of this book, with the sincere hope that it may prove an aid to those working in this field. At the same time, the authors' attempts to include the most recent developments in this extremely active field have inevitably resulted in inconsistencies in text and bibliography. It is hoped that these are minor in nature and will be condoned by the reader.

It is particularly pleasant to express to the managements of the Chemical Division and of the Research Department of the Koppers Company, Inc., the authors' very real appreciation for permission to publish this book, and for wholehearted support.

The kind permission to quote from an unpublished paper by Dr. H. Staudinger and Dr. F. Berndt is thankfully acknowledged. For review of the manuscript and valuable advice, the authors wish to express their gratitude to Dr. H. Mark; also to Drs. C. Cousin and H. Sack, Laboratoire de Recherches des Houillères du Bassin du Nord et du Pas de Calais, Bruay-en-Artois, France. The staff members of the Polyethylene Branch of the Research Department of the Koppers Company, Inc., Mr. J. J. Killoran, Mr. R. F. Kratz, Mrs. E. L. Lyle, and Dr. H. E. Tiefenthal, are cordially thanked for valuable discussions and comments, criticisms of the drafts, and proofreading the manuscript and galleys; and Mrs. J. B. Allison for painstaking assistance in typing and proofreading the manuscript.

Thanks are also extended to the publishers for their understanding help, and their patient and competent guidance of the production of the volume.

R. A. V. RAFF

J. B. ALLISON

Pittsburgh, Pennsylvania
June, 1956

CONTENTS

I. HISTORICAL DEVELOPMENT

1.1. Catalyzed Decomposition of Diazohydrocarbons

As early as 1898, von Pechmann (6) observed that small amounts of a white, flocculent substance which could be crystallized from chloroform separated from an ethereal solution of diazomethane on standing. While the presence of platinum or sodium somewhat catalyzed the formation of this solid, the amount of the product recovered was insufficient to permit further study. Two years later, Bamberger and Tschirner (7) collected a larger quantity of this very voluminous material, dissolved it in isopropylbenzene, and precipitated it by the addition of petroleum ether. The dried powder, somewhat soluble in boiling isopropylbenzene or boiling pyridine, melted at 128°C., corresponded by analysis to the formula $(CH_2)_n$, and was termed "polymethylene." Its formation had apparently taken place by the reaction $n(CH_2N_2) \rightarrow (CH_2)_n + n(N_2)$.

Much later, Buckley, Cross, and Ray (464) studied the copper-catalyzed decomposition of a series of aliphatic diazo compounds in ether solution. Straight-chain, high molecular weight, highly crystalline polymethylene was obtained from diazomethane. Polyethylidene and polypropylidene—hard, amorphous, brittle glasses, similar to polystyrene—were obtained from diazoethane and 1-diazopropane. The three compounds were given the structures:

$$-CH_2-CH_2-CH_2-, \quad \underset{\underset{CH_3}{|}}{-}CH\underset{\underset{CH_3}{|}}{-}CH\underset{\underset{CH_3}{|}}{-}CH-, \quad \text{and} \quad \underset{\underset{C_2H_5}{|}}{-}CH\underset{\underset{C_2H_5}{|}}{-}CH\underset{\underset{C_2H_5}{|}}{-}CH-$$

Products ranging from crystalline waxes to amorphous glasses were prepared by the decomposition of mixtures of diazomethane and increasing amounts of diazoethane.

The infrared absorption spectra of these polymers and copolymers are shown in Figure 1.

The molecular weights of these hydrocarbons were determined, where possible, by the cryoscopic method, benzene being used as the solvent. This was, however, unsatisfactory for molecular weights above 3,000; in such cases, the intrinsic viscosity was measured in diisobutene at 20°C. The relationship given by Oakes and Richards (411), $[\eta] = 1.08 \times \overline{M}_n^{0.7} \times$

1

10^{-3}, which may be used for polyethylene and polymethylene, was not considered applicable to polyethylidene and polypropylidene. Instead, the equation proposed by Flory (143), $[\eta] = 3.60 \times \overline{M}_n^{0.64} \times 10^{-4}$, which holds for polyisobutene, was used as the best available approximation. The combination of these two methods indicated that the polymers ranged

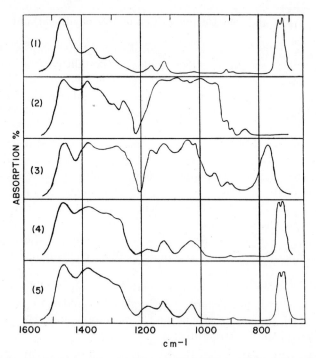

Fig. 1. Infrared absorption spectra of several diazo polymers: (*1*) polymethylene from diazomethane, (*2*) polyethylidene from diazoethane, (*3*) polypropylidene from diazo-propane, (*4*) ether-insoluble interpolymer No. 1 containing 3.0 moles % of diazoethane, and (*5*) ether-insoluble interpolymer No. 2 containing 6.7 moles % of diazoethane. (*J. Chem. Soc.*, **1950**, 2715.)

in molecular weight from 200 to 14,000. Studies by Leitch, Gagnon, and Cambron (478) followed along similar lines by introducing a deuterated polymer $(CD_2)_n$, obtained by the decomposition of diazomethane-d_2 These investigations, demonstrating the influence of chain-branching on crystallinity and of crystallinity on physical properties, were carried out for the purpose of clarifying the structure of polyethylenes made by other more involved processes. Actually, products similar to polyethylene obtained by the conventional catalyzed, high-pressure, high-temperature process, with their moderate degree of crystallinity and lower melting point, could be closely duplicated by the decomposition of mixtures of diazomethane and small quantities of diazoheptane and diazooctane. The significance of these results will be discussed in Sections 4.3 and 5.1.

A polymethylene of molecular weight greater than three million was prepared by Kantor and Osthoff (740) by treating diazomethane in diethyl ether with the diethyl ether-boron trifluoride complex at 0°C. The molecular weight of the resultant polymer was determined from the intrinsic viscosity obtained in xylene solution at 132°C. From the intrinsic viscosity and the Staudinger constants reported by Harris (606), a molecular weight of 3.3×10^6 was calculated. This method of preparation of polymethylene with a molecular weight of at least 500,000 has been recently patented in Germany (1095).

The polymer had a crystal melting point of 132°C., which is close to the convergence temperature of 137°C. for straight-chain paraffins derived by Mark (118) from thermodynamic data. An x-ray examination indicated a very high degree of crystallinity. The polymer had a tensile strength of 4,900 p.s.i. and an elongation at break of 500%. These values, being higher than those common for commercial polyethylenes prepared by high-pressure, high-temperature polymerization methods (compare Chapter VI), are indicative of the greater molecular weight and lower degree of branching of polymers prepared by this method. Dielectric constant, power factor, and breakdown voltage were comparable to those of the commercial high-pressure, high-temperature polyethylenes. Since the catalyst and solvent used in the polymerization are promoters of ionic reactions, Kantor and Osthoff believe that the polymerization takes place through an ionic rather than a radical mechanism.

A further study of the homogeneous decomposition of diazomethane to form high molecular weight polymethylene has been reported by Bawn and Rhodes (824). The reactions were carried out in toluene solution, and copper wire, copper stearate, and boron trifluoride were evaluated as catalysts. The rate of polymer formation, followed by titration and by measurement of the nitrogen evolved, was found to equal $K \cdot [Cat] \cdot [CH_2N_2]$, and an ionic reaction mechanism was proposed.

Molecular weights of the soluble polymers were determined by measurement of the intrinsic viscosity of a xylene solution at 95°C. and by substitution in the equation deduced by Harris (606), where $[\eta] = 1.35 \times 10^{-4} \times \bar{M}_n^{0.63}$. The average molecular weights obtained with copper wire, copper stearate, or boron trifluoride etherate as the catalyst were 17,000,

2,200, and 14,000, respectively. In most cases, linear, not crosslinked polymers resulted. Crosslinking appeared to have taken place when very low concentrations of $BF_3 \cdot O(C_2H_5)_2$ or $BF_3 \cdot CH_3COOH$ were used.

The melting points of most polymethylenes lie in the range of 127 to 135°C.; the higher melting points lie close to the limiting temperature of the paraffin series. The infrared spectra of the polymers were similar to those reported by Buckley, Cross, and Ray (464).

The kinetics of the decomposition reaction in ether solution of diazomethane, diazoethane, diazobutane, and of their mixtures, catalyzed by cupric stearate or boron trifluoride, were studied by Feltzin, Restaino, and Mesrobian (955), and some physical properties of the resultant polymers were determined. The results of experiments are summarized in Table I.

A polymerization mechanism involving propagation via a carbonium or diazonium ion, and termination by interaction of growing chains with diazohydrocarbons, is presented.

1.2. Action of Sodium on Decamethylene Bromide

An alternate route to essentially straight-chain, high molecular weight paraffins was explored by Carothers (20). By reacting decamethylene bromide with sodium, followed by distillation in the molecular still and by fractional crystallization, the following hydrocarbons (with corresponding melting points) were isolated from the reaction mixtures: $C_{20}H_{42}$ (35–35.6°C.); $C_{30}H_{62}$ (65–66°C.); $C_{40}H_{82}$ (80.5–81°C.); $C_{50}H_{102}$ (91.9–92.3°C.); $C_{60}H_{122}$ (98.5–99.3°C.); and $C_{70}H_{142}$ (105–105.5°C.). Carothers did not, however, succeed in producing appreciable quantities of hydrocarbons with more than 100 carbon atoms.

1.3. Fischer-Tropsch and Related Syntheses

The Fischer-Tropsch reduction of carbon monoxide with hydrogen is generally designed to yield low molecular weight products (567). However, by proper choice of the reaction conditions, essentially linear, highly crystalline solid paraffins can be obtained. Thus, Koch and Ibing (38) identified paraffins having a melting point of 117°C. and a molecular weight of 2,000 among the reaction products of the benzine synthesis. By the use of a ruthenium catalyst, paraffins melting from 117–132°C. and having average molecular weights of 7,000–9,000 were obtained by Pichler and Buffleb (100). The preparation of high molecular weight polyethylene (m.p. 133°C.) by the use of a metal tungstite catalyst is described by Arnold and Herrick in U.S. 2,726,218 [dupont (1105a)].

TABLE I.   Decomposition of Diazohydrocarbons in Ether

Reaction temp. °C	Catalyst	$RCHN_2$, moles/l.	Catalyst concn., moles/l.	Conversion,[a] %	Appearance of polymer	$[\eta]$ 20°C, toluene, dcl./g.	$\overline{M}_w$
			Runs with diazobutane				
8	Cupric stearate	0.5	3.17×10^{-6}	92	Glass	0.10	
8	Cupric stearate	0.5	25.4×10^{-6}	91	Glass	0.05	
8	BF_3	0.5	7.0×10^{-4}	28[b]	...	...	
8	$B(OCH_3)_3$	0.5	5.0×10^{-4}	16[b]	...	...	
			Runs with diazoethane				
8.5	$CuSO_4$	0.61	Insol.[c]	59	Glass	...	
8.5	Cupric stearate	0.61	6.2×10^{-6}	95	Glass	0.12	
8.5	$B(n\text{-}OC_4H_9)_3$	0.61	2.0×10^{-4}	23[b]	...	...	
8.5	BF_3	0.61	5.0×10^{-4}	25[b]	...	...	
			Runs with diazomethane				
0	BF_3	0.55	5.0×10^{-4}	100	Wax	16.2[d]	
0	Cupric stearate	0.55	12.8×10^{-6}	9[b]	...	...	
0	$B(OCH_3)_3$	0.55	2.0×10^{-4}	15[b]	...	...	
			Runs with diazomethane-diazoethane mixtures[e]				
0	$B(OCH_3)_3$	0.51(5/1)	2.0×10^{-4}	80	Rubber	7.3	
0	BF_3	0.41(8/1)	0.5×10^{-3}	94	Rubber	8.7	
0	BF_3	0.49(5/1)	0.8×10^{-3}	90	Rubber	7.2	
0	BF_3	0.22(4/1)	0.5×10^{-3}	91	Rubber	6.19	2.0×10^6
0	BF_3	0.56(4/1)	5.0×10^{-3}	98	Rubber	6.3	2.07×10^6
0	BF_3	0.55(1/1)	0.5×10^{-3}	40	Rubber	2.2	
0	Cupric stearate	0.53(4/1)	12.8×10^{-6}	8	...	...	

Source: *J. Am. Chem. Soc.*, **47**, 1517 (1955).
[a] Conversions are based upon amount of methanol-insoluble polymer obtained after total decomposition of diazohydrocarbon.
[b] Reaction exhibited a pronounced decrease in rate between 10 and 25% decomposition and proceeded at nearly the uncatalyzed rate for the remainder of reaction.   Successive additions of catalyst produced only temporary acceleration of decomposition rate.
[c] 0.3 g. of $CuSO_4$ suspended with stirring in 30 ml. of solution.
[d] Determined in xylene at 120°C.
[e] The numbers in parentheses under column 2 refer to the mole ratio of diazomethane to diazoethane.

1.4. Reduction of Polyvinyl Chloride

Hahn and Müller (963) believed that the structure of polyvinyl chloride could be studied more easily if these polymers were transformed into polyethylenes by reductive removal of the chlorine. Total reduction was achieved by the use of a surplus of lithium aluminum hydride under pressure at 100°C. or above, with a mixture of tetrahydrofuran and decalin as the solvent. The reduction products corresponded to the formula $(CH_2)_n$ and showed the same properties as polyethylene. Polyvinyl bromide was found to be easier to reduce than polyvinyl chloride, but the reduction of chlorinated or brominated polyethylenes gave completely insoluble, cross-linked products, as noted previously by Staudinger (633a).

1.5. High-Pressure, High-Temperature Polymerization Methods

Early studies of the direct polymerization of ethylene resulted mainly in its conversion into various gases, liquids, and mixtures of these by exceedingly complex reactions. In most cases, the polymerization was found to be accompanied by decomposition which became more pronounced as the reaction temperature was increased.

Direct polymerization of ethylene to polythene[1] was achieved in the course of a systematic study on the high-pressure chemistry of organic compounds undertaken by Imperial Chemical Industries, Ltd. This work was made possible by the development, by Dr. A. Michels of the University of Amsterdam, of a pump capable of giving a pressure of 3,000 atmospheres. During the course of this research, carried out in March, 1933, polyethylene was discovered as a trace of white powder in a reaction vessel. The results of these investigations were first reported by Fawcett and Gibson (29) in 1934; the basic patent relating to the production of polyethylene, Brit. 471,590 (60), was issued in the names of the original research team (Fawcett, Gibson, Perrin, Paton, Williams, and I.C.I.) in September, 1937. For its historical and technological interest, a facsimile of this pioneer patent is shown in Figure 2.

From the outset, the development of a commercial process for the production of polyethylene involved numerous technical difficulties. The polymerization reaction was found to be excessively exothermic and required strict control and elaborate safety measures in order to prevent explosive decomposition of the ethylene. As a result, polyethylene was not produced on a scale sufficiently large for technical evaluation until Decem-

---

[1] A generic name applied only to those polyethylenes which are suitable for use as plastics (225).

PATENT SPECIFICATION

Application Date : Feb. 4, 1936.   *No. 3372 / 36.*   **471,590**

,,   ,,   *March 16, 1936.   No. 7899 / 36.*

,,   ,,   *Aug. 21, 1936. No. 23093 / 36.*

One Complete Specification Left : Feb. 4, 1937.

(Under Section 16 of the Patents and Designs Acts, 1907 to 1932.)

Specification Accepted : Sept. 6, 1937.

PROVISIONAL SPECIFICATION

No. 3372 A.D. 1936

Improvements in or relating to the Polymerisation of Ethylene.

We, ERIC WILLIAM FAWCETT, REGINALD OSWALD GIBSON, MICHAEL WILLCOX PERRIN, JOHN GREVES PATON and EDMOND GEORGE WILLIAMS, all British Subjects, all of Winnington Hall, Northwich, in the County of Chester, and IMPERIAL CHEMICAL INDUSTRIES LIMITED, a British Company, of Imperial Chemical House, Millbank, London, S.W.1, do hereby declare the nature of this invention to be as follows :—

This invention relates to the polymerisation of ethylene, with the object of producing new and useful products therefrom by effecting the polymerisation under the operating conditions hereinafter described.

It is already known that ethylene and its homologues can be polymerised to yield a mixture of liquid organic compounds by the use of elevated temperatures, e.g. 200–400° C., and of moderate superatmospheric pressures, say up to 200 atmospheres, with or without the aid of catalysts. The liquid products range in character from relatively light oils up to fairly viscous oils of the lubricating oil type.

We have now found that ethylene may be polymerised to give solid products of a rubber- or resin-like character by the use of a very high pressure, i.e. a pressure of at least 1000 atmospheres, and by the use of reaction conditions such that the heat of the reaction is removed as quickly as possible. The products obtained under these conditions appear to be true polymers, i.e. they correspond to the formula $(CH_2)_n$, and they are of high molecular weight, e.g. those obtained at 2000 atmospheres have a molecular weight of the order of 3500. The temperature requirements of the reaction, in particular the initial temperature required for polymerisation to occur, have not yet been fully investigated, but it would appear that a moderate elevated temperature, of the order of 100–200° C.

should be employed.

It is necessary to provide for the efficient removal of the heat of reaction, otherwise it is impossible to control the reaction, which is then liable to give rise to an explosion of some violence, the end products being carbon and hydrogen. Suitable measures to achieve rapid removal of heat are the use of diluents for the ethylene (e.g. the use of industrial gases containing ethylene such as cracking still gases), and or the use of a reaction vessel constructed of or lined with a metal or alloy of high thermal conductivity. An internal heating element of small heat capacity, disposed within a cold-walled reaction vessel, is a convenient means of initiating the reaction.

In general, increasing the pressure at which the polymerisation is effected will increase the ultimate yield of the polymer. Alternatively increasing the pressure will permit of the same yield of polymer being obtained in a shorter time.

EXAMPLE.

Ethylene is compressed under a pressure of 2000 atmospheres in a steel bomb. The vessel is maintained in a constant temperature bath for 4 hours at a temperature of 170° C. According to whether the pressure is released before or after cooling to room temperature, the product is respectively a "coalesced" rubber-like white solid or a white powder. The product softens at about 120° C. At 170° it goes over to the form of a substantially clear resin-like or rubber-like material which has plastic properties and can be moulded into various forms at or above the softening temperature. It is fairly soluble in hot benzene and sparingly soluble in cold benzene, hence thin transparent coatings may be deposited on objects from benzene solution, followed by warming until the deposit coalesces. The product has a molecular weight of around 3500 and in composition corre-

Fig. 2. Pioneer British patent 471,590.   (*Continued on following page.*)

sponds to a true ethylene polymer, $(C_2H_4)_n$.

Dated the 4th day of February, 1936.
E. A. BINGEN,
Solicitor for the Applicants.

PROVISIONAL SPECIFICATION.
No. 7899 A.D. 1936.

Improvements in or relating to the Polymerisation of Ethylene.

We, ERIC WILLIAM FAWCETT, REGINALD OSWALD GIBSON, MICHAEL WILLCOX PERRIN, JOHN GREVES PATON and EDMOND GEORGE WILLIAMS, all British Subjects, and all of Winnington Hall, Northwich, in the County of Chester, and IMPERIAL CHEMICAL INDUSTRIES LIMITED, a British Company, of Imperial Chemical House, Millbank, London, S.W.I, do hereby declare the nature of this invention to be as follows :—

In co-pending Application No. 3372/36 we have described a process for the manufacture of solid polymerised products from ethylene, by subjecting the latter to the action of a very high pressure under conditions such that the heat of the reaction is removed as quickly as possible.

We have now found that the properties of the resultant polymer may be controlled, and products of different molecular weights may be obtained, by varying the reaction conditions and in particular the pressure employed.

The following table shows how the molecular weight of the solid product varies with the pressure employed, for the case of the polymerisation of ethylene at 190° C.

Pressure (atmospheres)	Molecular Weight of Polymer
500	2500
750	3750
1500	5500
1950	6800
3000	10750

(N.B. the above molecular weights should be regarded as approximate ; they were all obtained by the same method, i.e., one based on the measurement of the viscosity of a dilute solution of the polymer in tetrahydronaphthalene. The apparently discrepant value of 3500 given in Application No. 3372/36 for the product obtained at 2000 atmospheres was obtained by a different method, based on boiling-point elevation of a solution of the polymer. It will be noted that in the set of molecular weight values given above, there is a roughly linear relationship between the pressure used and the molecular weight of the product.)

The products made under different pressure conditions not only have different molecular weights, but certain other of their properties are also modified. Thus the products of high molecular weight are harder than those of low molecular weight, soften at a higher temperature and, when converted into a fibre or thread, are of greater strength.

Dated the 16th day of March, 1936.
E. A. BINGEN,
Solicitor for the Applicants.

PROVISIONAL SPECIFICATION.
No. 23093 A.D. 1936.

Improvements in or relating to the Polymerisation of Ethylene.

We, ERIC WILLIAM FAWCETT, REGINALD OSWALD GIBSON, MICHAEL WILLCOX PERRIN, JOHN GREVES PATON and EDMOND GEORGE WILLIAMS, all of Winnington Hall, Northwich, in the County of Chester, and all British Subjects, and IMPERIAL CHEMICAL INDUSTRIES LIMITED, of Imperial Chemical House, Millbank, London, S.W.I, a British Company, do hereby declare the nature of this invention to be as follows :—

In pending applications Nos. 3372/36 and 7899/36 methods are described for the production of solid polymers of high molecular weight from ethylene, in which the initial material is subjected to a very high pressure and the heat of the reaction is removed as quickly as possible.

Fig. 2. (*Continued.*)

471,590
3

It has now been found that the nature of the polymerisation is profoundly influenced by the presence of oxygen in the initial material in the following sense.

The course of the high-pressure polymerisation of ethylene to produce solid polymers is such that the reaction proceeds more or less rapidly to a definite point representing, for the particular conditions employed, a certain percentage yield of the polymer based on the ethylene treated, then the reaction ceases. For a given temperature and pressure, it has now been established that the yield of polymer is dependent upon the quantity of oxygen present, under the given reaction conditions, in the initial material; the yield increases with the oxygen content of the ethylene up to a limit beyond which explosion is liable to occur. Thus, a content of oxygen appears to be necessary in order that the reaction may occur and the said oxygen is or appears to be used up in the reaction and the oxygen content is an important controlling factor with respect to the yield of polymer obtained and also, inasmuch as the molecular weight of the resultant polymer appears to have an inverse relationship to the said oxygen content, with respect to the nature of the polymer.

If the oxygen content is very low, the requirement of rapid removal of heat of reaction is less important than when (within the allowable range) the oxygen content is relatively high, but the yield of polymer is lower in the former case than in the latter. It is also believed to be the case that, within limits, the more efficient the removal of the heat of reaction, the higher is the allowable safe oxygen content.

This oxygen content is in any case a relatively small one, e.g. it may be up to an amount of the order of 0.05—0.5 per cent. on the ethylene. These figures are, however, to be regarded as approximate, as it is probable that the maximum content of oxygen that can safely be employed (i.e. without liability of explosion) depends upon the reaction conditions—pressure, temperature and rapidity of removal of heat of reaction.

With the foregoing considerations in mind, the present invention may therefore be defined as comprising the polymerisation of ethylene under a high pressure and at a moderately elevated temperature, in the presence of a relatively small amount of oxygen, (suitably up to about 0.1 per cent. based on the ethylene) which may be added or present as such, or in the form of a substance furnishing oxygen under the reaction conditions, or of a suitable oxidising agent and preferably, though not necessarily in all cases, the reaction conditions being such that the heat of reaction is quickly removed from the reaction.

Suitable pressure for this process are 500 atmospheres or above, and suitable temperatures are about 200° C.

The invention further comprises a continuous process for the production of solid polymers of ethylene, in which the initial material contains a relatively small content of oxygen and is compressed and heated (e.g. by passage over a heated surface) to effect polymerisation, the oxygen content being at the same time used up; the resulting polymer is separated from the unconverted ethylene and the latter is recycled along with fresh ethylene and oxygen for a further polymerisation.

The following example is given for the purpose of illustrating the invention, but the invention is not limited to the conditions therein described.

EXAMPLE 1.

The initial material is ethylene to which has been added a certain amount of oxygen as shown below. The ethylene is compressed under a pressure of 1500 atmospheres in a steel bomb (from which all oxygen has previously been removed by sweeping out with nitrogen or with ethylene) and heated till rapid reaction occurs at a temperature of 210°. The yields of solid polymer obtained are as follows:—

Oxygen Content %, by Weight.	Yield of Solid Polymer (%)	Mol. Wt. of Solid Polymer
0.05	6	20000
0.10	50	6000

Dated the 21st day of August, 1936.
E. A. BINGEN,
Solicitor for the Applicants.

COMPLETE SPECIFICATION.

Improvements in or relating to the Polymerisation of Ethylene.

We, ERIC WILLIAM FAWCETT, REGINALD OSWALD GIBSON, MICHAEL WILLCOX PERRIN, JOHN GREVES PATON and EDMOND GEORGE WILLIAMS, all British Subjects, all of Winnington Hall, Northwich, in the County of Chester, and

Fig. 2. (Continued.)

IMPERIAL CHEMICAL INDUSTRIES LIMITED, a British Company, of Imperial Chemical House, Millbank, London, S.W.1, do hereby declare the nature of this inven-
5 tion and in what manner the same is to be performed, to be particularly described and ascertained in and by the following statement:—

This invention relates to the poly-
10 merisation of ethylene and more particularly to the production of new polymers of ethylene.

It is known that ethylene can be converted into a mixture of liquid organic
15 compounds, by treatment at elevated temperatures (e.g. 200—400° C.) and at moderate pressures (e.g. up to 200 atmospheres), with or without the aid of catalysts. The liquid products, which in
20 the main are not true polymers, range in character from relatively light oils to fairly viscous oils similar to lubricating oils.

Also, it has been proposed, in Speci-
25 fications 336,234 and 340,513, to treat gaseous olefines with catalysts comprising free silicon or acids of phosphorus or their salts, at elevated temperatures and at pressures of 5, 10, 20, 60, 100, 200, 1000
30 atmospheres or even higher. According to these prior proposals the products obtained consist mainly of liquid hydrocarbons such as gasoline-like products, middle oils and lubricating oils.

35 We have now found that, under certain reaction conditions, ethylene can be converted into polymers of a very different character from those hitherto known, namely into polymers of high molecular
40 weight (at least 2000) which are solid at ordinary temperatures. The said reaction conditions comprise:—(1) the use of very high pressures, i.e. at least 1200 atmospheres in the absence of oxygen and
45 at least 500 atmospheres in the presence of oxygen; (2) the use of moderately elevated temperatures between 100° C. and 300° C. and preferably between 150° C. and 250° C.; (3) careful control of the
50 thermal conditions during the polymerisation, in the sense that the heat of the reaction (which is exothermic) must be removed sufficiently rapidly to avoid an undue rise in temperature; (4) the oxy-
55 gen content (if any) of the initial material must not be allowed to exceed a definite small percentage, the value of which depends upon the temperature and pressure employed.
60 Unless these four conditions are observed, the products of any reaction that may take place will not consist of normally solid polymers. With properly chosen conditions, however, polymerisa-
65 tion takes place to give a product which

consists substantially of normally solid polymers, the molecular weight of which can be predetermined as explained later. At pressures between 500 and 1200 atmos-
70 pheres, and at rather higher temperatures than those at which normally solid polymers are exclusively formed, semi-solid or grease-like products are obtained, which apparently consist of solid polymers
75 mixed with a proportion of liquid products which are not all true polymers.

Experiments carried out under various conditions show that polymerisation may take place in either or both of two ways—
80 (1) by a relatively slow reaction, which may proceed over a number of hours, at the end of which time a large proportion (e.g. up to 90%) of the ethylene has been polymerised; (2) by a very rapid reaction,
85 occurring for a few seconds only, which converts a relatively small percentage of the ethylene (e.g. 5—20%) to the polymer. Both types of reaction require a very high pressure and a moderately
90 elevated temperature, and in both cases removal of the heat of reaction at a sufficient rate to prevent the temperature rising to too high a value is necessary to avoid explosion. The second type of re-
95 action appears, however, to require the presence of a certain quantity of oxygen, and in the absence of oxygen, or in the presence of too little oxygen, does not take place to any appreciable extent.

The oxygen present, which initiates the 100 very rapid reaction, is used up during the course of it and is attached chemically to the ethylene polymer; the remaining oxygen-free ethylene may then polymerise by the first-mentioned slow reaction. 105

The percentage of ethylene polymerised in this very rapid reaction, at a given temperature and pressure and under given conditions of heat transfer, increases with increasing oxygen content until the latter 110 reaches a certain critical value, which varies according to the reaction conditions. If more than the critical amount of oxygen is present the temperature rises locally in the gas so high that explosive decom- 115 position of the ethylene takes place. The oxygen content of the gas may suitably be from 0.03—3.0 per cent by weight. Generally an amount of oxygen of the order of 0.1 per cent by weight gives 120 satisfactory results, e.g. at a pressure of 1500 atmospheres 0.06 per cent by weight of oxygen may be used. The higher proportions of oxygen can only be used at pressures in the neighbourhood of 500 at- 125 mospheres and at relatively low temperatures since the critical amount of oxygen is lower the higher the pressure or the temperature employed.

In practice, conditions are chosen that 130

Fig. 2. (*Continued.*)

will give a rapid reaction and/or a good yield of polymer in a reasonable time. Rapidity is achieved if a small controlled quantity of oxygen is present. Good yield in a reasonable time is achieved by increasing the pressure and/or the temperature. At or above 1200 atmospheres we can use the quick reaction or the slow reaction or both for making normally solid polymers, but between 500 and 1200 atmospheres the quick reaction must be utilised, which, as previously stated, requires the presence of oxygen.

When making semi-solid or grease-like products, pressures between 500 and 1200 atmospheres are employed, more especially pressures below 1000 atmospheres in this range, and temperatures somewhat higher than those required to give exclusively normally solid products. The temperature range suitable for making the semi-solid polymers is from 200 to 400° C. Further, the proportion of oxygen may be higher than when working exclusively for solid polymers; it may range up to 5°/₀ by weight, although the higher proportions of oxygen can only be used at pressures in the neighbourhood of 500 atmospheres and at the lower temperature end of the stated range.

With both types of reaction, the effect of increasing the pressure is to increase the molecular weight of the product, also to accelerate the reaction; increasing the temperature will accelerate the reaction, but tends to give a product of lower molecular weight. Hence, for a given oxygen content, high pressure/low temperature conditions give products of relatively high molecular weight, and low pressure/high temperature conditions give products of relatively low molecular weight. Increasing the oxygen content, apart from its effect on the extent of reaction, also influences the molecular weight of the product, in the direction of lowering the same. Whatever the temperature/pressure/oxygen-content conditions chosen, the heat of the reaction must in all cases be suitably dissipated to prevent the temperature from reaching locally, i.e. in any part of the gas, the value at which, instead of polymerisation, explosive decomposition of the ethylene occurs. This critical temperature varies with the reaction conditions. When employing a pressure of 1500 atmospheres, and an oxygen content of 0.1 per cent., the critical temperature is in the neighbourhood of 400° C. and it must be ensured that at no part of the gas does the local temperature reach this value. If high pressures are employed the critical temperature is correspondingly lower. Suitable measures to achieve rapid

removal of the heat of reaction are:— the use of diluents for the ethylene, e.g. the use of industrial gases containing olefines, such as cracking-still gases (where the ethylene is accompanied by inert gases the partial pressure of ethylene in the mixture is reckoned as the pressure to which the ethylene is compressed); the use of a reaction vessel constructed of, or lined with, a metal or alloy of high thermal conductivity; e.g. copper or aluminium, or alloys thereof; efficient stirring of the gas during reaction either mechanically or by inducing turbulent flow. These, or any other suitable measures for dissipating the heat of reaction, may be adopted singly or in any combination. An internal heating element of small heat capacity, spaced within a cold-walled reaction vessel is a convenient means of initiating the reaction.

The invention further comprises a continuous process for the production of solid or semi-solid polymers of ethylene, in which the initial material contains a relatively small content of oxygen and is compressed and heated (e.g. by passage over a heated surface or through a heated reaction space) to effect polymerisation, the oxygen content being at the same time used up: the resulting polymer is separated from the unconverted ethylene and the latter is recycled along with fresh ethylene and oxygen for a further polymerisation.

The following examples are given to illustrate the operation of the invention, but the invention is not limited to the conditions therein described. The gas pressures are measured at the temperature to which the reaction vessel is heated.

EXAMPLE 1.

This example is designed to show the difference between the two types of polymerisation reaction, proceeding in the absence and the presence of oxygen respectively.

Oxygen-free ethylene is compressed in a steel vessel to a pressure of 1500 atmospheres. The vessel is immersed in a constant temperature bath for 2¾ hours at a temperature of 230° C. and during the course of the reaction the contents of the vessel are stirred by a suitable mechanical arrangement. At the end of the 2¾ hours 50 per cent. of the ethylene has been polymerised and during the course of the reaction the pressure has fallen to 1000 atmospheres. The polymer obtained is solid at the ordinary temperature.

Ethylene, containing 0.08°/₀ of oxygen, is compressed in a similar vessel to a pressure of 1500 atmospheres. The temperature of the vessel is then raised to

Fig. 2. (*Continued.*)

471,590

200° C. when a very rapid reaction at once takes place, as shown by a sudden fall in pressure of 150 atmospheres. After this reaction 12% of the ethylene has been polymerised and the remaining gas contains no measurable quantity of oxygen. The polymer obtained is solid at the ordinary temperature.

EXAMPLE 2.

This example is designed to show how the molecular weight of the polymer varies, for given conditions with the pressure employed for the polymerisation.

Ethylene containing 0.06% of oxygen is compressed in a steel vessel to various pressures and the temperature is raised to about 200° C., to initiate the reaction, after which the temperature is maintained constant. The table shows the initial pressure of the ethylene and the molecular weight of the polymer formed after 2 hours treatment in each case.

Pressure.	Molecular Weight.
520 atms	2000
1000	4000
1500	6—12000
3000	12—24000

The polymer of molecular weight 2000 is a soft solid at the ordinary temperature. The other polymers are solid at the ordinary temperature.

EXAMPLE 3.

This example is designed to show the effect of oxygen concentration on the percentage conversion and on the molecular weight of the polymer.

Ethylene, containing various concentrations of oxygen, is compressed in a steel vessel to a pressure of 1500 atms. and the temperature is raised to about 180—200° C. until the sudden fall in pressure shows that the rapid polymerisation reaction has occurred. The following table gives the initial concentration of oxygen, the percentage conversion and the molecular weight of the product in each case. All of the products are solid at the ordinary temperature.

Oxygen Content	Yield	Molecular Weight
0.01%	6%	18000
0.04%	9%	12000
0.07%	10%	10000
0.13%	15%	6000
0.16%	Explosive decomposition	

In a further series of experiments the gas is compressed initially to 1000 atms. and the following results are obtained:—

Oxygen Content	Yield	Molecular Weight
0.21%	6%	3000
0.63%	20%	2000
1.0%	Explosive Decomposition	

The polymer of molecular weight 3000 is solid at the ordinary temperature. The polymer of molecular weight 2000 is a soft solid at the ordinary temperature.

EXAMPLE 4.

This example is designed to show the possibility of carrying out the polymerisation of ethylene under such conditions that use is made of both the relatively slow reaction and the rapid polymerisation due to oxygen.

A steel vessel of 80 ccs. capacity is filled with ethylene, containing 0.06% of oxygen, to an initial pressure of 1500 atms. The temperature is raised to 180° C. when a sudden drop in pressure shows that the rapid polymerisation reaction has taken place. The temperature is kept constant and, after a period of about 15 minutes during which time the pressure has been falling slowly, more of the initial oxygen-containing ethylene is compressed into the vessel to bring the pressure back to 1500 atms. This procedure is repeated for 3 hours, after which time the vessel contains 26 grams of ethylene polymer of molecular weight 12000, which is solid at the ordinary temperature.

In Examples 1—4 the precautions taken to avoid the temperature in any part of the gas reaching that at which explosion would occur consist first in using steel reaction vessels of such internal surface to volume ratio that the heat of reaction is rapidly removed, and secondly in stirring the contents of the vessels throughout the experiments.

EXAMPLE 5.

This example is designed to show the possibility of polymerising ethylene by a continuous process depending essentially upon the rapid polymerisation due to oxygen.

Ethylene, containing 0.08% of oxygen, is compressed to 1500 atoms. and is forced, at this pressure, through a steel reaction vessel containing an internal heating element at a temperature of 230° C. The walls of the main reaction vessel are kept below 100° C. by means of a water jacket. After passing through the reaction space, the ethylene and the polymer which is formed are released through a suitable valve. In this experiment 15% of the ethylene passing through the vessel, is converted to a polymer of molecular weight 8000, which is solid at the

Fig. 2. (Continued.)

471,590   7

ordinary temperature.

The products of this invention have a chemical constitution corresponding to a homologue and true polymer of ethylene
5 —(C₂H₄)ₙ, viz, a straight chain hydrocarbon with one double-bond in the chain. In the case of the polymers formed in the rapid polymerisation due to oxygen, the very small proportion of the latter in
10 the polymer has a negligible effect on the chemical or physical properties. Products with molecular weights varying between 2000 and 24000 have been obtained, using experimental apparatus,
15 and there is no reason to believe that the latter figure represents the highest obtainable value. These values have been obtained by calculation from the elevation of the boiling point of a solution in the
20 case of the low molecular weights and from the relative viscosity of a solution in the case of the higher molecular weights.

The properties of the polymer depend to some extent upon the molecular weight;
25 thus the products of high molecular weight are harder, soften at a higher temperature, have improved mechanical properties and are less readily soluble than those of low molecular weight.
30 The solid polymers, as opposed to the semi-solid polymers of lower molecular weight, are negligibly soluble in cold organic solvents, but are quite soluble in the hot in most hydrocarbon solvents,
35 e.g. benzene. Their resistance to water, acids, and alkalis is outstandingly good, and only concentrated sulphuric acid causes slight charring.

The higher molecular weight solid
40 polymers melt at about 110—120° C. and may be moulded or cast to give shaped masses. The decomposition temperature of the polymers is relatively high (about 200° C. in air) and if heated in a high
45 vacuum they do not depolymerise, the vapour pressure being negligible up to temperatures of about 350° C., when a general breakdown of the long chain molecules begins.
50 Pliable, elastic and transparent films can be made from the solid polymers by known general methods, e.g. by heating the polymer above its melting point or by removal of a solvent from a solution of the
55 polymer; in the latter case it is essential that this process be carried out at a temperature above the softening point of the polymer in order to obtain a continuous film. Such films are very impervious to
60 water. It is also possible to impregnate materials such as paper and fabric with the polymer, using known methods. The polymer can be formed into threads by extrusion above the softening tempera-
65 ture. Owing to the great length of the

chains the molecules in such threads can be orientated by stretching the thread at room temperature; this produces a permanent elongation of about 500 per cent.
70 and a considerable increase in the mechanical strength. In a similar way, the molecules in films or tapes of the polymer can be orientated by cold rolling. The cold drawn threads may be worked up
75 into staple fibres similar to the staple fibres of textiles, which can be spun and woven. The polymers have outstandingly good dielectric properties and may be used for electrical insulation in general.
80 They are also useful for making vacuum tight joints at temperatures above or below the melting point of the polymers.

Having now particularly described and ascertained the nature of our said inven-
85 tion and in what manner the same is to be performed, we declare that what we claim is :—

1) A process for the conversion of ethylene into normally solid polymers of
90 ethylene, which consists in subjecting ethylene, compressed to a pressure of at least 1200 atmospheres, to a temperature of 100—300° C. for a sufficient period of time to effect polymerisation of a sub-
95 stantial proportion of the ethylene, during which time the temperature in any part of the gas is prevented from reaching the critical temperature at which explosive decomposition of the ethylene occurs.

100 2) A process as claimed in Claim 1, in which the ethylene is compressed to a pressure of at least 1500 atmospheres.

3) A process as claimed in Claim 1 or 2, in which the ethylene is maintained
105 at a temperature of 150—250° C. during the reaction.

4) A process for the conversion of ethylene into normally solid polymers of ethylene, which consists in subjecting
110 ethylene compressed to a pressure of at least 500 atmospheres and accompanied by a small proportion of free oxygen, not exceeding 3 per cent. by weight, to an elevated temperature sufficient to induce
115 reaction, the permissible amount of oxygen initially present being insufficient to cause explosive decomposition of the ethylene.

5) A process as claimed in Claim 4, in
120 which the ethylene is compressed to a pressure of at least 1500 atmospheres.

6) A process as claimed in Claim 4 or 5, in which, after the initial rapid reaction in which the oxygen is used up,
125 further oxygen-containing ethylene is mixed with the residual ethylene, without releasing the pressure, and the ethylene is again subjected to the reaction temperature, with or without separation
130 of the polymer between the reaction

Fig. 2. (Continued.)

8 471,590

stages

7) A process as claimed in Claim 4 or 5, in which the reaction is effected continuously by supplying a gas mixture consisting of ethylene containing a small amount of oxygen to a reaction zone, removing the polymer therefrom, withdrawing the residual ethylene and returning it to the reaction zone mixed with further ethylene and oxygen.

8) A process as claimed in Claim 4 or 5, in which after the initial rapid reaction in which the oxygen is used up, the residual ethylene, without releasing the pressure, is subjected to a temperature of 100—300° C. for a sufficient period of time to effect polymerisation of a substantial proportion of the ethylene, during which time the temperature in any part of the gas is prevented from reaching the critical temperature at which explosive decomposition of the ethylene occurs.

9) A process as claimed in Claim 4, 5, 6, 7 or 8, in which the amount of oxygen initially present in the ethylene is of the order of 0.1 per cent by weight.

10) A process as claimed in Claim 4, 5, 6, 7, 8 or 9, in which the oxygen-containing ethylene is heated to a temperature of 150—250° C.

11) A process for the conversion of ethylene into semi-solid or grease-like products, which consists in subjecting ethylene, compressed to a pressure between 500 and 1200 atmospheres, to a temperature of 200—400° C. for a sufficient period of time to effect conversion of a substantial proportion of the ethylene into a product containing a substantial proportion of solid polymer, during which time the temperature in any part of the gas is prevented from reaching the critical temperature at which explosive decomposition of the ethylene occurs.

12) A process for the conversion of ethylene into semi-solid or grease-like products, which consists in subjecting ethylene, compressed to a pressure between 500 and 1200 atmospheres and accompanied by a small proportion of free oxygen, not exceeding 5 per cent. by weight to an elevated temperature sufficient to induce reaction and lying within the range 200—400° C., the permissible amount of oxygen initially present being insufficient to cause explosive decomposition of the ethylene.

13) A process as claimed in any of Claims 1—12, in which the ethylene is accompanied by inert gases, the partial pressure of ethylene in the mixture being reckoned as the pressure to which the ethylene is compressed.

14) A process as claimed in any of Claims 1—13, in which the gas is maintained in turbulent motion while at the reaction temperature.

15) A process as claimed in any of Claims 1—14, in which the reaction is initiated by means of an internal heating element of small heat capacity housed within a cold-walled reaction vessel.

16) A process for the production of normally solid polymers of ethylene, substantially as hereinbefore described with reference to each of the foregoing examples.

17) Normally solid or semi-solid polymers of ethylene, whenever obtained by the process of any of Claims 1—16.

Dated the 4th day of February, 1937.
E. A. BINGEN,
Solicitor for the Applicants.

Fig. 2. (*Concluded.*)

ber, 1935. Important advances were made during the succeeding year, and by 1937 a continuously running pilot plant was put in operation by I.C.I. The years 1938 and 1939 saw the evaluation of pilot-plant data in terms of full-scale operations, and the fabrication of experimental lengths (one a mile long) of submarine cable insulated with polyethylene. A commercial-scale plant was erected by I.C.I. and ready for operation by the summer of 1939, but with the advent of the war, it was decided to

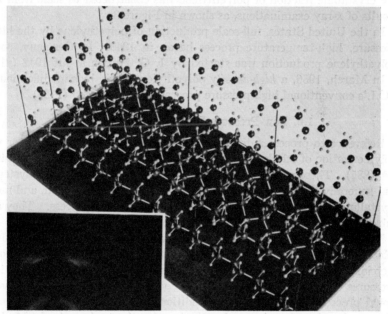

Fig. 3. Atomic model of the crystalline fraction of polyethylene. (*Endeavour*, **3**, 27, 1944.)

double its capacity before even one pound of the polymer had been produced. An entirely new plant was erected and in full production early in 1942.

In 1941, an American delegation, under United States Government auspices, visited the British plants and was furnished with pertinent information relative to commercial-scale operations. This resulted in the erection of two large-scale plants in the United States. Before this, however, a polyethylene-insulated cable had been laid as part of the multichannel trunk telephone line between New York and Washington, using material supplied to the Bell Telephone Company by I.C.I.

During the war, the bulk of the polyethylene produced was used for insulating cables, particularly high-frequency types, since its unique combination of properties made polyethylene especially suited for applications in the field of radar.

This brief outline of the British development may be supplemented by reference to the detailed presentations of the subject by Irwin (158), Swallow (162), Allen (173), Freeth (215), Renfrew (562), and recently Perrin (759). In the paper by Swallow, the picture of an atomic model of the crystalline fraction of polyethylene was constructed to scale from the results of x-ray examinations, as shown in Figure 3.

In the United States, full-scale production of polyethylene by the high-pressure, high-temperature process began in 1943. In Germany, some polyethylene production was started by I. G. Farben about 1942 (217).

In March, 1956, a *high-density* polyethylene made by a modification of I.C.I.'s conventional high-pressure process was announced (1120).

1.6. Low-Pressure Polymerization Methods

Reference to processes different from that discovered by I.C.I. for the polymerization of ethylene to solid products was made in a paper by Swallow (885). These processes were said to employ different catalyst systems, and generally the polymers are of higher density, less branched, and more crystalline than those made by the conventional I.C.I. process. They are subsequently referred to as high-density polyethylenes.

McSweeney and Kropa (994), in their review on "Plastics in 1954," relate that the polymerization of ethylene to polyethylene by the commercial process of Phillips Petroleum is carried out at relatively low pressures of the order of 500 p.s.i., as contrasted with the more conventional procedures which employ conditions requiring 15,000–30,000 p.s.i. This product has since been advertised under the trademark of "Marlex-50," and some of the properties of this highly crystalline, high-density polyethylene will be presented in Section 6.19 (compare also Section 3.5). The same authors mention further that unpublished evidence is accumulating to the effect that ethylene can be polymerized at atmospheric pressures, with reports of this accomplishment coming from both sides of the Atlantic.

Since then, references to a process for the polymerization of ethylene to high molecular weight polyethylene, developed by Prof. Dr. K. Ziegler and associates at Max Planck Institute for Coal Research at Mühlheim a.d.R., Germany, have been multiplying. It was announced (808) that the newly founded Arbeitsgemeinschaft für Olefinchemie has obtained from Steinkohlenbergbauverein in Essen all rights for the utilization of Professor Ziegler's patents for the production of polymers from olefins. The Steinkohlenbergbauverein had previously obtained from Professor Ziegler a general license for Germany and has now transferred the general license to the Arbeitsgemeinschaft, which was founded by about 20 mining industry companies. Interest in the production of polyethylene has been indicated by Gelsenkirchener Bergwerks AG, Essen; Mannesmann AG, Düsseldorf; Ruhrchemie AG, Oberhausen-Holten; Bergwerksgesellschaft Hibernia AG, Herne; and other companies. The last two companies already have polyethylene pilot plants in operation.

Somewhat later, in January, 1955, it was reported that Farbwerke Hoechst, under a license from Arbeitsgemeinschaft für Olefinchemie, was building a plant in Germany for the polymerization of ethylene and other olefins obtained from petroleum, and that polyethylene plants designed for operation of the same process were being operated by Ruhrchemie and by Bergwerksgesellschaft Hibernia. The properties of the Hoechst product, advertised under the trademark "Hostalen," were recently described in a trade bulletin and will be presented in Section 6.19.

Reference to a "stronger and more heat-resistant" polyethylene produced by Bakelite under conditions that "approximate" atmospheric pressure and temperature was made approximately one month later (927). Soon thereafter, also in 1955, Bakelite as well as duPont were reported (922,926b) to be in commercial production of low-pressure polyethylene, with Monsanto working on a low-pressure method (926a). At least a half dozen other firms were said to be interested in the Ziegler process.

Koppers Company subsequently announced (924) its "Super Dylan" polyethylene, the properties of which were described in a trade bulletin and will be presented in Section 6.19.

Speculations on Ziegler's and other low-pressure polyethylenes, reference to duPont's plans for a low-pressure polyethylene pilot plant at Orange, Texas, and mention of Dow, Goodrich-Gulf, and Hercules as others having an interest in the Ziegler method are the subject of still more recent (June, 1955) news releases (926,926a,929a).

Standard Oil, which has several U. S. patents covering various low-pressure routes (see Section 3.5), may be on the verge of competing with the Ziegler and Phillips processes (920a). Certain features are common to almost all of Standard Oil's patents: operating pressure is approximately 1,000 p.s.i.; temperature, 450–550°F.; the catalyst is probably a sub-hexavalent molybdenum oxide. Greaselike, waxlike, or tough, resinous solids with molecular weights ranging from 30,000–250,000 and even much higher are said to be obtainable by this process.

1.7. Future Development

An attempt to present a brief outlook for the future may be in order (see also Chapter X). With "accent on service," as *Chemical Week* (925) pointed out, "campaign platforms are being laid with carefully chosen planks in expectation of brisk competition in polyethylene. Sales promotion plans skirt extravagant claims, instead emphasize service, product quality, and versatility." But E. S. Childs of Monsanto asks, "Will the polyethylene gamble pay off?" In a discussion held at the 11th Annual National Technical Conference of the Society of Plastics Engineers, Inc., at Atlantic City during January, 1955, Childs posed this question. Significant conclusions drawn from the discussion at that meeting are quoted below:

1. There is a big potential market for this very versatile and useful new family of plastics.

2. New uses are being found steadily by thoughtful engineers and production men. Hardly a week goes by but that we hear of an exciting new application. Frequently, these new uses represent markets where no plastic material had been used previously. We are not replacing other plastics, but developing a host of entirely new large volume applications.

3. Polyethylene has its limitations which future development and research work is likely to reduce. Bear in mind that polyethylene has been a sellers' market for nearly its entire history. Increasing competition for your business will give you new and better products. Historically, this has been the case with every other plastic. Polyethylene will not be different in this respect.

4. Polyethylene is benefiting its users by giving better products at lower costs. It is increasing your customers' sales and profits. A material with such versatile applications and demonstrated performance cannot help but stimulate thinking by engineers of how they, too, can make better products at lower costs.

5. The polyethylene gamble of resin manufacturers is likely to pay off. The capacity now being built will not be absorbed immediately, but in time will come into closer balance with demand.

And how will the conventional high-pressure polyethylene and the novel high-density products stand up in competition with each other? This is an important question indeed if one considers that the producing capacity for all polyethylenes in 1960 was estimated in December, 1955, by M. Stringfellow (923c) of Spencer Chemical at 830 million pounds, of which 585 million will be high-pressure, and 245 million low-pressure polymer. According to the same source, Stringfellow foresees an advantage to the customer in having a wide array of properties, whereby the various types are expected to augment one another in meeting consumer requirements, without becoming as competitive as previously anticipated. This view is shared by J. G. Davidson of Union Carbide and Carbon who believes that each variety of polyethylene will find its own market.

II. ETHYLENE

2.1. Chemical and Physical Properties

Chemical Properties

Ethylene, the lowest member of the alkenes or olefinic hydrocarbons, is a colorless gas, sweetish in taste, and slightly soluble in alcohol or ether. Like most organic compounds, ethylene is combustible. As an unsaturated compound, ethylene is capable of undergoing addition reactions. Predominantly an electron donor, ethylene forms addition compounds with electrophilic agents, such as halogens and strong acids; no reaction is observed with nucleophilic agents or electron donors, such as weak acids or ammonia.

Of the addition reactions, the following deserve particular mention:

TABLE II

Miscellaneous Properties for Ethylene

Property	Value	Reference
Boiling point	$-103.71°C.$ (760 mm. Hg)	677
Boiling point variation with pressure (dt/dp)	$0.0224°C./mm.$ Hg (760 mm. Hg)	677
Triple point	$-169.15°C.$	677
Critical temperature	$9.90°C.$	749a
Critical pressure	50.5 atm.	749a
Critical density	0.227 g./ml.	749a
Flammability limits with oxygen	2.90–79.9 volume %	677
Flammability limits with air	2.75–28.60 volume %	677
Heat of combustion of gaseous ethylene ($-\Delta H_e^\circ$ at 25°C. and constant pressure):		677
To form H_2O (liq.) and CO_2 (gas)	337.23 kcal./mole 12,022 cal./g. 21,625 B.t.u./lb.	
To form H_2O (gas) and CO_2 (gas)	316.20 kcal./mole 11,272 cal./g. 20,276 B.t.u./lb.	
Heat of polymerization	See Chapter 3.1	

19

hydrogenation or reduction; bromination; chlorination; reactions with halogen acids, with sulfuric acid, and with hypochlorous acid; and addition of hydroxyl groups. The reaction of ethylene with itself to form products of the general formula $(CH_2CH_2)_n$ is called polymerization and represents, in its diversified aspects, the subject matter of this volume.

Physical Properties

The infrared and Raman spectra of ethylene have been the subject of several investigations to determine the molecular dimensions and funda-

TABLE III

Thermodynamic Properties of Ethylene

Temp. (°K.)	Heat content function $(H^0 - H_0^0)/T$ (cal./deg. mole)	Free energy function $(F^0 - H_0^0)/T$ (cal./deg. mole)	Entropy (ideal gas state) S^0 (cal./deg. mole)	Enthalpy $(H^0 - H_0^0)$ (cal./ mole)	Heat capacity C_p^0 (cal./deg. mole)	Heat of formation ΔH_f^0 (kcal./ mole)	Free energy of formation ΔF_f^0 (kcal./ mole)
298.16	8.47	−43.98	52.45	2525	10.41	12.496	16.282
300	8.48	−44.03	52.51	2544	10.45	12.482	16.305
400	9.28	−46.61	55.89	3711	12.90	11.766	17.675
500	10.23	−48.74	58.98	5117	15.16	11.138	19.245
600	11.22	−50.70	61.92	6732	17.10	10.600	20.918
700	12.18	−52.50	64.68	8727	18.76	10.142	22.676
800	13.10	−54.19	67.28	10480	20.20	9.760	24.490
900	13.96	−55.78	69.74	12560	21.46	9.448	26.354
1000	14.76	−57.29	72.06	14760	22.57	9.205	28.249
1100	15.52	−58.74	74.26	17070	23.54	9.02	30.16
1200	16.22	−60.12	76.34	19470	24.39	8.88	32.09
1300	16.88	−61.44	78.32	21950	25.14	8.76	34.03
1400	17.50	−62.71	80.21	24490	25.79	8.67	35.97
1500	18.07	−63.94	82.01	27100	26.39	8.61	37.92

1. The heat content function, $(H^0 - H_0^0)/T$, is the heat content at the given tempera ture less the heat content at 0°K., divided by the absolute temperature (°K.) of ethyl ene in the thermodynamic standard gaseous state of unit fugacity (1 atm.).

2. The free energy function, $(F^0 - H_0^0)/T$, is determined similarly, according to note 1.

3. S^0 is the entropy (exclusive of nuclear spin) of ethylene in the thermodynamic standard gaseous state of unit fugacity (1 atm.), at the temperature indicated.

4. $(H^0 - H_0^0)$ is the enthalpy at the given temperature less the heat content of 0°K. of ethylene in the thermodynamic standard gaseous state of unit fugacity (1 atm.).

5. C_p^0 is the heat capacity at constant pressure of ethylene in the thermodynamic standard gaseous state of unit fugacity (1 atm.).

6. ΔH_f^0 represents the increment in heat content for the reaction of forming ethylene in the gaseous state from the elements carbon (solid graphite), and hydrogen (gaseous), with all the reactants and the product in their appropriate standard reference state at the temperature indicated.

7. The increment in free energy, ΔF_f^0, is determined under restrictions as stated in note 6.

mental frequencies of this molecule. Further, Gallaway and Barker (134) succeeded in resolving the fine structure of several infrared absorption bands of C_2H_4 and C_2D_4. From the rotational constants so found, the C-C and C-H distances in this molecule were calculated to be 1.353A and 1.071A, and the H-C-H angle to be 119°55′. The far ultraviolet absorption spectra of C_2H_4 and C_2D_4 were recently investigated by Wilkinson and Mulliken (1042).

Miscellaneous properties of ethylene are compiled from various sources in Table II. A compilation of the thermodynamic properties of ethylene, taken from the American Petroleum Institute (Project 44) publication, "Selected Values of Physical and Thermodynamic Properties of Hydrocarbons and Related Compounds," is presented in Table III. From the same source, viscosity data for ethylene are quoted in Table IV.

TABLE IV

Viscosity of Ethylene

Temperature (°C.)	Viscosity (absolute) (centipoises)
−170	0.70[a]
−165	0.60
−160	0.51
−155	0.45
−150	0.39
−145	0.35
−140	0.31
−135	0.28
−130	0.26
−125	0.23
−120	0.21
−115	0.20
−110	0.18
−105	0.16
−100	0.15[b]

[a] For the undercooled liquid below the normal melting point (melting point, −169.4°C.; freezing point, −181°C.).
[b] For the liquid above the normal boiling point at saturation pressure.

Isotherms of ethylene from temperatures of 0–150°C. and pressures up to 3,000 atmospheres have been determined by Michels and Geldermans (138). In a later publication, Michels, Geldermans, and de Groot (221) presented elaborate data showing the energy, kinetic energy, specific heat, entropy, free energy, enthalpy, and thermodynamic potential of ethylene under pressures up to 3,000 atmospheres and temperatures of 0–150°C.

Values cited by Timmermans (487) for the specific heat of ethylene at very low temperatures are given in Table V. Timmermans' "best" values for the densities of liquid ethylene and of saturated ethylene vapor are shown in Table VI.

Data for the saturated vapor pressure of ethylene have been published both by the American Petroleum Institute (677) and by Timmermans (487). Determinations of the solubility of ethylene in water at temperatures in the range of 35–102°C. and pressures from 4.55–524 atmos-

TABLE V

Specific Heat of Ethylene (487)

t (°C.)	c_p (cal./g./°C.)
Solid	
−257.16	0.0286
−254.35	0.04634
−251.25	0.06853
−247.99	0.09118
−244.06	0.1199
−240.00	0.1530
−235.81	0.1850
−230.09	0.2156
−225.87	0.2473
−220.64	0.2786
−215.56	0.3067
−210.36	0.3310
−204.75	0.3560
−198.46	0.3849
Liquid	
−166.47	0.5890
−164.58	0.5883
−160.88	0.5861
−154.13	0.5826
−147.26	0.5808
−140.56	0.5783
−133.08	0.5747
−127.78	0.5740
−121.28	0.5736
−114.61	0.5719
−108.93	0.5722
−104.45	0.5740

pheres have been made by Bradbury, McNulty, Savage, and McSweeney (590). Thermal conductivity data for ethylene were reported by Lenoir and Comings (552), and for ethylene-nitrogen mixtures by Junk and Comings (739). Flame stability limits of ethylene, propane, methane, hydrogen, and nitrogen mixtures are presented in a paper by Grumer, Harris, and Schultz (962). The mutual solubility of ethylene with

TABLE VI

Densities of Liquid Ethylene and of Saturated Ethylene Vapor (487)

t (°C.)	Liquid	Vapor
−145.07	0.62465	. . . .
−129.90	0.60449	. . . .
−114.69	0.58380	. . . .
−103.01	0.56740	. . . .
−63.41	0.50588	0.012584
−48.15	0.47822	0.020407
−37.13	0.45610	0.029465
−24.33	0.42655	0.041854
−19.20	0.41313	0.051138
−14.18	0.39855	0.059942
−10.93	0.38818	0.067215
−7.70	0.37721	0.076050
+5.84	0.30840	0.13266
+6.50	0.30342	0.13716
+7.98	0.28726	0.15268

various polar and nonpolar relatively high molecular weight organic compounds at 1° and 10°C., respectively, above the critical temperature of ethylene, and at pressures up to 1,500 p.s.i. (absolute) was studied by Todd and Elgin (1037).

Ethylene compressibility factors have been reported by Walters, Tracht, Weinberger, and Rodgers (889) for temperatures ranging from −20 to +100°F., and pressures of 50–600 p.s.i. (absolute). These are illustrated in Figure 4. Compressibility factors for nitrogen-ethylene mixtures have been determined by Hagenbach and Comings (733) and are presented graphically in Figure 5.

Benzler and von Koch (932) recently published a modified Mollier diagram for ethylene, covering pressures up to 10,000 atmospheres (absolute). It is reproduced as Figure 6.

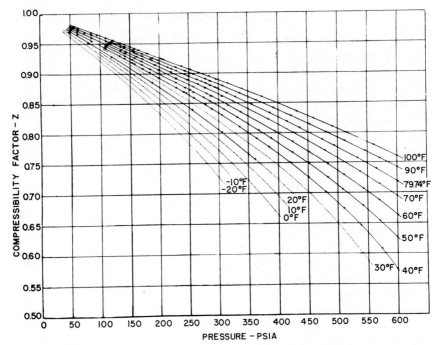

Fig. 4. Compressibility factors for ethylene: ——— experimental data; ······ values extrapolated from the experimental data using an equation of state. (*Chem. Eng. Prog.*, **50**, 513, 1954.)

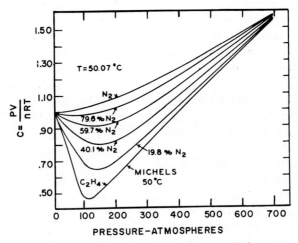

Fig. 5. Compressibility factors for nitrogen-ethylene system. (*Ind. Eng. Chem.*, **45**, 609, 1953.)

2.2. Manufacture

Ethylene is basic to the American petrochemical industry and is one of the most important of all chemical raw materials. Present annual production of petrochemicals in the United States amounts to some 4.6 billion pounds, or about 25% of total domestic chemical production. Olefins in the C_1 through C_4 bracket are the raw materials for at least 70% of all petrochemicals produced, and ethylene is the principal of these olefins. Approximately 2.2 billion pounds of ethylene was produced in 1953, and about 2.4 billion pounds in 1954. It has been conservatively estimated (818) that this figure will reach 3.0 billion pounds by 1956.

Ethylene as such is not present in crude petroleum or in natural gas. It does, however, represent up to 8 to 10% of the off-gases from refineries cracking petroleum stocks. Some 10% of the total ethylene produced in 1953 was recovered from this source. The remaining 90% was derived in large measure and in roughly equal amounts from the pyrolysis of propane and of ethane recovered from natural and refinery gases. A minor proportion was produced by the dehydration of ethanol.

Fundamentally, the manufacture of ethylene involves two principal operations: (a) the formation of ethylene; (b) its separation from other materials already present or concurrently produced. Further, there is no inherent technological connection between these operations. There are at least eight well recognized methods for the formation of ethylene, and at least five processes have been successfully employed for its separation and purification. Accordingly, the selection of the most desirable combination is predicated almost entirely upon the engineering economics involved.

Present processes for the formation of ethylene depend upon either the pyrolytic or the catalytic conversion of paraffinic hydrocarbons. Those most generally used in this country employ the high-temperature pyrolysis of petroleum fractions. Temperatures involved are of the order of 1300–1500°F., the lower being employed for crudes and gas oils, the higher for ethane and propane feed stocks. At these temperatures, any catalytic effects can usually be disregarded. Accordingly, most effort has been expended on the development of methods and designs intended to secure optimum time-temperature relations while minimizing carbon formation and equipment fouling. The following have been employed or proposed in consequence: (1) fired tubular furnace; (2) regenerative stove; (3) pebble heater; (4) partial combustion process; (5) electric arc process; (6) molten metal process.

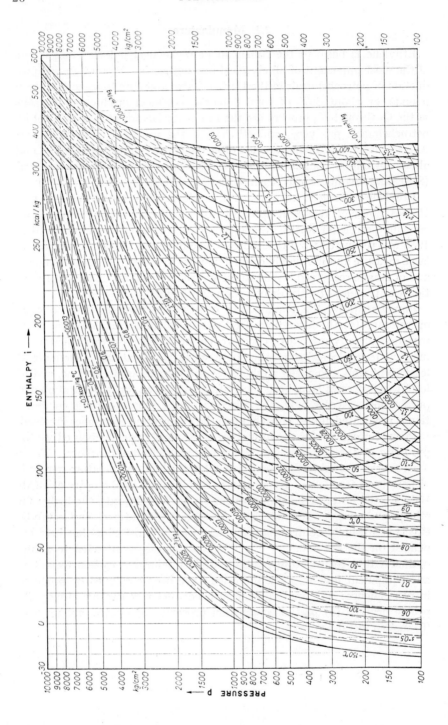

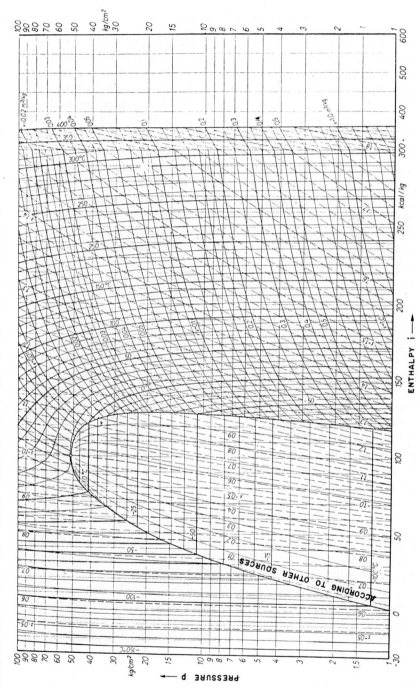

Fig. 6. Pressure-enthalpy diagram for ethylene: temperature, −150° to 400°C.; pressure, 1 atm. to 10,000 atm.; at critical point, $s = 1.00$, $i = 100.00$.   (*Chem. Ing. Tech.*, **27** [2], 71–5, 1955.)

Fired Tubular Furnace

The most commonly used method for the primary production of ethylene in this country involves the externally-fired tubular furnace. Essentially, the furnace is made up of a number of tubular coils. One section is equipped with means for external radiant firing, using gas or oil as the fuel. The feed stock to be cracked passes through the tubes, together with the quantity of steam necessary to suppress formation of coke on the walls of the tubes. The design of such units has been discussed in very considerable detail by Schutt (295). Operating at temperatures in the neighborhood of 1500°F. when ethane is used as feed stock, selection of the proper tube metal is of critical importance. Chrome or chrome-nickel alloy-steel is preferred. The most important control variables are, of course, temperature and contact time. At coil outlet temperatures within the range of 1400–1500°F., contact times of from 0.7–1.3 seconds are sufficient to permit conversions as high as 55% of the charge. Although a straight ethane feed requires coil temperatures of nearly 1500°F., a feed predominating in propane permits temperatures of about 1450°F. If virgin naphthas (400–450°F. end point) or gas oils (800°F. end point) are used as feed stocks, coil outlet temperatures of 1350°F. and 1250°F., respectively, are considered maximum. The quantity of steam necessary to minimize coke formation depends, of course, upon the particular feed stock being cracked. In the case of the high-boiling stocks just considered, up to four moles of steam per mole of hydrocarbon may be required. Since conversion is incomplete in the first pass, unconverted feed is generally separated in subsequent purification operations and recycled together with fresh feed to the cracking unit. It has been stated as a rough rule (566) that commercial ultimate yields of 75% (by weight) of ethylene may be obtained in cracking ethane in the fired tubular furnace. Ethylene yields from propane are about 48%, and yields from gas oils of 25–32% of ethylene should be normal.

Regenerative Stove

One of the oldest methods for the pyrolytic conversion of hydrocarbons to ethylene is the multiple, recuperative checker-brick furnace (regenerative stove). Although still used to some extent, high maintenance costs have sharply reduced the economic advantages of such installations.

In operation, the furnace is heated by passing combustion gases through it. Steam is then injected through the checker-work until a temperature of about 2000°F. is reached. At this point, feed stock is injected into the furnace from the end opposite the steam-injection port. Cracking is continued until the temperature has dropped to about 1500°F., at which point the furnace is reversed and the feed passed to a newly regenerated hot checker.

In the main, yields are comparable to those from fired tubular furnace operations. As charge stocks, naphthas, gas oils, and very heavy reduced crudes may be employed. Depending upon the feed stock, a more or less substantial amount of coke accumulates on the refractory brick by the conclusion of the processing cycle on any given checker. This is customarily removed by blasting with heated air. The heat of combustion of the coke serves in turn to reheat the checker-brick to cracking temperature.

In a modification of this system, the so-called Wulff process, the stoves are constructed of specially slotted carborundum bricks. This enables steam and feed stock to be charged from the same end. At the same time, the charging feed is limited to distillate stocks.

The Koppers-Hasche process, described by Farnsworth, Manes, McGurl, and Bretz (954), has been developed on a pilot-plant scale. It is based on an internally heated, regenerative furnace in which hydrocarbons are cracked by intermittent passage through hot refractory tiles of special design. Reported advantages of this process are: high efficiency of heat recovery, the possibility of using waste gases as fuel, and freedom from carbon accumulation.

Pebble Heater

An extremely flexible method for the production of ethylene is the moving pebble bed (the so-called Thermofor Pyrolytic Cracking or T.P.C.) system (340,857). It can be designed to utilize gaseous or liquid feed stocks. Carbon formation presents no problem, since it is burned off the pebbles continuously in the course of operations. For this reason, crude oils and heavy reduced crudes are as suitable feed materials as distillate stocks.

Essentially, the system is composed of a primary heater unit positioned over a reaction chamber. As heat-transfer medium, use is made of spherical (about $3/8$ inch diameter) refractory pebbles. These are raised by bucket or air lift and discharged into the top of the heater, where a pebble bed is maintained at constant height. In this unit, the pebbles are heated by the direct combustion of fuel gases in the bed to 1300–1750°F. At the same time, carbon deposited on the pebbles during cracking operations is burned off and vented. From the heater the pebbles flow by gravity into the reactor, where their heat serves to crack the charge stock. From the base of the reactor, the cooled pebbles, at a temperature of about 950°F., flow through a throttling valve into the base of the lift system for return to the heater. A system of baffles prevents channeling of pebble flow in both heater and reactor. The charge stock may be preheated outside the reactor, if desired. However, since the flow of charge stock is countercurrent to the direction of movement of the pebble bed, this is not essential. Instead, the feed may be introduced cold into the lower sections of the reactor, where residual pebble heat is available for preheating and vaporizing. Very rapid rates of preheating are possible, due to the favorable conditions for extremely high heat transfer rates—of the order of 15,000 B.t.u. per hour per degree Fahrenheit per cubic foot of pebbles. This is highly advantageous, since undesirable low-temperature cracking is thereby minimized. Cracking temperatures are controlled by the temperature of the pebble bed (1300–1750°F.) and by varying the ratio of pebble circulation to rate of hydrocarbon feed, generally within the range of 10–20. Hydrocarbon contact time is dependent upon the depth of pebble bed as well as upon the vapor velocity and is ordinarily within the range of 0.1 to 2.5 seconds. It is desirable to quench the cracked product gases as rapidly as possible to prevent decomposition. This may be accomplished by subjecting the gases to a primary direct water spray which reduces the temperature to the range of 400–700°F. A second quench then lowers the temperature to about 125°F. The vapors are then passed through an oil spray, a scrubber, and a mist extractor, to remove residual traces of tars and oils.

Partial Combustion

The partial oxidation of ethane as an alternative route to the production of ethylene has been proposed but never practiced commercially in this country. During World War II, an analogous process was developed and operated commercially in Germany for the large-scale production of acetylene from methane. The heat necessary for high-temperature cracking was supplied by the internal combustion of a portion of the methane feed in oxygen, air, or natural gas. The partial combustion of ethane for the production of ethylene was carried out on a commercial scale (13,000 tons of ethylene per year) at the I. G. Farben. Leuna works (284). The process depends for economic advantage upon a cheap source of oxygen.

Electric Arc

In Germany during World War II, a certain proportion of the production of acetylene (a raw material for the preparation of ethylene) was derived from methane by a process involving the electric arc for generation of the high temperatures required at short contact times. Various modifications of this process have been proposed in the United States, but so far none has found commercial acceptance.

Molten Metal

The Monsanto Chemical Company has developed and to some extent applied commercially a method for the production of ethylene from propane, involving the use of molten metal as heat-transfer medium. This system requires either charging volatile feed stocks into a packed tower through which a molten metal, such as lead circulates, or directly bubbling the feed stock through a bath of the liquid metal.

Catalytic Processes

Several catalytic processes for the production of ethylene have been proposed within the past 10 years. One of these, the so-called Catarole Process (221a,298), has been put into occasional commercial operation in England but has not yet found practical acceptance in the United States. Essentially, it involves passing the charging stock (naphtha) in vapor phase over a fixed-bed catalyst at temperatures within the range of 1200–1380°F., with pressures from 2–5 atmospheres and space velocities of the order of 0.5–1.0 per hour. The process is, of course, continuous.

According to a process described by Bludworth (337), ethane may be catalytically cracked to ethylene in the temperature range at which propane is usually pyrolyzed for the production of ethylene.

2.3. Separation and Recovery

Low-temperature, high-pressure, straight fractionation. The process most commonly used in this country for the separation of ethylene involves fractionation of the cracked gases under high pressures and at low temperatures. It has been estimated (224) that some 75% of all ethylene produced in the United States is recovered in this manner. Two principal fractionating towers are required. In the first, the so-called demethanizer, hydrogen, methane, and any other light products are separated from the ethylene, ethane, and higher components. In the second, the ethylene tower, the bottoms from the demethanizer are separated. Product ethylene is taken overhead, and the remaining still bottoms are either recycled to fractionation or to cracking operations, or removed from the system as fuel.

In a typical commercial operation, the ethylene-containing gases are first treated for the removal of butane and higher-boiling fractions, usually by oil absorption. The cracked feed gas is then compressed, usually in three or four stages, to a pressure of 530–600 p.s.i.g., and dried. Drying is effected in at least two steps. In the first, gas from the compressor is subcooled to about 65°F. This substantially dry gas is then passed through activated alumina or bauxite to remove residual moisture. As it leaves this step, the gas has a water dew point of about −100°F. The dried gas is then cooled to partial liquefaction by heat exchange and refrigeration, and is introduced into the demethanizer. Here the methane and hydrogen present are removed, together with the theoretical quantity (about 3 to 5 mole per cent) of C_2's required to saturate the overhead stream under the actual conditions of operation, i.e., a reflux condenser temperature of about −130 to −140°F., and an operating pressure of about 550 p.s.i.g. Ethylene is then removed overhead in a high degree of purity, ordinarily of the order of 94–96.5%. The residue is usually separated further by fractionation, and the remaining bottoms finally recycled to pyrolysis. Normally, the entire operation is continuous. Operating temperatures are sufficiently low to keep undesirable polymer formation and exchanger fouling at a minimum. At the same time, thorough dehydration of the gases avoids the formation of ice in the low-temperature equipment.

Special consideration must, of course, be given to the selection of materials of construction which are suitable for low-temperature fractionation operations. Carbon steel can be used only where operating temperatures are above −20°F., since this material is subject to cold embrittlement below this point. For service at lower temperatures, down to −150°F., 3.5% nickel steel is preferred, while 18–8 alloy steel is suitable for use at temperatures as low as −200°F. Some advantage has been claimed for the use of aluminum in permitting relatively inexpensive and rapid assembly of equipment by spot welding.

Low-temperature, low-pressure, straight fractionation. The low-pressure process for the low-temperature fractionation of cracked gases to separate ethylene has been developed in Europe. The first large-scale plant to operate by this scheme was constructed in England and was recently put into operation.

In this method, the cracked gases are quenched and the butane and heavier fractions removed by a conventional absorption operation. The cracked feed gases are then refrigerated by exchange, compressed to 100 p.s.i.g., and passed to a demethanizer, the top of which operates at −200°F. The residues are pumped to a de-ethanizer from which ethane and ethylene are removed overhead. These pass to a final ethylene tower from which ethylene is removed as overhead product.

Low-temperature absorption and fractionation. In low-temperature absorption operations, the cracked ethylene-containing gases are not scrubbed or otherwise treated to remove heavier fractions. Instead, the feed stock is compressed to about 450 p.s.i.g., and oil condensate formed during the operation is separated and recovered. The gases are then introduced into a fractionating absorber or absorber-stripper, where the bulk of the methane present is removed. To accomplish this, a portion of the aromatic distillate resulting from this process is circulated through the absorber at a rate of 3.0 to 4.0 pounds per pound of feed. At this rate, only moderate heat removal in the intercoolers results in the recovery, as bottoms, of about 99% of the ethylene present in the entering feed. About 96% of the methane, substantially all of the hydrogen present, and less than 2% of higher hydrocarbons are removed overhead. This mixture usually serves as a fuel gas. It is particularly desirable to remove at least 96% of the methane by controlling the bottoms to a methane concentration of 4% maximum. Higher methane ratios in the sorbate can be expected to result in operating difficulties in the low-temperature fractionation system which follows. From the absorber, rich oil passes to a stripper, operated at about 425 p.s.i.g. and 450°F., from which ethylene and higher hydrocarbons are removed as overhead. These gases are then dried to a water dew point of −40°F. before passing to the de-ethanizer. In this unit, the separation is made between ethane and propylene. The de-ethanizer column operates at a pressure of 450 p.s.i.g. and an overhead temperature of about +18°F. The overhead from this tower is introduced into an ethylene fractionating column, operated at 385 p.s.i.g. and overhead temperature of +1°F., where ethylene and ethane are separated. Normally, it is also desired to recover propylene. For this purpose, an additional tower is used to separate it from propane. Where this is not done, the entire C_3 fraction is recycled to pyrolysis with uncracked ethane. A portion of the aromatics from the depropanizer residues is used as make-up for the absorber lean oil; the remainder is delivered to aromatic distillate production. It is usually considered advantageous to add a small re-run tower to the system. This serves to eliminate the build-up of heavy polymers which otherwise would accumulate in the aromatic distillate.

Hypersorption. The hypersorption process is unique in separating the fixed gases from the charge stock by means of activated carbon rather than by low-temperature absorption or by fractionation.

After removal of C_5 and heavier fractions, the cracked gases are compressed to 70 p.s.i.g. and passed to the hypersorber column. This column contains a slowly moving bed of activated carbon which serves to adsorb the heavier components of the gases. The methane and lighter components are not adsorbed and are discharged at the top of the column. In the rectifying section of the column, the carbon containing the adsorbed components is brought into intimate contact with a reflux of C_3 hydrocarbons. This reflux is preferentially adsorbed by the carbon, resulting in concentration of the C_2's in the vapor phase. These are separated as a side-cut product. The carbon continues to pass downward, next entering into a stripping section. This usually is comprised of a vertical tube bundle heated by the circulation of diphenyl in the tubes. Just below this section, steam is introduced upwardly countercurrent to the carbon flow. This serves to strip the carbon practically completely of adsorbed components. These, with the steam, are disengaged above the stripping section, and are either recycled to pyrolysis or further separated into propylene and heavier fractions. The carbon leaving the stripper is raised to the top of the hypersorber tower by gas lift. Carbon reactivation by treatment with high-temperature steam is ordinarily undertaken in parallel with the hypersorber. Those lighter feed components, which are neither adsorbed nor displaced from the carbon by the C_2 product reflux, pass upwardly through the adsorption unit and are separated into two streams. The major stream may represent 80% of the combined overhead. It is disengaged as overhead below the cooler and usually serves as fuel gas. The minor portion is used to dehydrate the stripped carbon. The C_2 side cut disengaged from the hypersorber represents a substantially pure ethylene-ethane mixture. It is separated in the conventional manner, and pure (95%+) ethylene removed as overhead.

Solvent extraction. Solvent extraction is based upon the fact that a solution of cuprous nitrate in aqueous monoethanolamine exhibits a high equilibrium capacity for ethylene, and is nearly ideally selective with regard to fixed gases and paraffins. This principle was developed to semi-commercial unit size by the I. G. Farben. during World War II, but a projected full-scale unit was never erected. As practiced at the I. G. Oppau Works (296), the composition of the absorption liquor was as follows:

Cuprous copper	12.5	g./l.
Cupric copper	9	g./l.
Nitrate ion	190	g./l.
Monoethanolamine	383	g./l.
Ammonia	18	g./l.

The feed gas contained 36.25% ethylene, and absorption operations were carried out under a pressure of 300 p.s.i.g. Ethylene-rich liquor leaving the absorption tower contained some entrained ethane which was removed by reducing the pressure to 40 p.s.i.g. Ethane-ethylene mixture was recycled to the absorption stage. The de-ethanized solution was finally freed of ethylene by reducing the pressure to 150 mm. Hg at 100–105°F. Product ethylene was acid-washed to remove entrained ammonia, followed by an alkali wash to remove any carbon dioxide.

On a theoretical basis, the process appears to offer maximum advantage in operations where only ethylene or an ethylene-propylene fraction is to be recovered. Little or no advantage for it can be demonstrated where ethane recovery for pyrolysis to ethylene is also desired.

2.4. Purification and Testing

Ethylene for the manufacture of polyethylene must be essentially free of impurities which are known to affect the course of the reaction and the properties of the resultant polymers. This is to be expected for a polymerization reaction, and the theoretical and empirical basis for it will be made clear in subsequent chapters. According to a recent discussion (923a), the requirements for the purity of the ethylene used in the low-pressure polyethylene process discovered by Ziegler (see Section 1.5) are less rigorous than those for the high-pressure, high-temperature polymerization process. In the latter, ethylene of extremely high purity is required, since only a relatively low proportion of the ethylene is polymerized in a single pass. In the Ziegler process, on the other hand, this high purity of the ethylene is not essential, and even diluted gas can be used. However, certain impurities, such as carbon monoxide, acetylene, oxygen, and moisture, must still be removed from the feed gas.

Polymerization processes described in Brit. 579,666 (252), 579,676 (253), and 579,938 (258) to Forsyth and I.C.I. require the use of ethylene containing less than 0.02% of carbon monoxide; saturated compounds containing all of the elements carbon, hydrogen, oxygen; and olefins and saturated hydrocarbons, respectively. The later Brit. 585,814 to I.C.I. (313) claims that yields and molecular weights of polyethylenes are improved by using ethylene monomer which contains less than 0.1% by volume of acetylene. According to Brit. 582,334 (272), ethylene polymers of uniform quality may be prepared in good yield by using ethylene containing not more than 0.2% by volume of hydrogen. Here and in other instances, e.g., Tani (300); also Brit. 587,378 to Hunter, Feachem, Richards, and I.C.I. (317), a suitable grade of ethylene may be prepared by careful dehydration of ethyl alcohol.

According to Austrian 171,701 to Asboth (662), pure ethylene is obtained by the catalytic hydrogenation of carbon monoxide at 180–265°C. under 0.05–1.0 atmosphere pressure. The carbon monoxide-hydrogen ratio is less than 1/1, preferably 1/1.5. Incompletely reduced iron catalysts (density 1.1–1.3), containing 50–90% inert fillers, are used.

Purification. A number of patents have been issued relating to the purification of ethylene prior to polymerization. U.S. 2,388,138 to Greenewalt [duPont (202)], and Brit. 584,309 to I.C.I. (305) suggest the use of liquefied ethylene in the production of polyethylene. According to this process, ethylene is liquefied by compressing to 20–150 atmospheres and cooling to −35 to +5°C. The pressure is then increased to 800–3,000 atmospheres, and polymerization is effected at 50–400°C. by oxygen or peroxide-type catalysts introduced into the reactor in aqueous solution. Liquefaction under pressures less than those required for polymerization is claimed to prevent contamination of the product by lubricants in the compressor, since this lubricant is much more soluble in liquid ethylene at high pressures.

U. S. 2,581,088 to Etherington and Scheeline [Standard Oil (646)] describes process and apparatus for fractionating low molecular weight hydrocarbons, such as ethylene, from gaseous mixtures. Box in U. S. 2,587,680 to Phillips Petroleum (652) describes a process for separating acetylene from gaseous hydrocarbon mixtures by scrubbing with liquid acetic anhydride in an absorber, stripping dissolved acetylene, and recirculating. This process is based upon the fact that one volume of acetic anhydride dissolves 8.6 volumes of acetylene at 24°C. and at atmospheric pressure, but only 1.2 volumes of ethylene. Under the same conditions, the contact of 250 volumes of gas containing 92.7% ethylene and 7.4% acetylene with 30 volumes of acetic anhydride yields a gas containing 96.8% ethylene and 3.2% acetylene. U. S. 2,590,322 to Imhoff and Berg [Union Oil (654)] relates to an absorption process for separating ethylene from ethylene oxide and other gaseous constituents. The absorption column has a diameter of 11 feet and is 130 feet high. Operating pressures are in the neighborhood of 60 p.s.i.g. The column recovers better than 95% by volume of ethylene, with a simultaneous recovery of more than 97% by volume of ethylene oxide.

According to U. S. 2,635,709 to Archibald, Konrad, and Haney [Standard Oil (791)], gaseous ethylene may be preferentially adsorbed from a mixture of ethane and propane. The acid sludge, a petroleum refining byproduct consisting of carbonaceous residues mixed with sulfuric acid and sulfamic acid, is brought into contact with hot petroleum coke in a proportion of from 2/1 to 6/1 coke to acid sludge, at 200–400°C., until the volatile content is distilled. The carbonized sludge is calcined at 315–650°C. for 5–25 minutes. Seven pounds of product are returned for carbonization for every pound removed as petroleum coke. Absorbability is increased if the product is treated with nitrogen for 15–60 minutes at 870–980°C. Unless steam is used for desorption, the petroleum coke will retain its properties.

Purity of the ethylene is also required if sensitive organometallic activators are used in the polymerization reaction. Ziegler and Gellert (compare Section 3.5) point out in U. S. 2,699,457 (1048) that organometallic activators react easily with oxygen, carbon dioxide, water, and other substances, and are decomposed by them. This would render the molecular weight and reaction rate determining mole ratio of ethylene to activator uncertain. This difficulty can be avoided by: (a) "titrating away" the impurities of the ethylene with small quantities of the activator; (b) pretreating the ethylene with activator, preferably trialkyl aluminum; (c) adding to the polymerization certain organometallic compounds which remove all contaminants except carbon dioxide, but do not disturb the polymerization.

Testing. The considerable influence of some impurities in ethylene on the polymerization and on the properties of the resultant polymers makes accurate and, at the same time, speedy methods of analysis necessary.

For the determination of the purity of ethylene, fuming sulfuric acid or bromine water may be used as absorbents in the Hempel pipette or similar equipment.

For the determination of impurities, e.g., CO, CO_2, CH_4, C_2H_2, and SO_2 in ethylene, infrared gas analyzers may be used (Baird Associates, Inc., Leeds and Northrup, Liston-Becker Instrument Company, Inc., The Perkin-Elmer Corporation) (547). For the determination of the "nonabsorbers" of infrared, e.g., H_2, Cl_2, H_2S, electroconductivity and thermal-conductivity analyzers are suitable (Davis Instruments). Oxygen analyzers (Beckman, Leeds and Northrup) (681) are based on the fact that this gas is extremely paramagnetic, whereas most other common gases are slightly diamagnetic. In the case of the Davis Oxygen Analyzer, the specific quantitative oxygen measurement is achieved through the utilization of a specially designed cell in which the oxidation-reduction potential is measured. A regenerative liquor consisting of a complex ammoniacal ammonium chloride solution containing cuprous ions makes up the closed cycle system. The concentration of oxygen, in the range 10 ppm to 2% by volume, within the process stream, is determined when a portion of the stream is passed through the analyzer.

Several interesting recording gas analyzers of foreign make (Hartmann and Braun A.-G., Frankfurt am Main, Germany) deserve mention. Their oxygen meter "Magnos" is based on the paramagnetism of oxygen (479). For small amounts of oxygen which cannot be determined by this method, the "Thermoflux" is recommended, the heat generated by gas absorption acting as measuring principle; H_2O, H_2S, and organic sulfur can also be determined by the use of different absorbing liquids. A still more sensitive method of gas analysis, based on the change of the electrical conductivity of absorbing reagents, is provided by the "Electroflux"; traces of O_2, H_2O, H_2S, SO_2, NH_3, and CO_2 may be determined. The "Bulliflux" is designed for the determination of N_2 and H_2, which cannot be measured by the above methods. In this instrument, bubbles of the nonabsorbed gas traverse a capillary strangulation, carrying alternating current for their electrovolumetric measurement; depending upon the number and volume of the gas bubbles, a decrease of the mean current value is recorded. A critical discussion of these methods, with particular emphasis on the measurement of oxygen, has been recently presented by Krupp (989). A recent paper by Pepkowitz (1011) describes an instrument based on the dew principle for the continuous detection and measurement of oxygen in common gases, such as nitrogen, helium and the other rare gases, hydrogen, and carbon dioxide; this information is frequently required in polymerization studies of ethylene. A sensitivity of at least 0.0005 volume per cent of oxygen is attained with a mean deviation for precision of ±0.0001 volume per cent. While these instruments are exclusively used for the analysis of inorganic gases, the infrared selective absorbing analyzer "Uras" is recommended for the analysis of organic gases, including C_2H_2.

Acetylene in ethylene can also be determined colorimetrically with the Ilosvay solution, which is based on the formation of red copper acetylide. Another method (14) is based on the absorption of acetylene in a 20% solution of $Hg(CN)_2$ in $2N$ NaOH.

An accuracy of ±0.01% is claimed for the methods of determination of oxygen in ethylene by $Cu-NH_3$ and by $Mn(OH)_2$, and of aldehyde by NH_2OH (302). Separation and determination of gases by a chromatographic adsorption method has been described by Cremer (530,531).

III. POLYMERIZATION OF ETHYLENE

3.1. Kinetic Studies (Polymerization in Gas Phase and Bulk)

The status of the present knowledge of the mechanism of polymerization reactions has been presented in several recent books (481, 730b, 835) and will not be dealt with in this volume. It may suffice to point out that vinyl polymerization, whether effected by purely thermal or photochemical means, or induced by radical-producing catalysts, ionic catalysts, or by sodium, may be assumed to proceed by a chain-reaction mechanism. Persuasive evidence may be cited for this conclusion (12,25,35,39,42,46,47, 53,55,70,78,80,122).

Korshak (400,401) noted that substituted ethylenes generally polymerize more readily than ethylene, and investigated the influence of the number and of the nature of substituents on the polymerizability. He concluded from the data available that polymerizability is directly connected with the dipole moment, and that an increase of polymerizability is caused by polarization of the $C:C$ link under the influence of the substituent.

The nature of the carbon-carbon double bond and the energy levels of ethylene have been discussed in order to explain the elementary processes of polymerization (4). Mark and Raff (120) attempted a comparison and correlation between heat of hydrogenation, activation energy of polymerization, and product of collision number and steric factor, for the polymerization of ethylene and other unsaturated molecules, by interpretation of values taken from Eirich (65) and Kistiakowsky (37,44).

An investigation of the theory of absolute reaction rates and the polymerization of ethylene has been made by Jahn (79). He found that, granting simple assumptions concerning the entropy of activation, calculations of the rate of homogeneous thermal polymerization agreed satisfactorily with experimental values determined by Eyring's activated complex method (34).

The earliest publication indicating that ethylene can be polymerized in the gas phase by free radicals is a paper by Taylor (16). Based on this study, Pease (21) demonstrated the dimerization of ethylene to an unsaturated hydrocarbon at temperatures between 350 and 500°C., and pressures between 2 and 10 atmospheres. The reaction progressed slowly at the lower pressure, but was accelerated as the pressure was increased; decomposition diminished and some higher molecular weight polymer appears to have formed. The collision efficiency was found to be 5×10^{-4}. In view of the low steric factor, Pease (26) subsequently carried out hydrogenation experiments in which polymerization was prevented by the use of an excess of hydrogen. From the data obtained, the collision efficiency was calculated to be nearly normal, i.e., about 0.1.

Studies of the kinetics of ethylene polymerization were conducted by Storch (31,40) with material carefully purified by different methods. Small amounts of oxygen greatly accelerated the reaction rate, and the presence of small amounts of sulfur or mercaptans decreased it. Actually, 0.1% of ethyl mercaptan decreased the rate of polymerization about tenfold, and did not eliminate the induction period, although markedly reducing its duration. The polymerization reaction, which was carried out under a pressure of 141.5 cm. Hg and at temperatures between 350 and 400°C., resulted in butylene as the primary and propylene as the secondary product. The energy of activation was determined to be 43,500 cal./mol, compared with a value of 35,000 cal./mol observed by Pease.

Russell and Hottel (69) investigated the polymerization of ethylene in the gas and liquid phases, the latter when dissolved in liquid naphthalene. Reaction conditions and composition of the resultant gaseous products are shown in Table VII.

Little difference was found in the reaction rates at the same ethylene concentration, despite the presence in the latter case of 14 moles of naphthalene per mole of ethylene. It was shown that, in the gas phase, the polymerization in its early stages is a second order reaction. In the liquid phase it is of an order between second and third. As polymerization proceeds, the reaction rate does not fall off, and it was concluded that secondary reactions take place between ethylene and its polymers. No detectable reaction occurred between the naphthalene and the dissolved ethylene. The addition of extra surface in the reaction bomb was without effect on the reaction, indicating the polymerization to be homogeneous. The effect of temperature on the primary reaction was to double the rate every 15°C. over the range of 335–415°C. The corrected energy of activation was determined to be 40,000 cal./mol for the liquid-phase reaction, and 42,100 cal./mol for the gas-phase reaction.

The ethylene polymerization studies so far reported were carried out at relatively low pressures and yielded gaseous or liquid reaction products. A very extensive series of investigations on the high-pressure polymerization of ethylene to form solid reaction products has been conducted by

TABLE VII. Polymerization of Ethylene

Inside reactor temp., °F.	Phase	Pressure during run, lb./sq.in.	Reaction time (cor.), min.	Vol. of product gas (70° F., 1 atm.), cc.	Analysis of product gas — C₂H₄, %	High polymers, %	Residue, %	C₃H₈, %	Concn. at start of polymerization, mole/l.	C₂H₄ Concn. at end of polymerization, mole/l.	Polymerized, %
777	Liquid	3030	68.9	375	87.0	6.7+	5.8+	(0.45)	0.362 −	0.111+	69.2
	Liquid	3030	31.8	636	95.5	2.6	1.4	(0.45)	0.358	0.2266	36.5
	Liquid	3030	19.2	732	97.25	1.4	0.9+	(0.45)	0.359	0.270	24.6
	Liquid	5800	9.4+	1133.5	96.75	1.7+	1.0+	0.5	0.540	0.415	23.2
	Gas	:	50.95	471	79.4	13.5	6.6	(0.45)	0.3596	0.134	62.7
	Gas	:	32.8	660	86.9	9.5	3.0	(0.45)	0.3595	0.2158	40.0
	Gas	:	17.45	779	91.3	6.4	1.8	(0.45)	0.3624	0.272	24.9
	Gas	:	11.92	810	93.05	4.75	1.75	(0.45)	0.364	0.290	20.2
	Gas	:	10.37	1175+	93.2	5.15	1.35	0.30	0.569	0.4145	27.0
733	Mixed	5800	34.7	1246	88.1	6.85	4.6	(0.45)	1.651	0.429	74. ?
	Liquid?	5800	28.0	1291	95.6	2.3	1.6	0.50	0.793	0.469	42.1 ?
	Liquid	5800	34.66	1055	96.05	2.2+	1.2 −	0.55	0.564+	0.3819	32.4
	Liquid	5800	28.4+	1113	97.45	1.65	0.5	0.5	0.571	0.410+	28.1
	Liquid	3030	90.7	629	(94.9)	?	?	?	0.3754	0.2225	40.6
	Liquid	3030	64.0	725.5	95.7	2.0	1.5	0.8	0.372+	0.263+	29.3
	Liquid^a	3030	64.17	689.5	93.8+	1.95	3.75	0.5 −	0.3706	0.2503	32.4
710	Liquid	5800	70.85	975	96.1	2.3	1.1+	0.5 −	0.5676	0.3485	38.6
	Liquid	5800	47.83	1183	97.15	1.15	1.2	0.5	0.5662	0.4385	22.6
675	Mixed	5800	48.9	2783	96.5	2.1 −	1.2 −	0.25	1.754	1.048	40.3?
	Liquid	5800	169.8	1019	96.45	2.0+	1.0+	0.5	0.580	0.368+	36.4
	Liquid	5800	126.0	1150	97.3	1.2	1.0+	0.5	0.579	0.4258	26.4+
	Liquid	5800	87.56	1260	97.4	0.9	1.25	0.45	0.576	0.469	18.5
	Liquid	3030	254.1	750	95.3	1.4	2.65	0.65	0.386+	0.2715	29.5
675	Gas	:	44.3	3204	96.9	1.65	1.0	0.45	2.012	1.180	41.3+
	Gas	:	115.4	1299	95.2	2.7+	1.7	0.35	0.578	0.479+	17.1
	Gas	:	203.8	820	93.5+	3.8	2.2	0.45	0.368 −	0.2968	19.26
640	Liquid	5800	336.6	1190	97.4+	1.4	0.7	0.5	0.5855	0.4425	24.4
518	Liquid	3030	51±	1075	98.9	0.0	1.3?	..?	0.420	0.416	Nil
249	Liquid	3030	480±		..........Not analyzed............				0.4935	0.491	Nil

Source: *Ind. Eng. Chem.*, **30**, 183 (1938).
^a Run was made with extra reactor surface added in the form of metal turnings.

Japanese research workers. Kodoma, Tahara, and Taniguchi (219) studied the polymerization of ethylene at 1,000–1,800 atmospheres and at 250–285°C., by measuring the decrease in pressure of ethylene in an autoclave. Similarly, the polymerization of ethylene under high pressure was studied by Kume (220), Tani, Mori, and Horie (302,303), and Tani and Sato (351). Preliminary experiments were carried out with liquid ethylene containing 0.02–0.06% oxygen. Pressure-temperature curves showed an inflection at about 160°C. and a maximum pressure at about 245°C. and 1,600 kg. per sq. cm., which is taken to indicate the beginning of polymerization. The experiment was repeated 45 times with purified ethylene and curves of about the same general form were obtained. When the ethylene was diluted with nitrogen, the reaction was smooth but the polymerization products were brittle and the yields small. In later experiments, the reaction gas was analyzed at intervals; the polyethylene produced was recrystallized from benzene, and melting point, refractive index, and electrical properties were examined. The pressure in the reaction tube was 415–1,035 kg. per sq. cm. at room temperature. When the temperature was raised gradually, the first vigorous reaction occurred at about 200°C., followed by a second reaction. If more than 0.033–0.045% of oxygen was mixed with the gas, the first reaction became an explosion. Ethylene containing 0.02% of oxygen gave a product having a molecular weight of 29,900, while a product with a molecular weight of 15,300 was obtained from ethylene containing 0.08% of oxygen. The addition of 0.3–0.9% of carbon monoxide did not alter the course of reaction, but the electrical nature of the product was greatly affected. Aluminum, nickel, and especially copper accelerated the second reaction. When reduced copper was used, the resultant polyethylene was insoluble in organic solvents. In one of this series of experiments (303), an attempt was made to prepare a polyethylene of the highest possible molecular weight. To further this end, a careful examination was made of the various factors affecting the reaction, such as the purity of ethylene, the reaction pressure, reaction temperature, and effect of metal. Some 70 experiments were performed under various conditions. A product with a molecular weight of 65,000 was the highest obtained. In most cases, the initial pressure was about 1,000 atmospheres (the highest 2,000, and the lowest 400 atmospheres), and the pressures at reaction temperature were 900–3,000 atmospheres. The first reaction step previously noted was studied in detail and fully characterized. It was established that when the reaction pressure is low and the ethylene is impure, the reaction proceeds in one step only. Other effects were noted. The purer the ethylene, the higher the molecular weight of the polyethylene. The higher the reaction pressure, the higher the molecular weight and the melting point of the resultant products. The higher the oxygen content, the more vigorous the polymerization reaction.

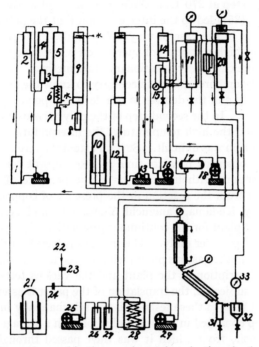

Fig. 7. Apparatus used in the experimental production of polyethylene

1. Alcohol storage tank
2. High storage tank
3. Rotameter
4. Evaporator
5. Drying unit
6. Cooling unit
7. Separator
8. Shell tank
9. Washing tower (water)
10. Storage tank for purified ethylene
11. Alkali washing tower
12. Alkali storage tank
13. Alkali pump
14. Ethylene liquefier unit
15. Liquid ethylene storage tank
16. Crude ethylene compressor unit
17. Ammonia storage tank
18. Ammonia compressor unit
19. No. 1 rectifying column
20. No. 2 rectifying column
21. Purified ethylene storage tank
22. Oxygen
23. Oxygen flowmeter
24. Ethylene flowmeter
25. Purified ethylene compressor
26. Dehydrator (dehumidifier)
27. Oil separator
28. Liquefier
29. Ethylene pump
30. Reaction tube
31. High pressure separator
32. Ordinary pressure separator
33. Gasmeter

(*J. Chem. Soc. Japan, Ind. Chem. Sect.*, **57,** 439, 1954.)

The allowable oxygen at about 2,000 atmospheres and 165°C. is 0.075%. If this limit is passed, an explosive decomposition reaction occurs and the products are mainly carbon, methane, and hydrogen. The rate of the second reaction step at 270°C. is three times as great as the rate at 240°C. Further studies (351) led to the interpretation that the polymerization is a chain reaction as in the case of vinyl compounds. The general reaction-rate equation of high-pressure polymerization was derived in terms of the observed pressure change by a stationary-state method. To determine the reaction velocity and order, it was necessary to know the volume coefficient or compressibility and the density of ethylene and polyethylene at the reaction conditions. In the second step of the polymerization, because of the high pressure and the high temperature, the interpretation of an accurate reaction mechanism was difficult. Several attempts were made to compare theoretical and observed pressure-time relationships at constant temperature. The reactions without metal or in the presence of aluminum are clearly different from the reaction in the presence of copper.

Quite recently, Kodama, Taniguchi, Yuasa, Ota, and Terada (858) have described a pilot plant for the continuous production of polyethylene at the rate of 10 kg. of polymer daily. The method is based on the polymerization of ethylene in the gaseous phase, with oxygen used as the catalyst. In the following description of the plant and the various tests to which this equipment was subjected, the translation of the paper is essentially quoted. The equipment used in these tests is shown schematically in Figure 7.

The first step consisted in pumping alcohol from a storage tank up to an elevated reservoir, from which it was then passed through a rotameter and pumped into an evaporator. The alcohol vapor produced in this stage was then passed through a drier filled with particles and fragments of alumina. The alcohol vapor was effectively dehydrated in this unit at a temperature of about 350°C., and the ethylene so produced was then passed through a water cooler. The next stage was to send it through a scrubber, the product from this operation then being stored in a special crude-ethylene storage tank.

Next, the still unrefined ethylene was sent through an alkali-washing tower, after which it was compressed to 35 atmospheres in an ethylene compressor, and upon cooling to −30°C. it was liquefied. One portion of the liquefied ethylene was pumped into a rectifying column and there "refined," while the remaining portion was sent into a cooling unit mounted in the upper part of the rectifying column and there used as the cooling agent. The refining or purification of the ethylene was carried out in two rectifying columns at a temperature of about −40°C. and under 15 atmospheres of pressure. The high-boiling fraction was removed from the lower part of the first column, while the low-boiling fraction was taken from the upper portion of the second column. The refined or purified ethylene which had collected in the lower portion of the No. 2 column was stored in the refined ethylene reservoir. As for the degree of purity of the refined ethylene, it is to be noted that the oxygen content of the latter was not more than 0.002%.

After the required amount of oxygen had been added to the ethylene from the refined ethylene storage tank, it was subjected to a pressure of 40 atmospheres and liquefied at a temperature of $-25°C$. In this operation, alcohol at a temperature of $-25°C$. was circulated in the outer jacket, and the thoroughly cooled liquid ethylene obtained by this method was then brought under the high pressure required for the reaction by the use of a plunger or piston-type pump (7 liters/hr.). When the ethylene-oxygen mixture had been compressed to the required reaction pressure, it was sent into the reaction tube. This reaction tube had an inner diameter of 15 mm. and a length of 5 m., and the outer part consisted of a jacket through which heating oil could be circulated in order to maintain the required reaction temperature. One portion of the polyethylene produced in the reaction tube was introduced into the high pressure separator and separated in the liquid state under the same pressure as that of the reaction, this fraction being drawn off at the bottom of the high-pressure separator, while at the same time another portion was subjected to decompression, after which the portion of the ethylene which had not reacted was separated in the atmospheric-pressure separator. The unreacted ethylene was pumped back to the storage tank for crude or unrefined ethylene. A quantitative analysis of the oxygen content of the ethylene was carried out by extracting some ethylene from the refined ethylene compressor, passing a part of it through the analytical apparatus where it was burned in the presence of a zinc catalyst, and measuring the rise in temperature produced by this combustion.

The molecular weight of the polyethylene was obtained from measurements of the viscosity of a tetralin solution at 75°C. as applied in Staudinger's equation, $\lim_{C \to 0} (\eta_{sp.}/C_{gm.}) = KM$ (where $K = 0.93 \times 10^{-4}$). It was found however, that the resultant products were rather nonuniform and that their molecular weights varied over a correspondingly wide range; this can be inferred from the wide range of melting points shown in Tables VIII and IX. It must accordingly be assumed that, in each case, under the conditions for the measurement of molecular weight, there remained an

TABLE VIII. Influence of the Reaction Temperature (Pressure, 1150 atm.)

Experiment number	Reaction temp., °C.	Oxygen content, %	Ethylene feed rate, kg./hr.	Total yield, g.	Yield, g./hr.	Yield, %	Molecular weight	Melting point, °C.	Mechanical properties		Electrical properties		
									Tensile strength kg./mm.²	Elongation, %	Frequency, mc.	Power factor, tan δ × 10⁴	Dielectric constant, ε
58	150	0.020	3.39	708	217	6.4	44,000	115~220	1.39	260	1.5	7	2.36
60	"	0.021	3.08	598	220	7.2	37,000	107~165	1.52	300	"	14	2.34
59	"	0.023	3.06	449	286	9.4	52,000	107~150	1.60	320	"	"	2.30
61	"	0.031	3.09	935	365	11.8	37,000	109~117	1.20	210	"	11	2.34
55	160	0.018	3.10	899	320	10.3	40,000	108~120	1.42	230	"	4	2.35
54	"	0.019	"	1180	367	11.8	38,000	"	1.25	450	"	3	2.34
57	"	0.023	"	1125	413	13.3	32,000	"	1.50	400	"	5	2.35
56	"	0.032	"	1120	361	11.6	35,000	102~116	1.77	420	"	3	"
65	170	0.016	"	1283	384	12.4	36,000	109~149	1.57	430	1.6	9	2.33
72	"	0.017	3.00	1651	392	13.1	35,000	110~145	..	..	..	..	..
64	"	0.020	3.07	1532	460	15.0	27,800	108~117	1.62	450	1.6	4	2.32
63	"	0.025	3.10	1100	456	14.7	32,000	101~108	"	460	"	"	2.34
62	"	0.028	"	1140	436	14.1	"	108~120	1.08	230	"	6	2.36
67	180	0.008	3.56	592	271	7.6	36,400	117~150	2.30	450	"	3	2.33
66	"	0.010	2.78	1131	303	10.9	38,000	112~134	1.66	460	"	5	"
68	"	0.013	3.00	1141	411	13.7	27,750	104~110	1.50	470	"	3	2.34
105	190	0.002	3.50	516	129	3.7	39,900	108~125	2.13	"	1.5	"	2.33
106	200	"	3.43	428	143	4.2	31,700	106~115	1.83	430	"	"	2.34
107	210	0.003	3.23	657	172	5.3	47,500	107~117	1.42	340	"	"	2.33
108	220	0.002	3.15	401	176	5.6	28,900	109~116	2.16	600	"	"	"
109	230	0.0025	3.28	595	187	5.7	26,800	102~110	1.72	570	"	"	"
137	"	0.0037	3.30	2016	295	8.9	25,300	95~108	..	..	..	..	..
135	"	0.0040	"	994	350	10.6	22,400	....	..	..	..	..	..
140	"	0.0042	"	1761	348	10.5	23,200	97~106	..	..	..	..	..
139	"	0.0043	"	2282	410	12.4	20,600	98~103	..	..	..	..	..
136	"	0.0045	"	1888	252	7.6	20,500	103~107	..	..	..	..	..
110	240	0.004	3.18	720	229	7.2	25,800	105~108	1.33	520	1.5	4	2.33

TABLE IX

Influence of the Reaction Pressure (Temperature, 160°C.)

Experiment number	Reaction pressure, atm.	Oxygen content, %	Ethylene feed rate, kg./hr.	Total yield, g.	Yield, g./hr.	Yield, %	Molecular weight	Melting point, °C.	Mechanical properties		Electrical properties		
									Tensile strength, kg./mm.²	Elongation, %	Frequency, mc.	Power factor, tan δ × 10⁴	Dielectric constant, ε
48	800	0.030	3.20	196	56	1.8	35,500	107~121	1.05	220	1.5	9	2.32
49	"	0.040	"	662	170	5.3	25,000	88~106	"	130	"	"	2.36
50	"	0.050	3.05	216	120	3.8	21,000	86~102	1.24	120	"	14	2.34
44	1000	0.025	3.14	140	140	4.6	32,000	110~185	1.64	500	"	8	2.32
46	"	0.030	3.20	877	240	7.7	33,000	105~112	:	:	"	5	2.33
52	"	"	"	1752	220	6.9	25,000	98~115	1.22	580	"	6	2.29
47	"	0.035	"	579	193	5.6	27,000	119~132	1.04	380	"	16	2.33
55	1150	0.018	3.10	899	320	10.3	40,000	108~120	1.42	230	"	4	2.35
54	"	0.019	"	1180	367	11.8	37,000	105~114	1.43	430	"	3	2.34
57	"	0.023	"	1125	413	13.3	32,000	108~130	1.67	400	"	5	"
56	"	0.028	"	1120	360	11.6	35,000	102~116	1.77	420	"	3	2.35
33	1350	0.016	3.00	783	309	10.3	83,000	145~260	:	:	:	:	:
34	"	0.018	"	1733	450	15.0	66,000	115~185	1.86	492	4.5	4	2.40
27	"	0.022	2.96	2166	476	16.0	41,000	105~125	1.60	440	4.2	6	2.35
37	"	0.023	3.00	6566	455	15.2	37,000	101~108	1.90	410	1.5	5	"
30	"	0.025	3.03	2684	255	8.4	:	::::	:	:	:	:	:

Source: J. Chem. Soc. Japan, Ind. Chem. Sect., **57**, 439 (1954).

undissolved portion in all of the test specimens. In the case of products
with a molecular weight of 20,000–25,000, this amount must have ranged

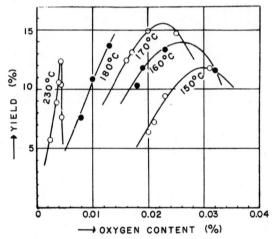

Fig. 8. Influence of reaction temperature (pressure 1,150 atm.).
(*J. Chem. Soc. Japan, Ind. Chem. Sect.*, **57**, 439, 1954.)

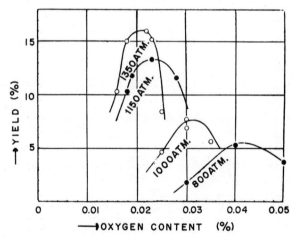

Fig. 9. Influence of reaction pressure (temperature 160°C.). (*J.
Chem. Soc. Japan, Ind. Chem. Sect.*, **57**, 439, 1954.)

up to 10%, while in the case of test specimens with a high molecular weight,
it might have reached as high as 70%. The figures for the molecular weight
given in the table show the values obtained for the dissolved portions. It

is to be observed, further, that when the test specimens were subjected to cold rolling or similar mechanical treatment, the low molecular weight specimens proved to be completely soluble, whereas the high molecular weight specimens, after similar mechanical treatment, showed that they retained an insoluble portion.

In order to show the influence of temperature and pressure on the reaction, Tables VIII and IX present, respectively, the changes in the oxygen increment under the various experimental conditions of temperature and pressure.

The reaction temperature shown in the tables is that of the heating oil which circulates about the reaction tube, as measured at the intake opening, where it begins to flow around the reactor. The yields, as given in Tables VIII and IX are shown in Figures 8 and 9, respectively, as a function of the oxygen content for various temperatures and pressures.

The influence of the oxygen content on the yield of polyethylene obtained by this process is shown in Figures 8 and 9, in which there is a correspondingly sharp point of maximum yield. When this point is passed and the amount of oxygen is increased, there is a sudden drop in the yield of polyethylene, as well as in its molecular weight; if this is continued to the point where the oxygen content becomes excessive, the reaction finally is converted into the explosive reaction given by the equation $C_2H_4 \rightarrow CH_4 + C$, with soot the only readily recognized product of the reaction. At the same time, it is to be observed that just before the oxygen content reached the explosive stage, the only recognizable product obtained was a substance with a molecular weight characteristic of the lower, waxy paraffins. Accordingly, in the industrial production of polyethylene very delicate control of the oxygen increment is absolutely necessary.

In general, there is a definite connection between the lowering of the molecular weight of the reaction products and the increase in the amount of oxygen. For example, this tendency is very clearly indicated in the experimental results shown in Table IX for the series conducted under a pressure of 1,350 atmospheres.

For a given oxygen content of the reacting mixture, the yield of the product obtained increases as the temperature rises. Thus, the maximum yield for the oxygen content which was considered most suitable above is shown in Figure 8, in which there is a small increase in yield for increases in temperature up to 170°C. However, when the reaction temperature is 230°C., the maximum yield is, on the other hand, less than that for 170°C. It is also apparent from the same figure that the range of oxygen content for maximum yield tends to narrow with rise in temperature, and that as the temperature rises, the oxygen content for maximum yield is displaced in the direction of less oxygen.   At 230°C., the allowed range of oxygen content is very narrow.   The data shown in Table VIII also indicate that the range of oxygen increment which was able to produce corresponding yields of polyethylene was only 0.0025–0.0045%.

It is further noted that there exists a general tendency for the molecular weight of the polyethylene produced to decrease as the temperature of the reaction rises.   This, too, can readily be seen when the molecular weight of the polyethylene is observed for the various temperatures in Table VIII.

As indicated in Figure 9, both the average yield and the maximum yield of the polyethylene produced for a fixed proportion of oxygen in the reaction mixture increase with an increase in the reaction pressure, but again the allowed range of oxygen increment becomes narrower with increase of pressure; and, as in the case of temperature, the oxygen content for maximum yield of polyethylene is displaced to the left, i.e., in the direction of a diminished proportion of catalytic oxygen, as the reaction pressure increases.

The fact that the molecular weight of the produced polyethylene increases with an increase in the pressure of the reaction can be seen by comparing the molecular weights with the various reaction pressures as these are given in Table IX.

From a theoretical standpoint, Bryant (529) has applied data on the free energies of formation of hydrocarbon free radicals to the mechanism of polyethylene synthesis.   It is demonstrated that initiation and chain propagation steps in the polymerization of ethylene are favorable thermodynamically.

The heat of polymerization of ethylene, 800–1000 cal./g. (347) [cf. (53)] is considerably greater than that of other monomers, e.g., styrene (164 cal./g.).   In addition to the difficulties inherent in all high-pressure reactions, the control of this high heat of polymerization is one of the most important problems in the polymerization of ethylene.   This is all the more true since the decomposition reactions occurring at elevated temperatures are also exothermic, and explosions may take place in the case of a run-away reaction.   In addition, the concentration of ethylene molecules under the conditions of high-pressure polymerization, i.e., approximately 1,000 atmospheres and 200–300°C., is closer to that of a liquid than a gas from the standpoint of density, although still above the critical temperature (9.90°C.) of ethylene.   Within limits, as is typical for polymerization reactions in general, an increase in the reaction temperature increases the rate of reaction but results in polymers of decreased molecular size.

Notwithstanding these data, the I.C.I. and similar processes to polymerize ethylene require high pressures and temperatures. This apparent contradiction, still more emphasized by the fact that ethylene can be polymerized to high molecular weight products under extremely mild reaction conditions by the use of special catalysts (see Section 3.5), is explained by Ziegler (1046) as follows. In the conventional activation with oxygen, the formation of some unknown peroxide of ethylene must be assumed which furnishes the radical initiators on subsequent decomposition. Since this decomposition apparently takes place fast enough only above 150°C., the concentration of ethylene, a gas, is too low at this high temperature and must be increased by the aid of high pressure to a level at which the reaction can proceed with sufficient speed.

3.2. Effect of Hydrogen and Other Gases

The addition of various gaseous components to ethylene prior to polymerization has been described in several patents. For example, U. S. 2,387,755 to Hanford [duPont (201)] relates to the use of ethylene containing 0.2–10% of hydrogen. This mixture is polymerized at a temperature in excess of 40°C. under a pressure greater than 50 atmospheres, in the presence of a peroxy-type compound or of oxygen as the catalyst. Preferably water and benzene are also present. A polymer produced in accordance with this process had a tensile strength at cold draw of 1,200 p.s.i. and at break of 1,200 p.s.i.; it had an elongation and a softening point of 188% and 79°C., respectively. Products of this type are said to be especially suited for domestic wax and for the preparation of shoe, floor, and furniture polishes.

The addition of inert gases (nitrogen, hydrogen, carbon dioxide, methane) to ethylene is claimed by Schmerling in U. S. 2,482,877 to Universal Oil (456) to favor the formation of liquid polyethylenes, while solid polymer was obtained in their absence under otherwise identical conditions. On the other hand, the presence of methane or dissolved oxygen is claimed not to affect the yield or quality of the polyethylene, when the polymerization of the ethylene is carried out according to the process described by Thompson and Schmerling in U. S. 2,568,902 to Universal Oil (585). In this process, an organic peroxide catalyst, a diluent, and a modifier are used.

3.3. Effect of Reaction Medium (Polymerization in Solution)

The presence of certain organic solvents and of water during the polymerization of ethylene at high pressure and temperature has been found helpful in dissipating the heat of polymerization, although such additions may also influence the reaction in other respects. Water alone as the reaction medium for the polymerization of ethylene is disclosed in Russian 59,036 to Dintses and Postnov (125). Polymerization is conducted at temperatures above 100°C. and at pressures greater than 1,000 atmospheres. The use of deaerated water as the reaction medium is described by Larson in U. S. 2,396,920 to duPont (238). According to this process, a stainless-steel reaction vessel is charged with 150 parts of deaerated water and 0.32 part of benzoyl peroxide. The vessel is closed, placed in an agitating rack, air removed from the system by sweeping with deoxygenated nitrogen, and the vessel pressured with ethylene containing 5 p.p.m. of oxygen, so that at temperatures of 64–71°C., the ethylene pressure is about 950 atmospheres. After a reaction period of 7 hours a reduction in pressure of 480 atmospheres is observed. Thirty-four parts of polyethylene are obtained. When the experiment is repeated with ethylene containing 200 p.p.m. of oxygen, the polymer yield decreases as the oxygen content of the ethylene is increased, and the quality of the product is also adversely affected.

Brubaker, in U. S. 2,396,677 (236) and Brit. 579,883 (257), both to duPont, describes the polymerization of ethylene in an aqueous medium. In an example, a stainless-steel reaction vessel is charged with 150 parts of water and 0.32 part of benzoyl peroxid eand the pH adjusted to 3.4 with formic acid. The vessel is closed, placed in an agitating rack, heated to 75°C., and pressured to 600 atmospheres with ethylene. During the reaction time of 10.75 hours, pressure is maintained at 840 to 985 atmospheres and the temperature at 74–78°C. The vessel is allowed to cool, excess ethylene bled from the system, and the contents discharged. The product, when filtered, washed, and dried, yields 62.5 parts of polymer melting at 119°C., with an intrinsic viscosity of 1.91. It is emphasized that the omission of a dispersing agent results in improved yields and in polymers of higher intrinsic viscosity.

Several patents relate to the polymerization of ethylene in an aqueous medium adjusted at different pH levels. Hanford, in U. S. 2,395,327 to duPont (232), claims that a reduced induction period results if the pH of the polymerization mixture activated with benzoyl peroxide is held between 2 and 4. Reaction temperatures between 20 and 350°C., and pressures above atmospheric, preferably between 300 and 1,500 atmospheres, are specified. British 578,584 to duPont (247) also discloses a process for the catalytic polymerization of ethylene in an aqueous medium at a pH below 7. A surface-active agent may optionally be used.

Brooks, Peterson, and Weber, in U. S. 2,388,225 to duPont (206), found that ethylene may be polymerized more quickly at a pH of 7–11, if agents such as borax, sodium bicarbonate, potassium bicarbonate, or sodium triphosphate are used to maintain the pH at the desired level. Similarly, Peterson, in U. S. 2,388,178 (205) and British 592,487 (327), both to du-Pont, discusses polymerization with oxygen-type catalysts in the presence of alkaline substances, such as sodium triphosphate or sodium hydroxide, at a pH between 11 and 14.

As to the most desirable ratio of ethylene to water, Downing and Wilcox in Brit. 612,056 to British Celanese (377), suggest that the polymerization of ethylene at 100–600 atmospheres be carried out in an aqueous liquid phase with a weight ratio of ethylene to water of at least two to one.

The polymerization of ethylene in an aqueous medium in the presence of a peroxide-type catalyst, in pressure-resistant, stainless steel-lined vessels, is further described by Young in U. S. 2,394,960 to duPont (231). In addition to water, the medium may consist of volatile organic compounds, such as isooctane, toluene, or butyl acetate. Surface-active agents may be used in the reaction which is carried out at temperatures between 60 and 250°C. and pressures of 300–1,500 atmospheres. Other monomers, such as vinyl propionate, dimethyl maleate, and methyl methacrylate, can be copolymerized with ethylene by this process, which may be adapted to continuous operation.

Similarly, Brit. 584,794 to duPont (308) claims the preparation of solid, waxy, or paste-like polymers of ethylene by reacting a mixture of ethylene, hydrogen (0.1–10%), oxygen (5–2,000 p.p.m.) or a peroxide compound, preferably with water (1 to 6 parts), and the optional addition of benzene, chlorobenzene, or isooctane, at temperatures from 40–400°C. and at pressures above 50 atmospheres. The preparation of copolymers with other unsaturated hydrocarbons, acids, esters, acid halides, amides, and anhydrides is included. A process for the manufacture of polyethylene at pressures between 50 and 3,000 atmospheres and temperatures up to 400°C., in the presence of a free radical producing catalyst and/or molecular oxygen in the presence of water, is also described in Brit. 717,533 to duPont (912). In this process, the water is separated from the unreacted ethylene and the polymer in a first separation step; in the second step, the polymer and unreacted ethylene are separated; the pressures and temperatures in both stages must be sufficient to maintain the polymer in a molten state.

Pressure polymerization of ethylene in the presence of benzene or chlorobenzene and water is claimed by Larson and Krase in U. S. 2,405,962 to duPont (260) to yield polymers with properties such as tensile strength, softening temperature, and tear resistance superior to those obtained without these additives.

A process for the polymerization of ethylene under pressure in methanol containing 10–50% of water is described in German Patent Appl. No. I73,031 by BASF (930). The polymerization catalyst is ammonium persulfate, and ammonia may be added to neutralize the acid formed on decomposition of the catalyst.

According to U. S. 2,409,996 to Roedel [duPont (269)], ethylene is polymerized in water or organic media such as benzene or *tert*-butyl alcohol by an alkyl hydroperoxide catalyst, preferably *tert*-butyl hydroperoxide. The oxygen content of the ethylene should be below 0.02%, and less than 0.001% of oxygen results in outstanding products. As would be expected, the molecular weight of the polymer is found to decrease with an increase in temperature and to increase with an increase in the ethylene pressure. Low molecular weight polymers obtained in this process are recommended for hot-dip coating and impregnating use; the high molecular weight polymers are suitable for films, oriented fibers, extruded tubing, and cable insulation. Copolymerization can be carried out with carbon monoxide, acrylics, styrene, vinyl esters and halides, and other unsaturated compounds.

Tert-butyl alcohol is also the medium in Brit. 585,969 to duPont (315) and in U. S. 2,467,234 to Sargent and Hanford [duPont (437)]. Polymerization of ethylene alone or with other monomers, including dimethyl fumarate, methyl methacrylate, vinyl acetate, and styrene is disclosed. A peroxide-type catalyst is used; temperatures range from 60–200°C., and pressures are between 200 and 1,500 atmospheres. The resultant polymers, which are described as clear and tough with good melt extrusion characteristics, can be formed into films and fibers.

Methylcyclohexane is claimed as diluent by Schmerling in U. S. 2,482,-877 to Universal Oil (456), with di-*tert*-butyl peroxide as the catalyst and an initial ethylene pressure of 40 atmospheres. When 60 atmospheres initial inert gas pressure (nitrogen, hydrogen, carbon dioxide, methane) was applied, liquid polyethylene formed after 4 hours at 180°C.; when no inert gas was used, solid polyethylene was obtained. The use of liquid polyethylenes in the preparation of sulfonated detergents is described.

Cyclohexane, in an amount of 0.15–15.0 parts per 100 parts of ethylene, is disclosed as a reaction medium by Franta in U. S. 2,586,322 to duPont (650). The cyclohexane is claimed to act also as a chain-transfer agent and to control branching of the resultant polymer. The products have a density of 0.925–0.950, a low melt viscosity, and a stiffness greater than 30,000 p.s.i. This patent is further discussed in Section 5.6.

The use of benzene or chlorobenzene and water as the medium in the polymerization of ethylene with an organometallic complex is described by Roedel in U. S. 2,475,520 (451), and in Brit. 592,486 (326) and 592,487 (327), all to duPont. The reaction is carried out at temperatures between 100° and 250°C. and ethylene pressures of from 400 to 1,500 atmospheres. The tensile strengths of the polymers are substantially above 3,000 p.s.i.

An aliphatic hydrocarbon solvent, particularly anhydrous pentane, is the reaction medium in the polymerization of ethylene by "Alfin" catalysts, according to U. S. 2,606,179 to Boyd [Monsanto Chemical Co. (663)]. The reaction temperatures range from −80 to +9°C.; the pressures from 10–55 atmospheres.

A diluent, such as an alcohol, an aromatic hydrocarbon, or a saturated hydrocarbon, containing at least three carbon atoms per molecule, is described by Thompson and Schmerling in U. S. 2,568,902 to Universal Oil (585). The catalyst is an organic peroxide, and β-thioethyl-substituted compounds are added as modifiers.

The polymerization of ethylene in the presence of liquid anhydrous ammonia is the subject of U. S. 2,467,245 to Whitman and Scott [duPont (438)].

The solution polymerization of ethylene with oxygen or an oxygen yielding compound as catalyst has been intensively investigated by Hopff and Goebel in Ger. 745,425 to I. G. Farben. (155). This work has been summarized by Hopff, Goebel, and Kern (472). As the solvent, methanol was found to be particularly suitable since it is a very good solvent for ethylene but does not dissolve polyethylene. The polymerization is carried out in equipment similar to that used in high-pressure polymerization in the absence of solvents, but temperatures in the range of only 110–120°C. are required. The polymer obtained by this process has been marketed by BASF as Lupolen N, a hard, yellow-to-brownish, wax-like, crystalline material of rather low molecular weight (2,000–3,000).

3.4. Polymerization in Emulsion

Ethylene, unlike vinyl chloride, vinyl esters or other vinyl monomers, cannot generally be polymerized in emulsion if the pH of the aqueous medium is 7 or lower. However, as described by Hopff, Goebel, and Kern (218,472), polymerization proceeds easily if the aqueous medium is strongly alkaline. It has since been discovered that successful polymerization in emulsion may also be carried out at a pH of 2–6, if the alkali is replaced by sodium tri- or hexametaphosphate. As an example, ethylene was emulsified under a pressure of 200–300 atmospheres in a solution of KOH or NaOH (0.25–2 kg.), an emulsifier such as a paraffin fatty acid (1.5 kg.), and a soluble peroxy compound such as potassium persulfate (0.6–2 kg.), in water (100 liters), and subsequently polymerized by heating. The

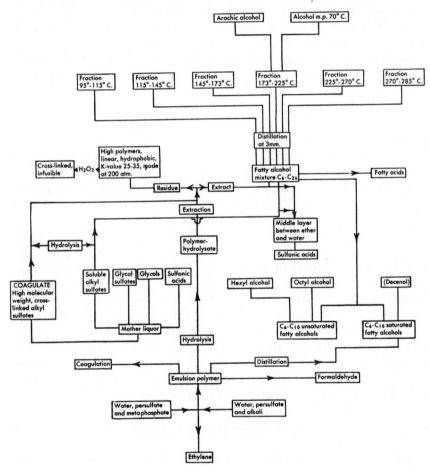

Fig. 10. Emulsion polymerization of ethylene. (*Modern Plastics*, **23** [10], 155, 1946.)

resultant emulsions were rather dilute and contained 5–20% of polymer. The solid product obtained after coagulation with electrolytes or methanol was found to contain hydrolyzable alkyl sulfonates, presumably formed from the persulfate and polymerizing ethylene. The polymer itself was not crosslinked, and could be drawn into filaments or rolled into sheets and films of poor strength but high water resistance. A scheme indicating the different compounds, including fatty alcohols, glycols, sulfonic acids, and alkyl sulfates, which may be obtained in addition to the ethylene polymer by processing the reaction products occurring in the emulsion polymerization of ethylene, is shown in Figure 10.

The ideas expressed in these publications are also the subject of several patents. French 865,102 to I. G. Farben. (127) and Ger. 737,960 and U. S. 2,342,400, both to Hopff, Goebel, and Rautenstrauch [I. G. Farben. (152) and General Aniline (164), respectively] relate to such emulsion polymerization processes.

An emulsion polymerization process applicable to ethylene, vinyl halides, vinylidene halides, vinyl acetate, acrylic and methacrylic acid esters, acrylonitrile and methacrylonitrile, styrene, fumaric acid esters, maleic acid esters, butadiene, chloroprene, and chlorinated styrenes or their mixtures is described by de Nie in Dutch 64,982 to N. V. de Bataafsche Petroleum (459). The compounds or mixtures are continuously passed at low temperatures in the form of an emulsion through a reaction apparatus, and fresh quantities of the polymerizable material are added at one or more places between the beginning and the end of the path covered by the polymerizing substance in the apparatus. The products obtained are highly polymerized and entirely free from low polymers.

Larson in U. S. 2,449,489 to duPont (373) describes a continuous two-step process. A nonemulsified polymer is obtained in the first step at elevated temperatures and pressures in the presence of an ethylene polymerization catalyst; in the second step, an emulsifying agent is introduced into the reaction mixture before the pressure is reduced. On discharging to atmospheric pressure, a stable emulsion of polyethylene is obtained.

The surface-active agent, probably a polymeric glycol, formed *in situ* during the polymerization of ethylene in contact with an alkali persulfate, is claimed in U. S. 2,462,390 to Harmon [duPont (428)] to result in the formation of a stable aqueous dispersion of polyethylene when ethylene is polymerized under elevated pressures and temperatures. In this reaction, a buffered aqueous solution of an alkali persulfate with a pH between 7.5 and 11 is used, containing from 3–20% (calculated on the weight of the water present) of the persulfate.

The emulsion polymerization of ethylene in the presence of both an ionic emulsifying agent and a water-soluble salt of a carboxylic polymer having a molecular weight of about 300 is claimed by Seed in U. S. 2,542,783 to I.C.I. (572). This process permits the preparation of emulsions, at temperatures above the softening point of the polymers, which have increased resistance to creaming. In an example, water (160 parts), sodium oleyl-*p*-anisidide sulfonate (2.6 parts), the ammonium salt of a polymethacrylic acid containing more than 45 carbon atoms (0.27 part), and a benzene solution (5%) of di-*tert*-butyl peroxide (1 part) are added to a stirred pressure vessel. Oxygen is removed by repeated flushing with oxygen-free ethylene, and ethylene (69.6 parts) is added. The vessel is kept at 200°C. and 1200 atmospheres for 10 minutes while additional ethylene (16 parts) is added to maintain pressure. When no further pressure drop occurs, the vessel is cooled and opened. The residual liquid polyethylene (16 parts) is a smooth, white dispersion, stable for three days. It can be coagulated and the polymer filtered, washed with distilled water and boiling ethanol, followed by vacuum drying at 60°C., giving solid polyethylene (27 parts) melting at 107–117.5°C., with a molecular weight of 17,000. If the sodium oleyl-*p*-anisidide sulfonate is omitted, only fused polymer is obtained; if the polymethacrylate is omitted, a coarse flocculate is formed which splits into two phases in one hour, and a semisolid surface cream is produced in three days.

The same inventor, in U. S. 2,592,526 to I.C.I. (655) claims the polymerization of ethylene in aqueous emulsion at 150–250°C. and 800–2,000 atmospheres pressure in the presence of 1–2% by weight of a nonionic emulsifier, such as polyvinyl alcohol, hydrolyzed polyvinyl acetate polymers, alkyl ether derivatives of cellulose, or monoethers of polyethylene glycols or polypropylene glycols, and 0.8–2.0% by weight of an organic sulfonic acid salt. In an example, water (1,000 parts), hexadecyl monoether or a polyethylene glycol containing 30 to 40 carbon atoms (16 parts), sodium oleyl-*p*-anisidide sulfonate (8 parts), di-*tert*-butyl peroxide (0.19 parts), and ethylene (1,200 parts), are heated to 230°C. until a pressure of 1,200 atmospheres is reached; ethylene (130 parts) is added, the reaction continued for one hour, and the reaction mixture cooled to room temperature. An aqueous emulsion (1,250 parts) of polyethylene containing particles from 0.5μ to 30μ in size resulted. Coagulation of the emulsion, washing the precipitate with water and boiling ethanol give, after 16 hours drying *in vacuo* at 60°C., a polyethylene powder (320 parts) of a molecular weight of 17,000, which is completely soluble in hot aromatic solvents.

The formation of a polyethylene latex, from which the polymer may be coagulated with acid, has been recently described in Brit. 721,678 to duPont (1050). The reaction is carried out by polymerizing ethylene at elevated temperatures and pressures in the presence of an emulsifying or dispersing agent, a peroxy compound, and a polyvalent metal ion in one of its lower valence states. Brit. 715,875 to Mathieson Chemical (906d) specifies the polymerization of ethylene of at least 99% purity in an aqueous emulsion of pH at least 10, and containing 0.5–2% of a substantially salt-free potassium soap, at least 2% potassium hydroxide, and 0.8–2% of potassium persulfate. The reaction is carried out at a temperature of 80–115°C. and at a pressure of 15,000–18,000 p.s.i.

A low temperature continuous process for the preparation in emulsion of copolymers of ethylene and vinyl acetate containing 1–30 moles of ethylene per mole of vinyl acetate is described by Roedel in U. S. 2,703,794 to duPont (1065). The reaction is carried out in the presence of a reducing agent and an oxidizing agent capable of generating a free radical by a reduction-oxidation (redox) process, at a temperature between 30 and 90°C., and at a pressure between 50 and 1,500 atmospheres.

A process for catalyzing the aqueous emulsion polymerization of substantially water-insoluble polymerizable materials, including ethylene, by using an electric current is claimed by Park and Bump in U. S. 2,726,204 to Monsanto (1105). In this process, an electric potential is applied to two electrodes immersed in the electrically conductive aqueous emulsion, causing electrolysis of the aqueous medium.

The preparation of polyethylene emulsions by emulsifying the polymer subsequent to its preparation is described in Section 8.12.

3.5. Polymerization Catalysts

Suitable ethylene polymerization processes were originally developed by using oxygen and peroxide catalysts. Subsequently many other initiators were disclosed, including azo compounds, azines, amine oxides, oximes, hydrazines, hypohalites, hydrides of boron, metals and metal oxides, Grignard reagents, "Alfin" catalysts, organolithium compounds, metal alkyls in general, and others.

Ionic Catalysts in General

Since the discussion of the polymerization of ethylene to liquid products is beyond the scope of this volume, the early investigations of the direct polymerization of ethylene will be treated only very briefly. Generally, ethylene polymerizes less readily with ionic catalysts than do most higher olefins, such as propylene or isobutylene. Actually, liquid ethylene at $-100°C$. is inert to boron trifluoride and to aluminum chloride to such an extent that the latter has been used commercially as a diluent for the low-temperature polymerization of isobutylene (628). However, under suitable reaction conditions, liquid hydrocarbons with relatively short chain length, frequently together with small amounts of solid, resinous substances, can be obtained from ethylene by the use of catalysts such as zinc chloride, aluminum chloride, and boron trifluoride.

Actually, Hofmann and Otto claimed in Ger. 505,265 (23) the preparation of liquid polymers of ethylene under pressure by the use of boron trifluoride as the catalyst. In subsequent Ger. 512,959 (24), the same inventors disclosed the addition of finely divided metals as being beneficial for this polymerization. As an example, 100 g. of ethylene in the presence of 10 g. of boron trifluoride under 70 atmospheres pressure yielded 20 g. of polymer after 12 hours; with nickel present on the walls of the reactor, a yield of 100 g. of polyethylene was obtained after 3–4 hours.

More recently, Fischer in Ger. 874,215 to BASF (790) succeeded in obtaining solid polymers by the polymerization of ethylene with aluminum chloride, if the reaction was carried out under pressure and at elevated temperature in the presence of titanium tetrachloride. The weight ratio of aluminum chloride to titanium tetrachloride should be around three to one; the reaction temperature is preferably between 130 and 180°C., the pressure between 30 and 80 atmospheres or above. It is further of interest to note that the inventors recommended that reactors be constructed in such a way that at least those parts which come in contact with the reactants consist of lead, tin, zinc, nickel, chromium, or nickel- or chromium-alloyed steels. The presence of a metal capable of binding hydrochloric acid, e.g., aluminum powder, during the reaction is recommended. [cf. (992).]

Phosphorus pentoxide as the catalyst in the polymerization of ethylene at atmospheric pressure and ordinary temperature was proposed independently by Desparmet (41) and by Malishev (45). They found it much more active than phosphoric acid, and reported good yields of liquid mixtures from which pure hydrocarbons could readily be separated. It has since been established that the products obtained in these ways were not actually simple polymers of ethylene, but rather the products of a series of steps of splitting and polymerization which could be promoted by various catalysts.

Thus, with the above exceptions, high polymers of ethylene cannot be prepared with these ionic catalysts, nor with peroxides under reaction conditions customarily employed for styrene and other vinyl monomers. Viscous oils, for example, were obtained by Wiezevich and Whiteley, as disclosed in U. S. 1,981,819 to Standard Oil (32) when ethylene containing a small amount of oxygen as the catalyst was heated at 200–400°C. under pressures up to 200 atmospheres.

Oxygen, Peroxy Compounds, and Ozonides

In connection with a study of the influence of pressure on organic reactions by Fawcett and Gibson (29), a process for polymerizing ethylene to solid polyethylene was developed and patented by I.C.I. in Fr. 817,374 (59), Brit. 471,590 (60), U. S. 2,153,553 (86), and Can. 388,355 (108) (compare Section 1.6). Essentially, the process involves subjecting ethylene, under a pressure of at least 1,000 atmospheres, to a temperature of 100–300°C., the temperature in any part of the gas being prevented from reaching the explosive decomposition point. Optionally, a small amount of oxygen, i.e., 0.03–3%, may be used as a catalyst, with a consequent reduction in the required operating pressures and temperatures.

Oxygen, peroxides, and peracids are the polymerization catalysts proposed in Brit. 587,378 to Hunter, Feachem, Richards, and I.C.I. (317). The ethylene used is obtained from ethyl alcohol, which is subjected to a dehydration catalyst (e.g., phosphoric acid, alumina, activated clay) between 350 and 1,500 atmospheres, and 300–600°C. The resultant ethylene is polymerized while still at elevated temperature and pressure.

The use of peroxides as catalysts for the polymerization of ethylene has been the subject of numerous investigations. For example, Brit. 584,794 to duPont (308) relates to the polymerization of ethylene at pressures above 50 atmospheres and temperatures ranging from 40–400°C. with a mixture comprised of 0.1–10.0% of hydrogen, 0.1–5% of a peroxide compound, 1–6 parts of water per part of ethylene and, optionally, benzene, chlorobenzene, or isooctane.

Alkyl hydroperoxides are proposed as polymerization catalysts by Roedel in U. S. 2,409,996 (269), and in Brit. 591,335 (324) and 612,266 (378), all to duPont. Ethylene is polymerized with *tert*-butyl hydroperoxide at 100–125°C. and 600–1,000 atmospheres pressure in 14 hours, to a white solid product having a molecular weight of 19,000–30,000, depending upon temperature and pressure. Similarly, ethyl hydroperoxide at 125°C. and 600 atmospheres for 18 hours catalyzes the polymerization of ethylene to a white product of a molecular weight of 11,800. Dialkyl dioxides have been found equally effective as catalysts, as proposed by Peterson in U. S. 2,425,638 (323), and in Brit. 592,517 (328), both to duPont, and in Brit. 582,890 to I. C. I. (275), when used in an amount from 0.001–5%. Catalysts of this type include dimethyl, diethyl, dipropyl, propylethyl, and propylmethyl dioxide.

Use of benzoyl peroxide as the catalyst, promoted by sodium dithionite, is the subject of U. S. 2,391,218 to Bacon and Richards [I.C.I. (208)].

In an example, a stainless steel bomb is half filled with water; benzoyl peroxide (3 parts) and sodium dithionite (0.15 part) are added; and ethylene containing less than 10 p.p.m. of oxygen is compressed in the bomb. The pressure is then increased to 750 atmospheres, the temperature to 75°C., and the bomb agitated for 4 hours. The yield amounts to 80 parts of polyethylene having a molecular weight of 17,000. When this procedure is repeated without sodium dithionite, the yield is only 40 parts of polyethylene of a molecular weight of 15,000.

2,2-Bis (*tert*-butylperoxy) butane as a catalyst for ethylene polymerization is disclosed by Boyd in U. S. 2,650,913 to Monsanto (801). Substantially oxygen-free ethylene is polymerized at 260–300°C. and at pressures ranging from 3,000–2,500 atmospheres for 2 hours in contact with the catalyst. Yields of 60–75% of solid, moldable polyethylene are obtained.

Organic polyperoxides are claimed as catalysts for the polymerization of ethylene by Roedel in U. S. 2,511,480 (508), and in Brit. 604,580 (366), both to duPont. Polyperoxides are defined as compounds containing two or more peroxy linkages, and are obtained from either a ketone or an aldehyde or mixtures thereof. Thus, a polyperoxide from acetone and methyl ethyl ketone is prepared by adding concentrated sulfuric acid (163 ml.) to water (130 ml.), cooling, adding 30% hydrogen peroxide (113 g.), cooling to −18°C., adding a mixture of methyl ethyl ketone (36 g.) and acetone (29 g.) in portions while stirring and maintaining the temperature below 0°C., allowing the mixture to stand for 15 minutes, and finally diluting to one liter with water. A colorless, viscous upper layer separates, which is freed from acid and unconverted traces of ketones by washing with water, dried over sodium sulfate, filtered, and purified by steam distillation. Many ketones and aldehydes which undergo this reaction are enumerated in the patent. From 0.1–2.0% by weight of these organic polyperoxides are used as ethylene polymerization catalysts, acetone–methyl ethyl ketone polyperoxide being particularly suited for this purpose. For example, an ethylene polymer of molecular weight 13,400 is obtained by charging a stainless-steel reaction vessel, previously filled with oxygen-free nitrogen, with anhydrous benzene (88 parts) and a benzene solution (0.35 part) of acetone–methyl ethyl ketone polyperoxide. The nitrogen is removed, ethylene is added to a pressure of 165 atmospheres and the reactor is heated to 125°C., at which point the ethylene pressure is raised to 500–600 atmospheres. The polymerization is allowed to proceed with agitation for 18 hours, maintaining pressure by the addition of more ethylene. At the end of this time, excess ethylene is bled off, and a white, solid polymer is obtained. A similar process is employed to produce a polymer having a molecular weight of 23,300, with a tensile strength of 3,250 p.s.i. at 490% elongation, by using a polyperoxide from acetone and cyclohexanone as the catalyst. With 3,6-diphenyl-s-tetroxane as the catalyst, a tough, extrudable product of 15,800 molecular weight, with a tensile strength of 2,163 p.s.i. at 620% elongation, is obtained. The organic polyperoxide catalysts do not give induction periods, are rapid and enduring in their activity, and are said to be particularly suited to the continuous polymerization of ethylene.

The polymerization of ethylene with a peroxydicarbonate ester as the catalyst, in the presence of a product carrier liquid (aqueous solution of methanol or tert-butanol) is claimed by Cerveny, Burney, and Weisemann in U. S. 2,685,577 to Standard Oil (905). Di-tert-butyl peroxydicarbonate as the polymerization catalyst is described by Friedlander in U. S. 2,728,756 to Standard Oil (1116). The polymerization process is carried out preferably at relatively low temperatures (25–75°C.), and at pressures ranging from 5,000–8,000 p.s.i. Tertiary-butyl ethylene may be used as a polymerization modifier with this and other types of catalysts, as specified by Brown in U. S. 2,728,752 to Standard Oil (1112).

The addition of a substituted phenol, such as 2,4-dialkyl-6-tert-alkylphenol, when polymerizing ethylene in alcohol solution in the presence of an organic peroxide, is proposed by Schmerling in U. S. 2,566,537 to Universal Oil (583). According to U. S. 2,566,538, also to Schmerling [Universal Oil (584)], the additive may be a p-aminoaniline, which serves to raise the melting point of the resultant polyethylene.

U. S. 2,391,218 (208) and Brit. 583,166 (276) to Bacon, Richards, and I.C.I. relate to promoters for peroxy-type catalysts generally, for use in the polymerization of ethylene. These promoters are water-soluble salts of an oxy-acid of sulfur with reducing properties, such as $NaHSO_2$, $NaHSO_3$, $Na_2S_2O_6$, and $Na_2S_2O_3$.

The addition of 0.03–1% by weight of an ether is claimed by Forsyth in Brit. 583,178 to I.C.I. (277) to double the rate of ethylene polymerization. Although ethyl ether is preferred, any ether containing up to 10 carbon atoms may be effective. It is speculated that the ether exhibits a catalytic effect due to formation of an unstable ether peroxide.

Saturated aliphatic esters of inorganic oxy-acids of phosphorus, sulfur, and silicon are proposed as catalysts by Hanford and Joyce in U. S. 2,478,390 to duPont (453). The reaction is generally conducted under pressure with or without an inert solvent, such as a saturated hydrocarbon. In an example, a silver-lined pressure-reaction vessel is charged with methyl sulfate, dioxane, and benzoyl peroxide; it is closed, evacuated, and charged with ethylene. The reaction is carried out at 90–120°C. and at a pressure of 400–500 atmospheres of ethylene. The product is precipitated with ether and filtered. Ethylene, polymerized in the same way with $Si(OC_2H_5)_4$ in the presence of benzoyl peroxide and dioxane, yields a white polyethylene containing 1.72% SiO_2, and melting at 112–113°C.

The use of $Na_2S_2O_8$ as the catalyst in aqueous solution (0.01–0.6%) buffered to pH of 7–11, is described in Brit. 579,881 to duPont (255).

A reaction medium which itself promotes polymerization catalytically is proposed by Larson and Krase in U. S. 2,405,962 (260) and in Brit. 592, 486 (326), both to duPont. This solvent may be comprised of benzene or chlorobenzene (0.1–0.5 part per part of ethylene) and water (1–6 parts per part of ethylene), the water serving a dual role in absorbing some of the heat given off in the exothermic polymerization reaction.

The polymerization of ethylene at elevated temperatures and pressures may also be catalyzed by ozonides of ethylenically unsaturated compounds. McArthur and Logan in U. S. 2,713,044 to Olin Mathieson (1079) describe the preparation of solid polyethylene by the ozonides of acrylonitrile, acrylic acid, and acrylic esters, diisobutylene, cyclohexene, cracked polyethylene, and others. These ozonides may be prepared by reaction of ozone from the usual ozone generator with the unsaturated organic compound.

Azo Compounds and Azines

The use of azo compounds and azines as catalysts is covered in a series of patents assigned to duPont. For example, according to U. S. 2,439,-528 to Roedel (363), $C_6H_5CH{=}NN{=}CHC_6H_5$ or $(C_6H_5)_2C{=}NN{=}C(C_6H_5)_2$ (0.5 part) in benzene (88 parts) effect polymerization of ethylene at 200–225°C. and 850–900 atmospheres to a tough, workable polymer. U. S. 2,471,959 to Hunt (448) and U. S. 2,520,338 to Robertson (515) also relate to azo compounds as catalysts for the polymerization of ethylene. Acetophenone azine dissolved in alcohol, together with palladium (10%) on charcoal, is claimed as the catalyst in Brit. 658,893 (586). According to an example, the polymerization is carried out in a steel vessel containing water and benzene at 900 atmospheres pressure and at a temperature of 100–175°C.

The literature on the use of the so-called Thiele azo compounds (4) as catalysts in various types of polymerization reactions has been reviewed by Ziegler (426). The possibility of substituting azodiisobutyronitriles for organic peroxy compounds in promoting polymerization and addition reactions generally is evaluated, and it is reported that ethylene has been successfully polymerized at 100 atmospheres pressure by dimethylazodiiso-butyrate.   Reaction is noticeable at slightly over 30°C. and is rapid at 50–60°C.; it proceeds slowly at room temperature in the absence of oxygen. The polyethylene product is a loose powder.

The use of azo-catalyst was recently reported by Hines, Bryant, Larchar, and Pease of duPont (1133) in the synthesis of linear, high-density, poly-ethylenes by a free radical route at very high pressures.

Azodisulfonates of lithium, sodium, potassium, bismuth, magnesium, calcium, strontium, and barium, or the salts of the organic bases, prefer-ably the tertiary amines, promote the rapid polymerization of ethylene and other ethylenically unsaturated compounds in high conversion at low tem-peratures, as described by Robertson in U. S. 2,468,111 to duPont (442). Potassium azodisulfonate is particularly valuable as a catalyst since it is outstanding in inducing rapid polymerization.   The catalyst is employed in an amount of 0.01–5.0% based on the weight of the monomer.   Poly-merization temperatures are within the range of -80 to $+60°C$., with a preferred temperature between 0 and 30°C.   As solvent, water and water-miscible compounds are preferred.

Amine Oxides and Oximes

Amine oxides, hydrates, and salts or hydrated salts are proposed to be used in an amount of 0.001–5%, preferably 0.1–2%, to promote polymeri-zation of ethylene, by Dorough in U. S. 2,398,926 (243) and in Brit. 585, 396 (309), both to duPont.   Of these compounds, trimethylamine oxide, triethylamine oxide, and dimethanolaniline oxide are stated to be par-ticularly effective.

The use of oximes as catalysts for polymerizing ethylene is disclosed by Roedel in U. S. 2,462,678 to duPont (429).   The catalyst is present in an amount of 0.001–5%.   An inert solvent may be used, and the reaction vessel should be substantially oxygen-free.   In an example, a silver- or stainless steel-lined pressure-reaction vessel is flushed with nitrogen, charged with benzene and $(CH_3)_2C:NOH$, evacuated, and charged with ethylene to 225 atmospheres pressure.   The temperature is raised to 175°C. and the pressure maintained for 14 hours at 850–990 atmospheres by the intermittent introduction of ethylene.   The yield amounts to 29 parts of a polyethylene having a tensile strength of 2,340 p.s.i., elongation at break of 470%, and a molecular weight of 18,900.   Oximes of the follow-ing are used as catalysts: benzoin, d-camphor, cyclohexanone, benzil, and butyraldehyde.   It is claimed that the oxime catalysts retain their activity for a long period and hence are suitable for continuous operation.

Hypohalites

Compounds containing a positive halogen are proposed as catalysts by Hanford and Salzberg in U. S. 2,435,256 (362) and in Brit. 590,816 (322), both to duPont. Typical of such compounds are inorganic hypohalites and *n*-haloaryl-sulfonamides and their metal salts, employed in an anhydrous reaction medium such as *tert*-butyl alcohol. Pressures of 800–1,000 atmospheres and temperatures of 100–200°C. are preferred.

Hydrides of Boron

Hydrides of boron, especially diborane and its homologs and analogs up to $B_{10}H_{14}$, are described as polymerization catalysts for ethylene and other ethylenically unsaturated monomers by Heiligmann and Benington in U. S. 2,685,575 to the Borden Co. (904). Solid polymers of ethylene with molecular weights ranging between 10,000 and 50,000 form at a temperature of approximately 55°C. and at pressures within the range of 1,200–4,500 p.s.i.

Metals and Metal Oxides

The influence of metals, alone and in various combinations, on the polymerization of ethylene, has been the subject of several patents. For example, Young in U. S. 2,394,960 (231) claims improved rates of reaction, yields, and color of product, when ethylene is polymerized in stainless steel-lined vessels with peroxide-type catalysts in aqueous media. The reactor steel is composed of chromium (18–20%), nickel (8–14%), molybdenum (2–4%), optionally modified with lead or manganese, and is claimed to exhibit negligible corrosion effects. U. S. 2,450,451 to Schmerling [Universal Oil (374)] relates to the liquid-phase polymerization of ethylene with a peroxide-type catalyst and a like amount of magnesium, cadmium, or mercury in a finely divided state. Temperatures of 150°C. and pressures of 30–100 atmospheres are stated to result in the production of waxes melting between 88 and 95°C.

Results of a study of the effect of metals on the polymerization of ethylene and on the properties of the polymer have been reported by Tani and Sato (304). They examined the effect of metals at reaction pressures of about 2,000 atmospheres by introducing plates of nickel, aluminum, copper, silver, and a wire net of tin into an autoclave constructed of chromium-molybdenum steel. It was found that silver and nickel clearly increased the rate of the second-step reaction, and the product was the same as in the case with aluminum or without metal.   Copper, especially in the reduced state, greatly accelerates the reaction rate.   With reduced copper, polyethylene adhering to the copper surface is colored red and insoluble in all of the solvents examined.   The copper itself becomes very brittle.   The polyethylene produced in the free space between copper plates is a white polymer, normally soluble in polyethylene solvents.   It is also concluded that if other conditions are equal, the metals affect the temperature of the first-step reaction.   At about 2,000 atmospheres, the reaction temperatures in the presence of different metals are as follows: nickel, 150°C.; aluminum, 160–165°C.; silver, 165°C.; and copper, 175–183°C.   With aluminum, the temperature of the first-step reaction is affected neither by the content of oxygen and carbon monoxide nor by reaction pressure and heating.   This effect, therefore, is considered to be due to metals and may be moderated by covering the metal surface with polyethylene.   The polymer in all cases except that of copper is white. The dark red color of the polymer adhering to the copper surface changes in time to green, and it was ascertained by x-ray studies that the substance is a mixture of polyethylene and metallic copper.   It is suggested that the products are crosslinked since, especially with reduced copper, most of them are insoluble in hot benzene.

Nickel oxide adsorbed on kieselguhr or silicon dioxide–aluminum oxide gel as catalyst for the polymerization of ethylene at low temperatures has been investigated in some detail by Koizumi (546).   It is concluded that the polymerization proceeds step by step between two, three, four molecules.   Lower olefins polymerize more rapidly than do higher ones; the ratio of the reaction velocities of ethylene, propylene, and butylene is approximately 100:10:1.   Olefin molecules are adsorbed anywhere on the catalyst and then reach active spots where polymerization takes place; the polymerization products then move to other positions on the catalyst. The rate-determining step is the process in which olefin molecules arrive at the active spots.   In the early stage of reaction, it is a simple displacement on the catalyst surface, whereas in the later stage it is a process similar to diffusion.   The transition between the two stages depends therefore upon the activity of the catalyst.

According to U. S. 2,470,166 assigned by Hetzel and Kennedy to Sun Oil (443), ethylene is polymerized at pressures of 30–150 p.s.i. and at temperatures of 350–450°C., with a catalyst comprised of silica gel (80–99.98%), aluminum oxide (0.01–10.0%) and nickel (0.01–10.0%).   Specifically, a catalyst containing silica gel (98%), aluminum oxide (1%), and nickel (1%), is prepared by adding $Ni(NO_3)_2 \cdot 6H_2O$ (97 g.) and $Al(NO_3)_3 \cdot$

$9H_2O$ (75 g.) to silica gel, 4–8 mesh (2 kg.).   The mixture is dried and heated at 300°C. for 9 hours.   Prior to use, it is heated again at 400°C. for one hour and then reduced with a slow stream of hydrogen for 9 hours at 400°C.   A similar process is described by Ciapetta and Buck in U. S. 2,589,189 to Atlantic Refining (653).   According to this procedure, the reaction is conducted at temperatures between 100 and 350°C. (preferably 200–300°C.) and pressures below 500 p.s.i., with a catalyst consisting of silicon dioxide–aluminum oxide impregnated with about 10% or less (preferably 1–5%) of a hydrogenation catalyst such as cobalt, nickel, iron, platinum, or palladium.

A hydrogenation catalyst, such as nickel or cobalt, is also employed by Boyd and Dickey, according to U. S. 2,666,756 to Monsanto (895), together with a promoter, preferably cerium or thorium, and in the presence of carbon monoxide and hydrogen.   Polymerization of the ethylene is carried out at temperatures between 100 and 400°C. and at pressures from 50–6,000 atmospheres.   Solid polymers with molecular weights in the neighborhood of 30,000 are obtained.

An alkali or an alkaline earth metal may be used as the catalyst for the polymerization of ethylene in accordance with U. S. 2,466,694 to Freed [duPont (434)].

Numerous patents on the polymerization of ethylene have been issued to Stand. Oil (Ind.).   Peters and Evering in U. S. 2,658,095 (805) contact ethylene with an activated carbon-supported metal such as nickel or cobalt at temperatures between 0 and 250°C. and a pressure of at least 500 p.s.i.   When the catalyst contains approximately 5% of the ethylene polymer, extraction with a liquid solvent is carried out and the polymer recovered from this solution.   Predominantly low-boiling hydrocarbons, together with high molecular weight wax-like and tough resinous polyethylenes, are obtained.   A similar process is described in Brit. 721,046 (919).

It was subsequently disclosed by the same inventors in U. S. 2,692,261 (911) that almost entirely solid polymers may be obtained by carrying out the process in a liquid hydrocarbon reaction medium, preferably an aromatic hydrocarbon.

Contact of ethylene with an alkali metal and one or more of the oxides of chromium, molybdenum, tungsten, or uranium, such as a partially reduced molybdenum trioxide extended upon a support, yields solid polymers of high molecular weight, according to U. S. 2,691,647 to Field and Feller (907).   The polymerization is carried out between 130 and 260°C. and at about 1,000 p.s.i. pressure.   The polymer tends to accumulate around and within the solid catalyst, and the presence of a liquid medium, preferably an aromatic hydrocarbon, serving both as a reaction medium and as a solvent for the polymer, is desirable.

A reduced molybdenum oxide combined with an activated adsorptive alumina, preferably in the presence of a liquid medium, particularly an aromatic hydrocarbon, is used in the conversion, of ethylene to solid polyethylene by Zletz, according to U. S. 2,692,257 (909). The reaction is conducted between 130 and 260°C. and at 1,000 p.s.i. pressure. The activation of the molybdenum catalyst (molybdenum trioxide, cobalt molybdate) before use is carried out by treatment at elevated temperature with a reducing gas, such as hydrogen, carbon monoxide, or sulfur dioxide.

A catalyst consisting of a hexavalent molybdenum-oxygen compound and oxides of titanium or zirconium is described in U. S. 2,692,258 to Roebuck and Zletz (910). The molybdenum-oxygen compound may be molybdenum trioxide, cobalt molybdate, iron molybdate, nickel molybdate, or aluminum molybdate. The catalyst is pretreated prior to polymerization with a reducing gas at elevated temperatures. A similar process has been claimed by E. F. Peters in U. S. 2,692,259 (910a).

When the subhexavalent molybdenum-oxygen compound combined with an active alumina, titania, or zirconia support is used as the ethylene polymerization catalyst, a substantial portion of the polymer remains deposited upon the catalyst surface and is difficult to remove, even with intensive solvent treatment. This deposition of the strongly adhesive polymer is reduced or even prevented by a treatment described by Peters in U. S. 2,700,663 (1057), whereby the catalyst is brought into contact with acetylene at elevated temperature.

A treatment of this catalyst to maintain uniform rate of polymerization, as well as yield and characteristics of the polymer, is described by Hoeksema and Peters in U. S. 2,702,288 (1060).

The conversion of ethylene to high molecular weight polymers by contact with $CaCl_2$, $SrCl_2$, or $BaCl_2$, and a catalyst comprising one or more of the oxides of chromium, molybdenum, tungsten, or uranium (for example, a partially reduced molybdenum trioxide extended upon a support) has been described by Seelig in U. S. 2,710,854 (1073). Other catalyst systems are described in the following patents recently issued to Standard Oil: an alkali metal hydride and nickel oxide in U. S. 2,717,888 to Feller and Field (1090); a metal borohydride and nickel oxide in U. S. 2,717,889 to Feller and Field (1091); an alkali metal and an oxide of a metal of group 6a of the periodic system of chemical elements in U. S. 2,725,374 to Mosher (1103); an alkali metal hydride and an oxide of a metal of group 6a in U. S.

2,726,231 to Field and Feller (1106); an alkali earth metal and an oxide of a metal of group 6a in U. S. 2,726,234 to Field and Feller (1107); activated carbon supported nickel or cobalt in U. S. 2,727,023 to Evering, Roebuck, and Zletz (1108); an alkali metal aluminum hydride and an oxide of a metal of group 5a in U. S. 2,727,024 to Field and Feller (1110); an alkali metal borohydride and an oxide of a metal of group 5a in U. S. 2,728,757 to Field and Feller (1117); a reactive metal borohydride and an oxide of a metal of group 6a in U. S. 2,728,758 to Field and Feller (1118); an alkaline earth metal hydride and an oxide of a metal of group 6a in U. S. 2,731,452 to Field and Feller (1145); and an alkali metal aluminum hydride with an oxide of a metal of group 6a in U. S. 2,731,453 to Field and Feller (1146).

Process modifications and improvements are considered in U. S. 2,728,753 to Russum, Hatch, and Weisemann (1113); in U. S. 2,728,754 to Evering and Peters (1114); and in U. S. 2,728,755 to Weisemann (1115).

Based on the discoveries protected by this patent structure, a recent (July, 1955) news release (920a), which has been discussed in a previous section (Section 1.6), foresees the entry of Stand. Oil (Ind.) in the commercial production of polyethylene.

A process for the polymerization of ethylene and propylene with chromium oxide as the catalyst, supported by at least one member of the group consisting of silica, alumina, and silica-alumina, is described in Belg. 530,617 (1056) to Phillips Chemical. This patent is of particular interest since it is claimed (920) that "Marlex" (see Sections 1.6 and 6.19) will be manufactured by this process in that company's projected commercial plant at Pasadena, Texas. This was essentially confirmed by the recent discussion (1128a) of the Marlex catalyst system by Clark, Hogan, Banks, and Lanning of Phillips.

While the description of the process in the patent deals principally with liquid phase operation, vapor phase operation without a diluent, or with a diluent in liquid phase, is also effective. The preferred temperature range for the polymerization of ethylene is 275–375°F. (actually, in all probability, about 310°F.), and for propylene and higher α-olefins, is 150–250°F. The pressure must be sufficiently high to maintain the diluent in the liquid phase and to assure that olefins not liquefied under these conditions are dissolved in the liquid phase in sufficient amount. This requires a pressure of at least 100–300 p.s.i., depending on the feed and the temperature, a pressure of approximately 500 p.s.i. being preferred. The reaction may be carried out in a fixed-bed or a moving-bed catalyst chamber; or may be effected in a catalyst slurry with the reaction product taken off for purification and the catalyst to be regenerated taken off as a slurry, washed to remove occluded hydrocarbons, and passed to regeneration.

For production of high molecular weight, flexible polyethylene, a slurry-type operation is preferable to a fixed-bed operation. The molecular weight is controlled by the temperature of catalyst activation, and by polymerization reaction pressure and temperature (1128a).

Chromium oxide as the essential ingredient associated with at least one member of the group consisting of silica, alumina, zirconia, and thoria is also the catalyst in Phillips Belg. 535,082 (1055). Particular emphasis is placed in this patent on the preparation of polypropylene and of ethylene–propylene copolymers. The higher melting point range of polypropylene in comparison to that of the polyethylene, and the flexibility of ethylene–propylene copolymers are stressed. Emphasis is placed on the application of these copolymers as films.

It may be mentioned in this connection that the preparation and properties of polypropylene were also investigated by Ziegler (1072); and particularly by Natta, *et al.* (1001,1002,1003,1004) in the course of their studies of "isotactic" polymers. While a discussion of this extremely interesting field is outside the scope of this volume, this increasing interest in polypropylene must not go unmentioned (1083b,1122).

Grignard-Type Compounds

Components of Grignard-type compounds may be used to polymerize ethylene, as described by Roedel in U. S. 2,475,520 (451) and in Brit. 592,486 (326) and 592,487 (327), all to duPont. An inert medium, such as benzene, is preferred. The catalyst comprises a mixture of metals and halogen compounds capable of yielding an organo-metallic complex of the general formula R-M-X, in which R is an alkyl, aryl, or aralkyl group; M represents zinc or magnesium; X is the halogen. The reaction is carried out at temperatures between 100 and 250°C., ethylene pressures from 400–1,500 atmospheres, and catalyst concentrations of 0.005–5%. The polymers are characterized by tensile strengths above 3,000 p.s.i. A similar process is described in British 592,335 to I.C.I. (325).

A process for the polymerization of ethylene under pressure with completely preformed magnesium alkyl chlorides at temperatures of 100–200°C. is claimed by Ziegler in German Patent Appl. Z1118 (658). The process may also be carried out in the presence of a solvent, e.g., ether, possibly with distillation of the ether from the reaction mixture.

"Alfin" Catalysts

"Alfin" type catalysts for the polymerization of ethylene in the liquid phase are described by Boyd in U. S. 2,606,179 to Monsanto (663). According to the patent disclosures, ethylene at temperatures of -80 to $+9°C.$, and pressures of from 10 atmospheres at $-80°C$. to 55 atmospheres at $+9°C$., is polymerized in the presence of a catalyst consisting of a mixture of a sodium alkenyl derived from an aliphatic olefin, and a sodium alkoxide derived from a methyl alkyl carbinol. In an example, liquid anhydrous ethylene (100 parts) is dissolved in anhydrous pentane (200 parts) at $0°C$.; to this solution, an equimolecular mixture of sodium isopropoxide and allyl sodium (0.1 part) is added with agitation. The reaction is carried out in the absence of air and oxygen; a temperature of $0°C$. and a pressure of 50 atmospheres are maintained during the reaction period of one hour. The resultant polymer has a molecular weight of approximately 20,000; it is assumed to be less crystalline than polymers prepared at high temperatures and pressures, and it yields clear and transparent articles on molding.

Organolithium Compounds

Friedrich and Marvel (21a) were the first to observe, as early as 1930, that lithium alkyls may cause the polymerization of ethylene to nongaseous products. In one experiment, a solution of 0.031 mole of butyllithium in 50 ml. of petroleum ether was found to absorb ethylene readily, and a white solid began to appear on the surface of the solution within two weeks.

The use of a hydrogenation catalyst (nickel) and an alkali-metal hydrocarbon, preferably butyllithium, in the polymerization of ethylene to solid products is described by Ellis in U. S. 2,212,155 (112), and in Brit. 536,102 (126), both to duPont. The polymerization is carried out at $50-100°C$., under $400-2,000$ p.s.i. pressure.

Later duPont patents, such as U. S. 2,377,753 to Brubaker (192) and U. S. 2,377,779 to Hanford, Roland, and Young (193) relate to the use of organolithium compounds alone as the catalyst, and a liquid aromatic hydrocarbon as the reaction medium. The latter patent in particular recommends the alkyl- and aryllithiums as catalysts in the polymerization of ethylene to hard, waxy polymers. Specially purified ethylene containing less than 0.1% of oxygen appears essential for this process, which is carried out in the presence of a nonpolymerizable liquid, such as benzene. The reaction temperatures may be quite low ($20-100°C$.), and the pressures range between 400 and 1,000 atmospheres.

Metal Alkyls and Ziegler Catalysts

Kraus, in U. S. 2,220,930 to Standard Oil (114) described the manufacture of high molecular weight polymers by the low-temperature polymerization of hydrocarbons of the olefin series, particularly isobutylene, catalyzed by halides of aluminum, gallium, and boron, which have a part of their halogen atoms substituted by monovalent hydrocarbon groups. Examples of compounds of this general class are dimethylaluminum chloride, diethylaluminum chloride, methylaluminum dichloride, ethylaluminum dichloride, diphenylaluminum chloride, dibutylboron chloride, butylboron dichloride, dimethylgallium chloride, and methylgallium dichloride. In addition, complexes of these compounds with inorganic halides or with ammonia or substituted ammonias are suitable catalysts. Methylaluminum dichloride-sodium chloride, $[Al(CH_3)Cl_2 \cdot NaCl]$, and dimethylaluminum chloride-dimethylamine, $[Al(CH_3)_2Cl \cdot NH(CH_3)_2]$, are compounds of this type. Also suitable as catalysts are all those formed by the replacement of one or more halogens of the metallic alkyl halides by an ether group, e.g., diethylethoxyaluminum, $[Al(C_2H_5)_2 \cdot OC_2H_5)]$.

It is found that the catalyst is consumed in the process of polymerization, and that the amount of polymer formed in a given reaction is roughly proportional to the amount of catalyst added. The catalyst may, to a large extent at least, be removed from the polymer by hydrolysis, as in treating with hot water, dilute acid, or with aqueous or alcoholic alkali solutions.

The preparation of a polyethylene of high density (0.97–0.99), high melting point (120–128°C., as determined by observing the disappearance of spherulites on a hot-stage microscope), considerable hardness and stiffness, and outstanding moisture-proofness, is described in Brit. 682,420 (670) and by Roedel in Can. 510,145 (1059), both to duPont. By this process, ethylene is contacted at a temperature below 9.6°C. with a catalyst capable of producing free radicals at this temperature. The most effective catalyst under these conditions is an oxidizing agent, such as a peroxide, in combination with either a silver ion or the ion of a metal having more than one valency in one of its lower valence states. Other catalysts which can be used include a metal alkyl, e.g., butylsodium, amyllithium, hexylzinc, butylmagnesium, and octadecylpotassium, in combination with a metal having more than one valency, an azo-disulfonate and water, and nitroso-acetanilide. Thus, the catalyst system is generally produced by adding two materials, which together produce free radicals at these low temperatures. Suitable ions of metals having more than one valency include titanium, vanadium, chromium, manganese, iron, cobalt, nickel, and copper and their combinations, ferrous ions being preferred. Silver is likewise suitable. The metal ion may be introduced in the lower state of oxidation, or reduced *in situ* by a supplementary reducing agent. As the latter, bisulfites, thiosulfates, sulfinic acids, benzoin, ascorbic acid, sodium formaldehyde sulfoxylate, primary, secondary, and tertiary amines, and alkanolamines may be used.

The process can be carried out in bulk, solution, emulsion, dispersion, and bead form. The pressures employed depend on the nature of the polymerization medium and the degree of polymerization desired, but must be sufficient to ensure that most of the ethylene is present as a liquid phase. Pressures in the range of 10–100 atmospheres are preferred, but higher pressures are operable.

Similarly, Can. 509,678 to Pease [duPont (1058)] deals with the polymerization of liquid ethylene with an active organic free radical produced by a compound of the group consisting of peroxy compounds, azo compounds, and metal alkyls (particularly butyllithium) at not higher than the liquefaction temperature of the ethylene.

The reactions of olefins with aluminum hydride, dialkyl aluminum hydrides, aluminum trialkyls, lithium aluminum hydride, and lithium alkyls, have been studied intensively by Ziegler (494,644,645,892). Based on the close resemblance, chemically, between the Al—H and the Al—C bonds an interesting sequence of reactions leading to polymers of ethylene could be carried out (644). Analogous to the reactions,

$$AlH_3 \xrightarrow{C_2H_4} Al\begin{smallmatrix} C_2H_5 \\ \diagup \\ \diagdown \\ H \end{smallmatrix}\!\!-H \xrightarrow{C_2H_4} Al\begin{smallmatrix} C_2H_5 \\ \diagup \\ \diagdown \\ H \end{smallmatrix}\!\!-C_2H_5 \xrightarrow{C_2H_4} Al\begin{smallmatrix} C_2H_5 \\ \diagup \\ \diagdown \\ C_2H_5 \end{smallmatrix}\!\!-C_2H_5$$

addition reactions such as,

$$Al\begin{smallmatrix} C_2H_5 \\ \diagup \\ \diagdown \\ C_2H_5 \end{smallmatrix}\!\!-C_2H_5 \xrightarrow{C_2H_4} Al\begin{smallmatrix} CH_2{-}CH_2{-}C_2H_5 \\ \diagup \\ \diagdown \\ C_2H_5 \end{smallmatrix}\!\!-C_2H_5 \xrightarrow{C_2H_4} Al\begin{smallmatrix} CH_2{-}CH_2{-}C_2H_5 \\ \diagup \\ \diagdown \\ C_2H_5 \end{smallmatrix}\!\!-CH_2{-}CH_2{-}C_2H_5 \xrightarrow{C_2H_4}$$

$$Al\begin{smallmatrix} CH_2{-}CH_2{-}C_2H_5 \\ \diagup \\ \diagdown \\ CH_2{-}CH_2{-}C_2H_5 \end{smallmatrix}\!\!-CH_2{-}CH_2{-}C_2H_5$$

may be realized.

While the first reaction step proceeds at 60–80°C., a temperature of 100–120°C. is required for the second. Actually, compounds of the general formula

$$Al\begin{smallmatrix} (C_2H_4)_x{-}C_2H_5 \\ \diagup \\ \diagdown \\ (C_2H_4)_z{-}C_2H_5 \end{smallmatrix}\!\!-(C_2H_4)_y{-}C_2H_5$$

are eventually formed.   By decomposition with water, saturated hydro-carbons of the general formulas $H—(C_2H_4)_x—C_2H_5$; $H—(C_2H_4)_y—C_2H_5$; and $H—(C_2H_4)_z—C_2H_5$ are obtained.   When the amount of ethylene was large in comparison to that of the aluminum alkyl, a range of hydrocarbons approaching the typical, high molecular weight polyethylenes was ob-tained.   It is estimated that molecular weights up to 5,000 were thus reached, as compared to 20,000–30,000 for commercial high molecular weight polyethylenes.

The kinetics of this reaction were studied by Natta, Pino, and Farina (869) using an aluminum autoclave and ethylene of extremely high purity to eliminate possible catalytic effects.   Operating at a temperature below 100°C. and at practically constant ethylene pressure, the addition of ethylene to triethylaluminum occurred with the formation of aluminum trialkyls, as shown in the above scheme.   These could be decomposed with ethyl alcohol to paraffins.

If the reaction between triethylaluminum and ethylene was conducted somewhat above 100°C., the formation of olefinic polymers of ethylene became noticeable.   This polymerization, which predominates over the addition reaction at temperatures above 140°C., may be interpreted ac-cording to Ziegler as a consecutive occurrence of the above addition re-action and the following reactions:

$$\begin{array}{c} R_1 \\ \diagup \\ Al—C_nH_{2n+1} \\ \diagdown \\ R_2 \end{array} \xrightarrow{\;C_2H_4\;} \begin{array}{c} R_1 \\ \diagup \\ Al—C_2H_5 \\ \diagdown \\ R_2 \end{array} + \; C_nH_{2n};$$

$$\begin{array}{c} R_1 \\ \diagup \\ Al—C_nH_{2n+1} \\ \diagdown \\ R_2 \end{array} \longrightarrow \begin{array}{c} R_1 \\ \diagup \\ Al—H \\ \diagdown \\ R_2 \end{array} + \; C_nH_{2n};$$

$$\begin{array}{c} R_1 \\ \diagup \\ Al—H \\ \diagdown \\ R_2 \end{array} \xrightarrow{\;C_2H_4\;} \begin{array}{c} R_1 \\ \diagup \\ Al—C_2H_5. \\ \diagdown \\ R_2 \end{array}$$

The tests were performed between 100 and 150°C. at 14 and 90 at-mospheres; under these conditions, the over-all reaction with respect to the concentration of ethylene in the liquid phase was of the first order.   Study of the reaction products by fractionation and determination of the olefins in each fraction indicated that the decomposition reactions must be assumed to take place simultaneously.

In a subsequent publication, Ziegler (893) distinguishes between two reaction steps and introduces the application of co-catalysts. The growth reaction takes place between the aluminum alkyl and ethylene at 100–120°C. and at 50–100 atmospheres pressure (to increase reaction rate), according to the scheme:

$$C_2H_5—al + CH_2{=}CH_2 \longrightarrow C_2H_5—CH_2—CH_2—al;$$

$$C_2H_5—CH_2—CH_2—al \xrightarrow{C_2H_4} C_2H_5—(CH_2—CH_2)_n—al \ (al = {}^1/_3 \ Al).$$

The displacement reaction takes place to an increasing extent at temperatures above 120°C., according to the scheme:

$$H(CH_2—CH_2)_n—al \xrightarrow{C_2H_4} H(C_2H_4)_{n-1}—CH{=}CH_2 + CH_3—CH_2—al.$$

It was found that very small amounts of nickel, called a co-catalyst, are capable of increasing the speed of the displacement reaction very considerably, thus permitting control of the ethylene polymerization by aluminum alkyls. If the ethylene polymerization is carried out in the presence of 0.1–0.2% of colloidal nickel, the displacement reaction is greatly favored over the growth reaction, and essentially the dimer of ethylene, α-butene, can be obtained by a continuous process. Higher olefins, on the other hand, can be obtained by a two-step procedure. First, the growth reaction is carried out in a reaction tower with the careful exclusion of any traces of catalyst. The tower is designed for continuous operation at 100–110°C. and 100 atmospheres ethylene pressure. Second, the displacement reaction, yielding the α-olefins, is carried out in another tower by exposing the aluminum trialkyl to ethylene in the presence of nickel at 60–70°C.

Based on these studies, the conversion of ethylene and mixtures of ethylene with other unsaturated hydrocarbons into polymers ranging from butylene to wax-like products is claimed by Ziegler and Gellert in U. S. 2,699,457 (1048) and in Ger. 878,560 (795a), and by Ziegler in Brit. 713,081 (906). The polymerization is carried out at temperatures between 60 and 250°C. in the presence of an activator which consists of hydrides, alkyls or aryls of beryllium, aluminum, gallium, or indium. The following examples of suitable activators are given: $Be(C_2H_5)_2$, AlH_3, $HAl(CH_3)_2$, $H_2AlC_2H_5$, $Al(CH_3)_3$, $Al(C_2H_5)_3$, $Al(C_6H_5)_3$, $Ga(CH_3)_3$, $In(CH_3)_3$, $Be(C_6H_5)_2$, $Al(C_6H_{13})_3$, $Al[CH_2—(CH_2)_{16}—CH_3]_3$, $Ga(C_6H_5)_3$, and $In(C_6H_5)_3$. These activators may also be present in the form of their (in many cases, very stable) organic molecular compounds with ethers, thioethers, or amines. They may also be present in complex linkage with alkali metal hydrides, alkyls, or aryls. Examples of these activator compounds are $NaBe(C_2H_5)_3$,

LiAlH$_4$, LiAl(C$_2$H$_5$)$_4$, NaAl(C$_2$H$_5$)$_4$. Activators of the general formula R'—Me—R", where Me represents Mg, Ca, Sr, or Ba, and R' and R" represent, in any desired combination, hydrogen or a monovalent saturated aliphatic or aromatic radical, and where the metal Me is linked directly to hydrogen or carbon, are claimed by Ziegler in Ger. 889,229 (800c). The dimerization of unsaturated, straight-chain hydrocarbons with more than two carbon atoms in the molecule, e.g., propylene and higher olefins, by the use of these activators is described by Ziegler and Gellert in U. S. 2,695,327 (913).

The use of nickel, cobalt, or platinum as co-catalysts in combination with an aluminum alkyl as the activator is specified by Ziegler in Belg. 527,736 (897a).

Organometallic activators are sensitive compounds which react easily with, and are decomposed by, oxygen, carbon dioxide, water and other compounds, and special emphasis must be placed on the use of very highly purified ethylene. Observing these precautions, it is claimed that about 500–2,000 g. of colorless polyethylenes melting from 110–135°C., with molecular weights ranging from 10,000 to 30,000, may be obtained for each gram of triethylaluminum employed. According to an example, a paraffinlike material with a melting point of 70–80°C. was obtained by heating purified ethylene with tri-n-hexylaluminum to 140°C. under constant ethylene pressure of 110–160 atmospheres. Under otherwise identical reaction conditions, an increase in pressure to 500 atmospheres yielded a product with an increased melting point of 110–120°C. The technically important properties of the polyethylene are still further improved when the ethylene pressure is increased from 1,000 to 2,000 atmospheres.

Ziegler et al. (1044,1045,1046) recently described vividly how the previously mentioned nickel effect was discovered, and how this discovery led to the study of other co-catalysts and finally to the Mülheim normal pressure polyethylene process, generally called the Ziegler process. Holzkamp, one of Ziegler's students, had frequently prepared higher aluminum alkyls, e.g., aluminum hexyl, or octyl, by heating aluminum triethyl with ethylene to 100°C. in an autoclave at 100 atmospheres. One day, instead of obtaining the higher aluminum alkyls, he noted a quantitative formation of butylene-1 besides unchanged aluminum triethyl. After some search for the co-catalyst responsible for this change in reaction mechanism, traces of colloidal nickel were found in the crevices of the wall of the autoclave, which had previously been used for hydrogenation experiments. At this stage, a systematic search of the periodic system was undertaken by Breil.

Besides Ni, only Co and Pt were found to catalyze the displacement reaction. Fe and the other metals of group 8 of the periodic system were practically ineffective, as were Cu, Ag, and Au. When, however, Zr-acetylacetonate was used as the additive, solid polyethylene was obtained. This was then also found to be possible with combinations of aluminum alkyls and all transition elements of groups 4, 5, and 6, including Th and U. The most efficient catalysts were built on the basis of Ti compounds. These results then led Martin to the discovery that with certain highly active catalysts, especially titanium catalysts, the polymerization could be effected at uncommonly low pressures, and finally at atmospheric pressure. The following description of such an experiment is a verbatim translation from pages 544 and 545 of the paper by Ziegler, Holzkamp, Breil, and Martin (1046):

In a large 5 l. glass cylinder we stir 2 l. of a solution or suspension of catalyst in a suitable medium, such as Aliphatin [Fischer-Tropsch-Dieselöl], and pass ethylene in at room temperature. The temperature rises at once, and in a few minutes afterwards, the precipitated polyethylene powder can be seen. When the temperature reaches 70°C., we cool the vessel by airblast. The velocity of ethylene absorption easily reaches 200 l. per hr. per l. of solution; in this case, therefore, about 400 l. per hr. All of the ethylene is absorbed and practically none escapes. The mixture becomes thicker and thicker, and after one or one and a half hours can no longer be stirred. The polymer which is gray to brown colored, depending on the nature of the catalyst, becomes snow-white on exposure to the air. It is then washed with dry alcohol and loses almost all its inorganic constituents. Apparently, aluminum alcoholates and titanium esters are formed, both of which are readily soluble. Ash content of 0.01% after filtering and drying is easily obtained. The above described experiment gives about 400 g. of polyethylene, and the process can be set up on a larger scale directly.

The molecular weight of the first product thus made by Ziegler was about 300,000. It is now known how to control the molecular weight in the range down to 10,000, and up to 2 or 3 million. The 50,000–100,000 range product can be processed on conventional plastics machinery, but is superior to conventional polyethylene in many respects, as will be shown in Section 6.19.

The Ziegler catalysts also permit the polymerization of α-olefins under somewhat modified reaction conditions, as well as the preparation of copolymers of ethylene and α-olefins (1045).

As far as the reaction mechanism is concerned, publications to date leave very little clue as to its nature. Ziegler (1046) points out that diethyl aluminum chloride alone does not add ethylene at 100°C. and 100 atmospheres pressure, while a highly active catalyst for the normal pressure polymerization is obtained in the presence of $TiCl_4$. He concludes that the polymerization catalyst must perform a new role, unrelated to the old growth reaction. In another paper, Ziegler (1045) expresses the opinion that neither a radical chain, nor a cationic chain mechanism is likely, but that perhaps an anionic mechanism may be assumed. However, he points out the possibility that the polymerization does not follow any of the three schemes. Additional information on the functioning of the Ziegler catalyst is in Belg. 538,782 to Montecatini and Ziegler (1072).

According to Anderson and Merckling in U. S. 2,721,189 to duPont (1097), complexes are formed in the polymerization mixtures by the reduction of a titanium compound having a valence state above two with agents such as a Grignard reagent, a metal alkyl or aryl, a metal hydride, an alkali metal or an alkaline earth metal, to a valence state of two. These complexes are believed to be the active catalysts or catalyst components which are capable of initiating the polymerization in an extremely active manner.

In discussing the synthesis and properties of crystallizable polymers, Mark (992) pointed out that catalysis in polymerization until now has essentially meant accelerating *initiation* or delaying *termination*. The important discoveries of Ziegler and Natta, for the first time, seem to indicate clearly that one also can influence in a favorable manner the *propagation* reaction itself. To achieve this it seems to be essential to initiate the reaction at a *solid surface* and to add the individual monomers at the point of initiation in such a manner that the growing chain is pushed away from its origin and the macromolecule grows like a hair. To make this process efficient, a delicate balance of several factors, is needed: (a) the carrier surface, which absorbs the monomer and the initiator; (b) the initiator, which forms the active complex with the monomer on the surface; (c) the solvent, which removes the polymer molecules from the active surface and permits hereby a reproduction of the cycle.

Apparently, it is possible to establish a successful cooperation of these factors in many different ways. Most prominent are the Ziegler catalysts with insoluble lower valence states of heavy metal halides ($TiCl_2$, $TiCl_3$, and corresponding halides of Zr, V, Cr, etc.) as carriers, soluble metal alkyls or alkylhalides (BeR_2, AlR_3, AlR_2Cl, ZnR_2, $MgRCl$, etc.) as initiators, and aliphatic or aromatic hydrocarbons as vehicles.

According to M. Fischer, the system $TiCl_4 + AlCl_3$ or Al metal and ethylene, in an aliphatic vehicle either represents directly, or produces at the beginning of the reaction, conditions which favorably influence the propagation reaction of ethylene polymerization. [Compare (790).]

According to A. A. Morton, alkali halides complexed with alkali alkyls promote and control in a specific manner the polymerization of dienes.

According to the Standard Oil of Indiana and the Phillips Petroleum

Company, it is possible to use finely divided metal oxides (Al_2O_3, Cr_2O_3, SiO_2, etc.) as carriers, alkali metals, alkali hydrides or alkali alkyls as initiators, and aliphatic or aromatic hydrocarbons as vehicles.

The use of these heterogeneous "catalysts" does not only permit one to carry out polymerization reactions under unusually mild conditions and to carry them to unexpectedly high molecular weights, but it also influences the details of the chain structure in a most remarkable manner. Natta has demonstrated that catalysts of the above type are able to produce "isotactic" and "syndiotactic" polymers of propylene, alpha-butylene, and styrene which have an unexpected capacity to crystallize and, as a consequence, display melting points very much higher than the softening ranges of their presently known glassy or amorphous counterparts (165°C. *versus* 25°C.; 135°C. *versus* 10°C., and 230°C. *versus* 80°C.). Already, Schildknecht (1140) has observed the existence of a crystallizable modification of polyvinylbutyl ether, and Nyquist and Kropa have reported a crystalline type of poly-alpha-methyl-para-methylstyrene. Natta together with Rigamonti disclosed the existence of a crystalline polystyrene as early as 1935.

Mark has repeated these experiments during the last year and has obtained evidence that crystallizable (isotactic or syndiotactic), vinyl type head-to-tail polymers result only if there is a finely divided solid component present while the polymerization takes place. Its presence seems not only to accelerate the stepwise addition of monomers to the growing chain but also to control the specific conditions of the entry of every individual monomer in such a manner that either isotactic (block meso-type polymers) or syndiotactic (regularly alternating meso-type polymers) are formed.

Additional experiments indicate that surface catalysis of vinyl polymerization is a rather general principle which can be embodied in many different specific ways demanding the cooperation of: (*a*) A *carrier*, which has a high specific surface development, is capable of adsorbing the monomer, and above that is capable of forming a moderately stable complex with the initiator and the monomer. Beyond the materials already mentioned, it seems that any finely divided metal or metal compound displaying reducing and complexing capacity is capable of being used in this connection (finely divided metal powders, metal acetylacetonates, carbonyls, etc.). (*b*) An *initiator*, which is capable of complexing with the carrier and the monomer to give a system of moderate stability, so that the monomer can be added in an "adiabatic" manner and the chain can grow without losing its contact with the point of its origin (metals, metal hydrides, metal alkyls, metal-halide alkyls, etc.). (*c*) A *vehicle* which removes the polymer molecule from the surface at which it is partially adsorbed and, according to Mark, hereby renders the initiating complex available for the reiteration of the process of growing another polymer molecule, fed by monomer which is adsorbed on the surface of the carrier.

The Ziegler process, to date, is the subject of four Belgian patents. In Belg. 533,362 (1071), Ziegler claims: the use, as catalysts, of mixtures of trialkylaluminums with compounds of metals of groups 4 to 6 of the periodic system, including Th and U, and particularly Ti, Zr, and Cr; a pressure of less than 10 atmospheres (preferably atmospheric or less than atmospheric); and a reaction temperature above 50°C. The polymerization is carried out in the presence of vehicles, and polyethylenes ranging in molecular weights from 50,000–3,000,000 are specified.

In Belg. 534,792 (1049), Ziegler claims the use, as catalysts, of mixtures of compounds of metals of groups 4 to 6 of the periodic system, including Th and U, with aluminum compounds of the general formula R_2AlX, where R is hydrogen or a hydrocarbon radical or residue, and X is hydrogen, an alkoxy or aryloxy group, or the radical of a secondary amine, a secondary acid amide, mercaptan or thiophenol, or of a carboxylic or sulfonic acid.

In Belg. 534,888 (1051), Ziegler claims as catalysts mixtures of organic compounds of magnesium and/or zinc, and compounds of metals of the groups 4 to 6 of the periodic system, including Th and U. Alkylmagnesium or alkylzinc, and Grignard compounds or the corresponding zinc compounds are specified.

In Belg. 540,459 (1086a), Ziegler explains how the polymer molecular weight is controlled by the mol ratio of the two catalyst components.

3.6. Polymerization Inhibitors

The inhibition of the polymerization of ethylene by nitric oxide, over the temperature range of 400–525°C. and at approximately atmospheric pressure, has been investigated by Burnham and Pease (92,131). The courses of the experiments for both the normal polymerization and the nitric oxide–inhibited polymerization at 500°C. are shown in Figure 11. The inhibitory effect of the nitric oxide was found to fade out as the polymerization proceeded. Surprisingly, the polymerization of propylene was found not to be inhibited but slightly accelerated by the addition of nitric oxide.

A resin obtained by the condensation of hydroquinone, a phenol, and an aldehyde is claimed by Kropa and Welcher in U. S. 2,703,792 to American Cyanamid (1063) to inhibit the polymerization of many monomers, including ethylene.

The addition of styrene or an alkyl-substituted styrene causes, according to U. S. 2,512,472 to White [duPont (509)], the termination of the ethylene-vinyl acetate copolymerization reaction.

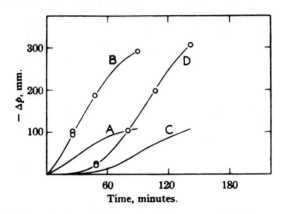

Fig. 11. Inhibition of polymerization of ethylene at 500°C.: A, pressure decrease, p_0 of C_2H_4 = 713 mm.; B, ethylene consumed in A; C, same as A with 10 mm. of nitric oxide; D, ethylene consumed in C.   (*J. Am. Chem. Soc.*, **64**, 1405, 1942.)

3.7. Induced Radical Polymerization

Apart from the thermal polymerization of ethylene, numerous studies dealing with induced polymerization were reported prior to 1938. These dealt with induction by ions, atomic hydrogen, free radicals from dimethyl-mercury and azomethane, by photo-decomposition of ammonia, acetone, ethyl iodide, and with excited mercury, cadmium, and sodium (57,120). More recently, Steacie and co-workers (102,136,139) investigated the cadmium- and zinc-photosensitized reactions of ethylene and of ethylene-hydrogen mixtures. The polymerization of ethylene by alkyl radicals from alkyl iodides has been reported by Jungers and co-workers (57,67,97).

With lead alkyls, methyl- and ethyl-radical induced polymerizations of ethylene and of propylene were carried out by Beeck and Rust (115) in static as well as in flow experiments. The latter allowed collection of enough reaction products for analysis by low-temperature distillation, which indicated that most of the formed polymer was of low molecular weight.

The effect of temperature on the methyl-radical induced polymerization of ethylene was studied by Rall and Danby (415). When a mixture of acetaldehyde vapor and ethylene is irradiated with ultraviolet light at temperatures between 200 and 350°C., methyl radicals from the aldehyde photolysis induce a chain polymerization of the olefin to products of small average molecular weight. From the temperature coefficient of the reaction, the activation energy of the step, $CH_3^* + C_2H_4$, was estimated to be 6.8 kcals.

The reaction between free hydroxyl radicals, formed from water vapor in a glow discharge, and ethylene was studied in the gaseous phase by Milas, Stahl, and Dayton (406). Ethylene was converted mainly to carbon dioxide, small amounts of peroxides, formaldehyde, formic acid, and possibly ethylene glycol. With a large excess of ethylene, no carbon dioxide was formed, but formaldehyde, formic acid, traces of ethanol, possibly ethylene glycol, and acetylene resulted. A white deposit, probably polyethylene, was found to cover the inner surface of the discharge tube.

3.8. Polymerization by Irradiation

Alpha radiation from radon was used by Lind, Bardwell, and Perry (17) to initiate the polymerization of ethylene at 25°C. and at approximately one atmosphere. Olefins of higher molecular weight and gases such as hydrogen and methane resulted.

Solid polymers, usually yellowish or brown in color, were obtained by Bretton *et al.* (591) from the polymerization of ethylene by gamma radiation at one atmosphere pressure and at temperatures ranging from room conditions to 167°C.

White, solid polyethylene resulted from the irradiation of ethylene with cobalt-60 γ-rays by Lewis, Martin, and Anderson (861). Some of the products were fluffy powders; others were tough, coherent masses. Their physical properties are described in Table X.

Compared with a sample of Bakelite DYNH, the samples obtained by irradiation showed high crystallinity, and some appeared to have crosslinked. The tensile properties presented in the table are probably somewhat influenced by the molding conditions, and a direct comparison with the data given for the Bakelite sample may not be possible.

In detailed evaluation of the experimental data, the radiation yield has been related graphically to the dose of irradiation, and to molecular weight, melting point, tensile strength, and crystallinity of the polymers.

Acetaldehyde, acetone, air and acetone, air and water, and carbon dioxide had no effect on this irradiation-initiated polymerization of ethylene. The addition of sulfur dioxide did result in the production of a white powder which proved to have a sulfur content close to that of an equimolar addition product of sulfur dioxide and ethylene. Similar reactions between

TABLE X

Properties of Polyethylenes Obtained by Irradiation

Dose, megarep	Radiation yield, A[a]	Melting point, °F., lower/ upper	Density, g./cm.^{3}	Ultimate tensile, lb./sq. in.	Elongation, per cent at rupture	Crystallinity, per cent	Molecular weight	
							by melt viscosity	by solution viscosity
1.55	95	219/226						
0.61	37	216/225						
0.58	71	205/217						
0.60	63	207/214						
0.54	52	196/205						
1.91	750	241/244	0.951	450	4	77	26,300	Insol.
0.37	28	234/235						
3.09	2400	248/689	0.941	2200	42	71	34,400	Insol.
2.40	730	210/248	0.951	770	2	77	28,100	4200
0.45	0.1							
0.57	790	203/252						8800
0.91	298	199/207						Insol.
6.97	2200	234/720	0.943	2100	29	72	40,500	Insol.
6.43	1900	241/610	0.941	2300	79	71	37,300	Insol.
4.29	745	241/244	0.951	630	3	77	11,900	3700
Bakelite DYNH			0.921	1500	550	61	21,800	20,000
								Assumed

Source: *Chem. Engr. Prog.*, **50** (5), 249 (1954).

[a] The A value represents $\dfrac{\text{weight fraction ethylene reacted} \times 10^6}{\text{molecular weight of ethylene} \times \text{dose, megarep}}$.

sulfur dioxide and ethylene under ultraviolet light have been reported by Matthew and Elder in Brit. 11,635/1914 (11) and by Snow and Frey (71).

Initial rates of polymerization of ethylene by gamma radiation have been derived by Hayward (967) from total pressure measurements on batch systems of ethylene. Initial rates between about 0.1 and 60% per day were obtained at temperatures between 27° and 238°C., pressures between $1/2$ and 21 atmospheres, and a radiation intensity of the order of 100,000 r./hr. The products obtained in these experiments were generally liquid; however, a white waxy solid was obtained at room temperature and the higher pressures. The reaction was found to be homogeneous and strongly inhibited by a trace concentration of oxygen. A simplified version of a free-radical polymerization mechanism is presented, according to which the ion-neutralization energy is ineffective in the initiation of ethylene polymerization and, furthermore, the chain-transfer process by which the liquid product is formed at elevated temperatures is suppressed by an increase in pressure. The initial radiation yields and the nature of the products obtained in Hayward's work, as well as the results of Lind, Bardwell, and Perry (17) on the polymerization of ethylene initiated by alpha particles, and the results of Lewis, Martin, and Anderson (861) on the polymerization of ethylene initiated by gamma radiation are generally consistent with the type of mechanism postulated by Hayward.

Reference has been recently made to the studies of Callinan (926c), as having obtained high-density polyethylenes in substantially quantitative yield by γ-irradiation of ethylene. The fact is emphasized that these products contain no residual catalyst to cause color or odor problems.

The production of vinyl polymers in general by ionizing irradiation was discussed by Chapiro, Magat, Prévot-Bernas, Reinisel, and Seban (941). Electrons, it is pointed out, are absorbed in a relatively thin layer of the material, and produce locally very strong concentrations of ions and free radicals. These favor termination reactions, and a large number of chains of low molecular weight are produced. Gamma rays, on the other hand, are capable of penetrating very deeply and producing free radicals in locations which are, on a molecular scale, widely separated. One thus obtains only low concentrations of growing chains and, therefore, molecules of higher molecular weight. For this reason, sources of γ-radiation, such as cobalt-60 appear preferable, in spite of the problem of protection involved.

The possibility of chain grafting by the application of high intensity radiation will be discussed in Section 4.2.

There has been recently much speculation on the possible commercial application of high intensity radiations in promoting polymerization reactions, and Ballantine (823b) has summarized some of the advantages which γ-radiation offers as an initiating agent. Much thought is given to the industrial future of radiation chemistry in publications by Manowitz (756a,863a), also of the Brookhaven National Laboratories, who analyzed the potential and the cost of radiation power for polymerization reactions. As to the polymerization of ethylene in particular, Manowitz considers the use of known reactor technology for this purpose economically feasible. Similar optimistic statements have also come recently from Britain's atomic engineers.

A process for the manufacture of polymers and copolymers of ethylene, particularly solid and semi-solid polymers, by exposing liquid or compressed ethylene to a source of penetrating radiation, particularly γ-rays, x-rays, or neutrons, is specified in Brit. 714,843 to I.C.I. (906b). The polymerization of ethylene under the influence of ionizing radiation, preferably γ-radiation from radioactive materials, e.g., cobalt-60, and in the presence of a chain transfer agent, such as an aromatic or chlorinated aromatic hydrocarbon, is described in Austral. 6253/55 to Monsanto (1052). The patent also includes the preparation of copolymers, and relates density and crystallinity of the resultant polyethylenes to the production variables.

3.9. Polymerization by Silent Electric Discharge

While the electric arc and spark have, in general, the same effect upon ethylene as intensive heat treatment, the silent electric discharge causes polymerization mainly through butene and hexene to heavy oils and, in some cases, to solids (120,558,738). Pryanishnikov (19) finds the process of silent electric discharge polymerization of ethylene hydrocarbons in general highly reminiscent of the high-temperature, high-pressure polymerization of such hydrocarbons studied by Ipatieff (10). The nature of the products depends largely upon reaction conditions, especially exposure time. Hydrocarbons of the formula $(C_2H_4)_n$, regarded as polymers of ethylene, were reported as polymerization products by Losanitsch and Jovitschitsch (5,8,9), and by Demyanov and Pryanishnikov (13,18). Szukiewicz (48) obtained the fractions, including solid deposits, from 14.8 g. of a reaction product obtained by silent electric discharge in an atmosphere of ethylene, as shown in Table Xa. Power input was approximately 35 watts per tube, and the rate of ethylene flow was 120 liters per hour.

De Saint-Aunay (28), in a study of the polymerization of hydrocarbons by the silent electric discharge, noted a film adhering to the walls of the discharge tube representing 5 to 10% of the weight of ethylene introduced

TABLE Xa

Reaction Products Obtained by Silent Electric Discharge

Fraction	% Total weight
From −10° to −5°C.	3.2
−5° to +5°C.	55.0
+5° to +10°C.	3.1
+10° to +20°C.	3.3
+20° to +50°C.	1.7
+50° to +90°C.	3.5
Above +90°C.	14.8
Deposit in glass tubes	9.8
Deposit in aluminum tubes	5.6

Source: *Roczniki Chemji.*, **13**, 245 (1933).

Baladin, Eidus, and Zalogin (30) polymerized ethylene in a closed system at
20°C. by means of high-frequency discharges.   Depending upon the duration of the discharge, low-boiling hydrocarbons and thick oils up to semi-
solid films formed on the walls of the discharge tubes.

3.10. Thermal Depolymerization

While partial degradation of polymeric materials is in some cases carried
out intentionally and under controlled conditions (as by milling to achieve
easier workability and more desirable properties), uncontrolled degradation

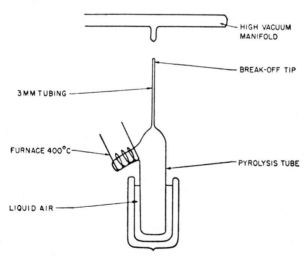

Fig. 12. Diagram of pyrolysis apparatus. (*J. Research
Nat. Bur. Standards*, **41**, 315, 1948.)

deteriorates polymers and renders them in many cases unusable. The study of degradation processes and of means to prevent degradation in polymers is, therefore, an important field of polymer chemistry; it is treated very capably in a recent monograph by Jellinek (972). Depolymerization frequently proceeds at higher temperatures, but even at relatively low temperatures, e.g., room temperature, oxygen or air will cause oxidative aging through formation and breakdown of hydroperoxides (776).

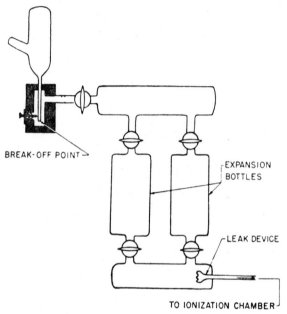

BREAK-OFF POINT

EXPANSION BOTTLES

LEAK DEVICE

TO IONIZATION CHAMBER

Fig. 13. Diagram of mass spectrometer inlet. (*J. Research Nat. Bur. Standards*, **41**, 316, 1948.)

The stability of high-polymer hydrocarbons toward thermal depolymerization was determined by Seymour (350) as the lowest temperature at which volatile products are produced; polyethylene was found to be more stable than polystyrene, and the latter more stable than polyisobutylene.

The thermal decomposition of polymers, including polyethylene, was studied at 400°C. by Wall (355), using a mass spectrometer to identify the products of pyrolysis. A diagram of the pyrolysis apparatus is presented in Figure 12. A simplified diagram of the mass spectrometer inlet system is illustrated in Figure 13.

A comparison of the volatile products obtained in the pyrolysis of

TABLE XI

Pyrolysis of Vinyl Polymers

Vinyl polymer	Volatile pyrolysis products[a]	Mole per cent
Polyethylene[b]	Approximately 30 compounds consisting of n-alkenes, n-alkanes, n-dienes, and cyclics.	
Polyisobutylene	Isobutylene	78
	Neopentane	10
	Diisobutene	4
	Ethane	2
	C_7H_{14}	1
	C_6H_{12}	0.5
	CH_4	0.5
	C_7H_{12}	0.4
	C_3H_4	0.4
	$C_{10}H_6$	0.1
Polystyrene	Styrene	94
	Ethylene	3
	Ethylbenzene	1
	Toluene	1
	Benzene	1
	Isopropylbenzene	0.5

Source: *J. Research Nat. Bur. Standards*, **41**, 316 (1948).

[a] The volatile products represent 66% of the polyisobutylene and 34% of the polystyrene.

[b] In polyethylene, it proved impossible to compute an analysis since the products were so varied; however, the ethylene produced was certainly less than 1%.

various vinyl polymers is presented in Table XI. It appears that polyisobutylene and polystyrene decompose chiefly into their respective basic monomers, isobutylene and styrene. Polyethylene when pyrolyzed *in vacuo* under the same conditions, decomposes into about 30 compounds consisting of normal alkanes, alkenes, dienes, and cyclic compounds.

Oakes and Richards (411) followed the thermal degradation of ethylene polymers at temperatures above 290°C. by changes in average molecular weight and in the infrared spectra. Figure 14 shows changes in the intrinsic viscosity of a sample of polyethylene as a function of time at 315 and 360°C. The broken lines indicate the course of the intrinsic viscosity and time curves which would have been found if the initial rate of reaction had been maintained throughout the course of the experiment. From the changes in number average molecular weight, the degradation was calculated in terms of the number of carbon-carbon links broken after various times of heating. Figure 15 shows the effect of time of heating on the number of chain links broken.   If all bonds were equally likely to break, the plot of amount of degradation against time would be a straight line.

Although molecular weight decrease was marked in the range of 300–400°C., ethylene or other volatile products were not formed in quantity

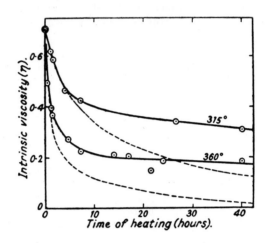

Fig. 14. Degradation of polyethylene on heating, as expressed by decrease in viscosity. (*J. Chem. Soc.*, **1949**, 2930.)

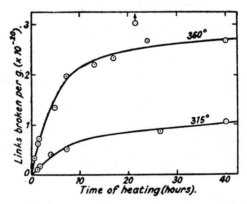

Fig. 15. Degradation of polyethylene on heating, as expressed by number of broken chain links. (*J. Chem. Soc.*, **1949**, 2930.)

below about 370°C.   In this respect, the degradation is in contrast to that of styrene or methyl methacrylate polymers, which in some circumstances evolve monomer in quantity before the molecular weight of residual polymer is appreciably reduced. The results of these polyethylene degradation experiments are interpreted in terms of a chain-reaction mechanism in which the rupture of weak links, present in very low concentration, initiates a further degradation, mainly at points adjacent to branches in the polymer molecule.

Hopff (609) heated polyethylene in the absence of oxygen, either in a nitrogen atmosphere without pressure, or under its own pressure in a closed vessel. At 400°C., continuous transition was observed from the viscous,

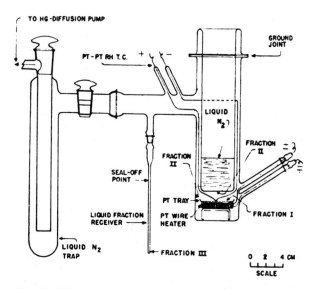

Fig. 16. Diagram of pyrolysis apparatus. (*J. Research Nat. Bur. Standards*, **42**, 500, 1949.)

plastic state, through a petrolatumlike, intermediary state, into a thick, oily liquid with partial separation of gaseous decomposition products. The higher the initial molecular weight of the polyethylene, the faster decomposition was found to take place.

The pyrolysis of polyethylene and other polymeric compounds in a high vacuum was carried out by Madorsky, Straus, Thompson, and Williamson (403,480) in the modified pyrolysis apparatus shown in Figure 16. A polyethylene sample of an average molecular weight of 20,000 was pyrolyzed at 300–475°C. *in vacuo* (10^{-6} mm. Hg), and the resulting fractions subjected to mass spectrometric analysis and to microcryoscopic determination of molecular weights. The first fraction was volatile at -196°C., had an average molecular weight of 16, and contained a trace of CH_4. The second fraction was liquid at $-75°C.$, had an average molecular weight of 53, and contained C_4H_8 (25%), $n\text{-}C_4H_{10}$ (19%), C_3H_8 (15%), C_2H_6 (12%), C_5H_{10} (8%), and lesser amounts of C_2H_4, propa-, penta-, and hexadienes, C_3H_6, C_5H_{10}, $n\text{-}C_5H_{12}$, C_6H_{12}, $n\text{-}C_6H_{14}$, and $n\text{-}C_7H_{16}$. The third fraction was liquid at $25°C.$, had an average molecular weight of 150, and

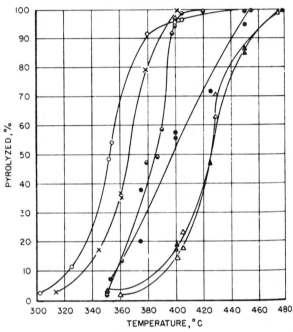

Fig. 17. Pyrolysis of vinyl polymers. O, Polyisoprene; X, polyisobutene; ◓, polystyrene; ●, GR-S; ▲, polybutadiene; △, polyethylene. (*J. Research Nat. Bur. Standards*, **42**, 512, 1949.)

gave evidence of a 15-carbon chain polymer structure. Finally, a waxlike fraction, volatile at the temperature of pyrolysis, with an average molecular weight of 692, and soluble in hot but insoluble in cold benzene, was separated. The residue was a horny mass, insoluble both in benzene and in cyclohexane.

The thermal decomposition of various polymers is compared in Figure 17.

In subsequent investigations, Madorsky (616) measured the rate of degradation of polyethylene in a vacuum by determining the rate of loss in weight with a very sensitive tungsten-spring balance.   Approximation to a first-order reaction was noted, and the activation energy was calculated on the basis of degradation rates at various temperatures between 300 and 400°C.   Values of 48 kcal. at the start, and 68 kcal. for subsequent degradation, were found.   The kinetics approximate those for random rupture of the carbon-carbon links, although there are some indications that rupture occurs preferentially at the points where the molecule branches. This further supports the earlier investigations of Oakes and Richards (411).   Comments on alleged discrepancies between the reports of Madorsky were made by Jellinek (737).

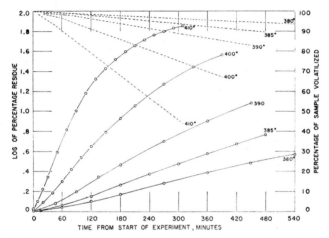

Fig. 18. Pyrolysis of polymethylene.   ———, Percentage of sample volatilized *versus* time; -----, log₁₀ of percentage residue *versus* time.   (*J. Research Nat. Bur. Standards*, **53**, 365, 1954.)

The thermal degradation of polymers as a function of molecular structure was investigated by Madorsky and Straus (863).   When heated in a vacuum at temperatures of about 200–500°C., polymer chains were found to break up into volatile fragments of various sizes, depending on the nature of the polymer.   Some polymers, like poly-α-methylstyrene, yield the monomer exclusively.   Other polymers, like polymethylene, yield a whole spectrum of fragments consisting of from two carbon atoms in the chain to about 50 or more.   The polymethylene used in these experiments was prepared by the decomposition of diazomethane with trimethyl borate as the catalyst.   Thermal degradation of this polymethylene is shown in Figure 18.

Intermediate between these two types of polymers are those like poly-isobutylene, which yield partly monomer and partly large fragments. The rates at which these fragments are formed and vaporized also vary for different polymers. On comparing rates of volatilization of a series of polymers at 350°C., it is found that polytetrafluoroethylene is the most thermally stable polymer, having an initial rate of volatilization of 0.0000016 weight % per minute. These differences in the thermal behavior of polymers can be correlated with the molecular structure of the polymer chains and with the nature and frequency of side groups.

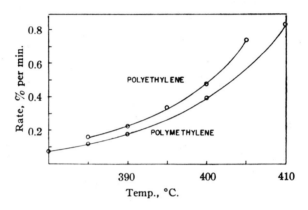

Fig. 19. Comparison of the rates of decomposition of polymethylene and polyethylene *versus* temperature. (*J. Amer. Chem. Soc.*, **76**, 3431, 1954.)

The same authors reported recently (991) on the thermal degradation of polytrifluoromonochloroethylene (Kel-F), poly-α,β,β-trifluorostyrene, and poly-p-xylene in a vacuum.

Wall, Madorsky, Brown, Straus, and Simha (888) studied thermal depolymerization rates and molecular weight changes of polymethylene and polyethylene and obtained spectrometric analyses of the volatile products. The polymethylene used in these investigations was obtained by treating ether solutions of diazomethane with boron trifluoride etherate. When the results of the polymethylene depolymerization experiments were compared with those similarly obtained for commercial and for radiation crosslinked polyethylenes, it was concluded that crosslinking had little effect on the rate of thermal depolymerization. Chain-branching is, however, assumed to be responsible for the increased rate of decomposition of polyethylene over polymethylene (Figure 19). The rate for polymethylene exhibits a characteristic maximum as a function of conversion which is absent in polyethylene (Figure 20) but is predicted by theory.

Florin, Wall, Brown, Hymo, and Michaelsen (847) attempted to improve the stability of polytetrafluoroethylene, the most stable polymer known, at high temperature.   Their methods were suggested by the structure and kinetics of its thermal decomposition.   Neither the use of a large number of different catalysts during polymerization, nor the addition of foreign structural units, such as sulfur, selenium, hydrocarbon, and fluorocarbon groups to the polymerizing mixture, brought about any improvement in thermal stability.

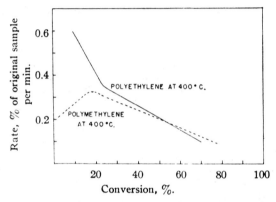

Fig. 20. Schematic comparison of experimental rate of pyrolysis curves of polymethylene and polyethylene. (*J. Amer. Chem. Soc.*, **76**, 3431, 1954.)

The kinetics of depolymerization reactions of the chain type were developed by Simha, Wall, and Blatz (486), by postulating an initiation, followed by propagation, transfer, and termination of radicals.

A novel method for investigating molecular degradation has been applied to polyethylene by Kiyama and Kinoshita (613), in which the degradation of the polyethylene molecule is effected by a high-pressure jet.   A 1% solution of polyethylene (molecular weight 26,900) in tetrahydronaphthalene was expelled through a 0.42-mm. nozzle at pressures of 2,000 and 4,000 atmospheres and temperatures of 10 and 100°C. on a plate immersed in water.   Degradation was favored by the higher temperature and pressure, as well as by closer proximity of nozzle and plate.

Patents relating to the pyrolytic degradation of polyethylene have been assigned to I.C.I. (191) and to duPont (188).   The first of these, Brit. 569,043 to Richards, is concerned with the pyrolysis of polyethylene by

heating in the absence of air or oxidizing agents at a temperature above
290°C., preferably 330–600°C., until no further pyrolysis occurs. According to the second patent, U. S. 2,372,001 to Joyce, polyethylene of molecular weight 14,750 may be degraded by heating at reduced pressures
(10 mm. Hg) until distillation ceases. The resultant product is a waxy
hydrocarbon having a molecular weight of 400 and an iodine number of
53. It is emphasized that no charring or tar formation occurs, and that
the molecular weight and unsaturation of the products, while dependent
upon the nature of the polymer degraded, can be controlled by temperature,
pressure, and the addition of such catalysts as nickel or kieselguhr.

3.11. Oxidative Degradation

While polyethylene is quite stable at elevated temperatures in the absence of oxygen, changes in physical and electrical properties indicative of
oxidation and degradation take place readily in the presence of oxygen.

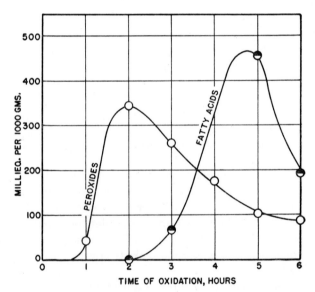

Fig. 21. Formation of peroxides and fatty acids in paraffin wax oxidized at 163°C.
(*Ind. Eng. Chem.* **41**, 1442, 1949, [406a].)

As an example of what to expect, the formation of peroxides and fatty
acids in paraffin wax, oxidized at 163°C., is shown in Figure 21. These
changes influence the processing behavior of the polyethylene in the molten
state and impose certain limitations on its use possibilities in the solid

state.   Changes in color to yellow, brown, and even black, together with
the development of a rancid odor, are accompanied by changes in molecular weight and eventual deterioration in mechanical strength.

The oxidation of polyethylene is most easily followed by milling the
plastic on a hot mill and measuring the change in electrical properties,
particularly the increase in power factor.   Myers (620) has determined
the degradation rate of a commercial polyethylene (Bakelite DYNH) by
measuring the change of power factor at various temperatures for different
lengths of time of milling.   These data are shown in Figure 22.   Oxidation

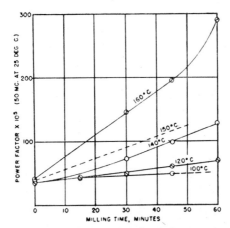

Fig. 22. Degradation of polyethylene on hot-
milling. (*Ind. Eng. Chem.*, **44**, 1096, 1952.)

of polyethylene is accompanied by an increase in the weight of the sample,
while the infrared spectrum shows the introduction of carbonyl groups,
resulting from the autocatalytic decomposition of hydroperoxide and peroxides.   The increase in carbonyl oxygen with time of milling is shown
in Figure 23.

Oxidation, usually associated with crosslinking of the molecules, tends to
cause an increase in melt viscosity, the melt becoming more rubbery, resulting in deterioration of the processing characteristics and formation of insoluble matter.   Continued oxidation, especially at high temperatures,
leads to degradation of the chains, liberation of volatile compounds such as
carbon dioxide, water, and fatty acids, and the formation of a brittle,
wax-like product.

Normally, polyethylene resins employed in high-frequency dielectric
applications contain an antioxidant to prevent oxidative degradation dur-

ing thermal processing. Figure 24 demonstrates the protective action of a commercial stabilizer, Akroflex C (65% phenyl-α-naphthylamine and

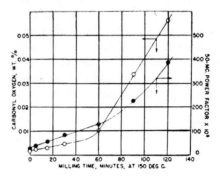

Fig. 23. Oxidation of polyethylene on hot-milling. (*Ind. Eng. Chem.*, **44**, 1097, 1952.)

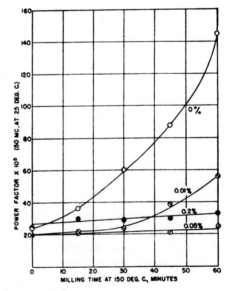

Fig. 24. Milling stability *versus* stabilizer concentration. (*Ind. Eng. Chem.*, **44**, 1097, 1952.)

35% diphenyl-*p*-phenylene diamine), on the polyethylene during milling in air at a roll surface temperature of 150°C.

The effect of temperature on the rate of oxidation of a 1-mm. sheet of polyethylene supported on a glass plate and exposed to air is shown in Table XII.

TABLE XII

Atmospheric Oxidation of Polyethylene Sheet in Air

Temp., °C.	Time for oxygen content to reach 0.2%, hrs.
35	25,000
50	3,000
75	300
100	60
150	1.5

Biggs and Hawkins (706,707) have pointed out that the oxidation of polyethylene follows the pattern set by lower homologs such as paraffinic waxes and oils. It is autocatalytic in nature, the rate of oxidation increasing as the amount of oxygen absorbed by the polyethylene increases. The rate of oxidation also increases with the amount of chain-branching, and also with the initial number of oxygen-containing groups. The rate of degradation in the dark at room temperature was found to be extremely low. The oxygen uptake of polyethylene at elevated temperatures was also measured by Wilson (1043) at approximately 1 atmosphere pressure of oxygen. The oxidation reaction was found to have a pronounced induction period, followed by a constant-rate stage and eventually by a gradual decrease in rate. The induction period could be greatly increased by the addition of antioxidants, and the amounts of the increase were found to be proportional to the concentration of the antioxidant. A subsequent report by Wilson (1142) dealing with the relation of oxidizability and structure is discussed in Chapter VI.

Hard waxes of molecular weight above 5,000 may be prepared by the controlled oxidation of polyethylenes. According to Brit. 579,666 to Forsyth and I.C.I. (252), this may be accomplished by treating polyethylene either with 60% nitric acid for 6 hours at 120°C., or with ozone at 70–100°C., or by heating in air at 140–250°C. for 2–10 hours in the presence or absence of oxygen carriers, such as tetralin. Such oxidation products are stated to be useful as synthetic waxes, polishes, and in coating compositions.

Controlled oxidation procedures applied to increase the bonding properties of polyethylene and to render polyethylene surfaces printable, are discussed in Chapter VIII.

3.12. Photochemical Degradation and Weathering

The photocatalyzed oxidation of polyethylene which takes place when the material is exposed to sunlight is a more serious problem than thermal oxidation, since it is difficult to control by antioxidants and protection is less readily accomplished. Photo-oxidation of polyethylene, according to Biggs and Hawkins (706,707), is rapid in contrast with that of saturated, low molecular weight aliphatic hydrocarbons. Furthermore, antioxidants

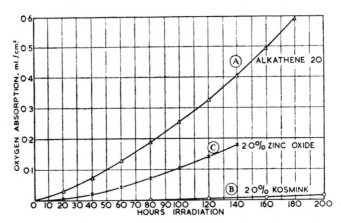

Fig. 25. Stabilization of polyethylene against degradation by irradiation. Oxygen absorption of polythene: alone (A); with added carbon black (B); with added zinc oxide (C). (J. Chem. Ind. [London], 69, 115, 1950.)

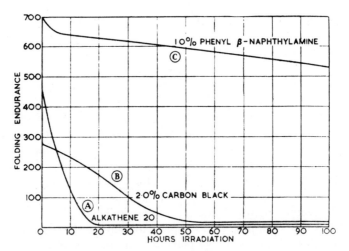

Fig. 26. Stabilization of polyethylene against degradation by irradiation. Folding endurance of polythene: unpigmented (A); with added carbon black (B); with added phenyl-β-naphthylamine (C). (J. Chem. Ind. [London], 69, 114, 1950.)

are of little benefit in protecting against exposure to light. Opaque pigments are of great value, finely divided carbon black being particularly effective in reducing the effects of light.

Experiments on the deterioration in sunlight of polyethylenes with molecular weights ranging from 11,000 to 20,000 were conducted by Pross and Black (485). Embrittlement, measured by the folding endurance test, and degradation of electrical and mechanical properties were determined.

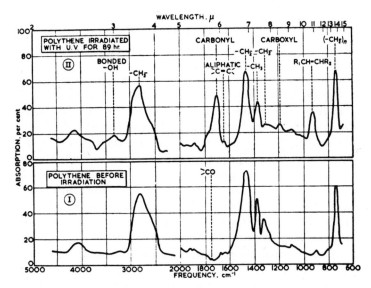

Fig. 27. Infrared absorption spectra of polyethylene before and after irradiation.
(*J. Chem. Ind.* [*London*], **69,** 115, 1950.)

Measurements were also made of the oxygen absorption of samples of polyethylene exposed to irradiation from a mercury lamp. Known areas of the polymer were placed in quartz tubes filled with oxygen and connected to mercury manometers fitted with compensating tubes. The pressure changes observed were considered to be due to the absorption of oxygen. Samples of polyethylene containing various pigments were treated in a similar manner and the relative effects of the pigments are shown in Figure 25.

The folding endurance was found to decrease rapidly as the brittleness of the polymer increased on aging. After 25 to 30 hours under the ultraviolet lamp, the endurance was negligibly small. Folding endurance was found to be improved by the presence of 2% of carbon black or 1% of phenyl-β-naphthylamine in the polymer, as indicated by Figure 26.

The ultraviolet absorption spectrum indicates that attack by irradiation is probably due to the presence of carbonyl groups in the polyethylene. Infrared absorption spectra between 2.5μ and 15μ, taken before and after irradiation, have established the presence of hydroxyl, carbonyl, and carboxyl groups, as shown in Figure 27.

The results of this investigation establish the probability that light absorption by the carbonyl groups present in the polyethylene is largely responsible for initiating the chain mechanism of oxidative deterioration, where both oxidation and deterioration must be assumed to occur simultaneously.

Results of experiments on the behavior of polyethylene (929), carried out in tropical Nigeria, West Africa, and in the United Kingdom, indicate that the material is less affected by the moisture of tropical climates than by the tropical sun in jungle clearings and, more particularly, on the beach and in the desert. The tests were carried out over a period of 12 months on two grades of British polyethylene, Alkathene 7 and Alkathene 20, both containing 0.1% of antioxidant, while some samples also included 0.1% of carbon black. No difference in the performance of the two grades was observed; in practically all cases, however, adverse effects were greatly reduced by the presence of carbon black. Thus, samples without carbon black exposed for 12 months in jungle undergrowth had a green coloration, while those containing carbon black were unaffected. In a jungle clearing however, even specimens protected by carbon black had isolated spots of green fungus after 6 months. Electrical property tests on specimens with carbon black in jungle undergrowth indicated that neither resistivity nor power factor was much affected; without carbon black, there was considerable deterioration. In semi-desert and surf-beach sites, even carbon black did not provide protection for more than 6 months; under the worst conditions of the test, there was a 30-fold rise in power factor without carbon black, and a 10-fold rise with it. Continuous exposure to the tropical sun resulted in surface cracking, increased brittleness, loss of flexibility and extensibility, and a rise in cold bend temperature. Progressive loss in specimen weight was noted at all sites, even after only 3 months. It is concluded from these results that while carbon black is helpful and should be included in polyethylene for use in the tropics, additional protection will have to be provided if more than limited service in direct sunlight is desired.

The reasons for the failure of thermal antioxidants to stabilize polyethylene against photo-oxidation were studied by Burgess (717), and other possible methods of stabilization were examined. Since saturated hydrocarbons do not absorb wave lengths shorter than 2000 A., the sensitization of polyethylene is attributed to aldehyde or ketone groups produced by the oxidation process, presumably formed by the breakdown of the peroxides. From the calculated quantum efficiencies of carbonyl formation and literature data on photolysis to free radicals, a kinetic chain length of 10 is derived, which should be much smaller in intense sunlight. The high rate of initiation and short chain length are mainly responsible for the failure of thermal antioxidants. By using absorbers stronger than carbonyl, attempts were made to prevent the initiation of oxidation chains altogether. Experiments with various amines indicated that the classification of absorbers as sensitizers or as stabilizers depends on the test method and particularly on the thickness of the sample. An excited absorber, to perform properly, must lose its electronic energy rapidly. Fluorescence is too slow, since materials fluorescing in the visible or ultraviolet ranges are generally sensitizers. The only compounds of photo-stabilizing efficiency similar to carbon black are certain metal chelate complexes of copper or nickel which, however, are also highly colored. Visible color may, according to Burgess, be necessary to approach the efficiency of carbon black.

3.13. Stabilizers against Degradation

The same types of materials useful as antioxidants for rubber are capable of reducing or completely inhibiting the thermal oxidation of polyethylene, at least temporarily. This is particularly true of phenols and amines. Freedom from color and odor, and low volatility to avoid loss on subsequent processing of the stabilized polymer, are essential requirements of a suitable stabilizer. Materials which have been used successfully include di-*o*-cresylolpropane[4,4'-isopropylidenebis(2-methylphenol)], and *p*-phenylenediamine. In general, the amount of stabilizer required to give adequate protection is less for polyethylene than for rubber. About 0.1% is usually sufficient to assure stabilization without significantly affecting the electrical properties.

Bosoni (830) determined the thermal oxidation of polyethylene by measuring the power factor at 50 Mc. (compare also Section 6.11). It was found to increase with temperature, milling time, and milling speed. Heating initially caused lowering of the molecular weight because of chain-breaking, then rapid increase in viscosity and softening point because of crosslinking by absorbed oxygen. Akroflex C (0.2%) (see Section

11, this Chapter), was found to stabilize polyethylene during milling for 7 hours at 150°C. Carbon black (2%) stabilized the polyethylene against photochemical oxidation but caused changes in electrical and mechanical properties.

The addition (0.0005 to 0.20%) of a nonprimary aromatic amine or of a phenol having a molecular weight of at least 250 is recommended in Brit. 571,943 to Baird, Forsyth, and I.C.I. (199) to improve the physical, chemical, and electrical stability of polyethylene to the action of heat, light, and outdoor exposure. British 594,891 to Western Electric (331) proposes a mixture of phenyl-α-naphthylamine and diphenyl-p-phenylenediamine as an antioxidant for incorporation in polyethylene compositions.

U. S. 2,434,662 to Latham and Strain (358), U. S. 2,435,245 to Strain (359), and Brit. 585,504 (310) (all to duPont) disclose the use as stabilizers for polyethylene of 1,3-bis(4-hydroxy-m-tolyl)propane; 1,3-bis(p-hydroxyphenyl)propane; a liquid acetone-diphenylamine condensation product; and a solid mixture of this with diphenyl-p-phenylenediamine. The acetone-diphenylamine condensation product can be prepared by heating 2 moles of acetone with 1 mole of diphenylamine in the presence of hydrogen iodide in an autoclave at 190–250°C. for a period up to 24 hours. These stabilizing agents are incorporated with the ethylene polymers in minimum quantity (0.005–2%) by a melt process at temperatures in excess of 145°C.

The incorporation of thiodipropionates, such as the didodecyl or dioctadecyl esters (0.001–5%) is proposed by Gribbins in U. S. 2,519,755 to duPont (513) to improve the stability of polyethylene to milling and to outdoor exposure. The stabilization of polyethylene against oxidative degradation by the addition of diphenylamine (0.2%) is described in U. S. 2,543,329 to Myers [Union Carbide (573)]. Diphenylamine is claimed to be superior to other secondary aromatic amines and quinones in not coloring the polymer originally or during thermal treatment in milling, extrusion, or casting operations. Constant power factor values during aging at 100°C. for up to 100 hours were used as the criteria for oxidative stability.

The use of butylated hydroxyanisole as a stabilizer for polyethylene is described by Conwell, Busse, and Caracciolo in U. S. 2,698,463 (1047).

For a hydrolyzed copolymer of ethylene and vinyl acetate, Gray and Latham in U. S. 2,516,980 to duPont (511) recommend small amounts of hypophosphorous acid as a stabilizer. The resins, which are stable and free of discoloration, are recommended as finishes and coatings for fabrics, yarns, and films.

Polyethylene and other polymeric organic materials which tend to deteriorate on exposure to heat and light and through oxidation are stabilized by the addition of nitrogen-containing monomeric organic compounds, generally by immersion of the polymer product in a solution of the nitrogen-containing compound, having magnetic susceptibility at 20°C. of $(11-15) \times 10^{-4}$ electromagnetic units per molecule in the solid state. The preferred compounds, according to McQueen in U. S. 2,619,479

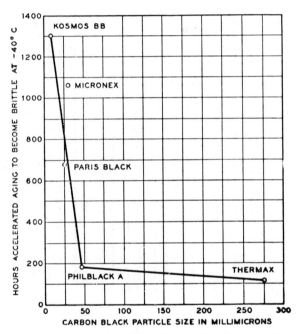

Fig. 28. Effect of carbon black particle size on accelerated aging of polyethylene. (*Ind. Eng. Chem.*, **42**, 2320–5, 1950.)

[duPont (673)] are the nitroxides, hydrazyls, and phenazyls, used in amounts of 2% or less by weight of the polymer. In examples, 2,2-diphenyl-1-picryl-hydrazyl and N-ethylphenazyl are described as being useful in the treatment of polyethylene and, additionally, in the treatment of nylon, rayon, polychloroprene latex, and polymethyl methacrylate.

The addition of 0.01–1% of a ricinoleate ester of polyethylene glycol containing 2–10 ethoxy groups per molecule, such as polyethylene glycol di- or triricinoleate, for light-stabilization of polyethylene or paraffin wax, is recommended by Young and Smith in U. S. 2,625,491 to Standard Oil (779).

As heat stabilizer, a similar amount of a 2,4,6-trialkylated phenol, such as 2,6-di-*tert*-butyl-4-methylphenol, is recommended. The addition to polyethylene of 0.01–0.5% of a 2,2′-methylene bis-(4,6-dialkyl phenol) as a stabilizer against oxidative deterioration is claimed by Pullman in U. S. 2,675,366 to American Cyanamid (898). Substituted dihydroxyphenols or their metal (Al, Ba, Ca, Mg, Sr, Zn) salts are proposed as stabilizers for

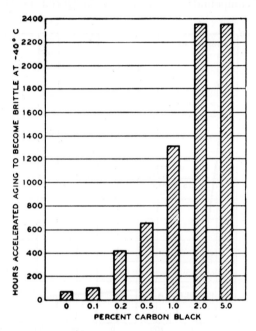

Fig. 29. Effect of carbon black concentration on accelerated aging of polyethylene. (*Ind. Eng. Chem.*, **42**, 2320–5, 1950.)

polyethylene in Austral. 3669/54 to I.C.I. (906e). A sulfide of a dialkylphenol is claimed in Austral. 4410/54 to Monsanto (911a). The addition of imidazoles, e.g., 2-mercaptobenzimidazole, 2-mercaptoarylenoimidazole, or a methylol reaction product of formaldehyde and a 2-mercaptoaryleno-imidazole is recommended by Vincent in U. S. 2,727,879 to duPont (1111) to achieve improved resistance to weathering. Chlorosulfonated polyethylene may be stabilized against decomposition by the addition of phenylglycidylether, as proposed by Brooks and Smook in Can. 516,510 to duPont (1089).

Austral. 8094/55 to I.C.I. (1068) suggests the addition of antioxidants to

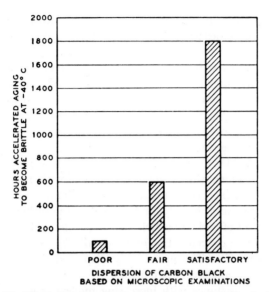

Fig. 30. Effect of carbon black dispersion on aging of polyethylene. (*Ind. Eng. Chem.*, **42**, 2320–5, 1950.)

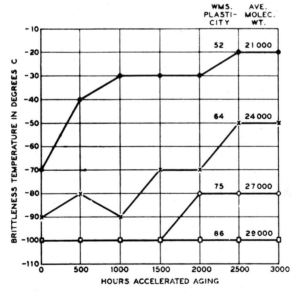

Fig. 31. Accelerated aging *versus* molecular weight of polyethylene. (*Ind. Eng. Chem.*, **42**, 2320–5, 1950.)

the vessel in which the polymerization of the ethylene takes place, whereby the antioxidant becomes incorporated in the polymer during the polymerization reaction.

A method for improving the resistance of polyethylene to ultraviolet light, proposed by Buckles and Williams in Brit. 652,730 to Pirelli-General Cable Works (574), consists of the addition to the polymer of a small quantity, less than 1%, of a substance which possesses a strong absorption spectrum in the ultraviolet light region. Naphthalene, anthracene, and fluorene are given as examples.

Wallder, Clarke, De Coste, and Howard (491) developed an accelerated weathering test which shows good correlation with natural aging (see Section 7.3). It is especially suited for the evaluation of the aging characteristics of compounds of polyethylene containing carbon black. Figure 28 shows the effect of carbon particle size on accelerated aging.

The influence of a concentration of carbon black (Kosmos BB) is demonstrated by Figure 29. The more finely dispersed the carbon black, the better its efficiency, as shown in Figure 30.

Improved age-resistance with increasing molecular weight of the polyethylene is demonstrated by Figure 31.

IV. MODIFIED POLYETHYLENES

When polymerized in the presence of unsaturated compounds, ethylene forms copolymers in which the second component is built into the resultant chain with a certain regularity. Other compounds are capable of terminating or transferring chain growth when the ethylene polymerization is carried out in their presence. The polymers formed are substantially composed of hydrocarbon chains, but have terminal groups derived from the second component. For the most part, compounds of this class contain active hydrogen or halogen atoms. Chain grafting is defined as taking place when a polymer chain is reactivated and side chains consisting of another monomer are made to grow onto the existing polymer. While these modifications take place during polymerization, polyethylene can also be modified by after-treatment. These procedures may be either of a chemical nature, such as chlorination, chlorosulfonation, or stabilization; or of mechanical nature, such as irradiation, drawing, refining, or blending.

4.1. Chain-End Modifiers (Telomers)

Chain-transfer agents are frequently used in polymerization processes to control the molecular weight of the polymer, to change its solubility, or to add various chemical groups to the ends of the polymer chains. In these reactions, the growing polymer radical can react with the chain-transfer agent to destroy the free-radical character of the growing chains. The transfer-agent molecule will then become a free radical and initiate a new polymerization chain. Thus, the chain-transfer process proceeds by a sequence of reactions in which the fragments X and Y of the transfer agent XY attach themselves to the ends of growing polymer chains, to form telomers of the general formula $X(C_2H_4)_n Y$. Typical chain-transfer agents are acetaldehyde, carbon tetrachloride, chloroform, hydrogen chloride, and hydrogen itself, all of which lead to essentially saturated ethylene polymers. The role of inert solvents as chain transfer agents, causing a decrease in the molecular weight of the polymer, was discussed by Flory (53).

Formaldehyde as the telomer is used by Hanford in U. S. 2,373,561 to duPont (189). A white solid (melting point, 105–106°C.), having an ethylene-to-formaldehyde ratio of 11:4, was obtained when ethylene at 750 atmospheres was compressed into formalin (37%) at 75°C. for 9 hours. The resultant polymer could be crosslinked with hexamethylenediisocyanate through the hydroxyl groups introduced by telomerization.

An aldehyde or a ketone containing an alpha hydrogen atom is proposed by Cramer [U. S. 2,432,287 to duPont (332)] as chain-end modifier in the polymerization of ethylene, propylene, or isobutylene in the presence of a free-radical producing catalyst. In an example, a silver-lined pressure vessel is charged with water (100 parts), freshly-distilled paraldehyde (50 parts), and benzoyl peroxide (0.5 part). The pH is adjusted to 2.3 with dilute hydrochloric acid, and the vessel is evacuated, charged with ethylene at a pressure of 500 atmospheres, and shaken for 9.5 hours at a temperature of 98–101°C., to yield a white solid (66 parts), melting at 111–113°C., and having an ethylene-aldehyde ratio of 4.5:1. Catalysts used in other examples comprise ethyl ether, $(NH_4)_2S_2O_8$, $N_2H_4 \cdot 2HCl$, $NH_2OH \cdot HCl$, and C_2Cl_6.

Highly purified acetals, aldehydes, ketones, ethers, and esters are claimed as chain-transfer agents by Hanford and Roland in U. S. 2,457,229 (381) and in Brit. 583,181 (278), both to duPont. Polymerization is carried out at 400–1,000 atmospheres, and 50–300°C., in the presence of a peroxy compound as the catalyst. Specifically, ethyl malonate, ethyl acetoacetate, sec-butyl alcohol, sec-butyl acetate, methyl propionate, methyl methoxyacetate, methyl butyrate, ethyl formate, dimethyl adipate, methyl acetate, 1,4-dioxane, tetrahydrofuran, 1,3-dioxolane, ethylal, acetone, cyclohexanone, propionic acid, propionic anhydride, methanol, ethanol, and ethyl ether are used. The resultant products are claimed to be useful as substitutes for carnauba wax in automobile polish, floor-paste wax, and shoe polish, as well as for moisture-proofing paper and textiles, as a paper size, and as an anti-flooding agent for enamels.

Cyclohexane is used as the chain-transfer agent in the high-pressure, high-temperature polymerization of ethylene by Franta in U. S. 2,586,322 (650), and in Brit. 694,271 (800a), both to duPont. By controlling chain growth during polymerization, cyclohexane (0.05–15%) is claimed to give a polymer of high density and high stiffness. At the same time, the melt viscosity is maintained at a level sufficiently low to permit rapid and satisfactory molding. The polymerization is preferably carried out in the presence of water or of benzene, chlorobenzene, or tert-butyl alcohol. Since these substances are resistant to attack by growing free radicals, their effect upon the course of the polymerization reaction is negligible. A more detailed discussion of this patent is presented in Section 5.6.

Hydrogen can also react as a chain-modifier, and ethylene polymers prepared in its presence are substantially saturated. As an example, U. S. 2,387,755 to Hanford (201) and Brit. 584,794 (308), both to duPont, describe the use of ethylene containing 1% of hydrogen and 382 p.p.m. of oxygen, passing this mixture together with water and benzene, at 1,000 atmospheres and 200°C. through a tubular converter, and obtaining a low molecular weight, waxlike, soft polymer (melting point, 69.5°C.). The resultant products are recommended for domestic waxes in the preparation of polishes.

Polymerization of ethylene in the presence of hydrogen chloride as the telomerizing agent is described in Brit. 582,663 to I.C.I. (274). According to one experiment, water (50 parts), hydrochloric acid (37%, 50 parts), and benzoyl peroxide (0.5 part) are charged into a kettle and ethylene admitted to a pressure of 200 atmospheres. Increase in temperature to 100°C. raises the pressure to 500 atmospheres. As long as decrease in pressure is noted, ethylene is added intermittently to maintain 400–500 atmospheres in the reactor. The reaction product consists of n-butyl, hexyl, octyl, decyl, dodecyl, tetradecyl, hexadecyl, octadecyl, and eicosyl chlorides, totalling 56 parts by weight; and 40 parts by weight of higher alkyl chlorides. The residue is a soft grease which contains 7% chlorine.

Chloroform is used as the telomerizing agent by Hanford and Joyce in U. S. 2,440,800 to duPont (364). A series of products of the general formula $Cl(CH_2CH_2)_nCCl_3$ is obtained.

The use of β-thioethyl-substituted carbonyl compounds as modifiers in the polymerization of ethylene is described by Thompson and Schmerling in U. S. 2,568,902 to Universal Oil (585). The reaction is conducted in the presence of an organic peroxide catalyst and a diluent, such as an alcohol, an aromatic hydrocarbon, or a saturated hydrocarbon with at least three carbon atoms per molecule. Specifically, the process consists of the addition to the reaction mixture of compounds such as bis[β,β-dimethyl-β-(ethylthio)ethyl] ketone, [β-phenyl-β-(propylthio)-ethyl]phenyl ketone, or 2,6-dimethyl-2,6-bis(ethylthio)-4-heptanone. The yield and quality of the product are stated to be unaffected by the presence of other hydrocarbons, for example methane, or of dissolved oxygen. The polymerization is preferably continuous, and the polymer is separated from the reactor effluent by fractionation. The diluent or unconverted ethylene may be recycled to the reaction cell. Pressures of 15–500 atmospheres, and temperatures at least as high as the initial decomposition temperature of the peroxide catalyst, are recommended. In batch operations, and in flow operations without packing, material contact times of 10 minutes are preferred. In fixed-bed operations, the space velocity (volume of liquid charged per hour per superficial volume of packing) is about 0.1–10. The presence of the modifier is claimed to increase the yield and to cause the melting point of the polymer to be raised considerably. The consistency of the product varies from a grease to a softer or harder wax.

Saturated aliphatic esters of inorganic oxy acids of silicon, phosphorus, and sulfur, particularly alkyl sulfates, phosphates and silicates, are proposed as telomerizing agents by Hanford and Joyce in U. S. 2,478,390 to duPont (453).

Alcohols (particularly isopropanol), certain ethers, ketones, esters, acids, acid anhydrides, aldehydes, ethylene oxide, acetals, lactones, furanes, as well as toluene, cumene, and other compounds boiling not above 200°C. at 760 mm., are used as co-reactants in the preparation of wax by the polymerization of ethylene, according to U. S. 2,683,141 to Erchak [Allied Chemical (903)]. In U. S. 2,713,071 and 2,717,910, assigned to Allied Chemical (1080, 1092), Erchak applies the telomerization of ethylene and saturated monohydric alcohols to the production of alcoholic products containing 5–30 carbon atoms in the molecule.

4.2. Chain Grafting

Scott, Field, and Standard Telephones and Cables, Ltd. [Brit. 507,323 (87)] have proposed dissolving polyethylene in monomeric styrene and polymerizing the solution by heating for 2 days at 120°C. With 2% polyethylene, a nonuniform polymeric material was obtained which was homogenized by milling. The resultant sheet was less brittle than a polystyrene sheet. The use of 5% polyethylene gave a more flexible product, while the addition of 10% polyethylene appeared to weaken it. With 40% polyethylene, a rubbery elastic solid was produced which showed good tensile strength and a good recovery after 100% elongation. The products were considered promising for electrical insulating purposes.

Condensation products of ethylene and rubber are claimed by West in U. S. 2,556,158 to Universal Oil (577). Ethylene, when subjected to the action of an organic peroxide in the presence of a saturated hydrocarbon diluent and a minor amount of a natural or synthetic rubber, polymerizes to a product different from that obtained in the absence of rubber. The resultant waxes are harder, have a higher melting point, and have other properties different from the greaselike polymers produced in the absence of rubber.

The possibility of preparing graft copolymers of polyethylene by the use of high intensity irradiation was suggested by experiments reported by

IV. MODIFIED POLYETHYLENES

Magat and Chapiro, of the Laboratoire de Chimie Physique de la Faculté des Sciences de Paris. Grafting of acrylonitrile on polyethylene films which had been subjected to controlled oxidation yielded products which were insoluble in dimethylformamide, even if the copolymer contained as much as 97% acrylonitrile.

According to a recent joint publication by Ballantine, Glines, and Metz, of the Brookhaven National Laboratory, Upton, Long Island, New York, with Behr, Mesrobian, and Restaino, of the Polytechnic Institute of Brooklyn, Brooklyn, New York (1127), graft copolymers of polyethylene may be prepared by the following methods: (a), the polyethylene is

TABLE XIIa

Gamma-Ray Irradiation of Some Polyethylene-Monomer Systems at Room Temperature

Run no.	Initial monomer	Dosage,[a] Mrep	Composition of copolymer[b]
1	Styrene	0.52	10.2
2	Acrylonitrile	0.25	23.8

Source: J. Polymer Sci., 19, 219 (1956).

[a] Source intensities employed were in the range of 200,000–300,000 rep per hour.

[b] Calculated as weight of converted monomer over the total weight of copolymer times 100.

TABLE XIIb

Physical Properties of Polyethylene Graft Copolymers

Weight % of grafted monomer	Dosage, Mrep	Tensile strength,[a] p.s.i.	Ultimate elongation,[a] %	Initial modulus of elasticity,[a] p.s.i.	Melt viscosity[b] at 156°C. (poise) × 10⁻⁴
Experiments with Styrene					
0	0	2480	700	17,400	6.51
2.0	0.124	2450	655	17,500	—
5.3	0.253	2340	605	20,300	112.8
11.3	0.523	2220	535	22,300	235.0
20.8	1.06	1700	415	30,400	—
30.4	1.76	1590	275	34,200	921.0
Experiments with Acrylonitrile					
1.2	0.21	—	—	—	126.0
7.4	0.06	2625	635	18,100	—

Source: J. Polymer Sci., 19, 219 (1956).

[a] Tests run at 30°C. on samples initially 4 mil thick. Values are averaged from measurements in machine direction and at cross section to machine direction.

[b] Determined in a parallel plate plastomer on samples initially 50 mil thick and 1.125 inch diameter.

swollen in the monomer and irradiated by γ-rays from a Co-60 source; or (b), a film of polyethylene is immersed in a large volume of the monomer and the entire system is irradiated. Both experiments shown in Table XIIa were performed by the latter procedure. Since only relatively small irradiation doses were required, no appreciable polymerization of the styrene or acrylonitrile *not* in contact with the polyethylene was noted. Some physical property measurements of polyethylene graft copolymers are shown in Table XIIb.

4.3. Copolymerization

An understanding of the properties to be expected in copolymers requires a brief consideration of the numerous investigations which have been made into the relations between structure and properties of polymeric materials. Simril (297), among others, has summarized a number of these in an attempt to outline a simple and consistent physical picture of these relations. The elastic and plastic properties of high polymeric materials are functions of the forces holding the molecules together and of the ability of small segments of the chains to move about relative to other segments. Copolymerization upsets the regularity of the molecular spacings and alters the inter- and intramolecular forces of the polymer aggregate. The extent of variation in these forces, and in internal plasticization, is the result of the differences in the monomer character, their relative amounts, and their mode of distribution.

The effects of specific modifications of the structure of a polymer on the freedom of segmental motions and on the strength of intermolecular forces are as follows. The introduction of unsaturation into the main carbon chain of polymers generally increases flexibility, as a consequence of the possibility of both *cis-* and *trans-*configuration about the unsaturated position.

Apolar side groups, such as methyl, ethyl, and phenyl, may either decrease or increase flexibility, depending upon which of two factors predominates: the plasticizing effect of side groups which separate neighboring chains, or the stiffening effect of bulky side chains. The first acts to decrease interchain forces and to increase flexibility; the second prevents free rotation of chain segments about carbon-carbon bonds in the main chain. The effect of side chains, increasing with bulkiness, on the hydrocarbon chain of polyethylene is to reduce the crystallinity, lower the melting point, and to render it more flexible and rubberlike. Experimental proof for the influence of side chains on the properties of the polymer was presented in Section 1.1.   Little or no reduction in crystallinity of the polymer takes place if the side group introduced is small and causes no distortion (e.g., fluorine, hydroxyl, or carbonyl).   This applies to ethylene-tetrafluoroethylene copolymers, and to the ethylene-vinyl alcohol co-polymers obtained by hydrolysis of ethylene-vinyl acetate copolymers. These retain the crystallinity of the original polyethylene and are fiber-forming polymers.   The carbonyl group, similar in size to the methylene group, can also take its place without causing distortion; thus, copolymers of ethylene with moderate amounts of carbon monoxide have crystallinity similar to polyethylene.

The substitution of polar groups into the polymer chain generally re-sults in the formation of a stiffer polymer, since the polar groups increase the forces between chains through dipole-dipole interaction.   Similar di-pole interaction between segments of individual chains also stiffens the polymer.   However, particularly bulky chains may be expected to decrease intermolecular forces somewhat, because of the resistance offered to close chain packing.   Thus, the final flexibility characteristics of a polymer are the result of a complicated balance of all the molecular forces tending si-multaneously to increase and decrease stiffness.

Ethylene can copolymerize with a great number of unsaturated com-pounds (e.g., styrene, methyl methacrylate, vinyl acetate) and with some compounds which polymerize by themselves by free-radical mechanisms only with difficulty (e.g., propylene, isobutylene) or not at all (carbon monoxide, carbon dioxide, sulfur dioxide, maleic anhydride).   In spite of the great amount of work which has been devoted to this field, and the large number of patents which have been issued, copolymers of ethylene do not appear thus far to have found any major commercial applications. However, according to a recent (December 15, 1955) news report (927c), duPont is expected to offer copolymers of ethylene soon.

Unsaturated Compounds in General

Mark and Ruppel, as early as 1930, claimed in Ger. 650,038 to I. G. Farben. (61) that ethylene or other olefins, which do not polymerize alone simply by warming with peroxide catalysts, can be made to copolymerize with unsaturated compounds, such as vinyl acetate, styrene, or acrylic acid, under the usual conditions of polymerization.   The copolymerization of ethylene with unsaturated compounds in general was first proposed by Perrin, Fawcett, Paton, and Williams in Brit. 497,643 (75), Fr. 836,988 (85), and U. S. 2,200,429 (109), all to I.C.I.   According to the disclosures of these patents, ethylene may be polymerized in the presence of one or more organic compounds containing one or more double bonds and capable of forming dimers or higher polymers, at a pressure of at least 500 atmospheres and a temperature of 100–400°C. Polymerization catalysts, such as small amounts of oxygen or benzoyl peroxide, and a gaseous diluent (e.g., nitrogen) may be present. In examples, ethylene is heated under pressure in the presence of benzoyl peroxide with isobutylene, or in the presence of oxygen with 2-pentene, styrene, stilbene, limonene, diethyl-maleate, -fumarate, -itaconate, or -citraconate, methyl or butyl methacrylate, glycol dimethacrylate, methyl or butyl methacrylate, vinyl acetate, or butadiene, and with a mixture of styrene and methyl methacrylate. Copolymerization, it is pointed out, appears in general to result in compounds in which other groups are interposed at various intervals in the normal chain of CH_2 groups. Alternatively, crosslinked or branched chain compounds may be formed in which single chains of the ethylene polymer (or of the copolymer type) are linked or branched together directly or via intermediate groupings.

Copolymerization of ethylene with unsaturated compounds in the liquid phase is described by Hopff and Goebel in U. S. 2,334,195 to General Aniline (154). The reaction is conducted in the presence of water or of an inert organic solvent medium at a temperature of 55–180°C., and 100–300 atmospheres pressure. The catalyst is preferably oxygen or a peroxide. The unsaturated compounds may be those capable of polymerizing by themselves (propylene, isobutylene, butadiene, styrene, acrylic acid esters), or those which do not so polymerize (diethyl and dimethyl maleates).

Hanford, in U. S. 2,396,785 to duPont (237) discloses a process for the copolymerization of ethylene with other unsaturated compounds, whereby a moderate pressure is maintained by the periodic introduction of additional ethylene. For example, an aluminum-lined steel reaction vessel is charged with acrylonitrile (100 parts) and benzoyl peroxide (0.2 part), placed in an agitating rack, and pressured with ethylene to about 600 atmospheres. During the reaction time of 11 hours, the temperature is maintained at 85°C. and the pressure at 860–950 atmospheres. The total pressure drop amounts to 200 atmospheres. The reaction mixture is steam-distilled to remove unreacted acrylonitrile, and is then washed and dried at 70°C. There is obtained a hard, yellow resin (19.7 parts) containing 23.5% nitrogen; the ethylene-acrylonitrile ratio is calculated to be 1:4. In the same way, copolymers may be prepared from ethylene and maleic anhydride, vinyl phthalimide, vinyl formate, divinyl formal, methacrylic anhydride, and vinyl acetate. Copolymerization of ethylene with a large number of unsaturated compounds (e.g., propylene, butylene, dichloroethylene, vinyl ethers, vinyl esters, vinyl ketones, stilbene, styrene, terpenes) is described in Brit. 578,584, also to duPont (247).   Intimate contact with water during the peroxide-catalyzed polymerization is required.   The reaction is carried out at pressures above 50 atmospheres and temperatures of 60–120°C.

British 578,992 to duPont (249) relates to the production of solid polymers and copolymers of ethylene and propylene in the presence of peroxide catalysts and organic solvents free of active hydrogen at a pressure greater than 200 atmospheres and a temperature of 50–130°C.   Silver-lined, aluminum-lined and stainless-steel reaction vessels are used.   Copolymerization is preferably carried out with unsaturated compounds which are easily hydrolyzable, such as methacrylic anhydride, maleic anhydride, methylene dimethacrylate, and divinyl acetals.   Further examples include the following monomer-solvent systems: maleic anhydride-ethylene-toluene;   N-vinylphthalimide-ethylene-isooctane;   vinyl formate-ethylene-toluene;   divinyl formal-ethylene-isooctane;   propylene-ethylene-isooctane; and vinyl acetate-ethylene-isooctane.

Polymerization of ethylene and its copolymerization in aqueous emulsion with such unsaturated compounds as vinyl esters, vinyl chloride, acrylic esters, styrene, and dienes (isoprene and butadiene), are claimed by Hopff, Goebel, and Rautenstrauch in U. S. 2,342,400 to General Aniline (164). Polymerization is conducted at superatmospheric pressures, preferably with oxygen-supplying catalysts and with polymerization regulators such as aldehydes.

Different Olefins

The polymerization of ethylene containing 6.4% isobutylene was studied by Kodama, Taniguchi, and Zenbutso (477) at 254–283°C. under pressures of 1,400–1,600 atmospheres. The molecular weights of the resultant copolymers were about one-third those of polyethylenes prepared under the same conditions. The reaction was found to be of the second order.   The rate constants were 1.2–1.5 times as large as those of polymerization reactions of ethylene alone, so that the velocity of the chain initiation and that of the chain termination must be four to five times as large in this copolymerization as in ethylene polymerization. The apparent activation energy of the copolymerization reaction is about 38 kcal.

Frolich, in U. S. 2,456,265 to Jasco, Inc. (379), discloses a low-temperature process wherein isobutylene, liquefied ethylene, and zinc stearate are polymerized with a Friedel-Crafts active halide catalyst, to yield a fine-grained, noncoalescing slurry of solid polymer. A diene, for example iso-prene, may also be present in the active olefin feed at −50 to −150°C. When isoprene is present, 1.5–5.0% of butyl rubber is made.

According to U. S. 2,470,190 to Schmerling [Universal Oil (444)], an olefin such as propylene is polymerized with ethylene in the presence of a metal phosphate catalyst by first converting the olefin to a monohalo-alkane which is then polymerized with the ethylene. Suitable catalysts are calcium monophosphate, calcium diphosphate, and calcium and silver pyrophosphates. Temperatures of 250–400°C. and pressures of 15–40 atmospheres are preferred for continuous operation. The copolymeriza-tion of ethylene and a higher olefin in the presence of a metal phosphate and hydrogen chloride is mentioned as an alternative procedure.

Diolefins

Butadiene and other diolefins (hexadiene, octadiene, decadiene) may be copolymerized with ethylene, as described by Friedman in U. S. 2,599,-249 [to Sinclair Refining (660)] at 75–300°C. and 100–1,000 p.s.i. ethylene pressure in the presence of a cobalt oxide catalyst. Thus, coconut char-coal impregnated with cobalt oxide is placed in a stainless-steel reactor tube and purified; ethylene is introduced at 72 vols./vol. catalyst/hr. and butadiene at 153 vols./vol. catalyst/hr., while the temperature is kept at 90°C. and the pressure at 200 p.s.i. From the reaction of 45 g. ethylene and 185 g. butadiene, 21 g. of liquid product is obtained.

Acetylene

Polymers from ethylene and acetylene are described by Paton and Wil-liams in U. S. 2,192,931 to I.C.I. (105). The pressures specified are above 500 atmospheres, preferably about 1,500 atmospheres; the temperatures above 100°C., preferably about 230°C.; oxygen is the preferred catalyst. When the proportion of acetylene is small, the product is solid; with in-creasing proportions of acetylene in the initial mixture, the molecular weight of the product decreases and the copolymer becomes more liquid. With proportions of acetylene in excess of 15%, the product is an oil characterized by outstanding drying properties.

Vinyl Acetate and Other Vinyl Esters

A continuous process for the copolymerization of ethylene and vinyl acetate is the subject of U. S. 2,395,381 to Squires [duPont (234)]. The polymerization is conducted at temperatures of 50–400°C., and pressures of 800–1,500 atmospheres. According to Brit. 569,927 to duPont (194), ethylene and organic vinyl esters are copolymerized under heat and pressure by a peroxide catalyst in the presence of a nonpolymerizable liquid such as water. Hanford, Roland, and Mochel, in U. S. 2,473,996 to duPont (449), describe the preparation of copolymers of ethylene with vinyl trimethylacetate, vinyl *tert*-butyl acetate, vinyl benzoate, vinyl diethylacetate, and vinyl-β,γ-dimethylvalerate, by agitating the monomers at 50–200°C. and at pressures of 1–1,500 atmospheres, with water and benzoyl peroxide catalyst (with or without emulsifiers). The compositions of the copolymers may be varied widely by varying the ethylene pressure. The resultant products are claimed to be strong, tough resins resistant to hydrolysis and capable of being cold-drawn and formed into fibers and films. The use of a redox polymerization system in the emulsion copolymerization of ethylene and vinyl acetate has been described by Roedel in U. S. 2,703,-794 to duPont (1065). A discussion of this patent has been presented in Section 3.4.

U. S. 2,377,753 to Brubaker [duPont (192)] describes the copolymerization of ethylene with a vinyl thiolester of an organic carboxylic acid, for example vinyl thiolacetate. By treatment of the product with potassium hydroxide in methanol solution, hard, tough, insoluble films which remain infusible at temperatures as high as 250°C. are formed.

McAlevy, Strain, and Chance in U. S. 2,388,169 to duPont (204) disclose the preparation of products ranging from soft, elastic materials to hard, horny substances by pyrolyzing (250–400°C.) a copolymer of ethylene and an organic vinyl ester, such as vinyl acetate. The pyrolyzate is compounded with sulfur, accelerators, metal oxides, and reinforcing agents. Final curing may be carried out with or without pressure.

Controlled hydrolysis of ethylene-vinyl acetate copolymers has been described by Roland in U. S. 2,399,653 (244) and by Plambeck in U. S. 2,467,774 (440), both to duPont. In the latter case, the hydrolysis is carried out at 80–85°C. by means of a methanol-water solution containing the theoretically required quantity of sodium hydroxide. The resultant product may be precipitated by the slow addition of sufficient salt to saturate the solution.

According to Brit. 582,093 and Brit. 634,140 (271,505) issued to I.C.I., copolymers of vinyl acetate and ethylene, preferably with a vinyl acetate-ethylene molar ratio greater than 1:5, are hydrolyzed in solution in an alcohol with alkali to the corresponding vinyl alcohol-ethylene copolymers. The hydrolysis may be complete or carried to any desired degree short of completion. The products may be converted to filaments which may be cold- or hot-drawn by a melt- or solution-spinning process. The products may also be molded to tough, strong compositions, calendered, or cast from solution into strong water- and oil-resistant films, or used in solution for coating paper or textiles. In an example, a copolymer (vinyl acetate-ethylene ratio 2.4:1, 400 parts) in 95% ethanol (1,700 parts) mixed with potassium hydroxide (185 parts) in 95% ethanol solution (900 parts) is refluxed for one hour after the exothermic reaction. After the ethanol is removed by steam distillation, dehydrolyzed (95%) copolymer (216 parts) is obtained. The copolymer may be melt-spun at 190°C. and the filament stretched five times its original length in a kerosene bath at 85°C. The drawn filaments have dry tenacities of 3.6 g./denier with 7% elongation, and wet tenacities of 2.1 g./denier with 7% elongation. The drawn filaments are oriented and have good receptivity to acetate- and oil-soluble dyes. Similar examples of hydrolysis of copolymers containing molar ratios of vinyl acetate to ethylene of 1:3.2 to 16:1 are cited. The process is also applicable to the hydrolysis of ethylene copolymers with vinyl esters of other carboxylic acids, and the hydrolysis may also be carried out with acid catalysts.

Hydrolyzed ethylene-vinyl acetate copolymers can be used as dispersing agents in suspension polymerizations. White, in U. S. 2,485,796 to duPont (458) describes the preparation of vinyl ester granules of uniform size and shape which require no further coating or lubricating. These are prepared by dispersion polymerization in water, in the presence of 0.28–0.66 parts of a granulating agent comprising hydrolyzed ethylene-vinyl acetate copolymer containing 2–8% of ethylene. If desired, the copolymer may be directly added without first being dissolved.

British 607,911 to duPont (369) relates to partially hydrolyzed ethylene-vinyl ester copolymers. The copolymers are dissolved in saturated secondary or tertiary aliphatic or cycloaliphatic alcohols. Solution of the copolymer is facilitated by benzene or toluene. An aqueous or alcoholic strong base, in an amount slightly less than that required to bring about the desired hydrolysis, is added, and the mixture containing at least 10% of alcohol is heated for several hours. The time and temperature of hydrolysis may be varied widely, and the pressure may be raised. The partial hydrolysis products of copolymers in which the ratio of ethylene to vinyl ester varies from 1:50 to 5:1, and the ratio of hydrolyzed to unhydrolyzed ester from 1:9 to 4:1, are especially suited for adhesives and for coated or calendered fabric compositions. They are substantially insoluble in hot and cold water, and they possess low-temperature toughness and pliability.   In an example, a copolymer prepared by passing ethylene at 1,000 atmospheres pressure into vinyl acetate at 65°C. containing a small quantity of benzoyl peroxide, and of vinyl acetate-ethylene ratio of 1:2.3, was dissolved in benzene (175 parts) and isopropanol (80 parts), and the mixture refluxed for 1.5 hours before steam distillation to remove the solvents.   The coagulated product was washed with cold water, then with hot water, and dried.   Compared with a similar product prepared when methanol replaced the isopropanol, the properties for the isopropanol and methanol preparations were, respectively: hydrolysis 51 and 86.5%; cold-crack, less than -60 and -60°C.; tensile strength, 1,725 and 4,320 p.s.i.;   elongation, 764 and 504%.

A hydrolyzed ethylene-vinyl ester copolymer, soluble in organic solvents, is insolubilized by mixing a free radical-generating compound with the solvent-swelled copolymer and heating the mixture to above 100°C. but below its decomposition temperature.   Following an example given by Alderson in U. S. 2,448,946 to duPont (372), a completely hydrolyzed ethylene-vinyl acetate copolymer derived from a polymer with an ethylene-vinyl acetate molar ratio of 3:1 (100 parts) is allowed to stand for 4 hours at room temperature in a solution of benzene (200 parts) and ethanol (200 parts).   The swollen product is blended with a solution of benzoyl peroxide (10 parts) in benzene (100 parts) on a rubber mill at 30–40°C.   Thin sheets of this material are heated in a press for 15 minutes at 130°C. to give a thermoplastic product with reduced solubility.

The preparation of oriented fibers from hydrolyzed ethylene-vinyl organic ester copolymers is described by Smith in U. S. 2,403,464 (246) and in Brit. 575,689 (235), both to duPont.   Water resistance is achieved by aftertreatment with polyfunctional compounds such as N,N'-bis(methoxymethyl)urea.

Filaments of hydrolyzed ethylene-vinyl acetate copolymers may be improved, according to U. S. 2,411,474 to Stevenson [duPont (273)], by drawing for a period of 1–5 seconds in steam at 90–100°C. and thereafter contacting the stretched filament with steam at 102–104°C. for a period of 5–20 minutes.

Isocyanates of hydrolyzed ethylene-vinyl ester copolymers may be prepared according to U. S. 2,451,963 to Loder [duPont (376)].   A benzene solution of an ethylene-vinyl ester copolymer is treated with a methanol solution of sodium hydroxide at about 30°C. for 4 hours and the mixture subjected to the action of ethyl, methyl, or phenyl isocyanates at temperatures between 30 and 200°C., in the presence of various solvents such as dioxane, 1,3-dioxolanes, formamide, and dimethylformamide.   Films were prepared from the dry N-alkyl carbamate polymers; the one made from a hydrolyzed 8:1 ethylene-vinyl acetate copolymer (10 parts), ethyl isocyanate (10 parts) and dioxane (240 parts), and treated at 90°C. under one atmosphere pressure for one hour, had a tensile strength of 4,350 p.s.i. at 800% elongation. These N-alkyl carbamate copolymers are further changed by treatment with formaldehyde at 20 and at 80°C. The N-substituted carbamate of the hydrolyzed copolymer is also prepared by treatment of a monoester of monoisocyanic acid (or the corresponding alkyl or aryl isocyanic acid) in a mutual solvent with the hydrolyzed copolymers of ethylene and a vinyl ester of an aliphatic, saturated, organic monocarboxylic acid.

Copolymers of ethylene with vinyl acetate, propionate, butyrate, or formate may be catalytically oxidized with nitric acid or higher nitrogen oxides. The oxidation, according to U. S. 2,360,673 to Hanford [duPont (170)] is carried out at 50°C. with ammonium vanadate, sodium vanadate, or vanadium pentoxide as the catalyst. The resultant products, α,γ-dicarboxylic acids, are said to be suitable for the preparation of condensation polymers such as polyesters or polyamides.

The preparation of ethylene-vinyl alcohol-acrylic acid terpolymers is described by Pickney in U. S. 2,566,244 to duPont (582). The products have a molecular weight of at least 50,000 and are used in the form of ammonium salts as pigment binders in paper coatings, since they have the property of becoming insoluble after drying.

Halovinyl Compounds

Hanford and Roland, in U. S. 2,409,679 to duPont (268), describe the copolymerization of ethylene with α-chloroacrylic acid, nitrile, amide, anilide, and esters. Preferred temperatures are within the range of 50–150°C.; pressures are from 200–1,000 atmospheres. A peroxide catalyst in an aqueous polymerization medium is employed. In an example, methyl-α-chloroacrylate is converted to a copolymer softening within the range of 145–148°C., with an ethylene-ester ratio of 19:1. In the same way, α-chloroacrylonitrile copolymerizes with ethylene to form hard products, softening at about 120°C.

Ethylene-vinyl chloride copolymers are claimed by Brubaker, Roland, and Peterson in U. S. 2,422,392 (319) and U. S. 2,497,291 (501a), both to duPont. The former patent describes the production of copolymers by heating ethylene (1 part to 99 parts) with vinyl chloride (99 parts to 1 part) under pressure at 50–300°C., in the presence of water (0.2 part to 5.0

parts), an organic peroxide catalyst (0.001–0.50%), and an oxidizable sulfoxy compound (0.001–0.10%), at a pH of 7–11, carefully controlled by an alkaline buffer such as borax. With mixtures containing a high proportion of vinyl chloride, the pressure is maintained at 5–50 atmospheres; with mixtures high in ethylene, pressures of 500–1,500 atmospheres are required. According to the latter patent, ethylene-vinyl chloride copolymers containing 74–90% of combined vinyl chloride, and soluble in aromatic hydrocarbons to the extent of at least 20% at 25°C., are obtained by the polymerization of ethylene and vinyl chloride in an aqueous medium of pH 8–11 in the presence of buffer salts, oxidizable sulfoxy compounds, and a peroxide catalyst at temperatures of 40–200°C. and pressures of 15–1,500 atmospheres. The buffer salts (0.25–1.0%) include such compounds as borax or Na_2CO_3, while the oxidizable sulfoxy compounds (0.001–0.1%) comprise Na_2SO_3, $NaHSO_3$, or $Na_2S_2O_3$. The resultant copolymers are especially suitable for use as finishing compositions; when modified with small amounts of maleic anhydride, they are particularly tough, flexible, and adherent to metals, glass, and wood.

Polymers of high tensile strength and stiffness, as described in U. S. 2,497,323 to Roedel [duPont (502)], are obtained by the copolymerization of ethylene with vinyl chloride, vinyl fluoride, styrene, and the like, in the presence of anhydrous benzene or a mixture of water and an inert organic solvent for ethylene, and a *tert*-alkyl percarboxylate (0.0005–2.0%) such as *tert*-butyl perbenzoate, at temperatures of 70–250°C. and pressures of 400–1,000 atmospheres. The process, which is exothermic, is adapted for continuous operation. The products are claimed to be especially suited for hot-dip and melt-spray applications for insulating materials and protective coatings.

Copolymers of ethylene and 3,3,3-trifluoropropene were prepared by Schroeder as described in U. S. 2,484,530 to duPont (457). These copolymers are transparent, much less stiff than polyethylene, and superior in tensile and tear strengths.

British 583,419 to duPont (279) relates to the copolymerization of ethylene and chlorotrifluoroethylene under pressure at 80°C. in the presence of a peroxide catalyst, in water or organic solvents. The copolymers of 1 : 1 molar ratio have higher softening points than either component when polymerized alone, and are useful as molding compounds, adhesives, fibers, and electrical insulation.

Copolymers of dichlorodifluoroethylene and ethylene are claimed by Hanford in U. S. 2,584,126 to duPont (648). These copolymers are formed in the presence of benzoyl peroxide in a stainless-steel reactor at 80°C., with pressures as high as 700 atmospheres. Films of the polymers have tensile strengths up to 1,800 p.s.i. and elongations of 600%.

The preparation of polymers of ethylene and vinylidene chloride is described by Hanford and Roland in U. S. 2,397,260 to duPont (239). The two components are caused to react in the presence of a peroxy compound catalyst, at a temperature between 40 and 350°C., and a pressure between 50 and 1,500 atmospheres. The same reaction may be carried out in an aqueous medium.

U. S. 2,468,054 to Ford (441) and Brit. 589,577 (320), both to duPont, relate to the copolymerization of ethylene and vinylidene fluoride. A stainless-steel vessel is charged with water (25 parts), benzoyl peroxide (0.1 part), and vinylidene fluoride (20 parts), and pressured to 450 atmospheres with ethylene at 25°C. Agitation and heating are started, and at 80°C. the pressure is maintained at 650–700 atmospheres by injection of ethylene (less than 20 p.p.m. oxygen content) until the absorption of ethylene ceases. The resulting copolymer, containing 5.11% of fluorine, may be molded at 200°C. to a transparent film. In another example, a silver-lined reactor is swept with oxygen-free nitrogen, closed, and evacuated, then charged with $(NH_4)_2S_2O_8$ (0.5 part) in deoxygenated water (100 parts) and $NaHSO_3$ (0.4 part) in water (100 parts). The reactor is cooled, charged with ethylene (40 parts) and vinylidene fluoride (2 parts), and agitated for 8.25 hours at 40°C. The resulting copolymer contains 74.46% of fluorine. Films pressed from it show no discoloration after 5 minutes at 300°C.

Copolymers of ethylene and vinylidene chloride, and terpolymers containing in addition another vinyl compound such as a vinyl ester, vinyl ether, or vinyl ketone, are described in Brit. 576,830 to duPont (241).

Styrene

U. S. 2,563,631 to Young and Smyers [Standard Oil Development (579)] relates to the preparation of liquid copolymers of ethylene and styrene. A gaseous mixture of the components, containing 1–30% by weight of styrene, is passed into an alkyl halide solution (C_2H_5Cl) containing 2–20 g. of a Friedel-Crafts catalyst ($AlCl_3$) per 100 ml. of solution at 0–20°C., under a pressure of 2–5 atmospheres. Besides styrene as such, substitution derivatives having halogen atoms or aliphatic groups containing up to 4 carbon atoms in the nucleus or side-chain of styrene, for example methylstyrene or p-chlorostyrene, can be used. The copolymers are claimed to be useful as thickeners for mineral lubricating oils and soap-oil greases; as solvent oils for gum fluxes in gasolines; as solvents for resins or insecticides; as dielectrics in electrical equipment; as plasticizers for natural and butyl rubber or neoprene; and as lubricating hydraulic oils *per se.*

Acrylic Esters

Copolymers of ethylene with an alkyl acrylate (e.g., CH_2=CHCOOCH$_3$) and an alkyl monoester of a 2-butene-1,4-dioic acid (e.g., HOOCCH= CHCOOCH$_3$) are described by Pinkney, Pratt, and Wayne in U. S. 2,599, 123 to duPont (659).   The resultant three-component copolymers may be crosslinked by heating with a curing agent to yield films useful in upholstery and coated fabrics.

Allyl Compounds

Copolymers of higher softening points than polyethylene are obtained by the copolymerization of ethylene and a dialkyl or divinyl ester of a saturated polycarboxylic acid.   Dialkyl oxalate, diallyl sebacate, and divinyl ether are proposed by Richards, Myles, and Whittaker in U. S. 2,526,773 (520) and in Brit. 584,324 (306), both to I.C.I.   The polymerization is carried out at elevated temperatures and pressures, in the presence of oxygen or of benzoyl peroxide catalyst.

Buckley, Ray and I.C.I. in Brit. 669,771 (654a) describe the preparation of waxlike products of improved dye compatibility by the pressure copolymerization of ethylene and allyl or methallyl alcohol in the presence of an organic peroxide or an azonitrile.   With allyl alcohol, the copolymer has a melting point of 100°C., a molecular weight of 1,500, and a hydroxyl content of 2.5%.   Proposed uses are as components of shoe polishes, wax crayons, and carbon paper.

Maleic Anhydride

An alkali-soluble copolymer of ethylene and maleic anhydride is obtained, according to Hanford in U. S. 2,378,629 to duPont (195), by heating a mixture of 1–4.6 moles of ethylene with 1 mole of maleic anhydride in contact with a peroxide catalyst and an inert diluent.   The reaction pressure is that generated by the reaction mixture itself under the given conditions, i.e., at a temperature which may be as low as 40°C.

9-Methylenefluorene

U. S. 2,533,207 to Dickey and Coover [Eastman Kodak (522)] describes the copolymerization of ethylene with 9-methylenefluorene in benzene solution in the presense of benzoyl peroxide. Polymers from monomer mixtures containing 2–95 mole % of 9-methylenefluorene are claimed.

β-Methylene-β-Propiolactone

Coffman, in U. S. 2,585,537 to duPont (649), proposes the copolymerization of ethylene or other vinyl monomers with β-methylene-β-propiolactone, to yield polymers useful for adhesives, molded objects, and unsupported films.

Vinyl Isocoumarans

U. S. 2,474,612 to Barney [duPont (450)] relates to copolymers of vinyl isocoumarans with vinyl monomers. Ethylene is mentioned as one of these monomers, together with methyl methacrylate, acrylonitrile, and methyl acrylate. For example 1,1,3,3-tetramethyl-4-vinylisocoumaran is copolymerized with ethylene in bulk, solution or emulsion, with peroxides as initiators. The copolymers show higher softening points than the corresponding copolymers without vinylisocoumaran, and are claimed to form superior products on molding, extrusion and fiber spinning. Films prepared from these copolymers are useful as dielectrics in condensers and batteries. The 1,1,3,3-tetramethyl-4-vinylisocoumaran may be prepared by the self-condensation of dimethyl(vinylethynyl)carbinol.

Alkylene Oxides

Copolymers of ethylene with 1,2-alkylene oxides of from 2 to 4 carbon atoms are described by Coffman in U. S. 2,516,960 to duPont (510). In the preferred method of preparing the copolymer, ethylene oxide is polymerized at 350–1,000 atmospheres and 200–250°C. in the presence of an azine catalyst, such as benzalazine. The resultant products are proposed as additives for lubricating oils, ingredients of waxes and polishes, coating and impregnating compositions, and as antistatic agents.

Amino Compounds

The copolymerization of ethylene and other olefins with cyclic imides of unsaturated dicarboxylic acids is described by Arnold, Brubaker, and Dorough in U. S. 2,301,356 to duPont (142). N-n-butylmaleimide and N-isobutylmaleimide are the preferred imides. Polymerization is carried out at fairly low temperatures (50–90°C.), with benzoyl peroxide as the catalyst. The preparation of copolymers of ethylene and N-vinyl derivatives of secondary amides, particularly N-vinylphthalimide, is described by Hanford in U. S. 2,402,136 to duPont (245). It is generally preferable to use a ratio of ethylene to N-vinyl derivative of at least 1 : 10. According to Sargent and Hanford in U. S. 2,467,234 to duPont (437), a strong, tough polymer, soluble in boiling xylene to the extent of about 30% by weight, results from the copolymerization of ethylene and a mixture of *tert*-butanol (78 parts) and sodium N-chloro-*p*-toluenesulfonamide (0.2 part) at 140–150°C. and 875–950 atmospheres pressure for 13.3 hours. The copolymerization of ethylene with N-vinylcarbazole is described in Brit. 706,412 to I.C.I. (897b).

Carbon Dioxide

The copolymerization of ethylene with carbon dioxide to form products useful as components of pastes, liquid polishes, and textile impregnants is described by Sargent in U. S. 2,462,680 (430) and in Brit. 620,963 (432) both to duPont. In an example, a stainless steel-lined vessel is charged with benzoyl peroxide (1 part) and, after evacuating, with carbon dioxide (75 parts). The vessel is pressurized to 500 atmospheres with ethylene and shaken at a temperature of 72–88°C. and a pressure of 760–1,000 atmospheres for a period of 13 hours; the observed pressure drop is 390 atmospheres. The product (10 parts; molar ratio of ethylene to carbon dioxide 29 : 1) melts at 110–112°C. to a free-flowing liquid.

Carbon Monoxide

The discovery of the free radical-initiated copolymerization of ethylene and carbon monoxide led Brubaker, Coffman, and Hoehn (593) to the synthesis of a family of polyketones ranging from liquids to microcrystalline linear polymers of high molecular weight. The molecular weight, deter-

TABLE XIII

Effect of Pressure on the Copolymerization of Carbon Monoxide with Ethylene

Pressure, lb./sq. in.	Carbon monoxide, %	Polyketone, molecular weight	Weight, g.
200	12.6	280	5
1000	28.1	700	18
2660	39.3	2420	80
4500	41.8	3400	170
14700	44.9	Insoluble	130

Source: *J. Am. Chem. Soc.*, **74**, 1510 (1952).

mined by an ebulliometric method, is about 400 for the mobile liquids, and increases to 1,000–3,000 for the viscous liquids to the crystalline waxes. The effects of pressure, monomer composition, and reaction temperature on the copolymerization are shown in Tables XIII, XIV, and XV. The densities, melting ranges, and molecular weights of the polyketones containing increasing proportions of carbon monoxide are listed in Table XVI.

TABLE XIV

Effect of Monomer Composition on the Copolymerization of Carbon Monoxide with Ethylene

Carbon monoxide, %		Polyketone	
In monomers	In polyketone	Molecular weight	Weight g. formed
13	17.8	2250	61
25	28.4	4310	90
33	34.3	1700	104
36	35.7	1420	113
42	36.7	1800	78

Source: *J. Am. Chem. Soc.*, **74**, 1510 (1952).

TABLE XV

Effect of Temperature on the Copolymerization of Carbon Monoxide with Ethylene

Temperature, °C.	Polyketone	
	Carbon monoxide, %	Molecular weight
120	22.8	360
135	18.5	240
150	12.5	280
165	9.1	250

Source: *J. Am. Chem. Soc.*, **74**, 1510 (1952).

TABLE XVI

Density and Melting Range of Polyketones

CO in copolymer, %	Density (23°)	Melting range, °C.	Molecular weight	Inherent viscosity
12.6	0.934	Liquid at 25°	280	..
17.8	0.952	70–82	2260	0.15
24.1	0.979	70–86	2710	0.13
34.3	1.068	70–97	1700	0.17
35.7	1.091	76–111	1420	0.20
36.7	1.105	70–117	1800	0.15

Source: *J. Am. Chem. Soc.*, **74**, 1510 (1952).

The presence of carbonyl groups and hydrocarbon fragments, as shown by infrared spectra, is consistent with a polyketone structure containing —CH$_2$—CH$_2$— and —CO— units. Further confirmation of the polyketone structure is furnished by the formation of derivatives characteristic of typical ketones. Hydrogenation of the polyketones yields polyalcohols without cleavage of the polymer chain; reaction with hydroxylamine and with hydrogen cyanide gives the corresponding oximes and cyanohydrins, respectively; nitric acid oxidation gives rise to polymethylene dicarboxylic acids ranging from glutaric acid through sebacic acid. These possibilities are indicated by the scheme shown below.

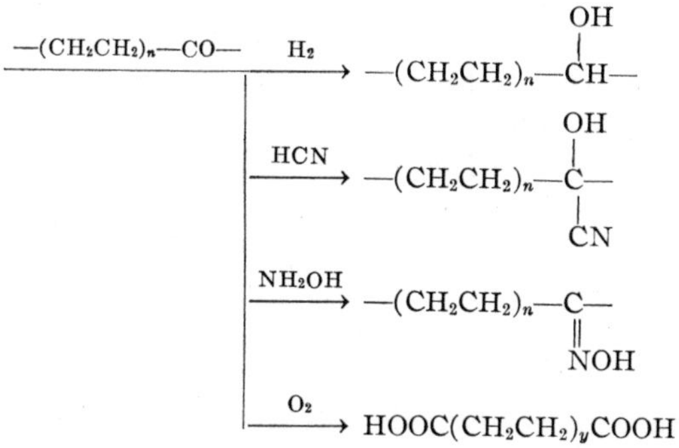

$$—(CH_2CH_2)_n—CO—$$

$$\xrightarrow{H_2} —(CH_2CH_2)_n—\overset{\displaystyle OH}{\underset{\displaystyle |}{CH}}—$$

$$\xrightarrow{HCN} —(CH_2CH_2)_n—\overset{\displaystyle OH}{\underset{\displaystyle |}{\underset{\displaystyle CN}{C}}}—$$

$$\xrightarrow{NH_2OH} —(CH_2CH_2)_n—\underset{\displaystyle \underset{\displaystyle NOH}{\|}}{C}—$$

$$\xrightarrow{O_2} HOOC(CH_2CH_2)_y COOH$$

The percentage of crystallinity of a typical waxlike polyketone, estimated from a plot relating intensity to angle of scattering, is about 38%. It closely resembles the microcrystalline petroleum waxes, displaying, however, the macromolecular properties of toughness and orientability.

An analysis of the data given in the above investigation led Barb (703) to suggest a reaction mechanism for the copolymerization of ethylene and carbon monoxide, which assumes that the reactants are the olefin and a one-to-one complex of the olefin and carbon monoxide.

Brubaker, in U. S. 2,495,286 to duPont (499), describes the preparation of copolymers of ethylene and other unsaturated organic compounds with carbon monoxide by means of peroxide catalysts under pressure of about 500 atmospheres. The properties of the resultant products vary, depending on the reaction conditions, some being infusible and orientable. Uses in protective coatings, as fibers, plasticizers, and adhesives, are proposed. A later patent by Brubaker to duPont [U. S. 2,680,763 (902a)] introduces the use of a chain transfer agent in the copolymerization reaction.

Ethylene-carbon monoxide copolymers may be modified by post-reactions. Hydrogenation to high molecular weight polymeric alcohols of ethylene-carbon monoxide copolymers in the presence of a hydrogenation catalyst is described by Scott in U. S. 2,495,292 to duPont (500). Similarly, polymeric polythiols were obtained by Scott, according to U. S. 2,495,293 to duPont (501), by the reductive thiolation of an ethylene-carbon monoxide copolymer with hydrogen and hydrogen sulfide.

The reaction of ethylene-carbon monoxide copolymers with an aldehyde, alone or in conjunction with urea, phenol, or an amine, in the presence of an alkaline catalyst is described by Hanford in U. S. 2,351,120 to duPont (167).

Polymeric ketones, including olefin-carbon monoxide copolymers, can be reacted with acrylonitrile in the presence of an alkaline condensing agent, according to Brit. 588,475 to duPont (318). The resultant products are polymeric ketones in which a number of the polymer units have at least one β-cyanoethyl group attached.

Pinkney, in U. S. 2,495,284 to duPont (497), describes the preparation of polycyanohydrins by reacting hydrogen cyanide with an ethylene-carbon monoxide copolymer.

Maynard, in U. S. 2,595,400 to duPont (657), describes the preparation of polyurea from polymeric polyamines obtained by the reductive amination of ethylene-carbon monoxide polyketones. Langkammerer, in U. S. 2,620,325 to duPont (674), describes the preparation of polymeric dioximes by treating ethylene-carbon monoxide copolymers with nitrous acid to form 1,2-ketooximes. By treatment with hydroxylamine, resins useful as chelating agents may be obtained.

Pinkney, in U. S. 2,495,282 to duPont (495), proposes the use of ethylene-carbon monoxide copolymers in the production of thermosetting compositions. In an example, the polymer is prepared by charging into a silver-lined pressure reactor, previously flushed with nitrogen, cyclohexane (100 parts) and *tert*-butyl peroxide (0.5 part). The vessel is closed, evacuated, charged with a mixture of carbon monoxide (44%) and ethylene (56%), and then heated to 135°C. while the pressure is maintained at 350–450 atmospheres. Termination of the reaction, as evidenced by cessation in pressure drop, results in a polymer containing 65.63% carbon and 8.45% hydrogen. The product is treated with alkali by dissolving it in dioxane (1,130 parts) and methanol (120 parts) and adding potassium hydroxide (7.4 parts, as a $0.7N$ solution in methanol). The mixture is kept at a temperature of 75–80°C. for 1.5 hours, poured into water (2,700 parts), and acidified with hydrogen chloride. A modified polymer containing 73.6% carbon and 7.78% hydrogen is obtained. The molding composition itself is prepared by dissolving the modified polymer (38 parts) in dioxane (220 parts) and furfural (38 parts) at 90°C., adding potassium hydroxide (1.4 parts, as a 0.7N solution in methanol), and maintaining the mixture at 90°C. for one hour.   It is then poured into water (400 parts) and acidified with hydrogen chloride.   The precipitate is separated, washed with water, and dried.   The product contains 37% combined furfural, based on hydrogen analysis.   To make a molding composition, this product (50 parts), paraformaldehyde (5 parts), 70–80 mesh white pinewood flour (50 parts), maleic acid (1 part), and zinc stearate (2 parts) are mixed together in a ball mill.   The composition is compression-molded at 160°C. and 3,000 p.s.i. pressure for 5 minutes, and forms a hard, rigid molding having a flexural strength of 12,900 p.s.i. and a yield temperature of 165°C.

Polymeric esters of natural drying-oil fatty acids may be prepared by heating drying-oil acids with polymeric alcohols.   Wayne, in U. S. 2,566,-218 to duPont (581), describes the use of these products to form insoluble, tough, and flexible protective coatings.   In an example, a hydrogenated ethylene-carbon monoxide copolymer (60 parts, hydroxyl number 281, molecular weight 1,927, carbon to hydroxyl ratio 12:1) was mixed with a stoichiometrically equivalent weight (82.5 parts) of linseed-oil fatty acids and xylene (10 parts) in a flask provided with a nitrogen inlet, thermometer, mercury-seal stirrer, and a condenser to separate refluxing xylene and water, in order to allow the water to be drawn off and the xylene to be returned to the mixture.   The mixture was blanketed with nitrogen and stirred and heated at 200–210°C. for 21 hours, at which time its acid number had reached 20.   The product was a clear, brown, oily liquid.   A film of this oil to which a cobalt drier (0.03% cobalt) was added air-dried much faster than a corresponding film of linseed oil and, after drying, was harder, tougher, and less tacky than the linseed-oil film.

According to U.S. 2,599,501 to Upson [duPont (661)], polyketones formed from the copolymerization of carbon monoxide and olefins are allowed to react with phosphorous trichloride or $(RO)_2POCl$ and either acetic acid or acetic anhydride to form polymers containing α-hydroxyphosphonic acid groups or their corresponding dialkyl esters.   In a typical preparation, the polyketone (34.45 parts, molecular weight 1,465, comprised of a 5.33 : 1 ratio of C_2H_4 to CO) is allowed to stand with PCl_3 (34.7 parts) for 2 hours, then added to acetic acid (36 parts), stirred for 3 hours, heated at 100°C. and 20 mm. pressure to remove volatile constituents, treated with 6N hydrochloric acid, evaporated *in vacuo*, and extracted with hot acetone and benzene to yield polymeric α-hydroxyalkane phosphonic acid (30 parts, softening about 145°C., containing 59% phosphonic acid groups at the sites of the original CO groups). The organic extracts yield a softened polymer containing 82% converted groups. Use of $(C_2H_5O)_2$-POCl similarly yields the analogous polymer containing diethyl ester groups of the above phosphonic acid derivative. The product from the 1.4:1 copolymer of ethylene and carbon monoxide made in this manner does not melt at temperatures as high as 300°C. and is proposed for the preparation of flame-resistant films or fibers.

Sulfur Dioxide

As early as 1914, Matthews and Elder in Brit. 11,635 (11) described a process whereby olefinic hydrocarbons, including ethylene, may be combined with sulfur dioxide, preferably under the influence of sunlight or ultraviolet light. As an example, a liquid mixture of the olefin and sulfur dioxide is sealed in a vessel with walls transparent to sunlight or ultraviolet light, and either heated in a water bath at 50°C. or, preferably, irradiated by exposure to bright sunlight or to ultraviolet light. It was suggested that the resultant product may be used to replace celluloid for transparent films, varnishes, or ornamental articles, or may be mixed with celluloid to reduce its flammability.

Snow and Frey (71) obtained resins from the reaction of ethylene and other olefins with sulfur dioxide under the influence of light and catalysts. The polymerization was weakly exothermic. The products obtained from 2-olefins showed higher softening points than those from 1-olefins and were more stable to the action of alkalies. The resins were fusible only under pressure. The ethylene resin was hard and insoluble in organic solvents; that of 1-decene was rubberlike and soluble.

The copolymerization of ethylene with sulfur dioxide and carbon monoxide is described by Lipscomb in U. S. 2,634,254 to duPont (789). In an example, a silver-lined reactor was charged with water (50 parts), sulfur dioxide (5 parts), and α,α'-azodiisobutyronitrile (1 part); carbon monoxide was admitted to 200 atmospheres pressure and then ethylene to a pressure of 400 atmospheres. The mixture was heated with agitation at a temperature of 80–90°C. for 6 hours to yield a powder (11.5 parts) containing 10.7% sulfur. The product could be separated into different fractions by extraction with xylene and chloroform. In another example, cyclohexane (50 parts), sulfur dioxide (0.1 part), and di-*tert*-butylperoxide (0.75 part) in a pressure reactor were charged with 300 atmospheres carbon monoxide and ethylene to a total pressure of 550 atmospheres, and heated at 130°C. for 8.5 hours to yield a solid (30.5 parts) containing 0.2% sulfur. A film of this material showed no sticking qualities below 165°C.

Hanford, in U. S. 2,398,426 to duPont (240), describes a process for the preparation of surface-active products containing sulfonic acid groups by reacting ethylene or other olefins with an aqueous solution of a water-soluble salt of sulfurous acid. Reaction temperature is 90–200°C. and the pressure is at least 400 atmospheres.

Formation of polymeric sulfones in high yields and of a satisfactory degree of polymerization is claimed by Ross and Noether in U. S. 2,698,317 to Celanese (918) by the copolymerization of sulfur dioxide with the olefin at very low temperatures. For example, a polymerization initiator is mixed with the olefinic component at a temperature at which the olefinic monomer is in the liquid phase and the resultant solution gradually added to an excess of cooled, liquid sulfur dioxide through which an inert gas is being bubbled. Polymerization starts quite rapidly and is usually complete shortly after the addition of the olefinic monomer. Propylene, but not ethylene, is enumerated among the olefinic monomers to which the process is applicable.

Also restricted to the use of propylene is U. S. 2,703,793 to Naylor [duPont (1064)] which describes the preparation of a copolymer of sulfur dioxide with propylene and an acrylate at 60–90°C.

Silicon Halides

Scott, in U. S. 2,407,181 to duPont (264), describes the preparation of waxlike polymers from ethylene and a silicon halide at pressures of 600–1,000 atmospheres and temperatures of 75–300°C., with or without an inert solvent such as cyclohexane. Described as suitable catalysts are diethyl peroxide and a combination of $KClO_4$ and MnO_2. The product has a molecular weight of 400–4,000 and melts at temperatures of 85–110°C. It may be used for polishes, paper coating, and as a lube oil modifier.

4.4. Chlorination

The chlorination of polyethylene, as described by Fawcett in Brit. 481,515 to I.C.I. (71a), proceeds rapidly with the evolution of hydrochloric acid if the polyethylene is dissolved in a solvent such as carbon tetrachloride, or with a finely divided suspension of the solid. Halogen carriers, such as iodine, an aluminum halide, or a ferric halide, may be present. The reaction proceeds rather slowly at room temperatures, with an elevated temperature above 50°C. preferred; light also accelerates the reaction. A wide range of products is obtainable by varying the amount of chlorine and the reaction conditions. As halogen is introduced, the material becomes more rubberlike, since its crystallinity is reduced; the softening point is also reduced and the solubility increases. When about 30% of chlorine or 60% of bromine has been introduced, a fairly sharp change occurs. Additional halogen yields fibrous products of high softening point and low solubility. Further increase in halogen leads to still stiffer products. A hard, transparent, tough, amorphous polymer, similar to unplasticized polyvinyl chloride, is obtained when a chlorine content of about 70% has been reached. Chlorinated polyethylenes are recommended for forming films, tapes, or threads; for coating or impregnating materials such as paper or fabrics, and for electrical insulation. Chlorinated polyethylenes are further discussed in Section 6.17.

A continuous process for the preparation of chlorinated polyethylene has been described by Myles and Jones in U. S. 2,398,803 to I.C.I. (242). In this process, a solution of chlorine and a normally solid polyethylene in an inert solvent are fed into a reaction zone maintained below 45°C. until about 50% of the chlorine has been introduced. The partially chlorinated reaction product is then passed into a second reaction zone maintained at 55–150°C., until a total of 55–75% of chlorine has been added.

McAlevy in U. S. 2,405,971 to duPont (261) claims a process of chlorinating polyethylene by reacting a solution of the polymer in carbon tetrachloride with sulfuryl chloride. Benzoyl peroxide is employed as the catalyst, and the temperature is maintained between 50 and 130°C. The chlorinated products contain little or no sulfur. Phosgene, oxalyl chloride, or thionyl chloride can be used in place of sulfuryl chloride. Heterocyclic nitrogenous compounds, such as pyridine, may be used as catalysts, or alternatively, the reaction may be accelerated by the action of light.

The chlorination of a finely divided suspension of polyethylene in water, preferably in the presence of a wetting agent, by gaseous chlorine at 40–100°C. is described in Brit. 627,376 (452) and in U. S. 2,592,763 to Taylor (656), both to duPont. The reaction mixture also preferably contains a wetting agent. Light may be used to accelerate the reaction. Calcium chloride may be added to the suspension to obtain a product of somewhat increased stability. The properties of polyethylene chlorinated in aqueous suspension are different from those of polyethylene chlorinated to a similar chlorine content in solution. This is demonstrated by the stiffness values shown in Table XVII. As initiators in this suspension chlorination process, aliphatic azo compounds, particularly α,α'-azobis-(α,γ-dimethylvaleronitrile), are recommended by Ernsberger in U. S. 2,503,252 to duPont (506).

TABLE XVII

Comparison of Chlorination of Polyethylene in Solution and in Suspension

Method of chlorination	Chlorine content, %	Stiffness, lbs./sq.in.
Solution in carbon tetrachloride	33	398
Water suspension	35.4	7680
Solution in carbon tetrachloride	37	585
Water suspension	37.5	1750
Solution in carbon tetrachloride	44	280
Water suspension	44.2	52600

Source: Brit. 627,376, Aug. 8, 1949, E. I. duPont de Nemours & Company.

Chlorination at 60–80°C. of an emulsion of polyethylene prepared by polymerizing ethylene in the presence of an emulsifying agent is described by Becker and Bayer in U. S. 2,695,899 to Farbenfabriken Bayer (915). The chlorination product precipitates immediately in an easily filterable form.

The manufacture of chlorinated polyethylene by the use of liquid chlorine, preferably under the influence of light, is described in Brit. 623,705 to duPont (445).

A process for at least partially dehalogenating chlorinated polyethylenes is described by Fawcett in U. S. 2,261,757 to I.C.I. (129). The term "dehalogenation" may include the removal of halogen as such or in the form of a halogenated compound, and its replacement by other atoms or groups. This procedure permits the preparation of a large number of derivatives of polyethylene.

Stabilization of chlorinated polyethylenes against deterioration by heat and light is claimed by Whittaker in U. S. 2,316,481 [I.C.I. (151)]. This is accomplished by the addition of salicylic acid and of esters of aromatic acids with mono-, di-, and trihydric phenols, preferably phenyl salicylate. According to U. S. 2,364,410 to Whittaker [I.C.I. (171)], sodium lactate may be added to impart heat stability to the chlorinated polymer.

The preparation of chlorinated and chlorosulfonated *polypropylenes* is described in Belg. 540,362 to Montecatini (1083b).

4.5. Chlorosulfonation

A modification of the chlorination process described by McQueen in U. S. 2,212,786 to duPont (113) permits the introduction of sulfur-containing groups into polyethylene. Differing from simple chlorinated polyethylene, chlorosulfonated polyethylene may be cured by crosslinking with metal oxides to form a rubberlike material with good mechanical properties and notable resistance to ozone and light. This permits its use without the addition of carbon black to give white and pale-colored compositions which do not show rapid deterioration like other elastomers. These compounds are further described in Section 6.18.

As one example, polyethylene (molecular weight, 10,000–20,000) is suspended in carbon tetrachloride in a reaction vessel provided with an agitator and means for illuminating the reaction zone with actinic light. A mixture of chlorine and sulfur dioxide is passed into the suspension over a period of 2 hours. The carbon tetrachloride is removed by distillation and the remaining sulfonyl chloride hydrolyzed with aqueous sodium hydroxide.

The chlorosulfonation of polyethylene by the use of azo catalysts is described by Beekley in U. S. 2,640,048 to duPont (795b). The preparation of ester derivatives of chlorosulfonated hydrocarbon polymers is claimed by Busse and Smook in U. S. 2,723,255 to duPont (1098a).

4.6. Oxidation, Crosslinking, and Curing

Controlled oxidation of polyethylene leading to various modified products, depending on the reaction conditions applied, is described by Whittaker and Forsyth in Brit. 581,279 to I.C.I. (266). Oxidation of polyethylene with 60% nitric acid for 6 hours at 120°C. yields high molecular weight dicarboxylic acids. A gaseous mixture of oxygen and ozone, when passed at 78°C. through a solution of polyethylene in carbon tetrachloride, causes the formation of waxlike materials, polycarboxylic acids, hydroxycarboxylic acids, and partially esterified polycarboxylic acids.

Mastication of polyethylene at 160°C. on heated rolls exposed to the atmosphere effects crosslinking of the polymer and results in increased viscosity after 6 hours of milling. The softening point of the material increases from 112 to 150°C.; the oxygen content is 0.3%, present as —CO—, as evidenced by infrared spectroscopy. A similar change takes place much faster if the polyethylene has been blended prior to milling with benzoyl peroxide (1%). Similarly, blending polyethylene or copolymers of ethylene and carbon monoxide or vinyl acetate on the rubber mill with an organic compound such as benzoyl peroxide, which generates free radicals on heating, is claimed in Brit. 597,833 to duPont (360) to decrease the solubility of the polymeric material. It is also claimed to impart increased resistance to deformation under load at elevated temperatures. The cured mixtures are particularly recommended for the calender-coating of fabrics.

The removal of crosslinked particles ("fisheyes") from polyethylene by refining procedures is described in Section 8.1.

Milling with stearic acid and a peroxy compound is stated by Alderson in U. S. 2,455,910 to duPont (380) to effect curing of polymers, halogenated polymers, and copolymers of ethylene.   In an example, polyethylene (molecular weight 15,000; 100 parts) is heated on rolls at 100–110°C., and stearic acid (10 parts) dissolved in xylene (100 parts) is added.   When the blend becomes homogeneous, a paste of zinc peroxide (8–10% by weight of active oxygen; 5 parts) and xylene (2 parts) is milled into the mixture. The composition is milled until free from solvent, then sheeted off the rolls.   Sheets, heated in a press at 160°C. for 15 minutes, are not soluble in boiling toluene, and have a zero-strength temperature of 170–200°C.

The preparation of ethylene polymers which may be crosslinked *after* shaping is described by Kent in U. S. 2,528,523 (521) and in Brit. 659,958 (586a), both to duPont.   The resultant product does not deform under load at elevated temperatures, and can yield smooth, extruded insulation coatings on wire.   The process consists in shaping polyethylene containing 2–5% of a tertiary peroxide at 150–180°C., until at least 50% of the polymer has become insoluble in boiling trichloroethylene.   The ingredients, including fillers, lubricants, or pigments, may be mixed by milling on hot rolls at 120–125°C., or by tumbling at room temperature.   When the blend is to be extruded, a liquid tertiary peroxide or a solution of a solid peroxide is incorporated from a device attached to the head of the extruder.

Removal of some or all of the halogen from halogenated polyethylenes leads to products of decreased solubility and increased melting point, according to a process described by Fawcett in Brit. 492,322 to I.C.I. (72).   Suitable substances for the removal of halogen are ammonia, caustic alkalies, sodium polysulfides, metals such as zinc or sodium, metal alcoholates, and amines.   Halogen removal may proceed in at least two ways: (a), by crosslinking between two or more molecules through links supplied by the reactive substances (e.g., —NH—, —O—, —S—, =C=O,

$$—NH—CO—NH—, \quad —NH—CH_2—CH_2—NH—, \quad —N\underset{CH_2—CH_2}{\overset{CH_2—CH_2}{\diagdown}}N—,$$

—O—CH_2—CH_2—O—, —NHC_6H_4NH—), leading to products of increased molecular weights; (b), by removal of hydrogen halide, apparently from a single chain, resulting in the formation of unsaturated bonds in the chain.

Halogenated polymers or copolymers of ethylene may also be cured by heating to at least 100°C. for at least 15 minutes with sulfur, a metal oxide (e.g., zinc, magnesium, calcium, or barium oxide) and a rubber vulcanizing accelerator.   The reaction, according to Brit. 585,711 to duPont (312), probably involves the removal of halogen, resulting in or followed by a crosslinking reaction.   Products with high solvent resistance, high softening point, and high tensile strength, are obtained.

4.7. High Intensity Irradiation

The physical properties of polyethylene and other polymers can be altered markedly by their exposure to radiation fields. An early paper by Winogradoff (492) describes the irradiation of polyethylene, polystyrene, and paraffin wax for periods up to 60 hours by radiation emerging from an x-ray tube. There was no evidence of brittleness, and x-ray diffraction patterns showed no definite structural changes. In the x-ray beam, all samples exhibited a bluish-white luminescence. After 60 hours of exposure, polyethylene and polystyrene showed no discoloration, while paraffin wax became slightly more opaque. Exposure to ultraviolet radiation caused marked luminescence of irradiated patches in polyethylene and paraffin wax. In polystyrene, the patch appeared almost black in comparison with a slight luminescence of the unexposed parts.

During recent years, the effects of radiation, particularly of atomic radiation, on plastic materials have been studied intensively, and the treatment of polymeric materials with high-energy radiation was included as a commercially feasible method by Mark (864) in his study of second-stage crosslinking. Some of the results of these investigations have now reached commercial exploitation, and the present status of this field has been very capably summarized by a number of distinguished contributors in recent issues of *Modern Plastics* (823a, 884, 933), and in publications of the United States Atomic Energy Commission, Oak Ridge National Laboratory, Oak Ridge, Tennessee (566a, 708a).

Various devices, called particle accelerators, which have been developed for producing high-energy beams of electrons or atomic and nuclear particles, are the most readily available sources of radiation energy for research and industrial processing; of these, the van de Graaff accelerators deserve particular mention (731). Nuclear reactions and artificial or natural radioisotopes are other sources of radiation (884).

This development is based essentially on the work of Charlesby, formerly of the British Atomic Energy Research Establishment at Harwell, England. Publication of Charlesby's findings began in 1952 (597; compare also 679, 684, 696, 840, 864, 947, and 973). Polyethylene, exposed in the Harwell pile, was found to become crosslinked, and a new type of plastic was produced which did not melt at about 115°C. or dissolve in organic compounds. The mechanical properties are also altered, especially above 115°C., when the plastic shows rubberlike elasticity. Crosslinking was assumed to arise primarily from the fracture of the carbon-hydrogen bonds and the liberation of hydrogen. The physical properties of the polymer can be studied as a function of the degree of crosslinking

which, over a wide range, is proportional to the incident radiation.   In
the presence of oxygen, oxidation takes place on the surface during irradia-

Fig. 32. Effect of radiation on melting of polythene.   Left: ordinary polythene, which
melts above 115°C.   Middle and right: irradiated polythene does not melt but becomes
transparent and elastic.   (*Plastics* [*London*], **18** [70], 143, 1953.)

Fig. 33. Elastic properties of irradiated polythene above 120°C.
Rigidity depends on quantity of irradiation to which specimen has
been subjected.   (*Plastics* [*London*], **18** [70], 143, 1953.)

tion while the crosslinking effect occurs uniformly throughout the specimen. A subsequent paper by Charlesby (720) deals with additional
observations on the changes of polyethylene subjected to the radiation of
an atomic pile, rendering the polymer insoluble, infusible, amorphous, and
resistant to sulfuric acid.   With drastic treatment, polyethylene becomes
glasslike, and its density increases from 0.92 to 0.96.   A very flexible and

Fig. 34. Elastic properties of irradiated polythene.   Right: irradiated polythene at 120°C. under load.   Left: recovery after removal
of load.   (*Plastics* [*London*], **18** [70], 144, 1953.)

nearly transparent modification of polyethylene can be obtained by irradiation at temperatures near its melting point.

The effect of irradiation on melting and on the elastic properties of
polyethylene is illustrated in Figures 32, 33, and 34.   Data on the changes
of density and mechanical properties of polyethylene caused by irradiation
are shown in Table XVIII.

While most polymers, including polystyrene, can be crosslinked by
similar treatment, polymers of tetrafluoroethylene are not crosslinked but
rather degraded, probably because the carbon-carbon bonds of the main

TABLE XVIII

Effect of Radiation on Density and Mechanical Properties of Polythene

Radiation dose[a]		0	5	10	20	40
Percentage crystalline at 20°C.		50	42	33	15	0
Density at 20°C.		0.92	0.915	0.91	0.92	0.96
Density at 150°C.		0.78	0.79	0.81	0.84	0.89
Coefficient of expansion $\times$						
10^{-3} (120°–160°C.)		0.90	0.87	0.83	0.75	0.57
Young's modulus						
(10^9 dynes/cm.^{2})	20°C.	3	1.6	1.6	2.2	4
	90°C.	0.4	0.5	0.7	1.0	2
	150°C.	melts	0.1	0.2	0.6	2

Source: *Plastics* (*London*), **18** (70), 144 (1953).
[a] 1 unit = 10^{17} slow neutrons–cm.^{2}/sec. with associated fast neutrons and γ-rays in BEPO.

chain, rather than the carbon-fluorine bonds, are broken.   Degradation instead of crosslinking was also observed in polymethyl methacrylate and in polyisobutylene.

The destructive effect of pile radiation on the crystallinity of polyethylene was found by Charlesby and Hancock (721) to predominate over the crosslinking effect of the radiation below about 4% crosslinking; a more flexible material was obtained at room temperature.   Young's modulus for polyethylene crosslinked by irradiation was measured by both static and dynamic means.   Below about 115°C., the modulus was found to decrease with temperature; above this temperature, the modulus increases again, in agreement with the theory of rubberlike elasticity, except for very high degrees of crosslinking, corresponding to a glasslike structure.

The results of an investigation of the effect of crosslinking on the density and melting point of polyethylene were reported by Charlesby and Ross (722).   The density of the polymer was studied in relation to temperature and to the degree of crosslinking produced by pile irradiation.   Crosslinking is found to result in a progressive reduction in the percentage of crystallized material at room temperature.   The transition temperature corresponding to melting in ordinary polyethylene is only very slightly decreased with increasing crosslinking, so that the temperature at which all crystallized structure vanishes is little affected.   However, because of the reduced amount of crystallized material present in the crosslinked polymer, the magnitude of the change of density at the transition temperature is considerably lessened.   The effect of crosslinking polyethylene is to increase the amount of amorphous material present at room temperature. There are, however, still rudimentary traces of crystallinity left if about 40% of the carbon atoms are crosslinked. For relatively high degrees of crosslinking (above about 15%), the density at room temperature is increased. The transition temperature at which the crystallized regions melt is but slightly reduced by crosslinking, although the change in density at this transition is considerably reduced. There is some evidence that transition temperature as measured by changes in density is somewhat higher than that measured by other means. All of the density measurements for amorphous polyethylene can be expressed in a form closely analogous to that for a gas whose molecules are of finite size and attract one another.

In a recent publication, Charlesby (840) points out that exposure to radiation provides a means of accurately controlling the degree of crosslinking of a polymer without the use of chemical agents or heat treatment. Charlesby (719a, 720, 840a) has further shown that the magnitude of the gel fraction formed on exposing many polymers, including polyethylene, to high energy radiation is a function both of the degree of crosslinking and of the initial molecular weight distribution of the polymer. The application of this method to determine the molecular weight distribution of polyethylenes will be discussed in Section 5.3.

Changes in the chemical properties of polyethylene, as well as of nylon, Koroseal, Buna-N, neoprene, Thiokol, and natural rubber, by long periods of gamma irradiation, have been measured by Ryan (765). Visual observations revealed that Koroseal and neoprene evolved materials that were corrosive to the aluminum containers in which the samples were sealed; the silver nitrate test confirmed the presence of chloride ions. In general, the mechanical deterioration processes resulted in a decrease of flow characteristics of the material tested. Gas evolution also occurred, as evidenced by the buildup of pressure in the containers, but neither qualitative nor quantitative measurements of gaseous products were made. The changes in physical characteristics brought about by radiation of plastics were also discussed by Ryan. As for polyethylene, x-ray diffraction measurements indicated major changes in structure, but the formation of crosslinkages preserves the mechanical properties at low dosages. After long exposure time, the crosslink formation overshadows the other reactions, as indicated by a decrease in the elongation and an increase in elastic modulus. The relative stability of polystyrene to radiation has been attributed to the presence of the phenyl group.

The gases liberated during the high-voltage electron irradiation of polyethylene were investigated by Lawton, Zemany, and Balwit (860) of General Electric.   The physical properties of irradiated polyethylene were measured by Lawton, Balwit, and Bueche (752, 859) to determine the magnitude of the changes brought about by irradiation with high-energy electrons and the efficiency of the electrons in the crosslinking process. Polyethylene irradiated with 800 Kv (peak) electrons has been studied over a wide temperature range.   The molecular weight range investigated was from 7,000–35,000 for irradiation doses up to 200 × 10⁶ roentgen units.

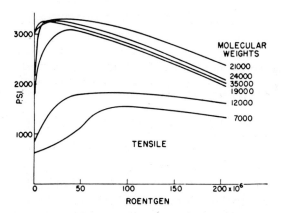

Fig. 35. Ultimate tensile strength *versus* irradiation dose at different initial molecular weights. Tests at room temperature, 800 kv. electrons. (*Ind. Eng. Chem.*, **46**, 1706, 1954.)

The improvements in tensile strength, elongation at break, and tension set were found to be dependent on the initial molecular weight of the polymers and the total irradiation dose.   In the case of a polyethylene of molecular weight 21,000, a dose of 15 × 10⁶ roentgens increased the tensile strength from 2,100 to 3,200 p.s.i., equivalent to an effective molecular weight increase of about 4,000.

In Figure 35, the tensile strengths of polyethylenes of different molecular weights are shown as a function of irradiation dosage.   The corresponding percentage of elongation at the point of break of the test sample is plotted as a function of irradiation dosage in Figure 36.

Above the melting point of the nonirradiated material, the irradiated polyethylene behaved as a noncrystalline, crosslinked elastomer.   The efficiency for crosslinking was found to depend on the initial molecular weight and the irradiation dose.   The irradiation of polyethylene by high-

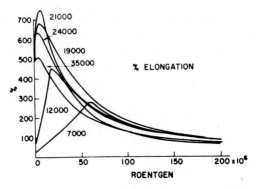

Fig. 36. Ultimate elongation *versus* irradiation dose at different initial molecular weights. Tests at room temperature, 800 kv. electrons. (*Ind. Eng. Chem.*, **46**, 1706, 1954.)

energy electrons can be used to improve its physical properties and high-temperature characteristics. This improvement is explained in terms of decreased crystallinity and increased crosslinking.

Dole, Keeling, and Rose (841) irradiated films and granules of poly-ethylene (molecular weight, 32,000) in the heavy-water pile of the Argonne National Laboratory, both *in vacuo* and in the presence of air. The composition of the gas liberated on irradiation in the absence of oxygen is shown in Table XIX.

TABLE XIX

Mass Spectrographic Analysis of Gas Liberated on Irradiation in the Absence of Oxygen

	% by vol.	
	pile irradiation in thimble	
	55 hr.	45 hr.
H_2	98.6	96.0
CH_4	0.2	0.4
C_2H_6	0.7	0.9
C_3H_8	0.1	0.2
C_3H_6	0.05	0.2
n-C_4H_{10}	0.3	0.7
i-C_4H_{10}	0.05	0.3
C_4H_8	. . .	0.2
N_2	. . .	1.1
Total	100.0	100.0

Source: *J. Am. Chem. Soc.*, **76**, 4306 (1954).

Comparison of the stress-strain curve of Figure 37 for the nonirradiated polyethylene with that of polyethylene irradiated for 45 hours *in vacuo* demonstrated that irradiation eliminated all of the cold-drawing properties of the polyethylene, made it more brittle and more like a three-dimensional polymer.   This was interpreted as being due to crosslinking.   A determination of the tensile strength at break demonstrated that the vacuum irradiation and thus crosslinking did not affect the tensile strength

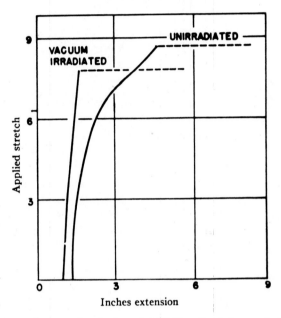

Fig. 37. Stress-strain curve for shock-cooled Visking film before and after irradiation in vacuum.   The units of the ordinate are arbitrary and different for the two curves. (*J. Am. Chem. Soc.*, **76**, 4308, 1954.)

significantly.   In the presence of air, however, the tensile strength was considerably reduced.   These relationships are shown in Table XX.   In the case of regular production, the polyethylene was extruded from the melt as endless tubing into air; shock-cooled polyethylene was extruded into a water bath at 0°C.

Bromine absorption, infrared absorption spectra, extent of gel formation, and viscosity of solutions were measured as functions of the time of exposure.   The most detailed studies were made on the vacuum-irradiated samples.   The first noticeable change in the composition of the film was

TABLE XX

Influence of Irradiation on Tensile Strength

Material T.D.—Transverse direction M.D.—Machine direction	45 hr.				90 hr.			
	Tensile strength		Standard deviation		Tensile strength		Standard deviation	
	Control	Irradiated	Control	Irradiated	Control	Irradiated	Control	Irradiated
Visking shock cooled—M.D.	3602	1653	138	17	3364	1471	89	13
Ventilated can	3594	1554	43	11				
Vacuum	3192	3298	29	198				
Visking shock cooled—T.D.	2182	1276	44	6	1619	1180	97	24
Visking regular product—M.D.	3069	1591	53	27	2771	1636	49	10
Ventilated can	1523	1614	24	16				
Vacuum	3245	3201	110	163				
Visking regular product—T.D.	1918	1384	129	12	1525	1642	6	34

Source: *J. Am. Chem. Soc.*, **76**, 4309 (1954).

the disappearance of the vinylidene group as hydrogen was evolved.   As judged by bromine absorption, 70–80% of the hydrogen evolution produced unsaturation.   The remaining 20–30% caused crosslinkages.   This is somewhat contrary to the concept developed by Charlesby, who assumed that practically all the hydrogen evolved came from crosslinking reactions, and that the formation of unsaturated groups was negligible.

Dole, Keeling, and Rose propose as a mechanism the so-called principle of migration of free-radical centers in the solid state.   Polyethylene is assumed to consist of essentially saturated straight chains, although there is a certain amount of branching, and each molecule is believed to contain one (unsaturated) vinylidene group.   Neutrons and gamma rays cause the ejection of hydrogen from the chain, creating an active free-radical center and also causing inactivation of the vinylidene groups.   The free radical centers are assumed to move along or across the chains through the random migration of hydrogen atoms attached to the chain.   On nearing a point favorable to reaction with the vinylidene group of a neighboring chain, crosslinking is assumed to occur.   Irradiation, it is concluded, appears to cause very little rupture of the carbon-carbon bonds within the main chain.   However, the carbon-carbon bonds in the side chain rupture as frequently as the carbon-hydrogen bonds in the material as a whole.   The detection of the small amount of hydrocarbon in the gases evolved provides the evidence for rupture in the side chains.

TABLE XXa

Changes in Physical Properties upon Exposure to γ-Radiation at 25°C.

Sample no.	Integrated field intensity, Mrep[a]	Ultimate elongation,[b] %	Tensile strength,[b] p.s.i.	Tensile creep[b]		Recovery after 10^4 sec. creep[b] (in %)		Deformation under compression[d] at 132°C.	
				10 sec. compliance, cm.[2] dyne[-1] $\times 10^9$	10^4 sec. compliance, cm.[2] dyne[-1] $\times 10^9$	at 10 sec.	at 10^4 sec.	h/h_0 at 1 min.	h/h_0 at 15 min.
0	0	650	2100	1.56	2.33	50.4	69.5	0.22	0.12
1	1	635	2180	1.42	1.80	78.6	100.	0.30	0.16
2	5	500	1734	1.15	1.57	73.5	79.5(?)	0.47	0.37
3	10	500	1729	0.93	1.15	71.5	100.	0.50	0.41
4	20	105	1385	1.09	1.20	76.5	100.	0.65	0.61
5	40	91	1510	0.81	1.06	85.5	100.	0.73	0.69
6	64	25	1540	0.80	0.80[c]	—	—	0.84	0.84

Source: *J. Polymer Sci.*, **13**, 410 (1954).
[a] The intensity of the source was 200,000 rep/hour.   Mrep = 10^6 rep.
[b] Test run at 30°C.
[c] Specimen failed after 1000 seconds.   Value given is for 10^3 seconds.
[d] Compression test in a parallel plate plastometer.   60-kg. load for 1 inch diameter specimen. h/h_0 is the thickness at the denoted interval divided by the initial thickness.

Changes in the physical properties of polyethylene upon exposure to γ-radiation at 25°C. were also determined by Ballantine, Dienes, Manowitz, Ander, and Mesrobian (823c). The results of this study, which included infrared examinations, are shown in Table XXa.

The effect of the chemical structure of vinyl polymers on crosslinking and degradation of ionizing radiation has been recently discussed by Miller, Lawton, and Balwit (865), and a mechanism for both reactions was proposed. Crosslinking, the authors assume, will occur if the polymer contains at least one α-hydrogen atom, i.e., if it has the structure:

$$(-CH_2CH_2-)_n \quad \text{or} \quad (-CH_2CH-)_n$$
$$\underset{R}{|}$$

Degradation will occur if the structure is

$$\left(-CH_2\underset{\underset{R}{|}}{\overset{\overset{CH_3}{|}}{C}}-\right)_n$$

It appears that the *direction* of radiation effect, as regards crosslinking or degradation, is independent of the nature of the R substituent, although this will, of course, influence the *efficiency* of crosslinking or degradation and will also influence byproduct formation, depending upon the susceptibility toward radiation damage of the substituent.

This correlation with chemical structure leads to a mechanism for crosslinking in which a radical stabilized by resonance with the R group, $-CH_2\dot{C}-$, is formed by loss of a hydrogen atom, which atom may then
$$\underset{R}{|}$$
form a similar radical by hydrogen abstraction on a nearby polymer chain. Thus, these radicals are in a favorable position to combine, and only one primary ionization event is required to form the crosslink. In the degrading polymers, radicals of the type suggested by Charlesby are not resonance-stabilized and may undergo C–C cleavage in the main chain to give a more stable form where one of the cleavage products is stabilized by resonance between the double bond and the R group:

$$-CH_2\underset{\underset{R}{|}}{\overset{\overset{CH_2\cdot}{|}}{C}}- \longrightarrow -CH_2\cdot + CH_2{=}\underset{\underset{R}{|}}{C}-$$

Changes in the density, percentage of crystallinity, and Young's modulus of polyethylene caused by irradiation at 80°C. in the Harwell pile were

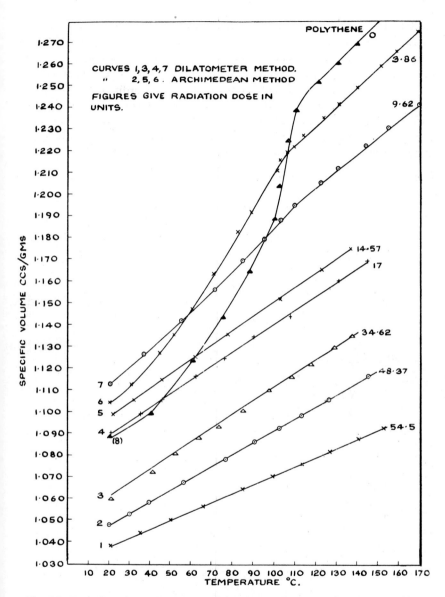

Fig. 38. Variation of specific volume of irradiated polyethylene with temperature. (Radiation temperature 80°C.) (*A.E.R.E. Report M/R 1401, 1954 Appendix* [*Declassified*], Dept. of Atomic Energy, Harwell, Berks., England.)

studied by Ross (879) and compared with earlier work (720, 721, 722) carried out at about 65–70°C., the normal working temperature of the pile. The change in specific volume of ordinary polyethylene and of polyethylenes irradiated with different radiation doses at 80°C. are shown in Figure 38. The change of slope at about 115°C. for ordinary polyethylene and for polyethylenes exposed to small radiation doses may be correlated with the decrease in crystallinity and increase in crosslinking; the decreasing slope of the volume expansion curves with increasing irradiation is consistent with previous findings on amorphous, crosslinked solids.

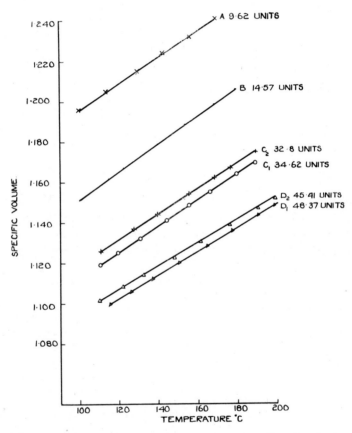

Fig. 39. Comparison of specific volume/temperature curves of irradiated polyethylene. Curves A, B, C_1, D_1 are for materials irradiated at 80°C.; curves C_2, D_2 are for materials irradiated at 60–70°C. (*A.E.R.E. Report M/R 1401, 1954 Appendix* [*Declassified*], Dept. of Atomic Energy, Harwell, Berks., England.)

Figure 39 shows the comparison of the specific volume curves over the range 110–190°C. for polyethylene irradiated for similar periods but at two different temperatures of irradiation.   From these curves, the values shown in Table XXI were prepared, in order to show the change in coefficient of expansion at 120–140°C. on irradiation; the specific volume at absolute zero is also shown.

TABLE XXI

Coefficient of Expansion (between 120 and 140°C.) and Specific Volume at 0°K. of Irradiated Polyethylene

Radiation dose in units[a]	Coefficient of expansion $\times 10^{-3}$	Specific volume at 0°K.
3.86	0.90	0.984
9.62	0.77	0.916
14.57	0.65	0.894
34.62	0.60	0.874
48.37	0.55	0.885
54.50	0.47	0.913

Source: *A.E.R.E. Report M/R 1401, 1954 Appendix (Declassified)*, Dept. of Atomic Energy, Harwell, Berks., England.
[a] 1 unit = 10^{17} slow neutrons–cm.^{2}/sec. with associated fast neutrons and γ-rays in BEPO.

The variation of the density of polyethylene at 20°C. with irradiation is shown in Figure 40.   The shape of this curve can be explained by considering the two competing causes of the density changes.   At first, the decrease in crystallinity caused by radiation decreases the density, since the crystalline structure has a density of almost 1.00, while the amorphous structure has an extrapolated density of 0.853.   When substantially all crystallinity is destroyed, increasing crosslinking causes a tighter packing and an increase in density of the material.

Figure 41, showing the variation of the percentage crystallinity of polyethylene with irradiation and temperature of irradiation, has been derived from the information presented in Figure 40.   Young's modulus changes with radiation dose, as indicated by Figure 42.   The shape of the initial portion of the curve resembles that of the density curve (Figure 41) for the same reasons.

The variation of Young's modulus with temperature for irradiated polyethylene is shown in Figure 43.

It is concluded that a whole series of amorphous, crosslinked materials may be obtained by exposing polyethylene to the effect of ionizing radiation.   The irradiated products will not melt or dissolve in organic solvents, and they vary in type from flexible to almost glass hard. When the temperature of irradiation is raised, crystallinity disappears at a lower radiation dose, and a more flexible, only slightly crosslinked material is produced.

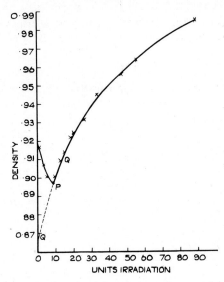

Fig. 40. Variation with irradiation of the density of polyethylene at 20°C. (*A.E.R.E. Report M/R 1401, 1954 Appendix* [*Declassified*], Dept. of Atomic Energy, Harwell, Berks., England.)

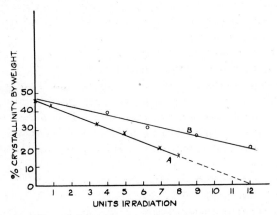

Fig. 41. Variation of the percentage crystallinity of polyethylene with irradiation and temperature of irradiation: O irradiated at 70°C; × at 80°C. (*A.E.R.E. Report M/R 1401, 1954 Appendix* [*Declassified*], Harwell, Berks., England.)

If these materials are heated *in vacuo* to 150°C. for several hours after irradiation, the initial drop in Young's modulus observed on heating can largely be eliminated, through removal either of low molecular weight fragments or of gas held internally in the material.

Reduced permeability to gases was noted by Szwarc, Stannett, Meyer, and Rogers (1030, 1035) for polyethylene films which had been crosslinked by irradiation (compare Section 6.3).   Sobolev, Meyer, Stannett, and

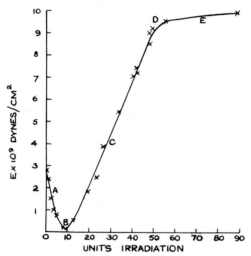

Fig. 42. Variation of Young's modulus of polyethylene with irradiation, measured at 20°C.   (*A.E.R.E. Report M/R 1401, 1954 Appendix* [*Declassified*], Dept. of Atomic Energy, Harwell, Berks., England.)

Szwarc (1028) conclude that irradiation and consequent crosslinking do not affect the solubility constant, but that the reduction in permeability is due to a decrease in a diffusion constant.

In conclusion it may be said that the basic mechanism of irradiation-induced reactions of polymers is still the subject of some controversy. This, Wall (1041) of the National Bureau of Standards explained, is partially due to conflicting experimental results caused by the particular influence of oxygen on the reaction.   Such influence was noted by Dole and co-workers, Charlesby, Little, Baskett, Ballantine and co-workers, and Stannett and co-workers.   The problem was studied in particular by Chapiro (940) who measured the softening points of irradiated polyethylenes by a novel technique.   He found that a crosslinking polymer such as polyethylene, crosslinks less in the presence of oxygen, and may even be de-

graded instead; a degrading polymer, however, degrades less in the presence
of oxygen than it does in a vacuum.   The phenomena observed on polyethylene were interpreted by Chapiro by assuming the formation of intermolecular bridges of a peroxidic structure which decompose at 150–170°C.

This assumption of peroxidic bridges may account for the presence of
carbonyl groups in air-irradiated polyethylene, while the reduced amount
of crosslinking observed in the presence of air may be explained by assuming that the macromolecular radicals, which would otherwise form crosslinks, are consumed by the reaction forming bridges of a peroxidic nature.

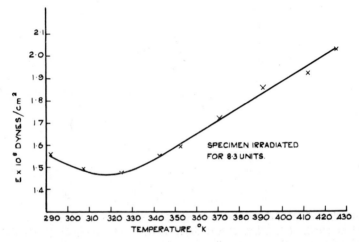

Fig. 43. Variation of Young's modulus with temperature for irradiated polyethylene. Temperature of irradiation 80°C. (*A.E.R.E. Report M/R 1401,
1954 Appendix* [*Declassified*], Dept. of Atomic Energy, Harwell, Berks., England.)

This interpretation may also explain certain results observed by Baskett
(823d), who found a larger soluble fraction in irradiated polyethylene when
he extracted the polymer with xylene at 140°C., instead of toluene at
100°C., or benzene at 78°C. It may be assumed that the peroxidic
bridges in the polymer break much more easily, the higher the temperature at which the extraction is carried out.   While Baskett had irradiated
his samples *in vacuo*, he had not degassed them prior to irradiation, which
Chapiro considers necessary, having found that polyethylene possesses a
very porous structure and occludes a considerable amount of air.   This
only seems to confirm Wall's originally cited argument

4.8. Blending

Polymers and copolymers of ethylene are compatible with certain plasticizers, resins, and waxes (compare Section 6.1). They may be incorporated in the usual way on mixing rolls or in a Banbury mixer at temperatures generally between 100 and 150°C. (compare Section 8.2) to give products with modified properties (compare Section 6.12). One of these, containing 10–20% of a high molecular weight polyisobutylene, has been widely used for cable applications. The outstanding advantages of such blends are generally improved processing behavior, higher flexibility at ordinary temperatures, decreased brittleness at low temperatures, and reduced tendency toward environmental cracking. The electrical properties usually remain unaffected. Antioxidants (compare Section 3.13), antistatic agents (compare Sections 8.7 and 8.16), pigments, dyestuffs (compare Section 8.2), and other additives may be incorporated by blending. Fillers, such as calcium carbonate and some carbon blacks, have a slight reinforcing effect and may increase the hardness and raise the softening point, but they impair other strength properties of the polymer.

Intimate mixtures of at least 50% by weight of polyethylene, 20–35% of antimony trioxide, and at least 6% of a solid chlorinated hydrocarbon (50–80% chlorine) can be molded or extruded into objects which have a high degree of flame retardance. Preparation and properties of the blends are described by Happoldt in U. S. 2,480,298 to duPont (454b).

When protection against radiation is required, this, according to Charlesby (944), may be achieved by incorporation within a polymer of small quantities of such compounds as thiourea or aniline capable of reducing the effect of radiation in causing degradation by a factor of three.

A polyethylene composition comprising 85–60% of a solid polyethylene and 15–40% of a styrene-isobutylene copolymer (about 60% combined styrene) is described by Young and Hardy in U. S. 2,655,492 to Standard Oil (802). These compositions are claimed to be especially adapted for making artificial fibers.

Compositions consisting of polyethylene (75–20 parts), polyisobutylene (25–80 parts), and optionally a wax, such as a paraffin wax (1–25 parts), may be formed into essentially transparent, thin films. According to Sparks in U. S. 2,339,958 to Jasco, Inc. (163), these blends are particularly suitable for food-wrapping sheets and similar applications.

A blend consisting of polyethylene (91 parts), a microcrystalline hydrocarbon wax (melting point 75–80°C., 8 parts), an antioxidant (phenols, 0.2 part), and zinc stearate (1 part), is claimed by Happoldt and Stockfleth in U. S. 2,448,799 to duPont (371) to be extrudable at a rate of 150 feet per minute.   Tausent in Span. 214,554 (912b) claims that the modification of polyethylene with paraffin permits injection molding at lower temperatures and results in more flexible moldings.   According to one example, polyethylene (90 parts) is heated to softening, paraffin oil (10 parts) is added, and the mixture heated to 65°C.   The blend, on cooling, forms a homogeneous mass which is again heated at 120°C. until fluid, and allowed to cool.   In Span. 214,555 (912c), Tausent claims the preparation of a range of plastics from soft and flexible, to hard and rigid, by modifying polyethylene with natural resins, such as colophony and copals, or with waxes, such as carnauba and beeswax.   In one example, polyethylene (50 parts) and colophony (50 parts) are heated until soft, the temperature raised to 94°C., and heating stopped immediately.   The homogeneous mass which forms on cooling is reheated to 120°C. for a few minutes until fluid, yielding a flexible molding compound on cooling.

A paper coating composition comprising a mixture of refined paraffin wax, polyethylene, and a low molecular weight polyethylene containing a terminal hydroxyl group (produced by polymerizing ethylene under 425–475 atmospheres at temperatures between 140 and 200°C., in the presence of isopropanol and hydrogen peroxide) is described by Thwaites and Hitchcox in U. S. 2,698,309 to Standard Oil (917).

A process involving the catalytic polymerization of ethylene in the presence of a molten petroleum wax to produce an intimate blend of polyethylene and wax is described by Newberg, Wilson, and Sayko in U. S. 2,706,719 to Esso Research and Engineering (1069).

According to Brit. 586,826 to Resinous Products and Chemical (316), a linear polyester of 1,2-propylene glycol and sebacic acid acts as a plasticizer without migrating into the polyethylene.   Polymers or copolymers of polyvinyl chloride and polyvinyl acetate containing this plasticizer may be used in conjunction with polyethylene as a high-frequency cable insulation covering.   The incorporation of a copolymer (2–10%) of vinyl chloride and octyl acrylate is claimed in Brit. 731,134 to Union Carbide (1071a) to improve the resistance of polyethylene to stress cracking.

A polymeric polyamide, obtained by reductive amination of an ethylene-carbon monoxide copolymer exhibits good properties as a water-repellant coating when blended with a wax, according to Werntz in U. S. 2,495,283 to duPont (496).

Blends of ethylene-carbon monoxide copolymers with waxes are claimed to be useful for the coating of paper, according to U. S. 2,495,285 to Hoehn [duPont (498)].

Chlorinated polyethylene compositions which may be molded or extruded into flexible, thermally stable sheeting are described by Fletcher and Taylor in U. S. 2,467,550 to duPont (439).   The blends contain litharge, a microcrystalline wax, and a metal salt of a fatty acid.   Use of these materials as insulation is proposed, because these materials can be extruded at high rates without the use of plasticizers.   In this way, stable wire coatings with smooth surfaces and satisfactory insulating properties may be formed.

Mechanical blends of polyethylene or of a halogenated polyethylene with a condensation product of phosphorous pentasulfide and a primary or secondary alcohol, amine, or mercaptan, are claimed by Burk in U. S. 2,480,296 to duPont (454) to exhibit improved transparency and surface characteristics.

Chlorosulfonated polyethylene together with a zinc compound (zinc oxide or zinc salts of fatty acids) is claimed by Peterson and Batts in U. S. 2,734,039 [U. S. Rubber (1148)] to accelerate the vulcanization of butyl rubber compounded with a dimethylolphenol as the curing agent.

Can. 522,921 to Derksen and Jacobs [N. V. Phillips' Gloeilampenfabrieken (1150)] describes a method of mixing polyethylene with asphalt bitumens to reduce the brittleness of the latter.   The polyethylene is first mixed with an asphalt bitumen of a melting point below 60°C. (measured by the ring and ball method), the mixture is melted and added while in the molten state to an asphalt bitumen of a melting point of above 75°C.

The preparation of mixtures of conventional low density polyethylene with high density (Phillips) polyethylene in solution, on rolls, or in a mixer, is described by Jones and Reynolds in Fr. 1,109,864 [Phillips Petroleum (1147)].   Preferably, mechanical mixing is carried out at temperatures between 104° and 127°C.   These mixtures are claimed to possess higher softening and heat-distortion temperatures, improved extruding and molding properties, and increased hardness and tensile strength.   A balance of properties may be achieved which, it is emphasized, makes these blends particularly useful as films.

V. MOLECULAR STRUCTURE OF POLYETHYLENES

Solid polyethylenes have the empirical formula $(CH_2)_n$ and show, in general, the properties to be expected for high molecular weight paraffins. Under the electron microscope, as observed by Rochow and Rowe (418), polyethylene appears to be composed of interlacing fibers or flakes, approximately 620 A–250 A in width, and roughly 20,000 A in length. Qualitatively, the structure is not unlike that of paraffin wax.

Measurements of the molecular weight of polyethylene can be carried out by absolute, e.g., osmotic or ebulliometric, methods, or more conveniently, by determining the solution viscosity of the polymer. However, physical properties of solid polyethylenes and of their melts are significantly modified by the presence of branches in the polyethylene chain. This may be demonstrated by infrared analysis, which also indicates the presence of methyl groups and of olefinic groups. Depending upon the catalyst systems and polymerization conditions employed, a wide variation in the degree of chain branching and hence of the crystallinity of the resultant polyethylene is observed.

For a detailed study of the principles underlying the subjects treated in this and the following Chapter VI, reference is made to the recent books by Burnett (835), Flory (730b), Mark and Tobolsky (481), and the series by Houwink (854b) and by Stuart (1034) on high polymers.

5.1. Crystallinity

An outstanding characteristic of solid polyethylene is its partial crystallinity, usually amounting to 60–70% for high-pressure, high-temperature polyethylene. Unbranched "polymethylene" is almost completely crystalline.* Comparative studies discussed previously (compare Chapter I) have demonstrated the relationship between crystallinity and chain-branching. Crystallinity may also be reduced by substitution, particularly copolymerization, chlorination, and irradiation (compare Chapter IV). Two specimens of about the same molecular weight may differ widely in both

---

* Consequently, the term "polymethylene" should not be applied to products like the Ziegler or Phillips polyethylenes, for which the term "high-density polyethylenes" was chosen in this book.

melting point and Young's modulus on account of differences in density and, consequently, of differences in the perfection of crystalline structure. The microcrystalline structure is also responsible for the fact that polyethylene ordinarily exhibits a white, waxy translucence, but that in thin sections it can be made substantially transparent by rapid chilling from a high

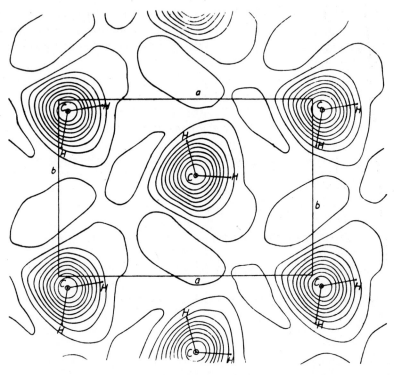

Fig. 44. Electron densities on plane perpendicular to c-axis, at $^3/_{12}c$ and (rotated 180°) $^9/_{12}c$. (*Trans. Faraday Soc.*, **35**, 489, 1939.)

temperature, as by quenching in water (63). Quenching additionally results in improved flexibility and toughness at low temperatures (145). The crystalline structure is also related to the capacity of polyethylene to be cold-drawn (62), with considerable attendant benefit to the mechanical properties through structural orientation.

Present x-ray and infrared techniques for estimation of the crystalline-amorphous ratio in polymers have been surveyed by Nichols (871), supplying representative data for some of the common crystallizing polymers and pointing out advantages and limitations of the methods discussed.   For a detailed study of x-ray diffraction procedures, reference is made to the recent book by Klug and Alexander (857a).   Of particular interest is the chapter dealing with the spectrometric powder technique and the section on the determination of the crystalline-amorphous ratio in textile fibers and other polymers.   In addition, reference should be made to the papers by Alexander, Ohlberg, and Taylor (929c), and by Aggarwal and Tilley (929b).   Some aspects of the crystallization of high polymers are presented

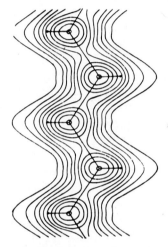

Fig. 45. Section through a polyethylene molecule.   (*Trans. Faraday Soc.*, **35,** 489, 1939.)

in a recent book by Schuur (1025); a survey of the literature about spherulites in high polymers, discussions of the mechanism of crystallization, the continuity of the crystal-lattice in high polymers, and the rate of crystallization and the melting range of high polymers are the subject matter of this publication.

An investigation of the percentages of crystalline and amorphous regions in various commercial and experimental polyethylenes by an x-ray diffraction technique, using a Geiger counter x-ray spectrometer which records the intensity of the diffracted radiation as a linear function of the Bragg angle, was reported by Bryant, Tordella, and Pierce (463).   A rapid method of resolving the area under the crystalline and amorphous diffraction peaks was devised for the determination of the amorphous percentage on a routine basis.   The results correlated with those obtained by density measurements, and amorphous contents ranging from about 10% to considerably over 60% were determined in the polymers studied.

An independent spectroscopic method to determine the amorphous content of polyethylene has been described by Miller and Willis (1135a).

The structure of the crystalline regions of polyethylene has been worked out in detail by Bunn (77) by means of x-ray crystallography, and confirmed by electron-diffraction measurements [e.g. (488)]. Very similar to that of a solid low molecular weight paraffin, the unit cell for crystals of the high molecular weight hydrocarbons is orthorhombic, with $a = 7.40$ A, $b = 4.93$ A, $c = 2.534$ A, the molecules lying fully extended in parallel planes. The molecular skeleton forms a zigzag of carbon atoms, with a zigzag angle of 112° and an aliphatic C—C distance of 1.53 A. Electron density diagrams have been obtained by three-dimensional Fourier syntheses of the x-ray data. They indicate that the apparent shape of a —CH_2— group is far from spherical, the electron cloud being much drawn out in the plane of the three nuclei. Figure 44 shows the electron densities in the plane perpendicular to c which passes through the atomic centers. Figure 45 is a section through one molecule, by the plane passing through all of the carbon nuclei of the molecule.

In a later paper, Bunn (833) considered the molecular characteristics which determine whether a long-chain polymer will crystallize at all, and if so, how readily. The criterion for crystallization is geometrical regularity of molecular structure, but absolute regularity is not essential; an approximation to regularity is sufficient, in that units which indiscriminately occupy corresponding positions in the structure must not be too different in size and shape. On the other hand, it is unlikely that quite regular molecules can be incapable of crystallizing. When such substances are repacked as noncrystalline, it is more likely that they crystallize only with difficulty, and the right conditions have not been found. Reluctance to crystallize is associated with a small interval between relaxation transition, i.e., second-order transition, and melting points. This interval appears to be influenced by the general shape of the molecule, though shape is not the only factor. The temperature range within which crystallization proceeds at an appreciable rate may be still further restricted if the chain repeat distance of the molecules is long, and this same factor may make crystallization at any temperature very slow.

Particular features of the physical behavior of a partly crystalline, long-chain polyethylene can be explained by the general concept developed and elaborately discussed by Mark (99) according to which very long molecules may pass through crystalline and amorphous regions. The mechanical behavior of a polymeric substance is determined by two different tendencies of the chains: the tendency to crystallization under the influence of molecular forces; and the tendency of the kinetic (statistical) rolling or curling up of the main-valence chains.   If the chains are relatively stiff, fit each other well, and the forces between them are large, the first tendency predominates, and rigid, strong, and inelastic fiberlike materials result.

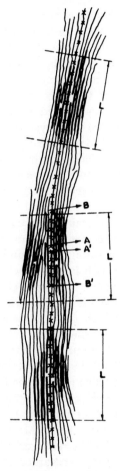

Fig. 46. Main-valence chains going through more than one micella.   (*J. Phys. Chem.*, **44**, 779, 1940.)

When, on the other hand, the chains are very flexible, bulky, poorly fitting, and their mutual forces are small, the statistical effect of entangling predominates, and soft materials with high rubberlike elasticity and peculiar thermoplastic properties are found.

A scheme of main-valence chains going through more than one crystalline region or micella (L) is presented in Figure 46. It is apparent that two adjoining molecular ends (A and A′), which are not inside a crystallized region in the material, can be separated from each other quite easily under the influence of a stress, since they are held together only by weak intermolecular forces. The work required to separate them would be small and, therefore, the tensile strength of the sample would be low. However, when the ends of the two molecules lie inside a crystallized region, they are kept in their positions not only by the forces between A and A′, but also by the van der Waals forces along the two lengths AB and A′B′. In order to separate the two molecules, it is necessary to pull them out of the lattice and to overcome all of the forces along their lengths with which they are held inside of the crystallized region. If parts of the main valence chains which belong to the crystalline region are long enough, then the total energy required to pull them out of this range will be great, because the two ends of the chains are entirely concealed in the center of the crystalline region and do not form a potentially weak spot for the rupture of the filament. These crystallized regions in the total structure have the effect of strengthening the fibers by covering up the chain ends inside the solid structure. The chains are of considerable length, and hence pass through several micellae cementing them together. As Mark further points out, the probability of finding the chain ends inside one crystallized region or another increases with increasing chain lengths. At the same time, the length of the track along which one chain must be pulled in order to separate it from its neighbors is also increased. Consequently, above a certain degree of polymerization, the chain length need no longer have a measurable influence on the tensile strength. The chain ends are distributed at random in the micellae and their effect in producing potentially weak spots is rendered negligible by the crystallizing forces. On the other hand, as the length of the chains approaches the length of the micellae, the end of a chain frequently coincides with the end of a micella, with the result that the tensile strength of the sample will be determined by the weak secondary-valence forces. Thus, Mark assumes the crystallized portions of the material to be the reinforcing backbone of the structure while the unordered regions are to be regarded as weak spots. The mechanical behavior of systems of high molecular weight is thus understood as a combination of crystallized regions with many chains emerging from their surface so that they are imbedded in an amorphous, movable medium formed by the flexible fringes. In this system, the crystallites act like temperature-sensitive crosslinks. The total behavior of the system is therefore influenced by the relative amounts of crystallized and amorphous fractions, the ratio between the average length of the main-valence chains and the average length of the crystallized regions, and the flexibility of the fringes and their sensitivity to swelling and to chemical reactions.

Molecular orientation and its influence on the physical properties of thin films of polyethylene have been studied by Freund and Mark (133), Funahashi (157), and Aiken (280) among others.   Charlesby (175) prepared thin films of polyethylene by placing one or two drops of a solution (0.5%) in xylene on hot water (90°C.) and evaporating the xylene.   The properties

Fig. 47. Thin film of polyethylene between crossed Nicols × 500.
(*Trans. Faraday Soc.*, **41**, 317, 1945.)

of these films were studied by means of electron-diffraction methods.   The structure exhibited a crystalline character, with the following axial spacings in the orthorhombic unit cell: $a = 7.428$ A; $b = 4.9324$ A; $c = 2.532$ A. In addition, the molecules are oriented by the action of the hydrophilic end group $-CH=CH_2$.   These can be incorporated in the structure only if the molecules are tilted so that the b-axis is parallel to the water surface, while the c-axis makes an angle of 56° instead of 90° with the water surface. The crystalline character of these thin films of about 1,000 A thickness contrasts with the amorphous structure of polyethylene in the bulk form. Upon stretching, the structure of thin films of polyethylene is found to consist of crystals in which the c-axis lies nearly parallel to the direction of the applied stress.   The intensity distribution in the electron-diffraction pattern leads to the postulation of intermolecular forces which stabilize the crystals in their new positions, until the temperature is raised to the neighborhood of the melting point, when the film reverts to some extent to its initial orientation.   On a metal surface, polyethylene molecules are found to be relatively mobile and can be oriented mechanically to a structure basically similar to that of stretched films.   The structure of a polyethylene emulsion is found to be very different from that of the crystalline film and quite similar to that of liquid polyethylene, being of a rather amorphous character.   There persists, however, evidence of a small portion of crystalline polyethylene.

Examination of suitably prepared thin films of polyethylene in the polarizing microscope between crossed Nicols was found by Bunn and Alcock (174) to show the existence of birefringent regions typical of spherulitic aggregations of crystals.   A spherulite consists of a large number of crystals radiating in all directions from a point, a particular direction of each crystal being consistently along a radius of a sphere.   A photomicrograph of a thin film of polyethylene between crossed Nicols is shown in Figure 47.   These spherulitic aggregations are believed to be the result of single crystal nuclei acting as centers for the growth of crystals in all directions.   Spherulites can only be seen in polyethylenes composed of average length of over 300 carbon atoms.

Bryant (281) points out that chain branching places an upper limit on the possible size of both crystallites and spherulites.   Other factors being equal, polyethylenes with the least-branched molecular structures give rise to the largest spherulites.   Spherulite sizes range from the submicroscopic to a few tenths of a millimeter in diameter.   Other factors affecting spherulite size are thermal history and mechanical working.

Careful annealing of polyethylene through the melting point effects realization of the maximum spherulite size permitted by the chain structure. Shock-cooling tends to preserve a more random arrangement with the result that crystalline segments are shorter and spherulite sizes smaller than in annealed material.   Because the spherulites in some shock-cooled specimens border on the limits of optical resolution, such polymers may exhibit unusual optical clarity in thin films.   Vigorous mechanical working immediately prior to shock-cooling decreases the spherulite size still further.

Crystallites in high polymers are conceived by Schuur (767,882) to be small collections of strongly oriented polymers which, on fusing, exhibit marked shrinkage in the direction of orientation.   Particles of amorphous material, therefore, stretch out in a certain direction during crystallization, causing substantial contraction in the other directions, a process termed "auto-orientation."   As the growing crystallite has to be fed from surrounding material, an orientation is initiated in the latter at right angles to the first crystallite.   As a result of this orientation, crystallites are formed there which are oriented perpendicularly to the first crystallite. These crystallites in turn induced orientation in their surroundings, and in this way crystallization becomes autocatalytic in character.   Spherulites owe their origin to the fact that the various sectors in a symmetrical spherical order mutually cancel out their stretching and shrinking tendencies.   In highly crystalline polymers with rapid nuclear formation, there first come into existence numerous randomly oriented nuclei which proliferate to small crystallites.   Wherever these small crystallites become arranged in a suitable position, their relative tensions will be cancelled out and they will grow into a spherulite.   Simultaneously, small crystallites which are in an unfavorable position will be consumed by the growing spherulite, or else oriented in the correct direction and incorporated.   As spherulites commonly measure from 10–50 microns, compensation between the tensions of the various sectors has to take place at long distances.   At higher temperatures, compensation is as a rule found at short distances. Therefore, "spherulites" varying individually come into existence as the crystallites are subject to other influences in addition to "auto-orientation." At very low temperatures, the primary, small crystallites are too stable to develop into spherulites.   The mechanism of crystallization as thus conceived implies that the melting point of a polymer depends not only upon the dimensions and perfection of the crystallites, but also upon the specific arrangements of the crystallites, i.e., the degree to which they stabilize each other by a mutual compensation of tensions.

The present position reached in a general study of the influence of fabrication conditions on the crystalline texture, and therefore on the properties of crystalline polymers, is reviewed by Morgan (866).   The mechanism by which long-chain molecules order themselves into some form of crystalline array is postulated to be one involving nucleation processes, modified to take into account the fact that polymers melt over a range of temperatures, and the nucleation act is followed by preferential growth in the direction of the polymer chains.   This mechanism, with the additional concept of coiling growth, is not inconsistent with the kinetics that fit the crystallization rate processes, on the one hand, and observable structure in crystalline polymers, on the other.   It is considered that lateral accretion of the polymer molecules to the long, helical polymer crystals present results in haphazard branching growth, with the new fibril developing along a path parallel to the parent crystal.   This leads to the formation of coiled families of fibrillar crystals.   This structure appears to be a suitable model on which to explain the many wide-angle and low-angle x-ray observations

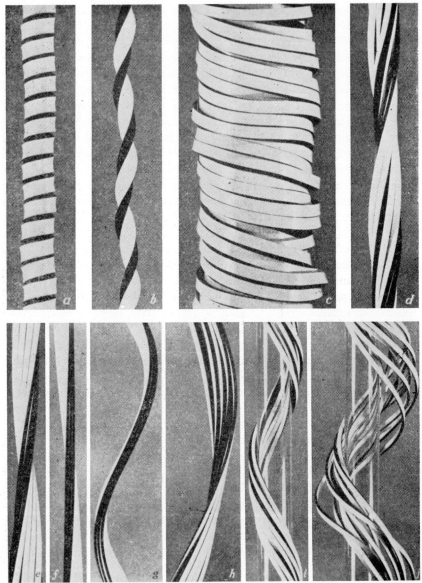

Fig. 48. Models of crystal arrangements. Molecular chain is along length of uncoiled fibril. For polyethylene the white face represents the 100 plane and the black face the 010 plane. The a-axis is across the black plane, the b-axis across the white plane, and the c-axis along the length of the uncoiled fibril.

Continued on next page

that have been made at various stages of the straining and relaxing of crystalline polymer filaments. Models of crystal arrangements are shown in Figure 48.

Birefringence, x-ray, narrow-beam x-ray, and infrared studies by Keller (611,745,746,976) and Keller and Sandeman (475a,977) have yielded experimental data that appear consistent with this arrangement of flat ribbons wound so as to form helices. Various positions of the unit cell in the helix, relaxed and in a state of elongation, are shown in Figures 49 and 50. When crystallization takes place while the melt is flowing, the flow produces lines of high nucleus density, leading to growth of the crystallites in all directions perpendicular to the direction of drawing. This results in elongated aggregates of helices, and the alignment of these complex units produces a unique type of orientation, which has been established from various angles. This row-orientation is shown in Figure 51.

Essential features of the crystallization of unoriented high polymers from the molten and supercooled liquid conditions were outlined by Bryant, Pierce, Lindegren, and Roberts (936) to provide a background for a proposed structure and mechanism of growth of spherulites. Homogeneous and heterogeneous nucleation mechanisms of crystalline growth were discussed. Spherulites are recognized as crudely oriented spheroidal aggregates of crystallites and their attached amorphous regions. Bryant *et al.* propose that a spherulite originates from a single nucleus and that growth proceeds thence in a statistically radial fashion until all crystallizable domains are utilized or until growth is arrested due to increasing viscosity of the medium. It is assumed that crystallite growth occurs by lateral accretion of suitably oriented molecular segments, and that nucleation proceeds from one crystallite to another by means of fine streamers of crystalline order, called protofibrils, which may grow either by longitudinal extension along fringes, or by lateral aggregation of very short segments. The predominant shapes of the crystallites are believed to determine the structure and optical properties of the spherulite. Bryant *et al.* prefer a

---

(*a*) Independently helically coiled single fibrillar crystal. (*b*) Twisted crystal obtained by fully extending (*a*). (*c*) Family of coiled fibrillar crystals. (*d*) Fully extended version of (*c*). (*e*) and (*f*) Representing the knitting-together of the drawn structure by crystallization of the inter-fibrillar amorphous material. (*g*) First stage of heat relaxing. The stronger cohesive forces are in the white plane, and separation of the structure will result in ribboning and the tilting of the white plane. (*h*) Further relaxation results in fibrillation into the main elements of the original structure. (*i*) and (*j*) With continued relaxation the fibrillar structure progressively opens up, giving spacings and orientations in accord with low-angle x-ray observations. (*J. Appl. Chem.*, **4** [4], 170, 1954.)

roughly conical arrangement of crystallites around a spherulite radius to a helical arrangement.

The study of the spherulitic structure of crystalline polymers with the

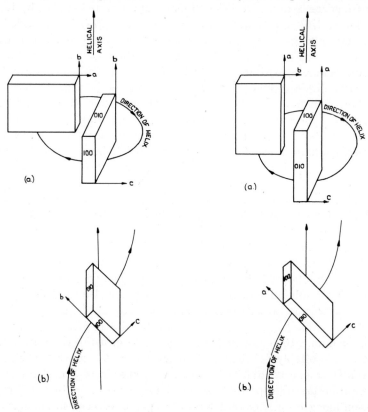

Fig. 49. The position of the unit cell in helix I; the *a*-axis is perpendicular to the helical axis. (*a*) The helix is closely coiled (helical angle ≈ 0°) with the *c*-axis perpendicular to the helical axis. (*b*) The helix in an intermediate state of elongation. (*J. Polymer Sci.*, **15**, 35, 1955.)

Fig. 50. The position of the unit cell in helix II; the *b*-axis is perpendicular to the helical axis. (*a*) The helix is closely coiled (helical angle ≈ 0°) with the *c*-axis perpendicular to the helical axis. (*b*) The helix in an intermediate state of elongation. (*J. Polymer Sci.*, **15**, 35, 1955.)

polarizing microscope was continued by Keller (978). Polyethylene (generally Alkathene 70) was fused at about 160°C. and crystallized in the form of both plugs and films. The spherulites showed the usual straight cross-extinction pattern. At the higher temperature of crystallization, this cross was less regular, bushy in appearance. In samples crystallized at 80°C. and above, a closely spaced, dark ring system was observed in addition to the cross, as shown in Figure 52. The spacings between the rings became increasingly narrower at lower temperatures of crystallization, until they could not be resolved any longer. This ring system was never quite regular and, under the highest power, the rings could often be resolved in a system of irregular lines changing their position along the radius with slight alteration of the focus.

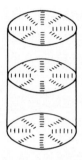

Fig. 51. Schematic representation of an ideal "row," showing three cross sections. The radiating rows of equidistant lines represent the helices. The structure of the helices is as shown in Figure 49 (a). (J. Polymer Sci., 15, 41, 1955.)

The growing spherulites are considered a crystalline part of the crystallizing melt. They are radiating fibrous structures, and the various observed extinction effects are interpreted by Keller in terms of fibrous units. These extinction effects varied for a particular substance with conditions of crystallization. Apart from the usual Maltese crosses, zigzag and ring-shaped extinction lines were observed between crossed Nicols. The zigzag lines were interpreted as resulting from the index ellipsoids lying along elongated helical paths, while the most plausible explanation of the rings is given by closely coiled or strongly twisted arrangements of the index ellipsoids.

Later papers by Keller (979, 980) deal with the problem of the molecular orientation in polymer spherulites, and with the geometrical factors in spherulitic growth and the fine structure.

The investigations of spherulite structure have thus far been confirmed by examination with the light or the electron microscope. An examination of the crystals in the very early stages of their formation has been described by Price (1015). Crystal development in polychlorotrifluoroethylene was studied by means of light scattering.

The infrared absorption band near 13.8 μ which arises from the rocking vibration of methylene groups in polyethylene was studied systematically by Stein and Sutherland (883b). This band exhibits in unoriented crystals of n-paraffins two components of equal intensity below the transition point; only the higher frequency component is found above the transition temperature and in the liquid state. In solid cold-drawn polyethylene, the two components are of unequal intensity, the low frequency component

Fig. 52. Section of polyethylene crystallized at 99°C. Crossed Nicols ×900. (*J. Polymer Science*, **17**, 291, 1955.)

being the stronger; in liquid polyethylene, only the lower frequency component is found. Polyethylene was studied in various states of crystallinity and orientation, with both polarized and unpolarized radiation. The results obtained may be consistently interpreted by attributing the higher frequency component to crystallites in the polyethylene, and by assuming that the lower frequency component is due partly to the crystalline and partly to the amorphous form of the polyethylene. The doubling of this frequency is believed to arise from some interaction between methylene groups which is peculiar to the crystalline state of long-chain n-paraffins below their transition points.

Confirmation of the stable coexistence of crystalline and amorphous regions in polyethylene and polyperfluoroethylene was further furnished by the nuclear magnetic resonance studies of Wilson and Pake (776a). The rigid crystal lattice is characterized by a broad absorption line; a narrow line similar to that observed for liquids is found in the amorphous zones. Decomposition of the complex resonance lines resulted in an estimated degree of crystallinity of about 64 ± 5% for the polyethylene, and about 72 ± 5% for the polyperfluoroethylene.

Dole, Hettinger, Larson, and Wethington (599) have contributed a statistical treatment of crystallite-length distribution based partly upon experimental and partly upon theoretical considerations.

Special crystallization and orientation phenomena in different polyethylenes have been discussed by Natta and Corradini (868). The crystalline structures of various types of linear and branched-chain polyethylenes and of polymethylenes were investigated (molecular weight ranges, 10^3–10^6). The polyethylenes and polymethylenes obtained by ionic polymerization show high crystallinity and rhombic structure of the paraffin. Products with low molecular weight (less than 3,000) were entirely crystalline (size of crystals, 500–1,000 A); those with higher molecular weight contained a smaller percentage of crystalline portion and smaller crystals (300–400 A). The investigation of orientation by the formation of films and stretching showed that moderate mechanical treatment broke the crystals, but not the molecules from which they were formed. It was observed especially on stretched material that in certain zones the zigzag line of the paraffin (*trans*-compound) isomerizes to the *cis*-configuration. These zones show different orientation, if the product is stretched to 50% or to 500%.

The effect of temperature on the crystallinity of polyethylene was investigated by Hunter and Oakes (179) by measuring density changes in the material. The observed specific volume of a sample is assumed to be related to the proportions and specific volumes of the crystalline and amorphous material by the expression

$$V_{obs.} = X \cdot V_{cryst.} + (1 - X)V_{amorph.}$$

in which X = weight fraction of $=CH_2$ groups in the crystalline form. The specific volume of the polyethylene crystal is 1.00 at room temperature (77); its volume expansion coefficient is assumed to be approximately 6×10^{-4} cc. per cc. per °C. From these data and the thermal expansion coefficient-temperature curve (Figure 53) the percentages of crystalline material at various temperatures have been calculated. These are presented in Table XXII.

The density of molten polyethylene was found to show little or no dependence on average molecular weight. However the temperature at which crystalline material first appears on cooling is raised by increase in molecular weight. Specimens of different composition differ markedly in density at 100°C. and consequently in their proportions of crystalline material at this temperature. Above 60°C., no severe hindrance to the setting up of an equilibrium between crystalline and amorphous phases was noted. There also appeared to be no bar to the shift of equilibrium with temperature, or to change in density of the amorphous regions with temperature

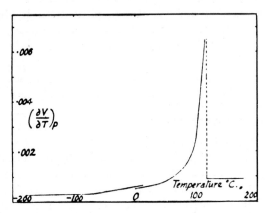

Fig. 53. Thermal expansion coefficient-temperature curve. (*Trans. Faraday Soc.*, **41**, 53, 1945.)

TABLE XXII

Crystalline Material at Various Temperatures

Temperature,°C.	0	20	40	50	60	70	80	90	95	100	105	110	115
Wt. % of crystalline material	55	55	55	55	55	55	50	45	45	40	35	25	10

Source: *Trans. Faraday Soc.*, **41**, 53 (1945).

by segmental movement. Below 60°C., the ratio of crystalline to amorphous material appears to be constant, although segmental adjustment with temperature changes continues in the amorphous regions. There are some indications that this may cease at a subnormal temperature.

The effect of temperature on the structure of polyethylene was studied by Charlesby (176) over a range extending from the temperature of liquid oxygen (−183°C.) to the temperature at which polyethylene exists in the liquid condition (169°C.). It was established that, as with much lower polymers, the ratio of the two axes, a/b, increases with temperature and tends to the value for a pseudohexagonal structure. Since fusion first sets in, however, this value is never attained. A change from a crystalline to an amorphous pattern occurs at temperatures below those generally taken as the melting point, but in agreement with that for which polyethylene transforms from a waxlike to a more transparent solid. The transition of structure extends over a number of degrees, and in this interval crystalline and amorphous patterns are superimposed. Orientation present in crystalline films is retained when the films are heated to temperatures well above the melting point and subsequently cooled. There is a remarkable similarity between the patterns of a polyethylene emulsion at room temperature and molten films of the polymer. This is taken as an indication that the intermolecular spacings and orientation must be similar, and hence that a polyethylene emulsion exists as a supercooled form of liquid polyethylene. In the molten condition, polyethylene presents an amorphous structure, represented in the electron-diffraction pattern by three haloes at 4.6 A, 21.5 A, and 1.22 A, that at 4.6 A being the most sharp and intense. Over a range of several degrees, the amorphous and crystalline types of structure coexist throughout the film. The conservation of the crystalline orientation initially present in the films, even when these are heated to 168°C., shows that the molecular arrangement is not entirely random, even at temperatures well above the melting point.

Crystallinity of polyethylene as a function of temperature was also investigated by Trillat, Barbezat, and Delalande (489,490). The weight ratios of amorphous and crystalline phases were determined from the ratio of the x-ray intensity of the amorphous halo to the intensities of the (110) and (200) crystalline diffractions for a sample of polyethylene having a molecular weight of 15,000. It was found that the proportion of the amorphous phase increases gradually with temperature from 20–80°C., and it is the only phase present from 120–180°C.

In further x-ray studies, Natta and Corradini (868a) determined the crystallinity of highly crystalline linear polymethylenes as a function of the temperature and compared the variation of crystallinity with that of more or less branched polyethylenes. Linear polymethylenes were found to keep their high degree of crystallinity up to temperatures of about 110°C., while a gradual variation of crystallinity with temperature was observed for branched polyethylenes, in agreement with the dilatometric behavior of these samples. Completely amorphous polyethylenes were obtained by attaching one C_2H_5 branch for every twenty carbon atoms of a polyethylene of medium crystallinity. It was found that when in chains such as $(CH_2—CHR)_n$, the R groups have a greater size than fluorine, the polymers are generally amorphous; one may expect a crystalline structure only when there is a regularity in the steric configuration of asymmetric carbon atoms.

Brown and Reding (715) determined the melting points and temperatures for the onset of crystallization of a series of polyethylenes of varying molecular weights and degrees of chain-branching by observing the 13.7-micron crystallinity band of the infrared spectrum. They showed that an increase in chain-branching decreases the melting point considerably, whereas a decrease in the molecular weight, at least in the range studied, lowers the melting point only slightly. On the other hand, an increase in chain-branching decreases, but a decrease in molecular weight apparently increases, the temperature at which crystallization starts at any given rate of cooling. The temperature for the onset of crystallization, the melting point, and the isothermal rate of crystallization of polyethylene were all found (877) to decrease with increasing chain-branching. In the molecular weight range studied, the melting point was shown to be independent of the molecular weight. The temperature for the onset of crystallization at any given rate of cooling appears to increase as the molecular weight is decreased. The isothermal rate of crystallization becomes much greater as the crystallization temperature is lowered. However, at a given temperature, the rate is affected only slightly by a change in molecular weight and is primarily a function of the degree of branching.

Kaufman (743) investigated the development of crystallinity in polychlorotrifluoroethylene (Kel-F) by x-ray methods at temperatures below the first order transition temperature of 211°C. Quick quenching of the heated polymer to a point below its transition temperature gives a glass-clear product with a low-intensity, broad diffraction line characteristic of a relatively disordered, amorphous structure. Extensive crystallinity with increasing opacity is developed by lengthening the residence time of the polymer at temperatures between 190°C. and the transition temperature. The increase in crystallinity is accompanied by a splitting of the broad amorphous line into two strong and relatively sharp lines, with less intense lines at the side. For a given heat treatment, the degree of crystallinity varies inversely with molecular weight. Fiber diagrams were obtained from highly crystallized fibers prepared by hot-drawing of the polymer. The patterns varied with the degree of orientation. The repeat distance along the fiber axis is 35 A. The unit cell is hexagonal with $a = 6.5$ A and $c = 35$ A. A spiral-chain structure accounts for the extraordinarily long fiber spacing; a planar zigzag chain structure is excluded. The calculated density is 2.10 g./ml.

Brittleness of polychlorotrifluoroethylene was observed by Reding and

Brown (876) on cooling the resin slowly from the melt, or on heating for prolonged periods at a temperature slightly below the melting point. The polymer chains in the spherulites of the resin were found to be oriented in such a manner that there are cleavage planes parallel to the spherulite radii; these spherulites form regions of weakness in the polymer, and size and perfection of the spherulites are correlated with the brittleness and breakdown voltage of the polymer. To minimize these undesirable properties, the size and perfection of the spherulites must be reduced.

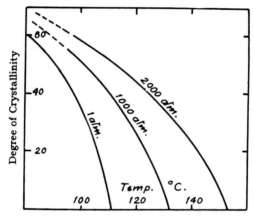

Fig. 54. Effect of pressure on degree of crystallinity near the melting point (approximate). (*Trans. Faraday Soc.*, **45**, 211, 1949.)

The effect of pressure on the degree of crystallinity of polyethylene in the range 100–160°C. is shown in Figure 54, taken from Parks and Richards (413). The high compressibility of solid polyethylene can be attributed to an increase in the proportion of the more dense material under pressure.

The kinetics of the crystallization of polyethylenes was recently studied by Kovacs (858b, 896, 1135). A dilatometer of the Bekkedahl type was used in which the reservoir was inclined about 90° to the axis of the capillary to prevent the melted polymer from dividing the dilatometer liquid (mercury) into two or more portions. The polyethylene samples were first degassed and desiccated under vacuum in the presence of P_2O_5 for several months; their weight was of the order of 1 gram.

Polyethylene, when rapidly cooled below a certain temperature, ceases to be in a state of thermodynamic equilibrium, and an isothermal time-dependent contraction of the volume is observed. Two concurrent processes are assumed to be responsible for this effect: (*a*) a rapid "exponential" contraction attributed to the autocatalytic formation of crystalline phase, and (b) a slow "logarithmic" contraction due to some rearrangement of the amorphous phase.

The apparent temperature of fusion of polyethylene is, according to Kovacs, a kinetic singularity which depends not only on the characteristic duration of the experiment, but also on the direction of the temperature variation: reheating or cooling. Therefore, if it is desired to determine a characteristic physical constant of polyethylene or any other crystallizable polymer, in which the determination has a "temperature direction," it is necessary that the sample be in a reproducible state, since it is never in equilibrium. Such a state can be obtained after a conventional thermal treatment, which may be defined by a series of temperatures and times, the starting temperature being well above the generally assumed fusion temperature.

This concept is emphasized by observations reported by Grams and Gaube (961) on high-density (Ziegler) polyethylene. On storage at temperatures of 60°C. up to the crystal melting point, an after-crystallization is noted which expresses itself in increased values for density and mechanical properties. The amount of after-crystallization is greater the lower the initial density (quenched material), and the higher the temperature at which the material is stored. This phenomenon does not, however, induce brittleness in polyethylene samples. At room temperature, no after-crystallization was noted in the course of one year.

5.2. Cold Drawing and Molecular Orientation

The microstructure of polyethylene can be altered physically by cold-drawing, resulting in orientation of the crystalline regions with an attendant increase in tensile strength. The application to polyethylene (of any except the softer grades) of a gradually increasing tension up to a certain critical value causes a gradual elongation. When tension is increased beyond a certain point, the material yields abruptly and is stretched to several times its initial length before any appreciable increase in tensional stress develops (145,162). Typical stress-strain curves for polyethylenes of various types are shown in Figure 55 from a paper by Bryant (281).

Measurements of the optical anisotropy induced by the application of known stresses were used by Kolsky and Shearman (146) to investigate the orientation and structural changes in polyethylene and other plastics. Another method to study the changes of the elastic properties of plastics with orientation and degree of crystallinity was recently described by Müller

(997d). Here, the velocity of sound is determined in filaments of poly-ethylene and other polymers subjected to cold-drawing.

The physical changes occurring during cold-drawing may be visualized as follows. During the initial stages of stretching, an orientation of the spherulitic aggregates or crystallites takes place which can be detected by

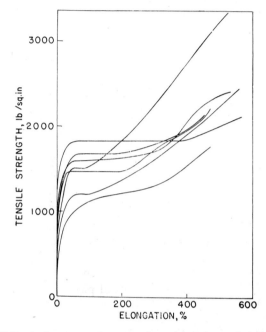

Fig. 55. Typical stress-strain curves for polyethylenes of various types: plotted from measurements made with microextensometer; stress based on initial cross-section. (*J. Polymer Sci.*, **2**, 558, 1947.)

measurement of the birefringence or by x-ray photography. On cold-drawing, the crystallites are pulled into approximately parallel orientation, the long molecules becoming parallel to the direction of drawing. During the process the crystals may to some extent be broken, but there may also be some reunion, since recrystallization may occur to a limited degree. On heating at temperatures below the melting point, this state of order tends to disappear, and the specimen retracts. The orientation can, how-ever, be removed completely only by heating above the melting point. In the case of polyethylenes of very high molecular weight, i.e., of very high liquid viscosity, extrusion or stretching results in some residual orientation of the molecules even above this temperature. It is of interest to compare this phenomenon with the stretching of rubber, where the rubber molecules themselves are oriented by stretching until crystallization takes place. This disappears on releasing the stress, since the freedom of rotation in unsaturated, substituted chains is greater than in the saturated polyethylene chains at room temperature. However, rubber at low temperatures will crystallize and will also show the phenomenon of cold-drawing.

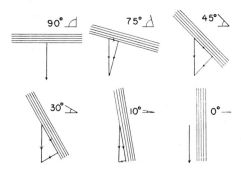

Fig. 56. Distribution of applied tension between lateral and longitudinal cohesive forces. (*J. Polymer Sci.*, **2**, 561, 1947.)

The mechanism of cold-drawing has been studied by Bryant (281). He considers it to be largely a rheological phenomenon, depending upon the relative weakness of the component of van der Waals' forces resisting lateral displacement of polymer molecules relative to molecules of the same species. Tension applied to the side of the polyethylene chains can increase the intermolecular spacing sufficiently to reduce the rather large force opposing the slippage of one molecule past another, provided the tension is applied at right angles to the chain. However, this advantage should decrease the smaller the angle between the direction of tension and the long dimension of the molecules. In the case of direct pull along the length of the molecules, there would be no tendency to separate, hence no diminution of the opposing van der Waals forces. Figure 56 shows the distribution of an applied tension between the components of the cohesive forces. Since there are numerous amorphous regions with somewhat reduced van der Waals' forces, these could serve as foci for the applied tension, so that it could more readily result in slippage. The rather low elongation of certain spherulitic polyethylenes may be due to crosslinkages; in others, a large, permanent amorphous content caused by extensive chain-branching appears to cause a similar result. The increased tension required in the later stages of cold-drawing is explained by the progressively smaller angle between the length of the molecules and the direction of applied tension. The observation that polyethylene with a high amorphous content has a low yield point is explained on the basis of the smaller magnitude of overall van der Waals forces operating between amorphous segments of chains. To explain the fact that the longitudinal breaking strength of some grades of polyethylene is increased as much as 60% as a result of redrawing, it is assumed that, in the presence of about 30% amorphous content, a single cold-drawing does not align the molecules as completely as sterically possible, and that this deficiency is largely rectified by redrawing.

X-ray diffraction patterns of oriented polyethylene indicate that the preferred direction of the crystallite-chain axis does not coincide with the direction of elongation after initial stretching but is inclined to it. As the elongation is increased, the crystallite orientation changes, until at elongations of about 500%, the chain axes practically coincide with the stretching direction. From an analysis of such patterns, Brown (385) concluded that, at elongations up to 200%, the long-chain axis of the crystallite is inclined at an angle of 64° to the stretching direction. On the other hand, Krimm (614) has taken the position that this analysis is not consistent with an angle of inclination of 64°, but rather the complement of this, *viz.*, about 26°. The inconsistency is held to arise from failure to distinguish between a direction in the real lattice, defined in terms of unit cell translations, and one in the reciprocal lattice, defined by the normal to a set of planes. Thus, the angle between the (001) and (011) directions in the real lattice of polyethylene, 62°48', is not the same as that between the vectors from the point of origin to the points (001) and (011) in the reciprocal lattice, which is 27°12'. The movement of the (011) reflection to the meridian would therefore imply a tilt of 27°12' with respect to the stretching direction.

The stretching and relaxation of polyethylene monofilaments have been studied by Horsley and Nancarrow (543). After extending and relaxing monofilaments 50 mils in diameter, micro x-ray diffraction patterns were made with a circular beam of 8 mils diameter at different positions in the region of the neck. When stretched at room or cold (−55°C.) temperatures, orientation in the direction of the (011) axis occurs at low stresses. Necking does not appear when the filament is extended at 96°C. Here, the crystallites align themselves gradually with their chain axes parallel to the fiber axis. The preferred orientation changes nonrandomly when stretched fibers are relaxed at 110°C. The chain axis parallel to the direction of stretch becomes perpendicular to this direction, and the crystallites align with their (100) or a-axis parallel to the fiber axis. The preferred orientation follows the contours of the neck at the edge of the specimen. The angular shift of the (110) maxima is about 27° in extension and 34° in relaxation, which is in agreement with calculated values. The orientation of the (011) axis is interpreted as the first step in the stretching mechanism. Shearing can take place easily here, since the chain makes an angle with the direction of stress. The torn-off portions of crystallites are then oriented in the final stage, with their chain axes parallel to the fiber axis.

Pierce, Tordella, and Bryant (623) have presented evidence for a second crystalline modification of polyethylene occurring in films subjected to the mechanical process of redrawing. The modification shows two strong crystalline interferences in the x-ray pattern, corresponding to spacings of 4.23 A and 4.55 A. Four to seven successive redrawings were necessary to obtain a high degree of sharpness and intensity of the new diffraction peaks.

According to Keller (745), a full understanding of the process of orientation can be gained only by taking into account a full range of dimensions, from microscopic units to molecules. The drawing of a polymer is assumed to affect all structural units present in the undrawn state, orienting those of elongated shape and uncoiling those capable of deformation. In terms of this morphology, the crystalline unoriented polymer consists of spherulites which themselves are built of helically coiled ribbons. The orientation of the molecules averaged over the whole material is random. The fully oriented polymer consists of these helical ribbons aligned and uncoiled, resulting in perfect fiber orientation with the molecules parallel to the fiber axis. This alignment and uncoiling of the submicroscopic and microscopic structural units can occur either simultaneously or in stages. This model enables explanation of the phenomenon of preferential tilt of the chains with respect to the fiber axis, anomalous orientation effects, and peculiarities in the drawing-relaxation process. It is particularly useful for the special case of perpendicular orientation. At the same time, it eliminates the geometrical difficulties encountered by assuming unidirectional tilt, zigzag arrangement, or conical arrangement.

Richards (564) noted oriented overgrowth of paraffin wax crystals from solution on the surface of cold-drawn strips of polyethylene and of polyethylene sebacate, but not on oriented gutta percha, rubber, nylon, or polyethylene terephthalate. The conditions under which oriented overgrowth can occur are similar to those for mixed-crystal formation, although it is only necessary to have similarity in atomic size or atomic spacings in one plane. The distribution of orientation of the individual overgrowth crystals about the direction of cold-drawing is a measure of the perfection of orientation of the surface crystallites in the polymer that have acted as nuclei for the paraffin crystals.   The distributions for the crystalline regions in the film as a whole are determined from the intensity in the polymer x-ray diffraction pattern of spots corresponding to the main crystal spacings at various distances from the equator.   The distribution of angles at which the platelike paraffin crystals lie on polyethylene is narrower than the angular distribution of the crystalline regions in the polymer as a whole. This suggests that the crystallites in the surface are more perfectly oriented than those in the interior.

The deformation of crystalline polymers over a wide temperature range was investigated by Kargin and Sogolova (742).   When exposed to stress,

Fig. 57. Experimental arrangement for determining biaxial stress-strain curve. Diaphragm of polymer, bearing coordinates, was subjected at instant it was photographed (camera behind floodlights) to gauge pressure of 250 p.s.i.   (*J. Appl. Phys.*, **21**, 208, 1950.)

three stages of behavior were noted.   Initially, the strain increases; then a plateau of constant strain follows where the deformation increases considerably (200–300%); finally, another increase takes place.   During the second stage, the sample shrinks in cross section and becomes anisotropic and oriented.   The strain level of the plateau is temperature-dependent, its extent temperature-independent.   Stretch in two directions causes orientation along both.   Polyethylene curves show gradual transitions owing to weak interchain forces, especially at higher temperatures where the polymer appears to be more amorphous.   The sorption ability of polyethylene for hexane was found by Kargin and Gatovskaya (975) to vary with the stretching of the polymer, pointing to a reduction in packing density during orientation.

Fig. 58. Device for applying gas or hydraulic pressure to polymer tube bearing coordinates. Tube is clamped into fittings within steel blocks. (*J. Appl. Phys.*, **21**, 209, 1950.)

Complex stressing of polyethylene has been investigated by Hopkins, Baker, and Howard of the Bell Telephone Laboratories (473). The experimental arrangement used for determining biaxial stress-strain curves of

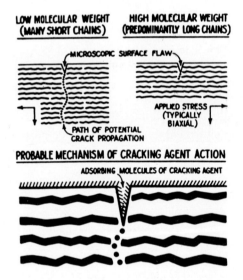

Fig. 59. Simplified scheme of possible cross-section of sheet of biaxially stressed polyethylene (in which one of the stress arrows should be imagined as perpendicular to the page). Crack propagation is shown by dotted lines; electron micrographs of crack replicas indicate that paths may run around crystallites or spherulites. Cross-sectional size of cracking agent molecules should be considered as about same as that of polymer molecules. Replicas have shown that tiny surface flaws are present. (*J. Appl. Phys.*, **21**, 212, 1950.)

polymer sheets is shown in Figure 57, and the device for applying gas or hydraulic pressure to a polymer tube in Figure 58. Strains are taken from coordinates printed on the samples by the silk-screen process. These authors have demonstrated that polyethylene of such molecular weight and structure that it readily fibers or cold-draws to 300–600% elongation by uniaxial tensile stressing may react quite differently under biaxial tension. When biaxial tension in a one-to-one ratio is applied to a diaphragm, some polymers show brittle fracture with less than 20% elongation at break. However, if a polymer having a higher average molecular weight is used, the orientation takes place under complex stresses. Elongation is then usually several hundred per cent before rupture. Variations in crystallinity are also significant. X-ray scattering of stressed samples suggests that preferred glide occurs on certain crystalline planes as the yield point is approached. These are such as to inhibit smooth alignment of the long chain axis in the direction of stressing.

While polyethylene in an unstressed condition is highly resistant to a wide variety of chemical environments, such as alcohols, soaps, and fatty oils, it may fail by cracking when exposed to these environments under polyaxial stress (compare Section 6.2). A possible mechanism of action by a cracking agent on biaxially stressed polyethylene, as proposed by the same authors, is illustrated schematically in Figure 59.

5.3. Molecular Weight Measurement and Distribution

Molecular weight, as one of the factors determining the properties of polyethylenes, is of fundamental importance in characterizing the polymer. It is equally basic to an understanding of the fine structure, and to its correlation with physical and mechanical properties. Molecular weights of high polymers may be determined directly by somewhat complicated physico-chemical measurements, or derived indirectly from viscosimetric determinations. The viscosimetry and rheology of high polymers have become independent fields, the discussion of which is outside the scope of this volume. For experimental and manipulative details, attention is drawn to a recent book by Umstaetter (640), while the recent discussions and investigations of the theoretical aspects of the subject by Flory and Fox (535,536,537) deserve particular mention.

Direct Methods for Determining Molecular Weights

Ebulliometric methods.—A sensitive method for measuring small boiling-point elevations, originally described by Menzies and Wright (15) and improved by Kitson and Mitchell (398) for the determination of polyethylene molecular weights in the region 5,000–20,000, has been applied by Morawetz (557). According to this scheme, a U-shaped differential thermometer which contains water in equilibrium with its vapor is used. One end of the thermometer is in contact with a boiling solution, the other end with the

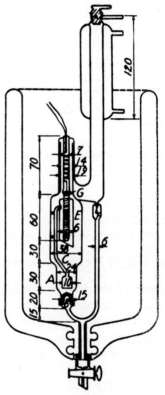

Fig. 60. Ebulliometer (dimensions in millimeters). (*Trans. Faraday Soc.*, **48**, 810, 1952.)

pure refluxing solvent. The temperature difference causes the water to exert different vapor pressures in the two legs of the U-tube and results in a head of water to counterbalance the vapor-pressure differential. Sensitivity is increased by using as solvents liquids of a higher boiling point than that of the differential thermometer fluid. By this method, the number-average molecular weight ($\overline{M}_n$) of an unfractionated sample of Bakelite DYNH (intrinsic viscosity in xylene at 100°C., 1.02) was determined as about 9,000. This is considered to be consistent with a weight-average molecular weight of about 20,000 estimated from the intrinsic viscosities of pure aliphatic hydrocarbons and polyethylene DYNH.

An ebulliometer claimed to be suitable for the measurement of polyethylenes in the molecular weight range of 5,000–30,000 has been described by Ray (625) and is shown in Figure 60. It consisted of a small boiler A, heated internally by a 2-ohm helix of 0.01-inch platinum wire B. Current was supplied from an autotransformer at 0–10 volts. The Cottrell pump C was mounted with its bell immediately over the heater and arranged to deliver boiling solution on the lower half of the thermocouple pocket D, which was wrapped with a helix of fine glass rod to promote spreading of the liquid over its surface. It was protected from cooled reflux by an "umbrella" E with a hole at the top to admit the outlet of the pump. The upper half of the thermocouple pocket was surrounded by a double jacket of vapor, as shown, and the reflux returned to the boiler via a calibrated dripper F. The outlet from the condenser was connected to a silica gel drying tube. The whole apparatus was placed inside a large Dewar flask with an opening in the bottom for the outlet tube. The ground joint between the latter and the stopcock outside the Dewar vessel was cemented with shellac, as it was only rarely necessary to take it apart. The stopcock itself was of capillary bore and was lubricated with glycerol-dextrin.

The thermal element was sealed into its tube with shellac and the two sets of junctions were embedded in Bakelite cement which ensured contact with the walls. The copper leads from the thermal element were coiled in such a way as to ensure contact with the upper part of the thermocouple pocket and thus minimize conduction of heat away from the junction. These leads were insulated with polyethylene and brought out to the galvanometer directly; no switch was incorporated in the main circuit. In order to safeguard the galvanometer when a large temperature difference existed between the junctions as, for example, when bringing a fresh portion of solvent to the boil, a shorting switch was connected in parallel with it.

The galvanometer was very sensitive both to vibration and to fluctuations in ambient temperature; for these reasons it was mounted on a heavy slab of concrete set well below ground level; here a very steady temperature could be maintained and vibration was also minimized.

Water for the condenser was stored in a 20-gallon aspirator at room temperature, and flowed by gravity at 5 ml./min. into an interchangeable reservoir at a lower level.

With toluene as the most suitable solvent, the molecular weights ob-

tained for several grades of I.C.I. polyethylenes are shown in Table XXIII.
The intrinsic viscosities given for comparison were obtained in tetralin
solution at 75°C. A value of 32,000 found by osmometry (354) for Grade
Number 5 is in good agreement with that of 34,000 obtained by the ebulliometric method.

TABLE XXIII

Molecular Weights of Polythene Samples

Grade no.	Intrinsic viscosity[a]	Molecular weight
5	1.09	34,000[b]
7	0.90	14,300
20	0.86	12,000
200	0.69	10,000
700	0.54	9,500

Source: *Trans. Faraday Soc.*, **48**, 811 (1952).
[a] In tetralin solution at 75°.
[b] This sample of grade 5 polythene was found to have a molecular weight of 32,000
by osmometry.

An ebulliometer similar to that described by Kitson, Oemler, and Mitchell
(399) was fitted by Harris (606) with a water-filled differential thermometer
and used for molecular weight determinations of polyethylene in the range
of 1,300–6,000. The solvent for most of the low molecular weight polyethylenes in this range was toluene, but the two lowest were determined in
benzene. Polymer concentrations up to 15% were used.

Cryoscopic methods. Cryoscopic determinations of molecular weights of
polyethylene have been described by Ueberreiter, Orthmann, and Sorge
(639). As the solvent, diphenyl with a melting point of 70°C. and a
cryoscopic constant of 8.35 was chosen. In a subsequent paper, Ueberreiter
and Orthmann (775) proposed phenanthrene as the solvent. Because of its
higher cryoscopic constant of 11.9 and higher melting point, errors due to
traces of moisture remaining in the sample would be eliminated.

Recently, Ashby, Reitenour, and Hammer (1126) reported on an improved cryoscopic technique.

Osmometric methods. Osmotic molecular weight determinations of
Lupolen H (BASF) and of its fractions were carried out by Staudinger and
Berndt (161) at 70°C. in an osmometer designed by G. V. Schulz, using
Ultracella membranes. By this method, the molecular weights obtained
on the same samples in toluene solution were found to be considerably
higher than in a solution of decalin. Viscosimetric studies, also at 70°C.,
showed, on the other hand, that the molecular weights were in all cases
considerably higher in decalin solution than in the other solvents. A com-

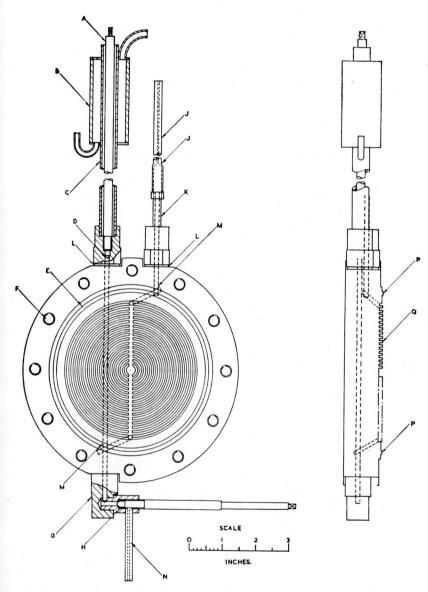

Fig. 61. Osmometer. (A) Upper valve rod for closing cell. (B) Condenser jacket. (C) Filling tube. (D) Upper valve seating. (E) Brass body of cell. (F) Bolt holes for clamping cell together. (G) Lower drainage valve. (H) Lower valve seating. (J) Glass capillary tube. (K) Copper tube. (L) Lead sealing washer. (M) Inner drainage channels. (N) Outlet drainage tube. (P) The two halves of the cell fit together here with a thin lead sealing gasket between. (Q) Rings for supporting membrane. (*J. Polymer Sci.*, **8,** 358, 1952.)

parison of these osmotic and viscosimetric molecular weights of polyethylene
is given in Table XXIV.

TABLE XXIV

Comparison of Molecular Weights

Solvent (70°C.)	Molecular weight	
	Osmometric	Viscosimetric
Toluene	32,000	10,500
Decalin	22,000	16,200

Staudinger and Berndt conclude from the observations obtained by
these two methods that polyethylenes are not molecularly dispersed in
some solvents but are associated into larger complexes. Among the sol-

Fig. 62. Osmometer. (*Makromol. Chem.*, **8**, 28, 1952.)

vents investigated, decalin was found the best solvent for polyethylene
(see also Sections 6.1 and 6.6).

Harris (606) determined molecular weights osmometrically within the
range 18×10^3 to 76×10^3 at 85°C., in xylene as solvent. The osmometer

used was based on the design of Fuoss and Mead (144), but modified as shown in Figure 61. Especially prepared and treated films of collodion were used as membranes. Measurement of the actual pressure was made by a static technique.

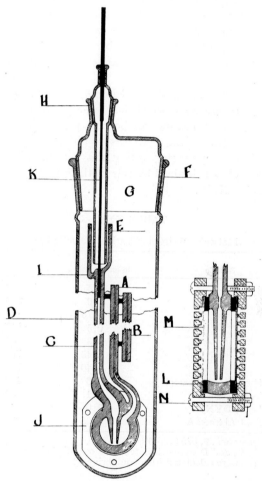

Fig. 63. High-temperature osmometer. (A) Measuring capillary. (B) Reference capillary. (C) Filling tube. (D) 57 mm. diameter jacket. (E) Filling bulb. (F) 60/50 standard taper joint. (G) Closure. (H) 24/25 standard taper joint. (I) Recess. (J) Stainless steel flange. (K) Stainless steel positioning rod. (L) Teflon gasket. (M) Gel cellophane membrane. (N) Stainless steel screw and nut. (*J. Polymer Sci.*, **9**, 575, 1952.)

Films of polyurethane of 0.025-mm. thickness were used as membranes by Ueberreiter, Orthmann, and Sorge (639) in an osmometer similar to that described by Herzog and Spurlin (22) and shown in Figure 62. Triple vacuum-distilled decalin was used as solvent at 70°C.

Pinner and Stabin (623a) found the widely used and simple Zimm-Myerson osmometer (229) unsuitable for high-temperature measurements since it cannot be filled in a vertical position, and designed a compact, robust osmometer capable of being filled by means of a heated pipet without removal from the bath. The construction of this instrument is shown in Figure 63.

Gel-cellophane membranes (supplied by American Viscose Corp., Sylvania Division) were used, which had been previously conditioned in xylene. Although these membranes became progressively embrittled in the course of 7 days at 98°C., there was no observable change in permeability or membrane asymmetry during this period. Molecular weights of various polyethylenes obtained by this method, in xylene as the solvent, are shown in Table XXV.

TABLE XXV

Molecular Weights of Various Polyethylenes

Sample	$h/c_{c=0}$ in cm./g./100 g.	$\overline{M}n$
A	10.5	28,000
B	1.0	300,000
C	0.75	400,000
D	0.5	610,000
E	9.3	34,000
F	0.45	700,000
G	0.40	790,000
H (Fractionated sample)	1.6	197,000
Bakelite DYNH	8.1	39,000
Bakelite DYNJ	7.0	45,000
duPont Alathon A	8.05	39,000

Source: *J. Polymer Sci.*, **9**, 575 (1952).
Values for A, B, C, and D were calculated from osmotic heights extrapolated to zero time, the remainder were calculated from equilibrium (24 hours) osmotic heights.

Osmotic pressures of polyethylene solutions in xylene at 90°C. were also measured by Billmeyer (708) in modified Zimm-Myerson osmometers with gel-cellophane membranes.

The simple osmometer shown in Figures 64 and 65 has been devised by Breitenbach and Forster (712a). In a subsequent publication (935b), the

determination of osmotic pressures of solutions of a commercial polyethylene in xylene at 75°C. is described by the same researchers, and the
advantages of the use of Ultracella membranes (supplied by Carl Schleicher
& Schuell Co., Keene, N.H.), are particularly emphasized.

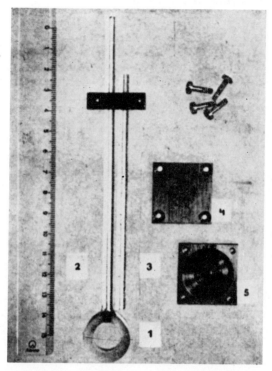

Fig. 64. Component parts of osmometer. (*Oesterr. Chem. Ztg.*, **54**, 346, 1953.)

Light-scattering methods. Light-scattering measurements on polyethylenes which may be carried out essentially by the usual techniques are somewhat complicated by the fact that such measurements must be made at
elevated temperatures to keep the polymer in solution. Billmeyer (708)
used α-chloronaphthalene and, in a few cases, o-dichlorobenzene and
cetane as the solvent. Moore (996) used α-chloronaphthalene. In all
cases, the measurements were carried out on conventional, high-pressure
polyethylenes at 125°C. Light-scattering studies on a commercial
Ziegler-type, high-density polyethylene (Hostalen) were recently reported
by Duch and Küchler (1129; compare also 1024). The experimental

arrangement described in this paper permits light-scattering measurements at temperatures up to 150°C. For the investigated polymers which not only differed in their molecular weights by a factor of 20, but which were also made under various experimental conditions, the following relationship between molecular weight and viscosity was found:

$$[\eta] = 2.36 \times 10^{-4} \bar{M}_w^{0.78}$$

Progress in molecular weight characterization of polyethylene by the light-scattering method based on an improved experimental technique and a refined theory was recently reported by Muus and Billmeyer (1136).

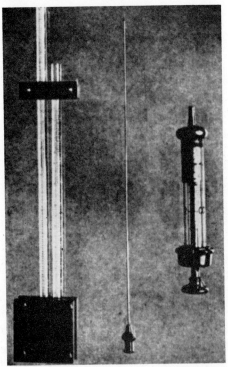

Fig. 65. Osmometer and syringe for filling. (*Oesterr. Chem. Ztg.*, **54**, 346, 1953.)

General comparison of methods. Measurement and significance of the molecular weight of conventional, high-pressure polyethylene were recently discussed critically by Hawkins (966). Since polyethylene, it was pointed out, is generally a mixture of a wide variety of molecules differing in size, it is necessary to express the results as an average molecular weight. The simplest and most useful is the number average $\bar{M}_n$ which is the one obtained by methods depending upon "colligative" properties. Up to a M_n value of 15,000, the ebulliometric method, developed by Ray (625) and subsequently improved by H. Smith, is the most useful and the results are very reproducible, provided a given technique is adhered to.

The region between 15,000 and 25,000 presents some problems since the appearance of frothing makes ebulliometry increasingly difficult as the molecular weight rises.   The osmometric method, described by Harris

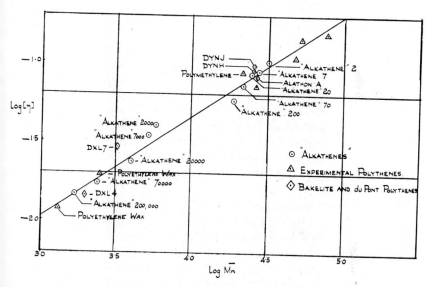

Fig. 66. Relation between number-average molecular weight and intrinsic viscosity.
(*J. Polymer Sci.*, **8**, 361, 1952.)

(606), suffers from the danger of solute diffusion when the molecular weight is too low, but is reliable and reproducible above 25,000. Over the whole range of molecular weights encountered, justifiable comparisons between two samples can be made only if the same technique is used for both.

For the determination of the weight-average molecular weight $\bar{M}_w$, there is at present available the light-scattering technique although, owing to the very high dissymmetries shown by some polyethylene solutions, practical and theoretical difficulties are considerable. It is found that the ratio $\bar{M}_w/\bar{M}_n$ for many polyethylene samples is very high (up to at least 20), showing that polyethylene can have a wide molecular weight distribution (compare Section 5.4).

Viscosimetric Methods for Determining Molecular Weights

For reasons of convenience, it is usually desirable to calculate molecular weights of high polymers from their intrinsic solution viscosities. Because of low solubility characteristics, viscosities of polyethylenes must be determined at temperatures of at least 75°C. or higher. Harris (606) carried out direct determinations of the number-average molecular weights of a variety of polyethylenes by ebulliometric and osmometric methods, and compared these with results obtained with an Ostwald viscosimeter. Covering a molecular weight range of 1.3×10^3 to 76×10^3, the following numerical intrinsic viscosity-molecular weight range relationship was established:

$$[\eta] = 1.35 \times 10^{-4} \bar{M}_n^{0.63}$$

This relationship is shown graphically in Figure 66. It holds irrespective of the degree of chain branching. Even a sample of completely unbranched polymethylene, synthesized by the method of Buckley, Cross, and Ray (464), shows no significant deviation, although the intrinsic viscosity of this crystalline and relatively insoluble material had to be determined at a higher temperature (95°C.) than the other polyethylenes; hence, it is not strictly comparable.

Billmeyer (708) determined the molecular weights of polyethylenes osmometrically and by light-scattering and measured viscosities of polyethylenes in α-chloronaphthalene at 125°C. For some polymers, viscosities were also measured in tetralin solution at 125°C., in xylene solution at 85°C., and in decalin solution at 70°C. Intrinsic viscosities in tetralin at 125°C. and in xylene at 85°C. were identical. Intrinsic viscosities in α-chloronaphthalene were 0.78 times those in tetralin or xylene, reflecting the lower solvent power of α-chloronaphthalene. Viscosities in decalin were 1.15 times those in xylene and tetralin. From these data, number-average molecular weights were calculated, according to the method of Harris (606).

Ueberreiter, Orthmann, and Sorge (639) determined molecular weights of polyethylenes cryoscopically and osmometrically. They derived the following numerical relationship for fractionated polyethylenes (molecular weight range, 2,600–35,000) which describes the molecular weight dependence of intrinsic viscosity in decalin at 70°C.:

$$[\eta] = 3.873 \times 10^{-4} \bar{M}_n^{0.738}$$

Umstaetter's free-flow viscosimeters (147) were used in these studies.

The molecular weight data given in the technical bulletin of one commercial producer of polyethylene (702) are derived by using the Ueberreiter equation. The technical literature of another polyethylene producer (568) presents molecular weights calculated from a modified Staudinger equation, using viscosity data determined in tetralin at 130°C. The following equation is employed:

$$\bar{M}_w = \frac{K_{cm} \log_{10} \eta_r}{C},$$

where

$\bar{M}_w$ = weight average molecular weight;
η_r = relative viscosity;
C = base molar concentration of polymer in tetralin at temperature of determination (4.0 g./l. at 130°C.)/14;
K_{cm} = 4.03 × 10⁻⁴ g./l. solution at 130°C.

Fractionation of Polyethylenes

Ueberreiter, Orthmann, and Sorge (639) fractionated eight polyethylenes (BASF Lupolens) with average molecular weights from 4,000–40,000 by dissolving in toluene at 80°C., adding n-propanol, and cooling. The fractionation apparatus is shown schematically in Figure 67. The solution

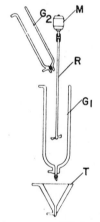

Fig. 67. Fractionation apparatus. (*Makromol. Chem.*, **8**, 23, 1952.)

and precipitation vessel was a cylindrical, jacketed tank (G_1) made of Jena glass, about 5 liters in capacity, and fitted with a drain cock. The drain was placed as close as possible to the jacket to ensure proper heating and to prevent clogging by solid polyethylene. The precipitant was preheated in a jacketed vessel (G_2) of similar form but considerably smaller size. The drain cock of this vessel was placed within the jacket for maximum constancy of temperature.

Contrary to the usual behavior of most polymers, the individual polyethylene fractions did not separate in a swollen state but as flocculent solids. It was possible, therefore, to separate them from solution by means of fluted filters. The process of filtration also had to be carried out at constant temperature to prevent clogging of pores or reprecipitation in the filter after the suspension of precipitate in the solvent-precipitant mixture had left the constant-temperature area. For this purpose, commercial fluted filters were placed in the jacketed copper funnel T equipped with a

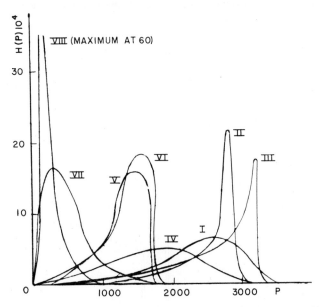

Fig. 68. Mass distribution functions of commercial polyethylenes. (*Makromol. Chem.*, **8**, 39, 1952.)

very short tube. The funnel and the two glass vessels carried the same circulating fluid at a constant temperature. The precipitator and the funnel were covered with watch glasses to prevent evaporation losses. The watch glass covering vessel G_1 had a hole in the middle to admit the delivery cock.

In each case, 10 g. of polyethylene was dissolved in 500 ml. of toluene at 80°C., and propanol was added gradually with vigorous agitation (3,000 r.p.m.) at the same temperature until the solution became turbid, and then dropwise until coagulation set in. The solution was then heated to about 85°C., whereupon the precipitate dissolved completely within a few minutes. In the course of about one hour, the temperature was reduced to 80°C. After another half-hour, agitation was discontinued, the precipitate began to settle and was filtered. The slimy filtered fractions were dried under vacuum at 65°C. and their molecular weights determined. The above cited Ueberreiter equation was used to derive molecular weights from intrinsic viscosities. Table XXVI lists the intrinsic viscosities $[\eta]$, the molecular weights, and the number of fractions obtained for the eight Lupolen samples investigated. The mass distribution functions of these polyethylene samples are plotted in Figure 68.

TABLE XXVI

Description of Lupolen Samples

Number	$[\eta]$	Molecular weight	Number of fractions
1	0.90	37,600	9
2	0.87	34,800	10
3	0.81	31,500	7
4	0.77	29,600	8
5	0.52	17,300	7
6	0.46	14,800	7
7	0.26	6,800	9
8	0.18	4,100	7

Source: *Makromol. Chem.* 8, 21 (1952).

Fractionation experiments by the gradual addition of a nonsolvent to a polyethylene solution have also been reported by Billmeyer (708). Polymers were divided into three fractions by successive additions of dibutyl phthalate to 2% solutions of polyethylene in α-chloronaphthalene at 125°C. After the addition of a predetermined volume of nonsolvent, the solutions were heated to 150–160°C., when all of the polymer dissolved. The solutions were then allowed to cool slowly to 125°C. After 24 hours at 125°C., the solution was poured away from the swollen polymer phase. The latter was dissolved in a small volume of xylene and precipitated in finely divided form by pouring into cold methanol. After the removal of two fractions in this way, the lowest molecular weight polymer was isolated from the remaining liquid by pouring it into a large volume of cold methanol. The precipitates were washed with methanol and dried *in vacuo* at 60°C. for 24 hours.

Fractionation of polyethylenes by extraction, based on a study by Desreux (389), has been described by Desreux and Spiegels (468). The polyethylene is deposited on Filtercell by evaporation from a solution in toluene. As shown in Figure 69, the polyethylene-covered Filtercell is then packed in column B between two layers of Celite. The bottom is formed by a porous glass plate C. The temperature of the column is kept constant by circulation of water through the jacket. Only one solvent, toluene, is used in the extraction process. The extraction temperature is increased step-wise, being kept constant at each step, until all of the fraction soluble at that temperature has been removed. Extraction (solubility) curves of several polyethylenes are shown in Figure 70. The molecular weights were determined by the equation of Richards (226): $\bar{M}_v = 20,000\ [\eta]$.

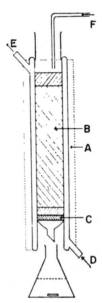

Fig. 69. Extraction column. (*Bull. soc. chim. Belges*, **59**, 478, 1950.)

Consistent irregularities observed by Desreux in the application of this method are attributed by Nicolas (757) to the partial crystallinity of the polyethylene film, whereby the amorphous portions show preferential solubility. This difficulty may be overcome by partially precipitating the polymer in solution as a liquid coacervate which can be separated by decantation. Toluene as the solvent, and a mixture of polyethylene glycols of average molecular weight approximately 225 as the precipitant, are proposed. The integral distribution curve determined by this method is shown in Figure 71.

The fractionation of a polyethylene sample by two methods was described by Socci and Lanzavecchia (883a). The fractionations were carried out both by using two different solvents (xylene and tetralin) and varying the temperature, and by using, at constant temperature, a solvent-nonsolvent mixture in variable proportions.

The formation of gel with radiation in many polymers was found by Charlesby (838b, 839) to offer a possibility of obtaining information as to the initial molecular weight distribution in a manner which has been calculated quantitatively. In order to obtain a full description of this initial

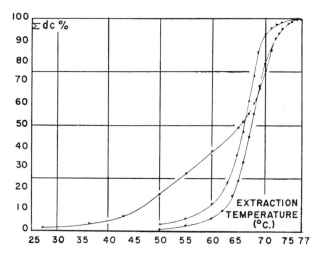

Fig. 70. Extraction curves of different polyethylenes. Curve 1 (left): Grade 7.P.3. (I.C.I.) $[\eta] = 1.05$, Mol. Wt., 21,000. Curve 2 (middle): Grade 2.P.5. (I.C.I.)$[\eta] = 1.17$, Mol. Wt., 22,400. Curve 3 (right): Grade DE2400 (Bakelite) $[\eta] = 1.02$, Mol. Wt., 20,400. (*Bull. soc. chim. Belges*, **59**, 482, 1950.)

distribution, the information derived from a study of the gel fraction must be supplemented by data on the sol fraction.

The theoretical derivation and a detailed description of this method, as applied to polyethylene, are given in a paper by Baskett (823d). Gel fraction curves were measured for a series of polyethylenes and corrected for the complicated effects of chain scission. As a result of this work, the following conclusions were reached: (*a*) it is possible to obtain molecular weight distribution curves by measurement of the amount of gel formed in the irradiated samples; (*b*) molecular weight distribution curves calculated by this method were found to be very wide, with the ratio of weight average to number average molecular weights lying between 5 and 20, thus confirming observations made by other methods; and (*c*) molecular weight distribution curves calculated by this method are similar to those predicted by a theory of chain transfer with dead polymer.

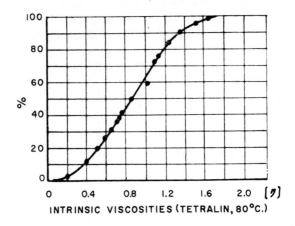

Fig. 71. Integral distribution function. (Alkathene, Grade 20.) (*Compt. Rend.*, **236**, 810, 1953.)

Several patents deal with the separation of polyethylenes into fractions of varying properties. According to Krase in U. S. 2,388,160 to duPont (203), polyethylene fractions varying in physical properties from hard, solid masses to waxy, semisolid masses and intermediate products can be obtained by condensing out the polymer from solution in the ethylene after polymerization. This is accomplished by either lowering the pressure in

TABLE XXVII

Fractionation at Constant Temperature

Run	Synthesis		Frac-tionation pressure, atms.	Melt visc.	Tensile strength at		Percent elongation
	Pressure atms.	Temp., ° C.			Cold draw	Break	
A₁	1,000	195	1,000	0.06	1,230	1,775	580
A₂	1,000	195	1	0.08	1,280	2,090	660
B₁	1,000	198	1,000	0.02	—	1,610	360
B₂	1,000	198	1	20.0	1,100	1,130	125
C₁	1,000	200	1,000	0.01	1,200	1,810	425
C₂	1,000	200	1	1.0	1,050	1,100	250
D₁	1,000	208	1,000	0.002	1,650	1,950	288
D₂	1,000	208	1	0.04	1,360	2,090	510

Source: U. S. 2,388,160, Oct. 30, 1945, p. 2, Krase, N. W. (E. I. duPont de Nemours & Company).

stages under substantially constant temperature; lowering the temperature in stages while maintaining the pressure substantially constant; or decreasing both temperature and pressure concurrently in stages and collecting the products from each stage. Tables XXVII and XXVIII illustrate a number of fractionations of this nature, together with melt viscosity, tensile strength, and the percent elongation of the fractionated product.

TABLE XXVIII

Fractionation at Constant Pressure

| | Synthesis | | Fractiona-tion temp., °C. | Melt visc. | Tensile strength at | | Percent elongation |
Run	Pressure atms.	Temp., °C.			Cold draw	Break	
A_1	1,000	204	191	0.1	1,260	1,760	525
A_2	1,000	204	125	2.0	1,415	1,415	120
B_1	1,000	200	191	0.01	1,230	1,795	480
B_2	1,000	200	125	0.1	1,290	1,960	600
C_1	1,000	200	186	0.1	1,000	1,300	470
C_2	1,000	200	94	0.3	1,190	2,020	640
D_1	1,000	200	190	0.03	1,080	1,630	510
D_2	1,000	200	104	0.3	1,135	1,430	550
E_1	1,000	200	191	0.04	1,060	1,480	480
E_2	1,000	200	106	0.05	1,100	1,430	470

Source: U. S. 2,388,160, Oct. 30, 1945, p. 2, Krase, N. W. (E. I. duPont de Nemours & Company).

Similarly, Hunter and Richards in U. S. 2,457,238 (382) and in Brit. 574,031 (209), both to I.C.I., disclose the fractionation of polyethylene by dissolving it in a paraffinic or olefinic gas of one to four carbon atoms, at a high pressure and temperature. The separated fractions are removed after each step, the higher molecular weight fractions precipitating first.

Melt Viscosity of Polyethylenes

The viscosity of molten polyethylene and its inverse function, the melt index, are both largely dependent on molecular weight, among other variables. The melt viscosity and flow mechanism of homologous polyethylenes were studied by Ueberreiter and Orthmann (637). Depending on the viscosity expected, three different viscosimeters were used. The curves presented in Figure 72 are typical of the melt behavior of polyethylenes. Here, the logarithm of the viscosity is plotted against 1/T. The right-hand branches of the curves express the melt viscosities of a normal liquid; the left-hand branches correspond to a condition in which crystalline regions are dispersed in a "liquid with fixed structure"; the near-vertical, medium portions of the curves indicate the temperature range in which the last remnants of crystalline connections are thermally disrupted. This leads to the conception of the macromolecule as a vibrating string, the vibrations being initiated during thermal energy distribution. The number of nodes

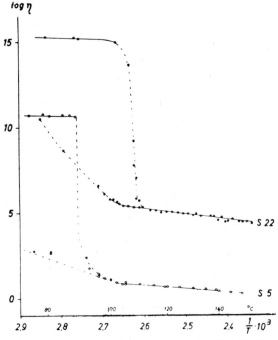

Fig. 72. Viscosity of polyethylenes (molten and as liquids with fixed structure).
(*Kolloid-Z.*, **126**, 141, 1952.)

which act as points of cohesion is small above the melting point; their concentration increases when cooled below the melting point, leading to the formation of a liquid with fixed structure; on further cooling, these nodes may become nuclei for crystal formation. Accordingly, the high viscosities measured in the region of liquids with fixed structure are only apparent viscosities which depend on the pretreatment of the sample and the load to which it is subjected. However, viscosities measured under equal conditions and temperatures appear to increase with the length of the chain.

Nine unfractionated polyethylene samples were investigated; the average molecular weights ranged from 4,000 to 38,000, and melt viscosities from 3 to 10^5 poises. Figure 73 shows this double dependence of melt viscosity on molecular weight and on temperature for the region of the

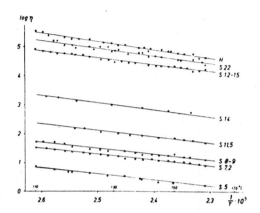

Fig. 73. Melt viscosity of polyethylene. (*Kolloid-Z.*, **126**, 142, 1952.)

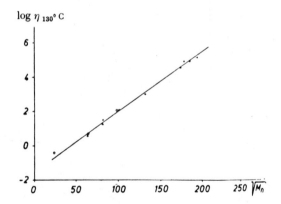

Fig. 74. Melt viscosity at 130°C. *versus* molecular weight of polyethylene. (*Kolloid-Z.*, **126**, 142, 1952.)

true melt. The isotherm at 130°C. which describes the relationship between molecular weight and melt viscosity is shown in Figure 74. This may be expressed numerically by the equation:

$$\log \eta_{130°} = 1.54 + 0.035 \, (\bar{M}_n)^{1/2}.$$

The volume-temperature curve (Figure 75) permits definition of the melting point.

The melting point viscosity is related to the molecular weight of the polyethylene as shown in Figure 76. Numerically, this may be expressed by the equation:

$$\log \eta_F = -1.206 + 0.0351(\bar{M}_n)^{1/2}.$$

Melts of high polymeric substances exhibit elasticity and are capable of a considerable amount of form recovery. This accounts for the "memory

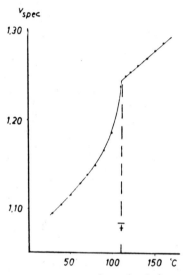

Fig. 75. Volume-temperature curve of a polyethylene. (*Kolloid-Z.*, **126**, 143, 1952.)

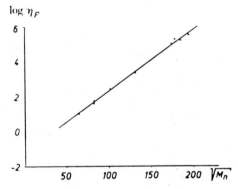

Fig. 76. Melting point viscosity *versus* molecular weight of polyethylene. (*Kolloid-Z.*, **126**, 143, 1952.)

effect," whereby markings in the texture of material extruded through a die replicate obstacles in its flow path; the spontaneous increase in diameter of an extruded rod or filament has also been ascribed to this effect.

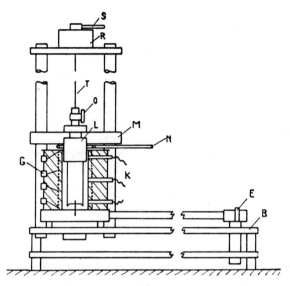

Fig. 77. Schematic drawing of elastoviscometer.   B, steel plate, base, leveled. E, eccentric drive.   G, "pot" with tapped heater windings.   K, thermocouples. L, "plunger."   M, exchangeable inertia disk.   N, supply of preheated nitrogen. O, mirror.   T, torsion-free suspension.   R, S, vertical and horizontal plunger adjustment.   (*J. Polymer Sci.*, **9**, 42, 1952.)

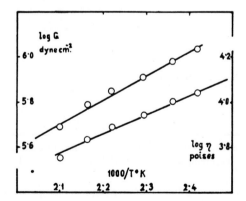

Fig. 78. Temperature dependence of shear modulus (G) and viscosity (η) for polyethylene of molecular weight 35,000.   (*J. Polymer Sci.*, **9**, 46, 1952.)

The elasticity of polyethylene melts was measured by Hoff (608) by inducing shear-resonance oscillations in the region of about 30 cycles per second
at small shear amplitudes.   The apparatus used is shown in Figure 77.

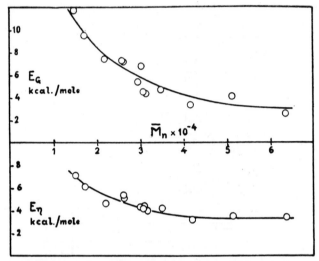

Fig. 79. Activation energies of melt elasticity (E_G) and viscous flow
(E_η) for polyethylenes of different molecular weights.   (*J. Polymer Sci.*, **9,**
46, 1952.)

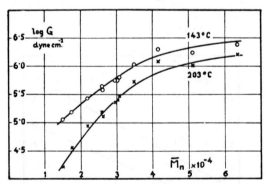

Fig. 80. Molecular weight dependence of the shear modulus of polyethylene
at two temperatures.   (*J. Polymer Sci.*, **9,** 46, 1952.)

The measurements extended over a range of temperatures (130–230°C.)
and of molecular weights (12,000–64,000) at a nearly constant shear rate
and at a small mean shear amplitude.

Shear moduli of the order of 10^5 to 10^6 dynes per sq. cm. were observed and a single relaxation time appeared sufficient to characterize the mechanical behavior of the polyethylene melt at a given temperature.

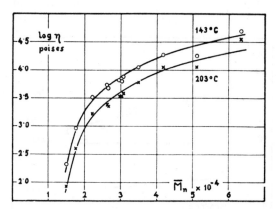

Fig. 81. Molecular weight dependence of the viscosity of polyethylene at two temperatures. (*J. Polymer Sci.*, **9**, 47, 1952.)

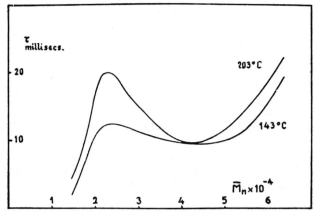

Fig. 82. Molecular weight dependence of the relaxation time of polyethylene at two temperatures. (*J. Polymer Sci.*, **9**, 47, 1952.)

Both shear modulus (G) and viscosity (η) of polyethylene are largely dependent on temperature. Their logarithms, when plotted against reciprocal absolute temperature, give reasonably straight lines for all samples investigated, as shown on Figure 78. The derived activation energies are shown plotted against molecular weight in Figure 79. Shear modulus and viscosity depend in a different manner on molecular weight, as shown in Figures 80 and 81. The relaxation times ($\tau = \eta/G$) were, therefore, found to show the S-shaped molecular weight dependence plotted in Figure 82. This was established by crossplotting from curves such as in Figure 83, which shows the temperature dependence of the relaxation times.

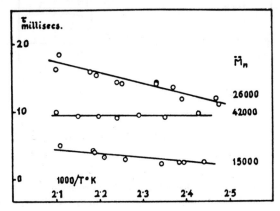

Fig. 83. Temperature dependence of the relaxation times of polyethylene for three molecular weights. (*J. Polymer Sci.*, **9**, 47, 1952.)

The variation of mechanical parameters with temperature and molecular weight may also be brought into relation with known data on the amount of chain-branching.

Melt viscosity and the effect of molecular weight and branching were recently discussed by Peticolas and Watkins (1138). (Cf. Section 5. 6.)

5.4. Chain-Branching, Unsaturation, and Infrared Spectra

Originally, polyethylene was assumed to be a straight-chain, saturated hydrocarbon of high molecular weight. The molecular weight was considered the most important single variable. It is now realized that molecular weight distribution and the range of individual molecular configurations introduce additional variables. As early as 1940, a branched-chain structure of polyethylene was assumed to account for the excess of methyl groups disclosed by infrared analysis. Fox and Martin (94) examined the infrared absorption spectra of two polyethylene samples in the region 2.6–3.8μ and found similarities to the spectra of long-chain normal paraffins. A band at 2960 cm.$^{-1}$, characteristic of the methyl group, was noted in all cases. The proportion of CH_3 to CH_2 groups was found to vary from $1:8$ for the most soluble part of the polyethylenes, to $1:70$ for the whole sample.

Thompson and Torkington (184) explored the reasons for the differences in physical behavior of various types of polymers, including plastics and rubbers. They surveyed the infrared spectra of a number of polymers and their basic monomers, extending the region studied to 20μ. Some typical infrared absorption spectra of high polymers are shown in Figure 84. Included in the study were polyethylenes and cracked polyethylenes, both of

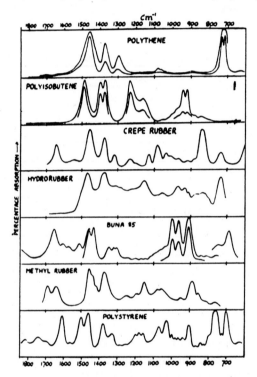

Fig. 84. Infrared absorption spectra of polymers. (*Proc. Roy. Soc. London,* **A184**, 3, 1945.)

different molecular weights. All were found to exhibit four bands which increased in intensity with the cracking and were attributed to the vibration of an unsaturated skeleton. In the polyethylenes studied, one methyl group was found for about every 50 methylene groups. One interesting feature is the weak absorption at about 1,720 cm.$^{-1}$, indicating carbonyl groups. These could arise if oxygen were taken up during the catalytic polymerization. Their presence at intervals along the carbon-carbon chain may markedly affect the electrical properties of the product. Thompson and Torkington also studied chlorinated polyethylenes. As illustrated in Figure 85, continued chlorination leads to well-marked changes in the spectrum, which may suggest the distribution of chlorine atoms along the chain.

Infrared methods were devised by Cross, Richards, and Willis (466) for the determination in ethylene polymers of methyl group concentration, the type and amount of unsaturation, and the nature and quantity of oxygen-containing groups. A strong correlation has been established for

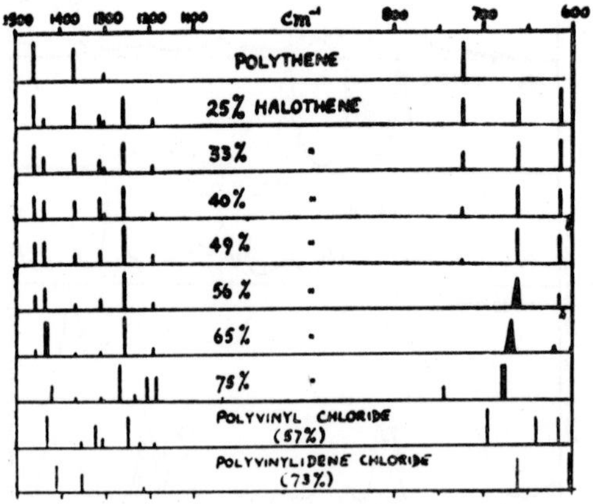

Fig. 85. Infrared absorption spectra of chlorinated polyethylenes. (*Proc. Roy. Soc. London*, **A184**, 3, 1945.)

higher molecular weight polymers between the extent of chain-branching and the degree of crystallinity. This is demonstrated in Figure 86, where the intensity of certain infrared bands, characteristic of methyl groups in crystalline or amorphous regions, is plotted against the degree of crystallinity expressed by the density of the material. Unsaturation determinations on a series of polyethylene fractions covering a wide range of molecular weights show that the total number of double bonds per molecule is of the order of 0.3 to 0.4. This is true both for the original polymer and for its fractions. While the $RR'C{=}CH_2$ type of unsaturation is most common in direct polymers of ethylene, the $RCH{=}CH_2$ type is prominent in low molecular weight, pyrolyzed polyethylenes, and in photo-oxidized polyethylenes. The relationship between the sum of the concentrations of $RCH{=}CH_2$, $RCH{=}CHR'$, and $RR'C{=}CH_2$ double bonds and the iodine number is shown in Figure 87. [Compare also Formigoni (847a).]

The oxygen-containing groups found by infrared methods in natural or oxidized polyethylenes were shown to be mainly ketonic or aldehydic, although some hydroxyl groups exist.

Rugg, Smith, and Wartman (764) investigated by infrared absorption spectroscopy a series of Bakelite polyethylenes having molecular weights ranging from 1,000 to 38,000.   Assuming that a CH_3 group is present at the

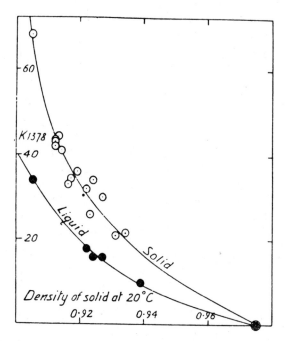

Fig. 86. Relation between chain-branching and crystallinity (density).   The extinction coefficient K is related to the ratio of the number of methyl groups to total number of carbon atoms in the molecule by the equation: $1.35 \times K_{1378}$ = $[CH_3]/[C]$.   (*Discussions Faraday Soc.*, 1950 [9], 238.)

end of each branch and at each chain end, the average number of branches per hundred carbon atoms was calculated by means of the following equation:

$$\frac{\text{branches}}{100 \text{ carbons}} = \frac{14}{15} \left(\% \text{ CH}_3 - \frac{3000}{\bar{M}_n} \right).$$

From the methyl content and the number-average molecular weight of each resin, the degree of branching was found to decrease as the molecular weight increases, a relationship shown in Figure 88. It was further demonstrated that each of the three types of double bond groups present, i.e., RHC=CH₂, RHC=CHR′, and RR′C=CH₂, decreases in concentration

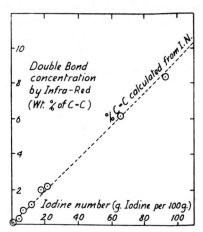

Fig. 87. Relation between sum of concentration of RCH=CH₂, RCH=CHR′ and RR′C=CH₂ double bonds and iodine number. (*Discussions Faraday Soc.*, **1950** [9], 241.)

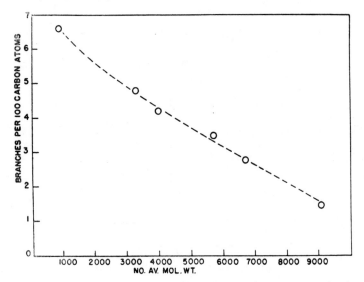

Fig. 88. Variation in chain-branching with number-average molecular weight for a series of polyethylene resins. (*J. Polymer Sci.*, **11**, 1, 1953.)

with increasing molecular weight.   Using polarized radiation, high-resolution grating spectra were obtained on polyethylene films which had been highly oriented by cold-drawing to 500%.   The results show that the CH_3-terminated branches are not predominantly oriented either parallel or perpendicular to the direction of stretch.   It is believed that the chain branches vary in length, with a considerable fraction short enough to be essentially at right angles to the long-chain axis, while others are sufficiently long to be parallel to the long-chain axis in stretched polyethylene. When a stretched polyethylene film is heat-relaxed (110–115°C.), its spectra from polarized radiation reveal the presence of crystallites in which the long carbon-to-carbon chain axes are predominantly oriented at right angles to the direction of stretch.

The two methods of determining molecular weight, by osmotic pressure and by ebulliometry, give results which are not in good agreement.   The number of double bonds would give a more reliable measure of the molecular weight if it could be assumed that there is one double bond per molecule. [See, however, Cross, Richards, and Willis, above (466)].   Experiments with polarized infrared light on stretched polyethylenes indicate that the methyl groups are not oriented; thus, the side chains are short, being substantially ethyl or amyl groups.

Also connected with chain-branching is thermal degradation.   This is assumed to be a chain reaction, initiation of which occurs at weak links. Depolymerization is then propagated preferentially through the points of branching.   [Compare (1142) in Chapter VI.]

Chain transfer, as represented by Equation 3 in Table XXIX (764), is

TABLE XXIX

Proposed Average Kinetic Life History of a Free Radical

Reaction no.	Reaction	Units of reaction	$\Delta F.°$ (kcal)
1	R + Oxygen → R·	1	
2	R· + CH_2=CH_2 → RCH_2CH_2·	5700	−12
3	R· + RCH_2R → RH + $R\dot{C}HR$	160	−6
4	$\begin{matrix} R \\ \diagdown \\ \diagup \\ R \end{matrix} \dot{C}$—$CH_2R$ → $\begin{matrix} R \\ \diagdown \\ \diagup \\ R \end{matrix}$C=$CH_2$ + R·	4	+19
5	$\begin{matrix} R \\ \diagdown \\ \diagup \\ R \end{matrix}$CH—$\dot{C}HR$ → RCH=CHR + R·	1.5	+16
6	$R\dot{C}H$—CH_2R → RCH=CH_2 + R·	1.5	+16
7	R· + R· → RR	0.5	−59

Source: *Ann. N. Y. Acad. Sci.*, **57**, 413 (1953).

suggested as the process responsible for chain-branching. This table attempts to illustrate other reactions which are part of a proposed average kinetic life history of a free radical in producing an experimental resin. Pertinent polymerization and structural data are summarized in Table XXX.

A calibration curve prepared from hydrocarbons of known methyl content is used by Slowinski, Walter, and Miller (1141) to determine quantitatively the degree of branching (methyl content) in ethylene polymers.

TABLE XXX

Some Pertinent Polymerization and Structural Data for an Experimental Polyethylene

Free radical/oxygen atom	1
% O_2 in ethylene	0.0016
% conversion	16
Ethylenes polymerized/free radical	5,720
No. av. molecular weight	20,000
Molecules/free radical	8
% methyl	1.8
Degree of branching	1.4
Branches/free radical	160

Source: *Ann. N. Y. Acad. Sci.*, **57**, 414 (1953).

Another approach toward the detection of branches in polyethylenes was chosen by Ueberreiter and Orthmann (638) in a comparison of unbranched, branched, and debranched polyethylenes. The specific volumes of *n*-paraffins, of fractionated, and of thermally degraded polyethylenes were measured over the temperature range −30 to +150°C., and the "Ordnungsgrad" (or degree of order) calculated from the volume-temperature curve. This is a measure of the degree of crystallinity expressed by the equation:

$$O_r = (V_{am.} - V)/(V_{am.} - V_{cryst.}),$$

where $V_{cryst.}$ = volume of the pure, crystalline material at t°C.;
  $V_{am.}$ = volume of the pure amorphous material at t°C;
  V = mixed volume at t°C.

This relationship is illustrated in Figure 89, in which F denotes the melting point of the polyethylene.

Ordnungsgrad of polyethylenes and of *n*-paraffins of various chain lengths (P) were determined at 20°C. and plotted for comparison in Figure 90.

The lower Ordnungsgrad of the polyethylenes, determined by the number of branches which do not fit into the paraffin lattice, decreases with increasing molecular weight. The distance (z) of two side chains in a molecule is related to its chain length (P) by the equation:

$$Z = 13.5 + 0.537\sqrt{P};$$

to its melting point $(F$ in °C.), by the equation:

$$Z = 21 + \frac{64}{114 - F}$$

in which F is below 114°C.

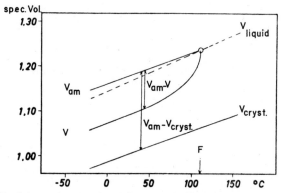

Fig. 89. Scheme for the determination of the Ordnungsgrad from the V-T curve of a polyethylene (molecular weight 23,400). (*Kolloid-Z.*, **128** [3], 125, 1952.)

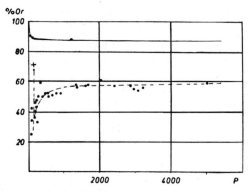

Fig. 90. Ordnungsgrad of polyethylene. Upper curve: *n*-paraffins; ●— denotes fractionated polyethylene, $Or = 60\text{–}3,000/P$ (*Or* in %; P above 100); ● → + — denotes increase in *Or* due to de-branching. (*Kolloid-Z.*, **128** [3], 125, 1952.)

Shock-cooling of solid polyethylene, it was found, does not markedly change the ordnungsgrad determined volumetrically, but only the mutual orientation of the crystallites. Thermal debranching causes an increase in the ordnungsgrad, with longer chains being thermally more unstable than shorter ones.

The concept of chain-branching in polyethylenes has been modified and refined by the investigations of a team of duPont research chemists. In the first of their series of publications, Roedel (762) pointed out that two types of branching, short-chain and long-chain, can occur during the free-radical polymerization of ethylene. These depend upon different polymerization variables and affect different physical properties of the polymer formed. Short-chain branching is believed due to intramolecular hydrogen transfer via transient five- or six-membered ring formation. It is dependent upon polymerization temperature, and mainly affects properties in the crystalline state. The following mechanism is postulated:

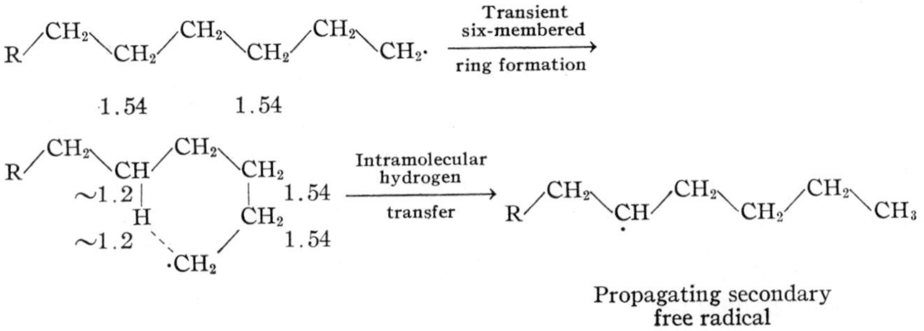

It appears probable that two short chains can originate from the same carbon atom, resulting from a repetition of the short-chain branching mechanism on the same carbon atom after addition of two more ethylene molecules to the secondary free radical. This process gives rise to a tertiary free radical before propagation continues, as shown in the following scheme:

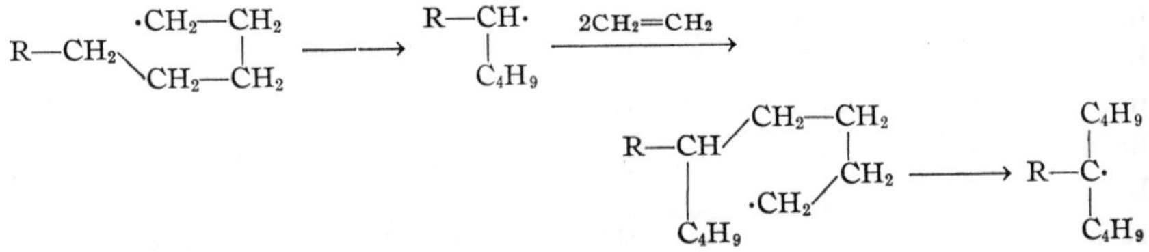

Long-chain branching, assumed to be due to intermolecular hydrogen transfer, is dependent on polymer concentration and mainly affects the rheological properties of the polymer. In accordance with Flory's intermolecular hydrogen-transfer mechanism (53,287), the following scheme is proposed:

$$R_1CH_2CH_2^{\cdot} + R_2CH_2CH_2R_3 \xrightarrow[\text{hydrogen transfer}]{\text{Intermolecular}} R_1CH_2CH_3 + R_2\overset{\cdot}{C}HCH_2R_3$$

| Propagating chain | Dead poly- mer molecule | | Dead polymer molecule | Propagating chain |

In their study on the determination of short-chain branching, dealt with in the second in the series of the duPont papers, Bryant and Voter (716) refined the infrared procedures to provide reliable measures of methyl and ethyl groups through absorption bands at 7.25 and 11.18μ, respectively. Preliminary observations were also made in the $13–14\mu$ region on bands related to branching. Corrections were applied for overlapping absorptions due to methylene and vinylidene groups and for intensity changes in passing from solid to liquid. The following conclusions were reached:

(1) No appreciable number of pendant methyl side chains are present. The methyl and ethyl groups are parts of longer chains most of which are believed to contain four carbons.

(2) Methyl groups in the unfractionated polyethylenes studied range from 0.2 to 4.6 per hundred carbon atoms.

(3) Predominance of short chains over long chains leads to a larger crystallite size and to a degree of crystallinity in better accord with x-ray results.

All these studies have served to establish firmly the relationship between crystallinity and the methyl or ethyl group content. Alkyl side chains, terminated by methyl groups, introduce disorder and thus reduce the fraction of polyethylene chain segments capable of crystallizing.

A new method for the determination of long-chain branching, published as the third in the series of the duPont papers, was developed and applied to polyethylenes by Billmeyer (708). Sensitive only to long branches, the method consists of comparing light-scattering molecular weight, and intrinsic viscosity of a branched polymer with values calculated for a linear but otherwise identical sample. It is found that a polyethylene molecule, in addition to its short-chain branches, has a small number of much longer branches, usually eight to ten per molecule calculated on a weight-average basis. These branches occur predominantly on the large molecules. As a result of the formation of long branches, the distribution of molecular weights in polyethylenes is very broad, and weight-to-number average molecular weight ratios as high as ten- or twenty-to-one are not uncommon.

Kinetic calculations of the effect of long-chain branching on molecular weight distribution are reported by Beasley (704) as the fourth in the series of the duPont papers. The short chains formed by transient six-membered rings are assumed to be distributed at random along all of the long chains. They cannot be part of the normal distribution of long chains calculated here because of their relatively high frequency of occurrence due to a different reaction mechanism. The number and distribution of long-chain branches were calculated, together with detailed molecular weight distribution functions, from kinetic equations describing the process of radical transfer to polymer. The presence of branching causes the molecular weight distribution to be broadened with the appearance of a long, high molecular weight "tail" on the distribution curve. The ratio of the weight-average to the number-average molecular weight may become much higher than the ratio for linear polymers. There is a very broad distribution in the number of branches per molecule, with a large fraction of the polymer remaining unbranched. The distribution functions and their averages are calculated in terms of two parameters. One is the reciprocal of the number-average degree of polymerization of all of the long chains. The other is a branching parameter, derived as the ratio of the total number of monomer units in the branches (number of branches times the average branch length) compared to the total number of monomer units in the polymer.

Results of light-scattering from polyethylene solutions were recently reported by Moore (996). Their interpretation, by considering the mechanism of long-chain branching presented by Roedel and by Beasley, leads to phenomenal molecular weight distributions having, in some cases, weight-to-number average ratios as high as 70 to one. [Compare (1126).]

5.5. Mechanical Relaxation Phenomena

The method of free torsion oscillations has been applied by Schmieder and Wolf (629,766) to the determination of mechanical relaxation properties (torsion modulus, G, and damping, Λ) as a function of temperature (T) for a series of polymers varying in molecular weight, branching, crosslinking, crystallinity, and chain flexibility. The measurements extended over the temperature range of -60 to $+165°C.$, and the frequency range from 0.2 to 60 hertz. A diagram of the equipment used in this study is shown in Figure 91.

The temperature curve of polyethylene obtained by this method is shown in Figure 92. Of the three maxima observed, the highest is due to the "melting" of the crystallites; the lowest to the softening of the "unstrained" amorphous regions containing side chains and chain ends.

The intermediate maximum is due to softening of the amorphous regions in which chains have been "strained" by having their ends clamped into two crystalline regions.   Of these, the high and the intermediate maxima may change their positions with respect to temperature, depending upon preparation and pretreatment of the sample.

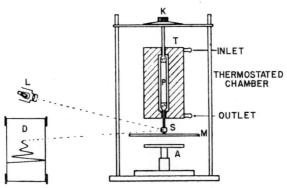

Fig. 91. Apparatus for registering torsion oscillations. A, arresting device. D, trace of oscillation. K, excitation knob. L, light source. M, disk. P, sample. S, mirror. T, temperature chamber. (*Kolloid-Z.*, **127**, 65, 1952.)

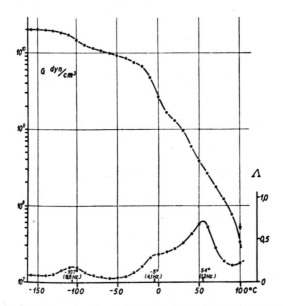

Fig. 92. *G* and $\Lambda = f_{(t)}$ of polyethylene. (*Kolloid-Z.*, **134**, 153, 1953.)

The effect of crystallinity on chlorinated polyethylenes prepared by passing chlorine into polyethylene solutions in carbon tetrachloride was studied. For lower-chlorinater products (0–28% chlorine), the temperature curves are shown in Figures 93 and 94. For higher-chlorinated products (28–77% chlorine), the temperature curves are shown in Figures 95 and 96. These curves are interpreted as follows: The crystallinity of the chlorinated

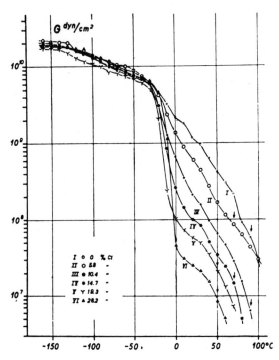

Fig. 93. $G = f_{(t)}$ for lower-chlorinated polyethylenes. (*Kolloid-Z.*, **134**, 162, 1953.)

products decreases with increasing chlorine content, disappearing at about 20% chlorine. The introduction of chlorine has two opposite effects which are superimposed: the bulk of the chlorine atom tends to decrease and its polarity tends to increase the softening temperature of the chlorinated polymer. In the case of the lower-chlorinated, still partially crystalline polyethylenes, the first effect predominates; in the higher-chlorinated polyethylenes, with the polar chlorine atoms crowding along the chain and stiffening it, the second effect prevails.

A recording instrument, shown in Figure 97, has been constructed by

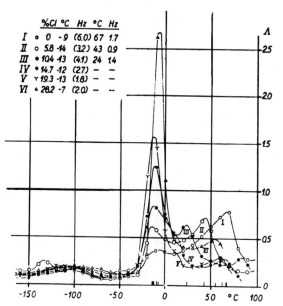

Fig. 94. $\Lambda = f_{(t)}$ for lower-chlorinated polyethylenes. (*Kolloid-Z.*, **134**, 162, 1953.)

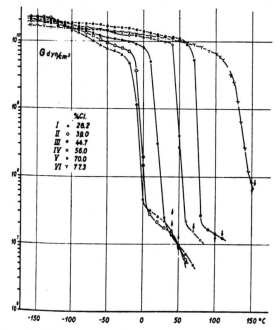

Fig. 95. $G = f_{(t)}$ for higher-chlorinated polyethylenes. (*Kolloid-Z.*, **134**, 159, 1953.)

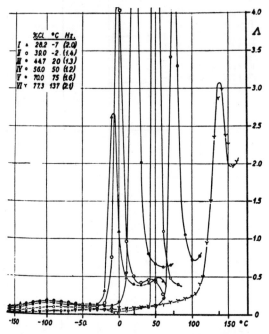

Fig. 96. $\Lambda = f(t)$ for higher-chlorinated polyethylenes. (*Kolloid-Z.*, **134**, 159, 1953.)

Nielsen (560) for measuring the dynamic shear modulus and mechanical damping of plastic and rubberlike materials, using the principle of the torsion pendulum. The mechanical oscillations are converted into electrical potentials for recording by a torque measuring device which is actuated by a differential transformer. This apparatus is capable of measuring the modulus and damping of materials over an extremely wide range.

This method was subsequently applied by Nielsen (872) to study six polyethylenes which differed widely in the degree of crystallinity. The crystallinity was determined from density measurements. Both the density and the dynamic mechanical measurements were made over the temperature range from 25°C. to above the melting point of the material.

The dynamic shear modulus was found to drop rapidly as the melting point was approached. The mechanical damping goes through a maximum near 60°C. and then through a minimum just below the melting point. It is possible to predict the density of any of the polyethylenes at any temperature below the melting point from the value of the shear modulus at the same temperature. The more crystalline materials have the higher shear moduli and the higher melting points.

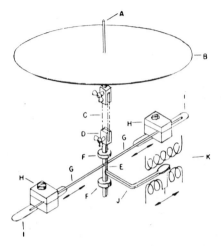

Fig. 97. Torsion pendulum showing details of torque measuring device. A, rod attached to fine suspension wire. B, moment of inertia disk. C, specimen. D, lower specimen clamp. E, shaft. F, ball bearings. G, spring rods. H, clamps for spring rods. I, slots for changing length of spring rods by changing position of spring clamps. J, arm which carries core of differential transformer. K, linear variable differential transformer. (*Rev. Sci. Instr.*, **22**, 690, 1951.)

More recently, mechanical relaxation phenomena on plastic materials were studied by Becker (931), and the applied methods were described in detail. The mechanical properties of polyethylene and other polymers were investigated over a temperature range from 80°K. to above room temperature and at frequencies in the range from 200 to 4,000 c.p.s. by Sauer and Kline (1023). The observed relaxation phenomena are discussed in terms of possible molecular mechanism and the results are correlated with specific heat measurements and other mechanical loss measurements.

5.6. Structure and Properties

The molecular structure and arrangement of polyethylenes as well as processing conditions and test methods determine those properties which make these polymers very desirable materials for many applications. The crystalline nature of the material, as Swallow emphasizes (162), must be kept constantly in mind. The complexity and interdependence of the various functions make it impossible to characterize a given sample of polyethylene adequately by any single physical property. Recently re-empha-

TABLE XXXI

Comparison of Properties of Two Polyethylenes of Same Melt Index (Grade Number)

	Polymer A	Polymer B
Melt index (grade number)	2.0	2.1
Intrinsic viscosity	0.85	0.84
Low temperature brittle point (°C.)	−70	−25
Solvent resistance (Bell test; hrs.)	200	1
Vicat softening point (°C.)	95	87
Relative rate of extrusion at high shear rate	0.36	0.78
Tensile strength (kg./sq. cm.)	187	138
Elongation at break (%)	630	630

Source: *Brit. Plastics*, **27** (9), 364 (1954).

sized by Hawkins (966), this has been illustrated by Swallow (885) in the example shown in Table **XXXI**, which compares the properties of two polyethylenes of the same melt index (grade number). This emphasizes the need to choose a polymer for a given purpose by subjecting it to tests which are representative of the service expected rather than on the basis of grade number alone.

The properties of polyethylenes to a first approximation were described by Richards (563) in terms of average molecular weight and degree of crystallinity. Properties which concern only slight movements of portions of the sample relative to each other are particularly dependent on crystallinity and depend little on average molecular weight. Properties which

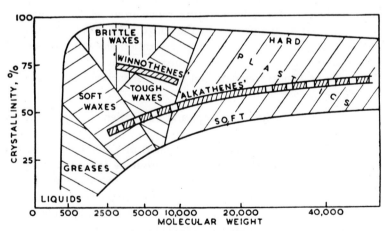

Fig. 98. Effect of molecular weight and crystallinity on mechanical properties.
(*J. Appl. Chem. London*, **1**, 372, 1951.)

TABLE XXXII

Classification of Properties

A. Properties mainly dependent on crystallinity

Melting point
Softening point under low load
Young's modulus in tension
Bending modulus
Yield point (tension to cause cold-drawing)
Surface hardness

B. Properties mainly dependent on molecular weight

Tensile strength of oriented specimen
Low temperature brittle point
Tear resistance

Source: *J. Appl. Chem. London*, **1**, 371 (1951).

involve more extensive movements, particularly rupture of the sample, are more concerned with average molecular weight and depend on crystallinity to a lesser extent.   Examples are given in Table XXXII.   The relation between the general physical properties, type of polymer, average molecular weight, and crystallinity is indicated in Figure 98.

The readiness of polyethylene to crystallize is primarily dependent on the

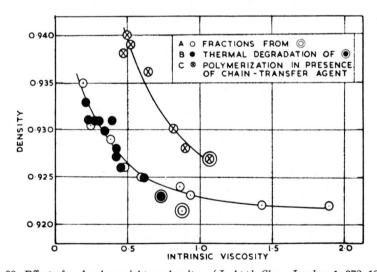

Fig. 99. Effect of molecular weight on density. (*J. Appl. Chem. London*, **1**, 372, 1951.)

extent of branching, although there are smaller effects on crystallinity associated with average molecular weight and with molecular weight distribution.   The effect of average molecular weight is that samples of relatively low molecular weight (between 2,000 and 5,000) crystallize more easily than do those of higher molecular weight (above 20,000).   Ease of crystallization is almost independent of molecular weight.   This is demonstrated by Figure 99 for three series of polymers, in each of which the degree of chain-branching is constant; the reduction in molecular weight causes a slight increase in density and hence in crystallinity.

The quantitative effect of chain-branching on crystallinity of polyethylenes at ordinary temperatures is illustrated in Figure 100.   Chainbranching, like substitution or copolymerization, has a profound effect on physical properties.   Table XXXIII compares the properties of a polymethylene having a molecular weight of 25,000 with those of a commercial polyethylene of similar molecular weight.   The polymethylene was prepared by the decomposition of diazomethane in ether solution in the presence of copper catalyst (464,478); the polyethylene was made by the high-pressure, high-temperature process.   The higher melting point, lower solubility, and greater hardness and stiffness of the entirely linear polymethylene are of interest.   This polymethylene was brittle at room temperature and could not be cold-drawn, while the polyethylene of similar chain length was flexible at −40°C. and lower, and could be oriented and cold-drawn readily.   As to flexibility at low temperatures, the average molecular weight, according to Richards, is the predominant phenomenon, but crystallinity and the texture of the polymer have important effects within certain ranges of molecular weight.   Samples with a molecular

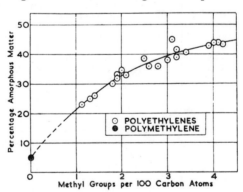

Fig. 100. Effect of branching on amorphous content.   (*J. Appl. Chem. London*, 1, 373, 1951.)

TABLE XXXIII

Effect of Chain-Branching on Physical Properties

Sample	Polymethylene	Polyethylene
Chain branching (CH_3 per 100 CH_2 groups)	nil	3
Density, g./cc.	0.98	0.92
Crystallinity at 20°C.	*ca.* 95%	*ca.* 60%
Melting point, °C.	130	110
Brittleness	Brittle at 20°C.	Flexible at −40°C.
Extensibility	<10%	Cold drawn to 400%
Cloud point for 5% solution in xylene, °C.	90	70

Source: *J. Appl. Chem. London,* **1,** 373 (1951).

weight of less than 20,000 are unlikely to be flexible below −35°C. Above 30,000, flexibility is exhibited at −70°C. or below; above 40,000, low-temperature brittle points of −140°C. were noted, corresponding possibly to a second-order transition. In the intermediate range of molecular weights, the brittle point is very sensitive to crystallinity. By reducing the rate of cooling from the melt and hence increasing the degree of crystallization, the brittle point could be raised in one sample from −70 to −25°C. Further, two samples of the same molecular weight, but of different degrees of chain-branching, may differ in low-temperature flexibility to the same extent.

Based on the previously discussed studies of Roedel (762), Bryant and Voter (716), Billmeyer (708), and Beasley (704), an attempt was made by Sperati, Franta, and Starkweather (772), in the fifth and last paper of the duPont series,* to present a consistent picture of the relationships between the molecular structure of polyethylene and various physical and mechanical properties. Combinations of three independent structural parameters, i.e., short-chain branching, long-chain branching, and molecular weight, were claimed (762) to control the various properties of polyethylene as indicated in the following scheme:

Short-Chain Branching	Density	
	Crystallinity	
	Moisture permeability	
	Stiffness	
	Yield point	
	Melting point	
	Cloud point	
	Sorption of reagents	
	Ultimate elongation	Molecular weight
	Hardness	Molecular weight
	Vicat temperature	Molecular weight
Long-Chain Branching	Ultimate strength	Molecular weight
	Melt elongation	Molecular weight

* This series was recently continued (1126, 1136, 1138).

TABLE XXXIV

Quantitative Relationships between Physical Properties

Relationship	Confidence limits, 95%	r^2	N	Range for which equation is applicable
Density = 2.0×10^{-3} (crystallinity) + 0.803	Graphical derivation			Crystallinity from 30 to 85%
Density = $0.9312 - 5.2 \times 10^{-3}$ (CH_3/100 C atoms)	±0.0019	0.87	84	CH_3/100 C from 0.4 to 5.0
Log (melt viscosity) = 5.95 − log (melt index)	Graphical derivation			Log melt index from 10^{-3} to 10^3
Log (melt index) = $5.09 - 1.53 \times 10^{-4} \overline{M}_n$	±1.085	0.85	14	$\overline{M}_n$ from 15,000 to 50,000
Log (melt viscosity) = $2.74 \times 10^{-2} \sqrt{\overline{M}_n} + 0.64$	±0.269	0.98	15	$\overline{M}_n$ from 1800 to 52,000
Log stiffness = 26.420 (density) − 19.889	±0.139	0.92	111	Density from 0.900 to 0.940
Yield point = 69600 (density) − 62300	±400	0.88	169	Density from 0.900 to 0.940
Cloud point = 728 (density) − 586	±5	0.89	37	Density from 0.900 to 0.940
Log (sorption of concn. HNO_3) = 31.07−32.10 (density)	±0.229	0.93	8	Density from 0.900 to 0.940
Log (sorption of lard) = 47.07−50.18 (density)	±0.357	0.93	8	Density from 0.900 to 0.940
Log (melt extensibility) = 4.752 − 0.609 log (melt viscosity)	Graphical derivation			Log melt viscosity from 5 to 6
Ultimate strength = 346 log (melt viscosity) − 320	±280	0.77	96	Log melt viscosity from 3 to 8
Vicat temperature = 1382 (density) + 9.29 log (melt viscosity) − 1233	±9	0.95	62	Density from 0.91 to 0.94; log melt viscosity from 0 to 7
Hardness = 1160 (density) + 2.80 log (melt viscosity) − 1000	±8	0.89	37	Density from 0.90 to 0.94; log melt viscosity from 1 to 7

Source: *J. Am. Chem. Soc.*, **75**, 6129 (1953).

TABLE XXXV

Preparation and Properties of Polyethylenes, According to U. S. 2,586,322

Run	P., atm.	T., °C.	Initiator		Inert solvent		Cyclohexane[b]	Contact time, min.	Conversion, per cent	Log_{10} visc. at 190° C.	Density, g./ml.	Olsen stiffness, p.s.i.	Tensile yield/break, p.s.i.	Elong., per cent	Softening point, °C.
			Kind	p.p.m.[a]	Kind	lb./lb. E[b]									
1	1,200	200	EP	120	Bz	0.7	—	3.5	23	6.6	0.914	17,000	1255/1830	695	88
2	1,200	230	EP	180	Bz	0.7	—	3.5	25	5.88	0.912	15,000	1180/1305	645	81
3	1,200	187	EP	140	Bz	0.7	—	3.5	20	7.5	0.915	17,000	1345/2040	650	91
4	1,200	180	EP	60	Bz	0.7	—	3.5	10	9.65	0.9162	18,000	1435/2440	650	97
5	1,200	125	A	200	Bz	0.15	—	6	6	>10	0.929	38,000	2360/2600	595	109
6	1,200	170	BP	300	Bz	0.175	0.025	6	17	8.85	0.9242	30,000	1710/1985	510	94
7	1,200	170	BP	300	Bz	0.15	0.05	6	12	7.28	0.9251	31,000	1680/1680	520	96
8	1,200	160	BP	300	Bz	0.14	0.06	6	12	7.68	0.9263	32,500	1900/1900	370	105
9	1,200	160	BP	300	Bz	0.13	0.07	6	13	6.90	0.9294	38,000	2110/2110	140	104
10	1,200	150	BP	300	Bz	0.14	0.06	6	15	6.62	0.9292	38,000	2110/2110	100	105
11	1,200	140	BP	300	Bz	0.16	0.04	6	11	7.52	0.9292	38,000	2080/2080	200	105
12	1,200	190	EP	80	Bz	0.45	0.3	3.5	20	3.25	0.9268	36,000	1700/1700	30	64
13	1,200	150	BP	300	Bz	0.16	0.04	6	12	8.60	0.9277	36,000	1900/2010	540	107
14	1,200	167	EP	225	Bz	0.1	0.2	3.5	15	4.18	0.927	35,000	1700/1700	0	75
15	1,200	150	EP	400	—	—	0.6	6	5	3.35	0.9314	42,000	—	—	—
16	1,200	120	BP	200	—	—	0.1	5	14	5.73	0.9360	56,000	2450/2450	50	105
17	1,200	120	BP	300	—	—	0.12	5	16	5.39	0.9349	51,000	2400/2400	50	102
18	1,200	233	EP	350	—	—	0.43	7	26	2.3	0.9124	16,000	—	—	—
19	1,200	230	EP	380	—	—	0.18	7	40	3.3	0.9149	18,000	—	—	—
20	2,000	300	EP	25	Bz	0.2	0.1	0.6	15	3.6	0.92	23,000	1410/1410	80	—
21	2,000	200	EP	27	Bz	0.2	0.1	0.9	17	5.0	0.92	23,000	1455/1455	110	—
22	1,000	75	PP	1,300	—	—	0.2	4.3	5	6.1	0.950	85,000	—	—	—
23	1,200	120	EPC	190	Bz	0.1	0.55	3.5	2	8.45	0.941	60,000	—	—	—

Source: U. S. 2,586,322, Feb. 19, 1952, Franta, W. A. (E. I. duPont de Nemours & Company).
A = Azobisdiisobutyronitrile.
BP = Benzoyl peroxide.
E = Ethylene.
Bz = Benzene.
EP = Diethyl peroxide.
EPC = Diethyl peroxydicarbonate.
PP = Perfluorobutyryl peroxide.
[a] Parts per million parts of ethylene.
[b] Pounds per pound of ethylene.

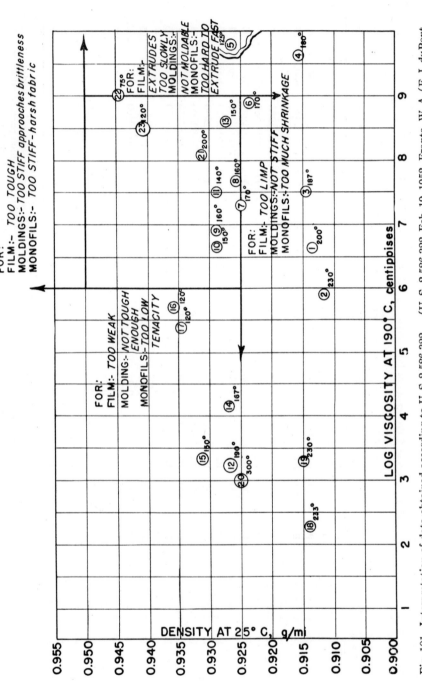

FOR:
FILM:- *TOO TOUGH*
MOLDINGS:- *TOO STIFF approaches brittleness*
MONOFILS:- *TOO STIFF-harsh fabric*

FOR:-
FILM:-
EXTRUDES
TOO SLOWLY
MOLDINGS:-
NOT MOLDABLE
MONOFILS:-
TOO HARD TO
EXTRUDE FAST

FOR:
FILM:- *TOO WEAK*
MOLDING:- *NOT TOUGH ENOUGH*
MONOFILS:- *TOO LOW TENACITY*

FOR:
FILM:- *TOO LIMP*
MOLDINGS:- *NOT STIFF*
MONOFILS:- *TOO MUCH SHRINKAGE*

LOG VISCOSITY AT 190° C, centippises

DENSITY AT 25° C, g/ml

Fig. 101. Interpretation of data obtained according to U.S. 2,586,322.   (U.S. 2,586,322, Feb. 19, 1952, Franta, W. A. (E. I. duPont de Nemours & Company.)

Quantitative relationships between physical properties and the ranges for which each equation is applicable are presented in Table XXXIV.

In recent studies by Peticolas and Watkins (1138) melt viscosity, unlike solution viscosity, was not found to be a function of long-chain branching.

Actual physical data, their determination and interdependence, will be presented in subsequent chapters.   The preparation of polyethylenes with desirable combinations of properties, by varying the reaction conditions and introducing a chain-transfer agent, has been described in Brit. 694,271 (800a) and in U. S. 2,586,322 to Franta (650), both to duPont.   The object of the process is to control chain-branching in such a way that polymers of improved stiffness and workability and relatively high density and low-melt viscosity are obtained.   Reaction conditions and some of the properties of the resultant polymers are presented in Table XXXV.

While interpretation of the effect of molecular structure on some of the properties of polyethylene requires the three-parameter system proposed by Roedel (762), a number of mechanical properties of the solid polymer are not affected by long-chain branching.   In such instances, a plot of crystallinity against molecular weight, as given by Richards (563), or the equivalent, a plot of density against log-melt viscosity, is sufficient to correlate the specific properties with the molecular structure of polyethylene. The latter mode of presentation has been chosen in Franta's patent, as shown in Figure 101, to interpret the data set out in Table XXXV.   It will be seen that the products contained in the rectangle bounded by log viscosity between 6 and 9, and between densities of 0.925 and 0.950 (i.e., Runs 7, 8, 9, 10, 11, 13, 21, 22, and 23) are superior for the preparation of films, monofilaments, and molding compositions.   The trend in deficiencies encountered in products outside the rectangle will also be apparent.

5.7. Commercial High-Density Polyethylenes

The foregoing sections of this Chapter have dealt essentially with the molecular structure of the low density, high-pressure, polymerized polyethylenes and, to some extent, with polymethylene.   While the study of these polymers, although by no means complete, has been pursued for many years and has led to a fairly consistent concept of their structure, comparable information with respect to the high-density polyethylenes, represented by the Ziegler and Phillips types, is not yet available.   The following discussion of the molecular structure of the Ziegler and Phillips polyethylenes is thus based on only a few publications, i.e., Grams and

Gaube (961), Krause (987), Schulz and Mehnert (1024), Ziegler (1044) and Ziegler, Holzkamp, Breil, and Martin (1046), and Smith (1141a).

Added in proof:

Ziegler polyethylenes, which may be obtained with molecular weights ranging from about 10,000 to 3 million, differ structurally from the conventional high-pressure polyethylenes by having a considerably reduced degree of short-chain as well as long-chain branching. These polyethylenes have pronounced spherulitic structure, as detected under the microscope in polarized light.

The Phillips polyethylene, otherwise apparently quite similar to the Ziegler product, has a somewhat higher density and degree of crystallinity. The comparison shown in Table XXXVa has been presented by Smith (1141a).

TABLE XXXVa

Comparison of Molecular Structure of Polyethylenes

	DYNH (low-density)	Super Dylan (Ziegler)	Marlex 50 (Phillips)
Density, g/ml	0.91–0.92	0.93–0.95	0.96
Double bonds/1000 C atoms	0.6	0.7	1.5
Unsaturation distribution, %			
$RCH=CH_2$	15	43	94
$RR'C=CH_2$	68	32	1
$RCH=CHR'$	17	25	5
Methyl groups/1000 C atoms			
Total	21.5	3	below 1.5
Terminal	4.6	approx. 2[a]	below 1.5[a]
Methyl branches	2.5[a]	...	...
Ethyl branches	14.4	1	below 1
Crystallinity, % by			
X-ray diffraction	64	87	93
Nuclear resonance	65	84	93
Crystallite size, Angstroms	190	360	390

Source: Paper presented by D. C. Smith, Phillips Petroleum Company. American Chemical Society, Dallas Meeting, April 8–13 (1956).
[a] Value estimated.

Two high-pressure polyethylenes (Alathon 10 and 34) with medium density (0.930) were recently announced by duPont (1120a). No details have as yet become known of the molecular structure of Alkathene HD, a high-density (0.940) polyethylene made by a modification of I.C.I.'s conventional high-pressure process (1120). Its properties are reported to resemble more the Ziegler-Phillips, low-pressure products than the conventional low-density, high-pressure polyethylenes. Some information on a high-density (0.955–0.970) polyethylene made by duPont at very high pressure (7000 atm.) but rather low temperature (60°C.) is contained in Can. 502,597 to Larchar and Pease [duPont (901a)]. Further details were presented recently by Hines, Bryant, Larchar, and Pease (1133) who concluded that all high-density polyethylenes of a given weight-average molecular weight have similar properties, regardless of synthesis route.

VI. PROPERTIES OF POLYETHYLENES

Polyethylene is a colorless material with a relatively soft surface. It is almost transparent in thin layers, translucent to opaque in thicker ones. Transparency can be influenced by manufacturing conditions as well as aftertreatment, such as annealing or quenching. Polyethylene is practically tasteless and odorless, and is nonpoisonous. As a pure hydrocarbon, its flammability is similar to that of high-melting waxes or paraffins. Down to about $-60°C.$, polyethylene is tough and flexible; at lower temperatures, hardening and possibly crazing take place.

Polyethylenes are thermoplastic resins and, as such, can be molded by either compression or injection methods and extruded into sheets, films, tubes, rods, filaments, and other shapes. They differ, however, from most thermoplastic resins in having a distinctly crystalline structure, and the amount and character of orientation are important factors affecting physical and mechanical properties.

As would be anticipated from the paraffinic nature of its structure, polyethylene is one of the most inert and stable of polymers, more so, for example, than polystyrene, and to a considerably greater extent than polyisobutylene (350).

The behavior of polyethylenes towards oxidation is dealt with in several sections, particularly in Section 4.6. The effect of specific structural groups in polyethylene on oxidizability can be determined by studying aliphatic low molecular weight hydrocarbons of well-known structure which may be considered to be prototypes for polyethylene. In general, their rates of oxidation are similar to that for polyethylene, but vary somewhat with structural changes. A study of the oxygen uptake of these polyethylene prototypes was recently reported by Wilson (1142). Oxidizability was found to be increased by branching. Terminal methyl groups in unbranched hydrocarbons were less easily oxidized than methylene groups; thus, the rate of oxidation increased with the chain length of the hydrocarbon. Side chain methyl groups, however, increased the rate of oxidation because of the presence of a tertiary hydrogen on the chain, e.g., $-CH_2-CH(CH_3)-CH_2-$. Carbonyl groups also were found to increase the oxidizability of the hydrocarbon. From this, the straight-chain, high-density polyethylenes may be expected to have a higher resistance towards oxygen than branched, conventional polyethylenes of comparable chain length.

The comparative immunity to ozone, by which it is much less affected than is rubber (162), is an advantage of polyethylene in electrical applications.

In the complete absence of oxygen, polyethylene is stable at temperatures up to 290°C. (749). At temperatures between 290 and 350°C., polyethylene decomposes to give lower molecular weight polymers, normally thermoplastics or waxes, but little or no ethylene. At temperatures above 350°C., gaseous products are produced in increasing quantities, the major component being butylene and not ethylene, as might be expected (411). In this respect, the degradation is unlike that of styrene or methyl methacrylate polymers, which evolve monomer in quantity before the molecular weight of the residual polymer is appreciably reduced (compare Section 3.10).

With respect to polymethylene, its thermal stability was found superior to polyvinyl fluoride, but inferior to polytrifluoroethylene, 1,1-polyvinylidene fluoride, and polytetrafluoroethylene, according to experiments carried out by Madorsky, Hart, Straus, and Sedlak (754).

6.1. Solubility, Compatibility, and Chemical Resistance

Polyethylene made by the conventional, high-pressure, process is practically insoluble in all solvents at ordinary temperatures. It is resistant to water and aqueous solutions and does not change its dielectric or other physical properties in an atmosphere of high relative humidity or on immersion. At room temperature, polyethylene is resistant to dilute sulfuric and nitric acids, and to the following compounds and solutions in all concentrations: hydrochloric acid, hydrofluoric acid, phosphoric acid, formic acid, ammonia, potassium hydroxide, sodium hydroxide, potassium permanganate, and hydrogen peroxide. Polyethylene is slowly attacked at room temperature by fuming sulfuric acid, concentrated nitric acid, nitrating acids (mixture of nitric and sulfuric acids), and cleaning solution (mixture of chromic and sulfuric acids). These properties make polyethylene valuable as a corrosion-resistant construction material (950, 1022).

No sign of metal contamination was noted by Sharaswathi Devi (879a) in water kept for three weeks in polyethylene bottles, when 1000 ml. of this water was concentrated to 10 ml. and tested on *Aspergillus niger*.

However, unusual behavior of liquids, resulting from exposure to polyethylene, was reported by Gatos (850).   He found that the dissolution rate of SAE 1020 steel in dilute hydrochloric and sulfuric acids is decreased in the presence of polyethylene; and that the corrosion rate of 1020 steel in tap water at room temperature was decreased by about 30% in the presence of polyethylene in tests of 25 days' duration.   It is recommended that care should be exercised when polyethylene equipment is being used in connection with polarographic and metal-dissolution studies.

At room temperature, aliphatic, aromatic, and chlorinated hydrocarbons cause a certain amount of swelling and a change in physical properties; the original properties reappear after evaporation of the swelling medium. Only nonvolatile or difficulty volatile materials, such as lubricating oil, vaseline, some animal and vegetable fats and oils, cause permanent damage.

At temperatures above 70°C., polyethylene is dissolved to some extent by toluene, xylene, amyl acetate, trichloroethylene, turpentine, chlorinated hydrocarbons, tetralin, decalin, petroleum ether, lubricating oil, and paraffin.   Above 100°C., polyethylene becomes miscible in all proportions with these.   Even at elevated temperatures, however, polyethylene remains insoluble in water, aliphatic alcohols, acetic acid, acetone, ether, glycerol, carbon disulfide, and linseed and certain other vegetable oils.   On cooling, polyethylene separates from its solutions and, depending on the temperature, pastes or gels are formed.

The phenomena of solubility and swelling of crystalline polymers, including polyethylene, are treated from a theoretical angle in Volume II of the series by Stuart (1034).

Staudinger and Berndt (161) (see Sections 5.3, and 6.6) have observed that polyethylene may not be dissolved molecularly in all solvents.   Association was noted in toluene, while decalin was considered the best solvent for polyethylene.

At room temperature, polyethylene is unaffected by chlorine, but does absorb the other halogens, and at elevated temperatures it absorbs sulfur. The chlorination of polyethylene was described in Section 4.4 (see also Section 6.17).   The preparation of fluorinated polyethylene by the action of fluorine on finely divided polyethylene in the presence of a metal (copper) is described by Rudge in Brit. 710,523 [I.C.I.(902b)].   Metallic sodium can be stored in polyethylene containers (1078).

Further pertinent data on the solubility characteristics and chemical resistance of polyethylene are given in the trade bulletins of its commercial producers (568,883).   From one of these (568), the information contained in Tables XXXVI through XL is quoted.   Table XXXVI shows the very low water absorption of polyethylene, determined by the increase in weight of sheets of polyethylene immersed in water. Table XXXVII shows the acid and alkali resistance of polyethylene. Table XXXVIII presents numerical data for the amount of swelling of polyethylene in various liquids. Tables XXXIX and XL present information on the compatibility of polyethylene with various materials.

The behavior of polyethylene in various chemical environments has been recently summarized in a trade bulletin (844) as a guide to the application of polyethylene. This survey is quoted *in extenso* in Table XLI.

Where paraffins are concerned, compatibility increases with their molecular weight. Paraffin oil separates in concentration of 3–4%, while a paraffin of 52–54°C. melting point does not separate until the concentration is 15%. The tensile strength of the polyethylene is greatly re-

TABLE XXXVI

Water Absorption of Polyethylene Resin[a]
(Mg./sq. in. of surface)

Time in Water	Water at Room Temperature	Water at 70°C.
1 month	0.03	0.2
3 months	0.06	0.8
1 year	0.2	0.2
2 years	0.3	1.6

Source: *Bakelite Polyethylene for Paper Coatings*, Bakelite Co., p. 6, 1951.
[a] Tests on samples immersed in salt water show somewhat lower values.

TABLE XXXVII

Acid and Alkali Resistance of Polyethylene Resin

	Degradation of Physical Properties of Resin DYNH After Five Days	
Reagent	25°C.	60°C.
Ammonium hydroxide, concentrated	No	No
Sodium hydroxide, solid	No	No
Nitric acid, fuming	Yes	Yes
Nitric acid, concentrated	Yes	Yes
Sulfuric acid, fuming	Yes	Yes
Sulfuric acid, concentrated	No	No
Chlorosulfonic acid, pure	Yes	Yes
Hydrochloric acid, concentrated	No	No
Glacial acetic acid	No	...
Phosphoric anhydride, pure	No	No
Hydrofluoric acid, 28%	No	...

Source: *Bakelite Polyethylene for Paper Coatings*, Bakelite Co., p. 5, 1951.

TABLE XXXVIII

Swelling of Polyethylene Resin DYNH in Liquids

Test Liquid	Swelling Index at 60°C. (Percent Volume Change of Resin DYNH at Equilibrium)
Silicone liquid (Type 200, viscosity 350 cstk.,[a] 25°C.)	−0.30
Silicone liquid (Type 200, viscosity 1,000 cstk., 25°C.)	−0.20
Methanol	Negligible
Acetone	Negligible
Water	Negligible
Lactic acid	0.015
Propylene glycol	0.13
Turkey red oil	0.30
Dimethyl carbitol phthalate	0.35
Dimethoxy ethyl phthalate ("Methox")	0.36
Linseed oil	0.45
Soya bean oil	0.65
Castor oil	0.65
Diethoxy ethyl phthalate ("Ethox")	0.75
Ethylene glycol monoethyl ether (Cellosolve solvent)	0.95
Tricresyl phosphate	1.3
Butyl Cellosolve solvent	1.7
Di-2-ethyl hexyl phthalate (Flexol plasticizer DOP)	4.5
Dibutyl sebacate	6.1
Methyl ethyl ketone	6.4
Trioctyl phosphate (Flexol plasticizer TOF)	6.6
Mineral oil ("Socony" No. 309)	8.7
Silicone liquid (Type 500, viscosity 0.65 cstk., 25°C.)	9.5
Methyl isobutyl ketone	10.3
Hexyl ether	18.5
Xylene	19.5
Chloroform	21.0
Butyl ether	22.6
Benzene	23.0
Dichlorobenzene	26.0
Tetrahydronaphthalene	36.0

Source: *Bakelite Polyethylene for Paper Coatings*, Bakelite Co., p. 7, 1951.
[a] 1 cstk., kinematic viscosity unit corresponding to centipoise; 1 cstk. = 0.01 stoke.

duced by the various additives.   Even small concentrations of paraffins and similar low molecular weight materials cause considerable tendency to environmental cracking.

TABLE XXXIX

Polyethylene Compatibility

(Materials dispersible but not mutually soluble at normal temperatures)

Materials dispersible in polyethylene, but not mutually soluble at normal temperatures, are shown below. Mixtures with good stability throughout a wide temperature range are formed by the addition of the following to polyethylene:

1. Paraffin wax
2. Polyisobutylene (high molecular weight)
3. GR-S Rubber
4. Butyl rubber
5. Polystyrene (high molecular weight)
6. Ester gum
7. Zyrox resin 3007 (up to about 50%)
8. Chloroparaffins (solid resins)
9. Chlorobutenes (solid resins)
10. GR-N (limited, poor dispersions)
11. "Stanco" S Resins (S-60-2)
12. Polyvinyl chloride resins
13. Vinylite resin VYNW
14. Dichlorostyrene
15. Gutta percha
16. Ethyl cellulose
17. Hard asphalt (gilsonite)
18. Chlorinated diphenyls (solid "Aro-chlors")
19. Hydrogenated castor oil (solid "Opal" wax)
20. Deproteinized natural rubber
21. o,p-Toluenesulfonamide ("Santicizer" No. 9)
22. Bakelite phenolic resin BR-3360
23. Bakelite phenolic resin BR-254
24. Beeswax
25. Inorganic fillers

Source: *Bakelite Polyethylene for Paper Coatings*, Bakelite Co., p. 12, 1951.

TABLE XL

Polyethylene Compatibility

(Materials dispersible but incompatible at room temperatures)

Materials dispersible in polyethylene, not mutually soluble, and incompatible at room temperatures are noted below. Incompatibility is shown by tendency for the components to separate after a period following the compounding into two distinct phases:

1. Mineral oil
2. "Paraplex" G-25 plasticizer
3. Hydrogenated soy bean oil
4. Fluid low molecular weight polyisobutylene
5. Fluid polypropylene
6. All organic solvents
7. Stearic acid (solid)
8. Ceryl alcohol (solid)
9. Laurone (solid ketone)
10. "Akroflex" C antioxidant
11. "Age Rite Alba" antioxidant
12. Low molecular weight alkylated phenols
13. "Vinsol" resin
14. Cocoanut oil
15. Palm oil

Source: *Bakelite Polyethylene for Paper Coatings*, Bakelite Co., p. 13, 1951.

TABLE XLI

The Application of Polyethylene Resins in Various Chemical Environments

Chemical	Conc., Wt. %	Polyethylene Can be Used at: 25°C.	60°C.
Acetaldehyde	...	Yes	No
Acetic acid	10	Yes	Yes
Acetic acid	Glacial	No	No
Acetic anhydride	...	No	No
Acetone	...	Yes	No
Acetphenetidine	...	Yes	...
Alcohol, allyl	...	No	No
Alcohol, amyl	...	No	No
Alcohol, benzyl	...	No	No
Alcohol, ethyl	35	No	No
Alcohol, ethyl	100	No	No
Alcohol, furfuryl	...	No	No
Alcohol, methyl	...	No	No
Alcohol, n-octyl	...	No	No
Alcohol, propyl	...	No	No
Allyl chloride	...	No	No
Alum	...	Yes	Yes
Aluminum bromide	Sat. aq.	Yes	...
Aluminum chloride	...	Yes	Yes
Aluminum fluoride	...	Yes	Yes
Aluminum hydroxide	...	Yes	Yes
Aluminum sulfate	...	Yes	Yes
Ammonia	...	Yes	Yes
Ammonium carbonate	...	Yes	Yes
Ammonium chloride	...	Yes	Yes
Ammonium hydroxide	28	Yes	Yes
Ammonium metaphosphate	...	Yes	Yes
Ammonium nitrate	...	Yes	Yes
Ammonium oxalate	...	Yes	Yes
Ammonium persulfate	...	Yes	Yes
Ammonium phosphate	75	Yes	Yes
Ammonium sulfate	...	Yes	Yes
Ammonium thiocyanate	...	Yes	Yes
Amyl acetate	...	No	No
Amyl chloride	...	No	No
Aniline	...	No	No
Animal oils	...	No	No
Antimony trichloride	...	Yes	Yes
Aqua regia	...	No	No
Argyrol	...	Yes	...
Arsenic acid	100	Yes	Yes

Continued

TABLE XLI (*Continued*)

Chemical	Conc., Wt. %	Polyethylene Can be Used at:	
		25°C.	60°C.
Aspirin	. . .	Yes	Yes
Atabrine	. . .	Yes	. . .
Barium carbonate	. . .	Yes	Yes
Barium chloride	. . .	Yes	Yes
Barium hydroxide	. . .	Yes	Yes
Barium sulfate	. . .	Yes	Yes
Barium sulfide	. . .	Yes	Yes
Beer	. . .	Yes	. . .
Benzaldehyde	. . .	No	No
Benzene	. . .	No	No
Benzenesulfonic acid	10	Yes	Yes
Benzoic acid	. . .	Yes	Yes
Bismuth carbonate	. . .	Yes	Yes
Boric acid	. . .	Yes	Yes
Brake fluid	. . .	Yes	. . .
Bromobenzene	. . .	No	No
Bromine	. . .	No	No
Bromine water	. . .	No	No
Butyl acetate	. . .	No	No
n-Butyl amine	. . .	No	No
Butyraldehyde	. . .	No	No
Butyric acid	. . .	No	No
Calcium carbonate	. . .	Yes	Yes
Calcium chlorate	. . .	Yes	Yes
Calcium chloride	. . .	Yes	Yes
Calcium hydroxide	. . .	Yes	Yes
Calcium hypochlorite	. . .	Yes	No
Calcium sulfate	. . .	Yes	Yes
Camphor oil	. . .	No	No
Carbon bisulfide	. . .	No	No
Carbon dioxide, dry gas	. . .	Yes	Yes
Carbon monoxide	. . .	Yes	Yes
Carbon tetrachloride	. . .	No	No
Carbonic acid	. . .	Yes	Yes
Cetane	. . .	No	No
Chloracetic acid	. . .	No	No
Chlorine gas, dry or wet	. . .	No	No
Chlorobenzene	. . .	No	No
Chloroform	. . .	No	No
Chlorosulfonic acid	100	No	No
Chromic acid	80	Yes	Yes
Cider	. . .	Yes	. . .

TABLE XLI (*Continued*)

Chemical	Conc., Wt. %	Polyethylene Can be Used at:	
		25°C.	60°C.
Citric acid	. . .	Yes	Yes
Copper chloride	. . .	Yes	Yes
Copper cyanide	. . .	Yes	Yes
Copper nitrate	. . .	Yes	Yes
Copper sulfate	. . .	Yes	Yes
Cresol	. . .	No	No
Cresylic acids	50	Yes	Yes
Crude oil	. . .	No	No
Cyclohexane	. . .	No	No
Cyclohexanol	. . .	No	No
Cyclohexanone	100	No	No
Cyclohexylamine	. . .	No	No
Decahydronaphthalene	. . .	No	No
Decanol	. . .	No	No
Dibutylphthalate	100	No	No
Dichlorobenzene	. . .	No	No
Diethylene glycol	100	Yes	Yes
Dihydronaphthalene	. . .	No	No
Diisobutylene	. . .	No	No
Diisopropyl ketone	. . .	No	No
Di-*n*-butyl amine	. . .	No	No
Di-*n*-butyl ether	. . .	No	No
Dioxane	100	Yes	. . .
Ether	. . .	No	No
Ethyl acetate	. . .	No	No
Ethyl aniline	. . .	No	No
Ethyl butyrate	100	No	No
Ethyl chloride	100	No	No
Ethyl ether	100	No	No
Ethylene chlorohydrin	100	No	No
Ethylene dichloride	. . .	No	No
Ethylene glycol	. . .	Yes	Yes
Fatty acids ($>C_6$)	. . .	No	No
Ferric chloride	. . .	Yes	Yes
Ferric nitrate	. . .	Yes	Yes
Ferric sulfate	. . .	Yes	Yes
Ferrous chloride	. . .	Yes	Yes
Ferrous sulfate	. . .	Yes	Yes
Fertilizers	. . .	Yes	Yes
Fluoboric acid	42	Yes	. . .
Fluorine	. . .	No	No

Continued

TABLE XLI (*Continued*)

Chemical	Conc., Wt. %	Polyethylene Can be Used at:	
		25°C.	60°C.
Fluosilicic acid	...	Yes	Yes
Formaldehyde	40	Yes	Yes
Formamide	...	Yes	No
Formic acid	100	Yes	Yes
Formic acid	50	Yes	Yes
Furfural	100	No	No
Gasoline	...	No	No
Gin	...	No	No
Glycerine	...	Yes	Yes
Heptane	...	No	No
Hydrazine hydrate	...	Yes	...
Hydrobromic acid	50	Yes	Yes
Hydrochloric acid	...	Yes	Yes
Hydrocyanic acid	...	Yes	Yes
Hydrofluoric acid	48	Yes	Yes
Hydrofluoric acid	75	Yes	No
Hydrogen peroxide	3	Yes	Yes
Hydrogen peroxide	30	Yes	No
Hydrogen peroxide	90	Yes	No
Hydrogen sulfide, dry gas	...	Yes	Yes
Hypochlorous acid	...	Yes	No
Iodine (in KI solution)	Conc.	No	No
Lactic acid	10	Yes	Yes
Lactic acid	90	Yes	Yes
Lauryl alcohol	...	No	No
Lauryl sulfate	...	No	No
Lead acetate	...	Yes	Yes
Linseed oil	...	No	No
Lubricating oil	...	No	No
Magnesium carbonate	...	Yes	Yes
Magnesium chloride	...	Yes	Yes
Magnesium hydroxide	...	Yes	Yes
Magnesium nitrate	...	Yes	Yes
Magnesium sulfate	...	Yes	Yes
Maleic acid	...	Yes	Yes
Mercuric chloride	...	Yes	Yes
Mercuric cyanide	...	Yes	Yes
Mercurous nitrate	...	Yes	Yes
Mercury	...	Yes	Yes
Methallyl chloride	...	No	No
Methane	...	No	No

TABLE XLI (*Continued*)

Chemical	Conc., Wt. %	Polyethylene Can be Used at: 25°C.	60°C.
Methyl bromide	...	No	No
Methyl chloride	...	No	No
Methyl ethyl ketone	...	No	No
Methyl formate	...	No	No
Methyl isobutyl ketone	...	No	No
Methyl salicylate	...	No	No
Methyl sulfuric acid	...	Yes	Yes
Milk	...	Yes	Yes
Mineral oil	...	No	No
Mixed acids	...	Yes	No
Naphtha	...	Yes	No
Naphthalene	...	No	No
Nickel chloride	...	Yes	Yes
Nickel nitrate	...	Yes	Yes
Nickel sulfate	...	Yes	Yes
Nitric acid	10	Yes	Yes
Nitric acid	20	Yes	Yes
Nitric acid	50	Yes	No
Nitric acid	95	No	No
Nitric acid vapors	...	Yes	Yes
Nitriding gases	...	Yes	Yes
Nitrobenzene	...	No	No
Nitroethane	...	Yes	No
Nitromethane	...	Yes	No
Nitropropane	...	No	No
Octanol	...	No	No
Octyl cresol	...	No	No
Oleic acid	...	No	No
Oxalic acid	...	Yes	Yes
Oxidizing gases	...	Yes	Yes
Ozone	...	No	No
Paper mill liquors	...	Yes	Yes
Paraffin	...	Yes	No
Perchloric acid	...	Yes	Yes
Petroleum ether	...	No	No
Phenol	94	Yes	No
Phosphoric acid	30	Yes	Yes
Phosphoric acid	85	Yes	No
Phosphorous oxychloride	...	No	No
Phosphorous pentoxide	...	Yes	Yes
Phosphorous trichloride	...	Yes	...

Continued

TABLE XLI (*Continued*)

Chemical	Conc., Wt. %	Polyethylene Can be Used at:	
		25°C.	50°C.
Photographic developers	...	Yes	Yes
Picric acid	...	Yes	No
Potassium bicarbonate	...	Yes	Yes
Potassium borate	...	Yes	Yes
Potassium bromide	...	Yes	Yes
Potassium carbonate	...	Yes	Yes
Potassium chlorate	...	Yes	Yes
Potassium chloride	Sat'd.	Yes	Yes
Potassium dichromate	40	Yes	Yes
Potassium ferri- or ferrocyanide	...	Yes	Yes
Potassium hydroxide	...	Yes	Yes
Potassium nitrate	...	Yes	Yes
Potassium permanganate	95	Yes	Yes
Potassium sulfate	...	Yes	Yes
Propylene dichloride	...	No	No
Propylene glycol	...	Yes	Yes
Silicic acid	...	Yes	Yes
Silver nitrate	...	Yes	Yes
Sodium acetate	...	Yes	Yes
Sodium benzoate	...	Yes	Yes
Sodium bicarbonate	...	Yes	Yes
Sodium bisulfate	...	Yes	Yes
Sodium bisulfite	...	Yes	Yes
Sodium bromide	...	Yes	Yes
Sodium carbonate	...	Yes	Yes
Sodium chlorate	...	Yes	Yes
Sodium chloride	...	Yes	Yes
Sodium cyanide	...	Yes	Yes
Sodium ferri- or ferrocyanide	...	Yes	Yes
Sodium fluoride	...	Yes	Yes
Sodium hydroxide	...	Yes	Yes
Sodium hypochlorite	...	Yes	No
Sodium nitrate	...	Yes	Yes
Sodium nitrite	...	Yes	Yes
Sodium sulfate	...	Yes	Yes
Sodium sulfide	...	Yes	Yes
Sodium sulfite	...	Yes	Yes
Stannic chloride	...	Yes	Yes
Stannous chloride	...	Yes	Yes
Starch	...	Yes	Yes
Stearic acid	100	Yes	Yes
Sulfuryl chloride	...	No	No

TABLE XLI (*Concluded*)

Chemical	Conc., Wt. %	Polyethylene Can be Used at:	
		25°C.	60°C.
Sulfur	...	Yes	Yes
Sulfur dioxide	...	Yes	Yes
Sulfur trioxide	...	Yes	Yes
Sulfuric acid	10	Yes	Yes
Sulfuric acid	50	Yes	Yes
Sulfuric acid	70	Yes	No
Sulfuric acid	96	No	No
Sulfurous acid	...	Yes	Yes
Tallow	...	Yes	No
Tannic acid	10	Yes	Yes
Tanning extracts	...	Yes	Yes
Tartaric acid	...	Yes	Yes
Tetrachloroethane	...	No	No
Tetrachloroethylene	...	No	No
Tetrahydronaphthalene	...	No	No
Toluene	...	No	No
Transformer oils	...	No	No
Trichlorobenzene	...	No	No
Trichloroethylene	...	No	No
Triethanolamine	...	No	No
Trisodium phosphate	...	Yes	Yes
Vegetable oil	...	No	No
Vinegar	...	Yes	Yes
Water, distilled	...	Yes	Yes
Whiskey	...	No	...
Wine	...	No	...
Xylene	...	No	No
Yeast	...	Yes	...
Zinc chloride	...	Yes	Yes
Zinc fluoride	...	Yes	...
Zinc sulfate	...	Yes	Yes

Source: Durethene Corp., Nov., 1954.

Mixtures of polyethylene and polyisobutylene retain the excellent dielectric properties and the resistance to chemicals of both components. In most cases, the mixtures process more easily than the components; they show increased compatibility with fillers, reduced tendency to crack, and reduced diffusion of some vapors.   The resistance to deformation and the hardness of such mixtures depend on the proportions of the components.

Polyethylene has a low compatibility for fillers, and only the pigments necessary for coloring should be added in order not to reduce the toughness of the material. Little or no effect upon the mechanical properties of the polymer is observed with a 2% loading with carbon black. This was found to be optimum from a protective standpoint, in order to increase the life

TABLE XLII

Resistance of A-C Polyethylene to Liquid Chemicals

Liquid or Solvent	Percent Change
Acetic acid, 10%	0.02 increase
Acetic acid, glacial	0.46 increase
Acetone	5.6 increase
Ammonium hydroxide, 10%	0.01 increase
Ammonium hydroxide, conc.	0.01 increase
bis(2-Chloroethyl) ether	0.50 increase
Calcium chloride, 15%	0.01 increase
Carbon tetrachloride	Swelled and disintegrated
Corn oil	0.01 decrease
Dioxane	2.5 increase
Ethyl alcohol, 95%	0.12 increase
Hydrochloric acid, 10%	0.01 decrease
Hydrochloric acid, conc.	0.01 increase
Lubricating oil	0.60 increase
Methyl ethyl ketone	1.5 increase
Mineral spirits	11 increase
Nacconol, 10%	0.05 increase
Nitric acid, 10%	0.01 increase
Nitric acid, conc.	0.55 increase
Oleic acid	0.61 increase
Pyridine	3.0 increase
Sodium hydroxide, 10%	0.01 decrease
Sodium hydroxide, 50%	0.02 decrease
Sodium hypochlorite, 3% (Chlorox)	0.01 increase
Sodium thiosulfate, 10%	0.01 increase
Sulfuric acid, 10%	0.01 decrease
Sulfuric acid, conc.	0.06 increase
Toluene	Swelled and disintegrated
Trichloroethylene	Swelled and disintegrated
1,2,4-Trichlorobenzene	20 increase
Triethanolamine	0.03 decrease

Source: *A-C Polyethylene*, Semet-Solvay Division, Allied Chemical & Dye Corp., New York, 1954.

of ethylene polymers exposed to weathering for periods of less than one year to more than 20 years.

The solubility and chemical resistance data presented above were determined for high molecular weight products.   Similar information for low

TABLE XLIII

Compatibility of A-C Polyethylene[a]
Grades 6, 7, and G
(50–50 Blends by Melting)

Alkyds (oil modified)	L	Polystyrene	L
Casein	I	Polyvinyl acetate (high molecular weight)	I
Cellulose acetate	I	Polyvinyl acetate (low molecular weight)	M
Chlorinated diphenyls	M	Polyvinyl alcohol	I
Chlorinated paraffin (70%)	I	Polyvinyl butyral	L
Coumarone resins	M	Polyvinyl chloride	L
Ethyl cellulose	M	Rosin esters (all types)	M
Hydrocarbon resins	M	Shellac	I
Hydrogenated castor oil	M	Soya oil	L
Linseed oil (bodied)	L	Soybean protein	I
Linseed oil (raw)	L	Starch and dextrin	I
Melamine-formaldehyde resins	I	Stearates (metal)	I
Methyl cellulose	I	Stearic acid	L
Oleoresinous materials	L	Stearone	M
Phenolics (modified)	I	Styrene-butadiene resins	L
Phenolics (pure)	I	Tar and asphalt	L
Plasticizers (most types)	M	Terpene resins	M
Polyacrylic esters	L	Urea-formaldehyde resins	I
Polyamide resins	I	Waxes (all types)	M
Polyisobutylenes	M	Zinc resinate	I

Source: *A-C Polyethylene,* Semet-Solvay Division, Allied Chemical & Dye Corp., New York, 1954.

M = After melting equal amounts of A-C Polyethylene together at 150°C., they were allowed to cool.   No separation was noted.

L = Limited compatibility after cooling to room temperature.   Due in most cases to excess A-C Polyethylene.

I = Incompatible in all proportions when heated to 150°C. and allowed to cool.

[a] Higher molecular weight resins were blended by means of a hot mutual solvent, usually toluene.   Films were prepared by evaporation of the solvent.

molecular weight (1,500–5,000) polyethylenes is shown in three tables reproduced from the trade bulletin of another commercial producer (883). Table XLII shows the resistance of low molecular weight polyethylenes to liquid chemicals.   Tables XLIII and XLIV show compatibility data.

The effects on high molecular weight polyethylene of inorganic reagents at 100°C., and of various solvents and chemicals after immersion for three

TABLE XLIV

Compatibility of A-C Polyethylene
(Blends by Milling)

Materials Which Form Compatible Mixtures with A-C Polyethylene

Beckacite 1113

Beeswax

Butadiene-styrene resins (some types)

Carnauba wax

Chlorinated paraffin (35%)

Chloroprene rubber

Crepe rubber

Cumar V3

Deenax

Geon Polyblend

GR-N rubber

GR-S rubber

Microcrystalline Wax

Octadecenamide (Acrawax-C)

Oleic acid

Paraffin wax (fully refined)

Polyisobutylene (lower mol. wt. range)

Polypale Ester 10

Polyvinylchloride (limited)

Staybelite Ester 10

Stearic Acid

Thiokol

Vinylchloride–vinyl acetate (limited)

Materials Which Do Not Form Compatible Mixtures with A-C Polyethylene

Chlorinated rubber (Parlon)

Ethyl cellulose[a]

Melamine-formaldehyde (Melmac 401)

Methyl cellulose

Phenolic resins

Polyisobutylene (Vistanex B120) (high mol. wt.)

Polystyrene (Bakelite)

Polystyrene resin (Piccolastic C75)

Polyvinyl butyral (Vinylite XYHL)

Rosin

Saran

Shellac

Source: *A-C Polyethylene*, Semet-Solvay Division, Allied Chemical & Dye Corp., New York, 1954.

[a] May be rendered miscible by the addition of a mutual solvent (hydrogenated castor oil, fatty acids).

The above materials were blended on a two-roll rubber mill, at the melting temperature of the blend, with various grades of A-C Polyethylene. Compatible mixtures formed clear melts both during milling and after cooling. Incompatible mixtures formed cloudy films or fell apart during milling.

The above data do not necessarily apply in formulations employing *emulsifiable* grades of A-C Polyethylene.

TABLE XLV

Effect of Reagents at 100°C. on Polyethylene

Reagent	Effect
Conc. HCl ⎫	
Dilute HNO₃ ⎬	None after 24 hr.
Dilute H₂SO₄ ⎪	
50% NaOH ⎭	
Conc. HNO₃	Some discoloration
Conc. H₂SO₄	Some charring

Source: *Ind. Eng. Chem.*, **37**, 530 (1945).

TABLE XLVI

Effect of Various Chemicals on Polyethylene after 3-Month Contact

| Reagent | On Removal from Reagent | | After 24 Hr. Conditioning at Room Temp. | | |
	Change in Wt., %	Appear-ance	Tensile Strength, Lb./Sq. In.	Elonga-tion, %	Resist-ance Rating[a]
A. Inorganic Acids and Bases					
H_2SO_4, conc.	+ 0.13	No change	1458	462	E
H_2SO_4, 10%	+ 0.04	No change	1370	483	E
HCl, conc.	+ 0.13	No change	1406	258	G
HCl, 10%	+ 0.20	No change	1442	336	E
HNO_3, conc.	+ 3.02	No change	1093	71	F
HNO_3, 10%	+ 0.22	No change	1387	325	E
NaOH, 50%	+ 0.13	No change	1432	313	E
NH_4OH, conc.	+ 0.31	No change	1378	371	E
B. Oxygenated Organic Compounds					
Ethanol (denatured)	− 0.02	No change	1550	421	E
Acetone	+ 0.03	No change	1363	379	E
Ethyl acetate	+ 2.76	No change	1295	325	E
Dioxane	+ 0.38	No change	1368	382	E
Butyraldehyde	+ 3.06	No change	1245	417	E
Linseed oil	+ 0.88	No change	1410	483	E
Triethanolamine	+ 0.08	No change	1408	379	E
Camphor oil	+17.42	Swollen	1375	483	G
C. Hydrocarbons					
Ethyl gasoline	+11.75	Swollen	1430	508	G
Benzene	− 0.86	No change	1464	429	E
Xylene	− 0.70	No change	1623	479	E
Lubricating oil	+ 7.54	Swollen slightly	954	167	F
Carbon tetrachloride	+22.35	Swollen	1560	475	E
Ethylene dichloride	+ 0.80	No change	1526	300	E
Trichlorobenzene	+26.33	Swollen	1450	442	G
D. Aqueous Solutions of Salts					
Na bisulfite, 10%	+ 0.17	No change	1310	483	E
Ca chloride, 15%	+ 0.70	No change	1380	483	E
Ca hypochlorite (bleaching soln.)	+ 0.06	No change	1330	375	E
Duponol ME (fatty alcohol sulfate), 10%	+ 0.04	No change	1225	463	G
Ferric sulfate, 15%	+ 0.02	No change	1307	467	E

Source: *Ind. Eng. Chem.*, **37**, 530 (1945).

[a] E = excellent, G = good, F = fair.

months, were determined by Hahn, Macht, and Fletcher (178), as shown in Tables XLV and XLVI.

Polyethylene was also found by Maybeck and Iwanow (619) to be resistant to an aqueous solution of NaClO$_2$ (0.5%), adjusted with acetic acid to a pH of 4.0 at 80°C.

The complex solubility behavior of polyethylene, with its structure intermediate between that of an amorphous polymer and an entirely

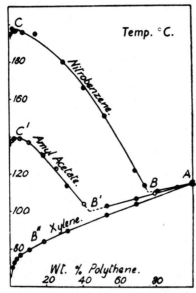

Fig. 102. Border curves for polyethylene in nitrobenzene, amyl acetate, and xylene. (*Trans. Faraday Soc.*, **42**, 11, 1946.)

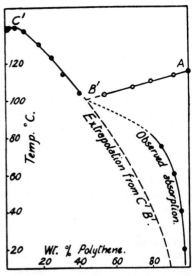

Fig. 103. Absorption of amyl acetate by solid polyethylene. Relation to liquid-liquid phase equilibria. (*Trans. Faraday Soc.*, **42**, 12, 1946.)

crystalline long-chain material, has been further investigated by Richards (226) and found in agreement with theoretical work by Huggins (117,137), Flory (116,132), and Gee (135). With poor solvents which are incompletely miscible with liquid polyethylene, such as nitrobenzene, a plot of the composition against the minimum temperature at which a single phase is stable shows a maximum. Good solvents such as xylene do not show such a maximum; in this case, the solubility curve represents the depression of the melting point of the polyethylene crystallites by the solvent. This is demonstrated in Figure 102.

Solid, semicrystalline polyethylene absorbs and reaches equilibrium with liquids. The amount of absorption increases with rise in temperature but is less than would be expected for a completely amorphous material. Precipitation of solid polyethylene on cooling a solution leads to a fractionation, the high molecular weight species being essentially precipitated first. This relationship is shown in Figure 103, which is based upon the data presented in Table XLVII.

TABLE XLVII

Equilibrium between Solid Polyethylene (M.W. 17,000) and Solvents

Temp., °C.	Weight % of Solvent in Swollen Polyethylene at Equilibrium		
	Xylene	Amyl Acetate	Nitrobenzene
20	14.7	3.0	1.8
40	19.7	4.5	2.4
60	31.0	8.0	5.0
75	..	15.0	11.0

Source: *Trans. Faraday Soc.*, **42**, 11 (1946).

High molecular weight polyethylenes are less soluble and absorb less liquid than low molecular weight products. When the solvent is not completely miscible with liquid polyethylene, the critical composition occurs at a lower polyethylene concentration. Of polyethylene samples of the same average molecular weight, those containing the higher proportion of short chain material are the more soluble and swell more in organic liquids. The increase in critical solution temperature with increased molecular weight is indicated in Figure 104. The effect of molecular weight on xylene absorption at 20°C. is shown in Table XLVIII; on xylene solubility at 70°C., in Table XLIX.

TABLE XLVIII

Effect of Molecular Weight on Xylene Absorption at 20°C.

Molecular Weight	Weight % Xylene in Equilibrium with Solid at 20°C.
9,400	21.4
14,000	18.2
16,000	14.7
17,000	11.7
23,000	11.2
40,000	9.9

Source: *Trans. Faraday Soc.*, **42**, 18 (1946).

TABLE XLIX

Effect of Molecular Weight on Solubility at 70°C.

Molecular Weight	Solubility in Xylene at 70°C. (Weight %)
9,400	12.0
11,000	10.0
13,000	2.0
16,000	0.3
31,000	0.05
40,000	ca. 0.01

Source: *Trans. Faraday Soc.*, **42**, 17 (1946).

It was further found by Richards that polyethylene samples of the same molecular weight can vary in their solubilities if their molecular weight distributions are different; those with the broader distribution have the greater solubility. The supporting experimental data are tabulated in Table L and presented graphically in Figure 105.

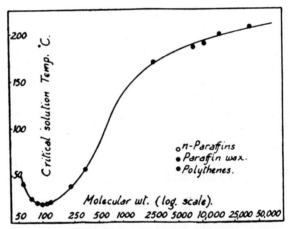

Fig. 104. Increase in critical solution temperature with rise in molecular weight. (Nitrobenzene as solvent.) (*Trans. Faraday Soc.*, **42**, 16, 1946.)

Chain-branching, by increasing the entropy of the amorphous region, reduces the melting point and crystallinity of polyethylene. Experimental evidence for this has been presented by Muthana and Mark (407) in a study of six polyethylene samples of increasing degrees of branching. A semi-empirical constant (μ), essentially independent of the molecular weight and characteristic for the interaction of the molecules of the solvent

TABLE L

Molecular Weight Distribution and Solvent Absorption

Liquid	Molecular Weight of Polyethylene	Percent Extracted by Benzene at 20°C.	Weight % of Liquid Absorbed
Xylene (20°C.)	13,800	1.1	15.1
	14,000	1.5	18.2
	13,500	12.0	39.0
Hydraulic oil (75°C.)	20,800	0.7	32.5
	20,000	1.5	40.6
	20,600	1.9	51.0

Source: *Trans. Faraday Soc.*, **42**, 19 (1946).

(xylene) with the segments of the macromolecules, is derived as a convenient measure of polymer solubility.   In Table LI, the polyethylene
samples are arranged according to the value of CH_2/CH_3, in decreasing

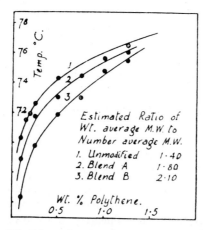

Fig. 105. Effect of artificial broadening of molecular
weight distribution on solubility in xylene. (*Trans.
Faraday Soc.*, **42**, 19, 1946.)

order of branching.   The density generally increases as branching decreases.   The μ values show a general tendency to decrease as branching
decreases, indicating that the solubility of the more highly branched polyethylene molecules in xylene is greater than that of the less-branched
molecules.   The refractive indices of the same samples were studied by
Baccaredda and Schiavinato (823); see Section 6.8.

Richards (226) further investigated the effect of solvent type on the solubility and swelling of polyethylene and the factors influencing the rate of swelling and solution. The best solvents, i.e., those liquids which dissolve a given quantity of polyethylene at the lowest temperatures, are absorbed to the greatest extent by solid polyethylene (hydrocarbons and halogenated hydrocarbons). The amount of absorption decreases as the heat of mixing, indicated by the differences between the cohesive energy densities of polyethylene and the liquid, increases.

TABLE LI

Relationship between Solubility and Crystallinity (Density) of Polyethylenes

Sample No.	Density[a]	Ratio CH_2 to CH_3[a]	Temp., °C.	$\overline{M}_n \times 10^{-3}$	μ Value
1	0.91	12	72.7	9.91	0.516
2	0.917	21	72.7	26.20	0.511
3	0.925	22	72.7	11.60	0.514
4	0.929	38	72.7	16.66	0.506
5	0.926	62	72.7	38.10	0.507
6	0.936	330	91.6	37.30	0.503

Source: *J. Polymer Sci.*, **4**, 528 (1949).
[a] These data were supplied by W. M. D. Bryant and W. Franta of duPont.

A test procedure for the determination of the maximum solubility of unfractionated polyethylene resins under equilibrium conditions has been reported by Myers (159,867). In Figure 106, equilibrium temperature-solubility data for four polyethylene resins in dilute solution are compared with similar data from the literature for several paraffin waxes and two normal paraffins. The equilibrium (cloud) temperature is the temperature at which a hot solution of known concentration shows gelation and/or precipitation upon cooling. The linearity of these curves was predicted on the basis of theoretical considerations.

Figure 107 shows the effect of solvent type on the weight percent solubility of a polyethylene as a function of temperature. While insoluble in all organic solvents at ordinary temperature, polyethylene begins to dissolve in a number of organic solvents at 50–60°C., in agreement with thermodynamic concepts for crystalline materials. Carbon tetrachloride is the most effective solvent, toluene and xylene are intermediate, and 1,1,2-trichloroethane is the poorest of the four solvents shown. The extreme temperature sensitivity of solubility is apparent.

Minimum equilibrium temperatures of solutions (1%) of the same

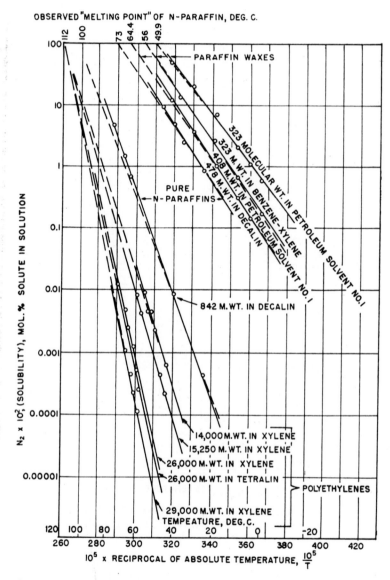

Fig. 106. Solubility of polyethylenes and paraffin waxes *versus* temperature.
(*J. Polymer Sci.*, **13,** 556, 1954.)

polyethylene in several solvents are presented in Table LII. The best solvents appear to be highly chlorinated ethylenes.

The solubility in xylene of a polyethylene resin is compared with that of two commercial paraffin waxes in Figure 108. The occurrence of gelation in the high concentration range for high molecular weight polyethylene is significant.

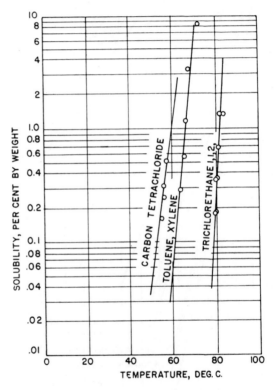

Fig. 107. Solubility of polyethylene DYNH *versus* temperature. (*J. Polymer Sci.*, **13**, 557, 1954.)

The solubility of four polyethylenes of different molecular weights (DYNH, 21,000; DYNF, 19,000; DYGT, 7,000; DYDT, 4,000) in a refined paraffin wax (m.p. 52°C.), a relatively poor solvent, is illustrated graphically in Figure 109.

A solubility phase diagram for a polyethylene resin in xylene, a good solvent, is shown in Figure 110. The line *AB* represents the solubility

TABLE LII

Comparison of Solvents for DYNH Polyethylene

Solvent	Incipient "Cloud" Temp., °C., of a 1% Soln. by Wt. of DYNH Resin
Carbon disulfide	>46 (B.P.)
Tetrachloroethylene	51.5
1,1,2-Trichloroethylene	55
Methylcyclohexane	56
Carbon tetrachloride	60
n-Heptane	62
Tetralin[a]	62
Hexachloropropane	63
Benzene	63
Xylene	66
Toluene	66
Solvent naphtha (Solvesso No. 2,[b] b. p. range 135–175°C.)	66
Trichlorocumene	66.5
1,1,2-Trichloroethylene, 1,1,2-trichloroethane (1:1)	68
Tetrachloroethane	68
Styrene	69
Hexachlorobutadiene	70
1,1,2-Trichloroethane	82
Paraffin wax, m.p. 52°C.	82
1,2-Dichloroethane	>83 (B.P.)
Technical white oil (Socony No. 309)[c]	86

Source: *J. Polymer Sci.*, **13**, 558 (1954).
[a] "Tetralin" Solvent, duPont.
[b] "Solvesso" Aromatic Solvent, Esso Standard Oil Company.
[c] "Socony," No. 309, Socony-Vacuum Oil Co.

curve; the line AC the border between insolubility and gelation, or partial solubility. Such gelation takes place primarily because of the high molecular weight and semicrystalline, semiamorphous nature of the polymer. The solvent is able to diffuse into amorphous regions and disperse the crystalline phase sufficiently to result in a gel, but it cannot disperse the gel entirely without the assistance of higher temperature.

The influence of chain-branching on solubility was established by comparing the solubilities in tetralin of a polyethylene and a polymethylene sample of similar average molecular weights. As shown in Table LIII, the polymethylene, melting at a higher temperature, is less soluble. A comparison of general properties relative to other hydrocarbon polymers characterized by extreme limits in crystallinity is presented in Table LIV.

The concept of average chemical resistance and of relative medium chemical resistance has been developed by Rocca (417) in an attempt to elucidate the relative chemical stability of high polymers. The average chemical resistance is expressed as the sum of the internal bond energies of the compound divided by the product of the total number of terminal atoms and their valencies. By dividing the average chemical resistance of a compound by the average chemical resistance of the corresponding hydrocarbon, the relative medium chemical resistance is obtained. The

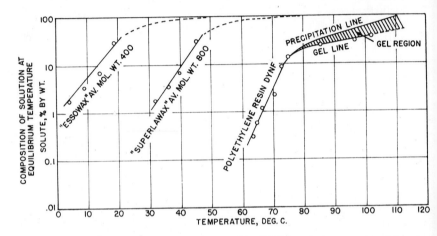

Fig. 108. Solubility diagram of polyethylene resin DYNF and some commercial waxes. (*J. Polymer Sci.*, **13,** 557, 1954.)

chemical stability of a high polymer then is expressed by the average chemical resistance and the relative medium chemical resistance of the unit cells. The polyethylene average chemical resistance is 116.6; relative medium chemical resistance is 1.00. For polytetrachloroethylene these figures become 105.8 and 0.91, respectively; for polytetrafluoroethyl-

TABLE LIII

Comparison of Properties of Polymethylene and Polyethylene

| | | | Solubility | |
Polymer	Average Molecular Weight	Melting Point, °C.	Cloud Temp. in Tetralin, °C.	Conc., wt. %
Polyethylene DXH-38	38,000	112	63	0.1
Polymethylene 88A-1008	38,000	140	84	0.1

Source: *J. Polymer Sci.*, **13,** 561 (1954).

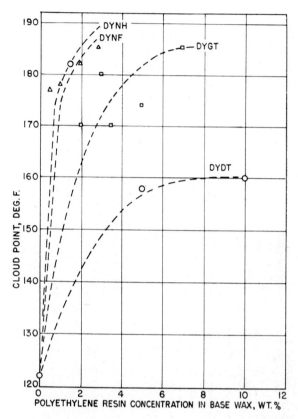

Fig. 109. Cloud point *versus* concentration of various molecular weight polyethylenes in paraffin wax. (*J. Polymer Sci.*, **13**, 559, 1954.)

TABLE LIV

Influence of Hydrocarbon Chain Structure on Properties

Property	Polyiso-butylene	Polyethylene	Polymethylene
Crystallinity	Nil	*ca.* 50%	*ca.* 90%
Solubility	High	Intermediate	Low
Softening temperature	Low	Intermediate	High
Stiffness modulus	Low	Intermediate	High
Intermolecular attraction	Low	Intermediate	High
Relative density	Low	Intermediate	High
Chain symmetry	Low	Intermediate	High

Source: *J. Polymer Sci.*, **13**, 562 (1954).

ene, 147.3 and 1.26; for polyisobutylene, 116.6 and 1.00; polymethyl-acrylate, 109.1 and 0.94; polymethyl methacrylate, 115.6 and 0.99; poly-styrene, 192.6 and 1.65; polyvinyl chloride, 131.9 and 1.13.

The usual effect of absorbed liquids, as pointed out by Richards (226), is a softening of the polymer. The observed reductions in yield point,

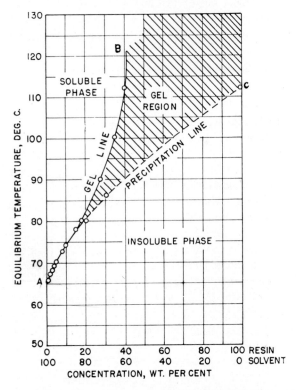

Fig. 110. Phase diagram for resin DYNH-xylene system.
(*J. Polymer Sci.*, **13**, 560, 1954.)

Young's modulus, surface hardness, and shear strength are approximately proportional to the amount of liquid present. While a low molecular weight polyethylene containing a high proportion of absorbed liquid can-not be cold-drawn, the higher molecular weight polymers can absorb large quantities of liquid (e.g., 10–20% of xylene), without losing their tough-ness and flexibility.

Grease Resistance

A procedure based upon a modification of TAPPI Method T454m-44 has been employed by Lavers to measure the grease resistance of a number of packaging materials (292b). Polyethylene was found to be considerably more resistant than glassine and just slightly less so than all grades of cellophane and cellulose acetate, cellulose nitrate, ethyl cellulose, Pliofilm, Vinylite, and Saran. Neither aging nor creasing appreciably affected the grease resistance of the thermoplastic films or of cellophane.

6.2. Environmental Cracking and Weathering

Environmental Cracking

When low molecular weight polyethylenes are exposed to mobile polar liquids, such as acetone, lower alcohols, acetic acid, or nitrobenzene, only slight absorption occurs. At the same time, intense embrittlement of the polyethylene takes place so long as the latter is in contact with the liquid. In the case of very low molecular weight polyethylenes, even the vapor of acetone or ethyl alcohol will cause embrittlement. Higher molecular weight polyethylenes do not show this effect. While alcohols, esters, ethers, and ketones have no measurable swelling effect on high molecular weight polyethylenes, these compounds may cause sudden cracks after a given length of time if a molded piece has internal strains. This phenomenon is referred to as stress cracking or environmental cracking (compare Section 5.2). DeCoste, Malm, and Wallder (533) list as active environments the following compounds: aliphatic and aromatic liquid hydrocarbons, alcohols, organic acids, ester-type plasticizers, vegetable oils, animal oils, mineral oils, metallic soaps, sulfated and sulfonated alcohols, alkanolamines, polyglycol ethers, sodium and potassium hydroxide, depolymerized rubbers, polybutenes, and silicone fluids (1123). The following compounds are listed as inactive environments: water, polyhydric alcohols, sugars, selected saponins, hydrolyzed proteins, rosin, selected asphalts, paraffin wax, bentonite, acid, and neutral inorganic salts.

The degree of crystallinity somewhat affects the readiness of polyethylene to crack. That is, samples which are slowly cooled and annealed are somewhat inferior in crack resistance to rapidly cooled and quenched samples. When the resin is cooled slowly from the melt, a greater degree of crystallinity results and the product is noticeably stiffer. This would introduce higher stresses which explains at least partially the greater tendency for the annealed specimens to crack. However, the improvement achieved by quenching is only temporary and disappears after 35 days of shelf aging. This is shown graphically in Figure 111. The high-density polyethylenes recently developed on a commercial scale, on the other

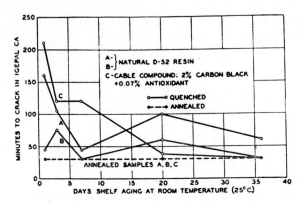

Fig. 111. Effect of shelf aging on crack resistance of quenched and annealed polyethylene. (*Ind. Eng. Chem.*, **43**, 120, 1951.)

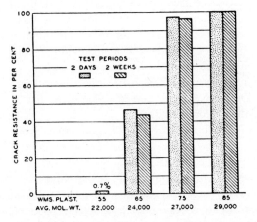

Fig. 112. Effect of molecular weight on crack resistance. (Cracking test; compounds contain 2% carbon black and 0.07% antioxidant.) (*Ind. Eng. Chem.*, **43**, 119, 1951.)

hand, are described as particularly resistant to environmental cracking (see Section 6.19).

The higher the molecular weight of a polyethylene, the more resistant it becomes to cracking, as demonstrated in Figure 112.

The stress-corrosion problem in polyethylene can be solved in many cases either by increasing the molecular weight or by adding other materials, such as polyisobutylene, butyl rubber, or certain petroleum resins. The effect of addition of polyisobutylene on the crack resistance of polyethylene is shown in Figure 113.   Some additives seriously affect the chemical resistance of the blend.   As pointed out by Bockhoff and Neumann (828), polyethylene can be very effectively improved in its stress-

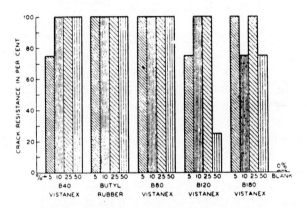

Fig. 113. Effect of addition of polyisobutylene on crack resistance of polyethylene. (Contains 2% carbon black and 0.07% antioxidant.) (*Ind. Eng. Chem.*, **43**, 120, 1951.)

cracking resistance without any appreciable decrease in its chemical-corrosion resistance, through the proper blending of several new types of resins.

Weathering

Biggs (527) of the Bell Telephone Research Laboratories has made a theoretical study of the effect of exposure of organic polymers to water, oxygen, and ozone.   Water attack may cause failure of the type in which surface effects are pronounced and in which electrical properties deteriorate. The attack of ozone is most pronounced in those organic molecules where unsaturation exists.   In this case, ozonides form and subsequently decompose with a consequent rupture of the molecular chain.   Cleavage of C—C or C═C bonds results in smaller molecular aggregates, causing a serious change in physical properties.   It is considered that in the case of polymers of high molecular weights, for example polyethylene, even a small weight percentage of oxygen, amounting to a relatively large number of oxygen atoms compared to the number of polymer molecules, can result in very drastic effects. Once some free radicals are formed, chain reactions may be set up at increasing rates that result in rapid failure. This would explain why a given amount of antioxidant is much more effective initially than if incorporated into the composition after partial degradation has already taken place. Carbon black is an effective inhibitor of the chain reactions, and in some cases phenyl salicylate may also be effective in absorbing actinic radiant energy which may activate free-radical mechanisms.

Crack resistance and weathering of polyethylene were studied by Haine, Smith, and Smith (605) from the point of view of extrusion conditions. They found that higher compounding temperatures and cold-quenching increased resistance to cracking. They also established that the addition of up to 5% of pigments, fillers, or antioxidants has no adverse effect on crack resistance, while additives such as rubber and polyisobutylene may improve it.

The effects of outdoor aging of various types of plastic materials under widely different climates were investigated by Yustein, Winans, and Stark (891). Mechanisms and types of chemical corrosion of polyethylene and numerous other plastics are treated and discussed by Eifflaender (601).

Blake and Kitchin (384) studied the effect of soil microorganisms on various insulating materials. Laboratory conditions were chosen purposely to favor and accelerate microbial attack so that failures simulating those occurring after 10 or more years of service took place in a few months or less. Parallel tests on sterile soil and on inactive soil established that failures were caused by living microorganisms. The mechanism of this microbial attack was not established and, in some cases, profound electrical failure occurred even without any visible surface defects. Insulating compositions of polyethylene, polyvinyl chloride, and Neoprene were found to be of inherently greater resistance than GR-S, butyl rubber, or gutta percha, while vulcanizates of natural rubber were most susceptible to microorganisms.

6.3. Permeability

The permeation of gases and vapors through elastic and plastic membranes is regarded as a combination of the two functions of solution and diffusion, that is, as a process in which the gas first dissolves in the solid, then diffuses to a position of lower concentration, and finally evaporates. Passage through pores or cracks is not assumed to play any role in the case of plastomers.   Otherwise, there is a great resemblance between the solubility behavior of a gas in an organic liquid and in an elastomer.   In the case of polyethylene, permeation by most polar-type organic liquids is very low.   Permeation of nonpolar organic liquids is somewhat higher because of the nonpolar nature of the polyethylene.

An important property of polyethylene is its low water-permeability (294).   On the other hand, polyethylene has a high permeability to organic vapors (e.g., dibutyl ether, diethyl ether, gasoline, carbon tetrachloride, carbon disulfide) and to gases (e.g., oxygen, carbon dioxide).   Permeability increases with temperature.

The combination of relatively high permeability to oxygen and carbon dioxide, with low permeability to water vapor, makes polyethylene most suitable for packaging fresh produce, since the latter can continue to breathe and remain fresh without the loss of water.   On the other hand, the permeability of polyethylene to many aromatic compounds and essential oils still limits its use as containers in the toilet goods and perfume industries (814).

Investigations by Reitlinger (160) of the relation of microstructure to gas permeability of polyethylene, polybutadiene, polystyrene, and other high polymer compounds led to the conclusions that permeability (a), rises with increased curvature of the primary valence chain and with the size of the side chains; (b), is independent of the length of the primary valence chains; (c), decreases with increased energy of intermolecular bonding.   Further, the main avenues of penetration for such molecules as hydrogen are along the interfaces of nonpolar groups or portions of the main macromolecular chains.   More recently, Houwink (289) has studied the influence of entropy and internal energy on the permeabilities of polyethylene, polyamides, polyvinyl chloride and polystyrene.

The permeability data reported in this section refer to high-pressure polyethylene only.   It will be shown in a subsequent section (Section 6.19) that a highly unbranched, highly crystalline, high-density polyethylene has considerably lower permeability for gases, liquids, and moisture vapor than high-pressure polyethylene.

Gas Permeability

The relatively high permeability of gases through polyethylene films (in 10^{-8} cm.^{2}-sec.$^{-1}$-atm.$^{-1}$) is demonstrated by the comparative data (474) shown in Table LV.

An isostatic method for the determination of gas permeabilities has been applied by Davis (213) to determine the permeability of polyethylene and

TABLE LV

Permeability of Gases Through Polymers

Material	Temp., °C.	H₂	O₂	CO₂
Polyethylene	20–22	3.9	1.	50
Polystyrene	20–22	11.3	1.4	7
Polyisobutylene	25	4.9	0.9	3.8
Pliofilm	25	0.9	0.07	0.12
Koroseal	21	. .	0.1	0.43
Vinylite	25	4	0.7	4
Saran	25	0.03	0.0006	0.001
Polyvinyl alcohol	8	. .	0.0003	0.0003
Cellophane	21	0.05	0.0003	0.001
Cellulose acetate	21	4	0.6	4.5

Source: R. Howwink, *Elastomers and Plastomers*, Vol. I, 315. Elsevier Publishing Co., Inc., Houston, Tex., 1950.

other sheet-forming plastic materials to oxygen and to carbon dioxide at various temperatures and relative humidities. In this method, the test sheet forms the partition between two chambers of a diffusion cell. The

Fig. 114. Partially assembled diffusion cell and press. (*Paper Trade J.*, **123** [9], 35, 1946.)

test gas is passed over one side of the sheet and a second "sweep" gas over the other, both gases being preconditioned to the desired humidity. The diffusion cell is illustrated in Figure 114. Method and apparatus for carbon dioxide permeability determination are presented in Figures 115 and 116; for oxygen permeability, in Figures 117 and 118. The carbon dioxide and oxygen permeabilities of polyethylene and other sheet materials determined by this method are shown in Table LVI.

The permeability of polyethylene to helium, hydrogen, and nitrogen has been determined by Barrer (76,91). The sorption of nitrogen and krypton on polyethylene and on nylon and collagen has been further investigated by Zettlemoyer, Chand, and Gamble (493) at the temperature of liquid nitrogen and liquid oxygen. The adsorption curves indicate a break where the monolayer is completed. The adsorption data gave surface areas that agreed very well for the two gases at different temperatures on the same sample. The thermodynamic functions for the adsorptions

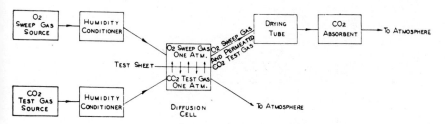

Fig. 115. Method for carbon dioxide permeability determination. (*Paper Trade J.*, **123** [9], 34, 1946.)

show that, for krypton, the heat of adsorption curves rise as more gas is added to the surface, and then fall off again after one monolayer is completed. The entropy curves for krypton on polyethylene and nylon fall toward limiting values as one layer is completed.

Gas-transfer characteristics of polyethylene and other plastic films over a considerable temperature range were determined by Freeman, Sheridan, and Renfrew (849) for the purpose of selecting the most promising materials to be used as plastic balloons in service at high altitudes. As indicated by Figure 119, the permeability of polyethylene to gases decreases with decreasing temperature. For example, the permeability at room temperature for helium is about one thousand times that at $-70°C$. Both molecular weight and film orientation appear not to affect the permeability of polyethylene films to any significant degree. Permeability studies on polyethylene and other plastic films in the higher temperature ranges are tabulated in Table LVII.

Table LVIII shows increases in porosity with flexing and resistance to damage from flexing as a function of thickness of polyethylene film.

A study of the permeability of plastic films has been reported recently

TABLE LVI

A. Carbon Dioxide and Oxygen Permeabilities of Various Sheet Materials

Sheet Material	Thickness, Inches	Temperature, °C.	Relative Humidity, %	Permeation Rate,[a] in Cc./Sq. Meter/ 24 hr.		Specific Permeability,[a] in Cc./Sq. Cm./Min./Cm. Thickness	
				Carbon Dioxide	Oxygen	Carbon Dioxide	Oxygen
Cellophane, No. 300 PT (regenerated cellulose)	0.0008	21	0	5	<1	0.0008×10^{-6}	$<0.0002 \times 10^{-6}$
Cellophane, No. 300 PT	0.0008	21	30	12	..	0.0017×10^{-6}	......
Cellophane, No. 300 PT	0.0008	21	75	99	49	0.014×10^{-6}	0.0069×10^{-6}
Cellophane, No. 300 MSAT (lacquered regenerated cellulose)	0.0009	21	0	24	<1	......	......
Cellulose acetate	0.0009	21	0	17,000	2,300	2.7×10^{-6}	0.36×10^{-6}
Cellulose acetate	0.0009	21	75	14,000	1,200	2.3×10^{-6}	0.19×10^{-6}
Ethyl cellulose	0.0010	21	50	120,000	22,000	21.0×10^{-6}	3.8×10^{-6}
Koroseal (polyvinyl chloride composition)	0.0012	8	0	1,000	..	0.22×10^{-6}	......
Koroseal	0.0012	8	75	450	..	0.095×10^{-6}	......
Koroseal	0.0013	8	0	1,000	480	0.23×10^{-6}	0.11×10^{-6}
Koroseal	0.0013	21	50	920	190	0.26×10^{-6}	0.055×10^{-6}
Vinylite (polyvinyl chloride composition)	0.0010	8	0	800	200	0.14×10^{-6}	0.036×10^{-6}
Vinylite	0.0010	8	75	..	150	......	0.027×10^{-6}
Saran (polyvinylidene chloride composition)	0.0013	21	50	14	4	0.0032×10^{-6}	0.0009×10^{-6}

Saran	0.0013	21	0	48	…	0.011 × 10⁻⁶	
Saran	0.0013	8	0	33	33	0.0075 × 10⁻⁶	0.0076 × 10⁻⁶
Saran	0.0013	8	75	35	31	0.0081 × 10⁻⁶	0.0072 × 10⁻⁶
Nylon (polyamide composition)	0.0009	8	0	302	63	0.048 × 10⁻⁶	0.010 × 10⁻⁶
Nylon	0.0009	8	75	170	46	0.027 × 10⁻⁶	0.0073 × 10⁻⁶
Nylon	0.0018	21	50	170	29	0.054 × 10⁻⁶	0.0091 × 10⁻⁶
Parafilm (rubber-wax composition)	0.0050	21	0	640	120	0.56 × 10⁻⁶	0.11 × 10⁻⁶
Parafilm	0.0050	21	75	550	120	0.49 × 10⁻⁶	0.11 × 10⁻⁶
Parafilm	0.0050	16	0	420	…	0.37 × 10⁻⁶	…
Parafilm	0.0050	27	0	840	…	0.74 × 10⁻⁶	…
Parafilm	0.0050	32	0	1,300	…	1.2 × 10⁻⁶	…
Pliofilm, tensilized (rubber hydrochloride)	0.0004	8	0	1,000	240	0.059 × 10⁻⁶	0.017 × 10⁻⁶
Pliofilm, tensilized	0.0004	8	75	…	230	…	0.016 × 10⁻⁶
Pliofilm, tensilized	0.0006	21	0	1,500	…	0.16 × 10⁻⁶	…
Pliofilm, grade NO	0.0009	21	0	310	110	0.049 × 10⁻⁶	0.017 × 10⁻⁶
Pliofilm, grade NO	0.0009	21	75	…	100	…	0.016 × 10⁻⁶
Pliofilm, grade NO	0.0013	21	0	1,500	…	0.34 × 10⁻⁶	…
Pliofilm, grade P2	0.0012	8	0	470	85	0.10 × 10⁻⁶	0.018 × 10⁻⁶
Pliofilm, grade P2	0.0012	8	75	320	66	0.068 × 10⁻⁶	0.014 × 10⁻⁶
Polyethylene	0.0010	22	0	14,000	3,5000	2.5 × 10⁻⁶	0.62 × 10⁻⁶
Polyethylene	0.0030	22	0	610	1,000	3.2 × 10⁻⁶	0.71 × 10⁻⁶

Continued

TABLE LVI (Continued)

Sheet Material	Thickness, Inches	Temperature, °C.	Relative Humidity, %	Permeation Rate,[a] in Cc./Sq. Meter/24 hr.		Specific Permeability,[a] in Cc./Sq. Cm./Min./Cm. Thickness	
				Carbon Dioxide	Oxygen	Carbon Dioxide	Oxygen
Polystyrene	0.0015	22	0	16,000	3,100	4.3×10^{-6}	0.81×10^{-6}
Polystyrene	0.0015	22	75	....	3,200	......	0.85×10^{-6}
Polyvinyl alcohol	0.0008	21	50	380	310	0.053×10^{-6}	0.043×10^{-6}
Polyvinyl alcohol	0.0010	8	0	<1	<1	$<0.0002 \times 10^{-6}$	$<0.0002 \times 10^{-6}$
Polyvinyl alcohol	0.0010	8	75	627	18	0.11×10^{-6}	0.0031×10^{-6}
Polyvinyl butyral	0.0042	21	0	16,000	2,300	12.0×10^{-6}	1.7×10^{-6}
Polyvinyl butyral	0.0042	21	75	16,000	2,400	12.0×10^{-6}	1.8×10^{-6}
Rubber, vulcanized dental dam	0.0087	21	0	45,000	...	69.0×10^{-6}	......
Rubber, RCMA pale crepe cast from solvent	0.0067	20	0	61,000	9,300	72.0×10^{-6}	11.0×10^{-6}
Butyl rubber cast from solvent	0.0195	20	0	810	180	2.8×10^{-6}	0.62×10^{-6}
Vistanex (polyisobutylene) cast from solvent	0.0119	20	0	1,200	160	2.5×10^{-6}	0.34×10^{-6}
Greaseproof paper, 30 lb. (24 × 36—480)	0.0022	27	75	3,100	1,800	1.2×10^{-6}	0.72×10^{-6}
Glassine, 25 lb. (24 × 36—480)	0.0012	21	0	570	660	0.12×10^{-6}	0.14×10^{-6}
Glassine, 25 lb.	0.0012	21	75	610	320	0.13×10^{-6}	0.067×10^{-6}
Glassine, 25 lb.	0.0013	21	0	14,000	17,000	3.3×10^{-6}	4.0×10^{-6}
Glassine, 25 lb.	0.0013	21	75	12,000	14,000	2.8×10^{-6}	3.3×10^{-6}

B. Gas Permeation Rates of Sheet Materials Exhibiting Variable Pore-Type Permeation

Sheet Material	Thickness, Inches	Temperature, °C.	Relative Humidity, %	Difference in Total Pressure, Inches Mineral Oil	Side with Higher Pressure	Permeation Rate[a] in Cc./Sq. Meter/24 Hr.	
						Carbon Dioxide	Oxygen
Sulfite paper, 23 lb.[b] supercalendered	0.0018	26	75	0.0	.....	130,000	.....
Sulfite paper, 23 lb.[b] supercalendered	0.0018	22	0	0.0	.....	120,000	.....
Sulfite paper, 23 lb.[b] supercalendered	0.0018	22	0	0.5	Test gas	250,000	.....
Sulfite paper, coated one side with 28 lb. of paraffin wax	...	26	0	0.0	.....	39	.....
Sulfite paper, coated one side with 28 lb. of paraffin wax	...	26	0	0.5	Test gas	38	.....
Vegetable parchment 35 lb.[b] lard liner	0.0024	21	0	0.0	.....	22,000	31,000
Vegetable parchment 35 lb.[b] lard liner	0.0024	21	0	1.0	Test gas	170,000	170,000
Vegetable parchment 35 lb.[b] lard liner	0.0024	21	0	1.0	Sweep gas	8,000	5,200
Aluminum foil	0.0010	22	75	0.0	.....	79	.....
Aluminum foil	0.0010	22	75	0.1	Sweep gas	.....	91
Aluminum foil	0.0010	22	75	0.6	Sweep gas	.....	91
Aluminum foil	0.0007	22	0	0.3	Sweep gas	1,700	.....
Aluminum foil	0.0007	22	0	0.2	Test gas	1,600	.....
Aluminum foil	0.0007	22	75	0.2	Sweep gas	1,400	.....
Aluminum foil	0.0007	22	75	0.9	Test gas	1,500	.....
Aluminum foil	0.0007	22	75	0.0	.....	.....	1,500
Aluminum foil	0.0007	22	75	0.8	Test gas	.....	1,500
Aluminum foil	0.0005	21	75	0.0	.....	10,000	.....
Aluminum foil	0.0005	21	75	0.6	Test gas	37,000	.....
Aluminum foil	0.0005	21	75	0.0	.....	1,400	.....
Aluminum foil, laminated to kraft paper, 25 lb., with 25 lb. of wax[b]	...	21	75	0.0	.....	8	.....

Source: *Paper Trade J.*, 123 (9), 38, 39 (1946).
[a] Corrected to 760 mm. Hg difference in partial pressure of test gas across test sheet.
[b] Basic ream size (24 × 36—480).

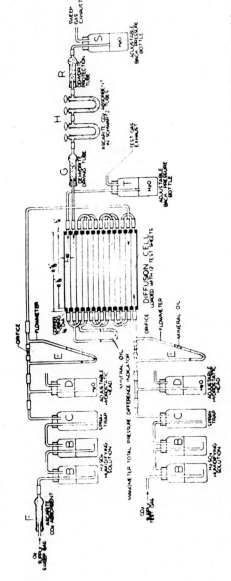

Fig. 116. Apparatus for carbon dioxide permeability determination. (*Paper Trade J.*, **123** [9], 39, 1946.)

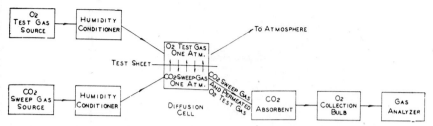

Fig. 117. Method for oxygen permeability determination.   (*Paper Trade J.*, **123** [9], 35, 1946.)

TABLE LVII

Typical Porosities of Various Plastic Films

| | Permeability Constant $\times 10^9$ $P = $ cc.-cm.-sec.-cm.²-cm. Hg | | | | | | | |
| | CO_2 | | H_2 | | O_2 | | N_2 | |
	20°C.	40°C.	20°C.	40°C.	20°C.	40°C.	20°C.	40°C.
Ethyl cellulose	4.10	4.70	2.60	4.00	2.15	3.40	0.66	1.05
Polyethylene	1.45	3.20	0.90	1.93	0.32	0.92	0.11	0.32
Polystyrene	3.50	3.90	9.00	9.20	2.42	2.35	0.78	0.77
Vinylite VB-1920	1.80	2.18	4.99	5.05	..	..	..	..

Source: *Modern Packaging*, **27** (6), 150 (1954).

by Szwarc, Stannett, and co-workers (1028,1030,1035).   A schematic drawing of the equipment used is depicted in Figure 120.   The two cells are made of stainless steel.   The membranes are held and seated in position by means of rubber gaskets and mercury seals.   For measurements with mixed gases, i.e., for mixtures of small amounts of carbon dioxide with large excesses of nitrogen or oxygen, different equipment, shown in Figure 121, was used.

TABLE LVIII

Effect of Mechanical Flexing at −50°C. on Film Porosity
(Helium test gas)

Time of Flexing, Min.	Loss Because of Flexing 1-Mil Film	2-Mil Film
0	0	0
5	0.26	0.10
10	0.28	0.13
15	0.36	0.17
20	0.48	0.27

Source: *Modern Packaging*, **27** (6), 150 (1954).

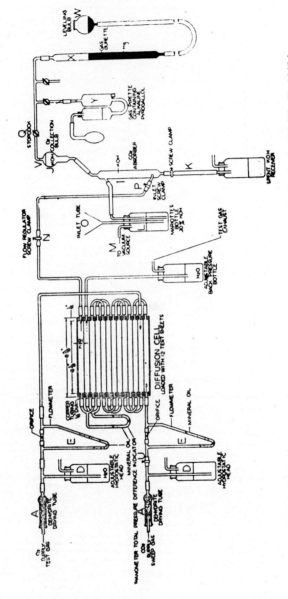

Fig. 118. Apparatus for oxygen permeability determination. (*Paper Trade J.*, **123** [9], 40, 1946.)

In order to measure the effect of mixed gases, measurements of the transmission of one gas in the presence of another were made.   It was shown that changes up to three-fold were sometimes experienced in the case of oxygen and carbon dioxide.   In general, however, the observed effects

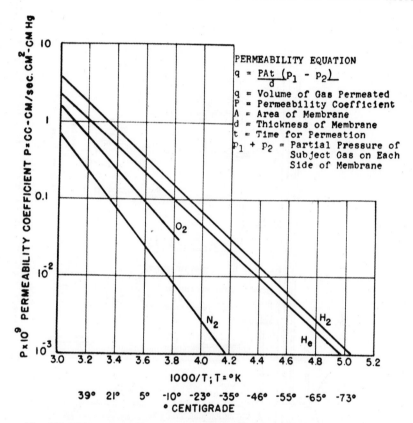

PERMEABILITY EQUATION

$$q = \frac{PAt\ (p_1 - p_2)}{d}$$

q = Volume of Gas Permeated
P = Permeability Coefficient
A = Area of Membrane
d = Thickness of Membrane
t = Time for Permeation
$p_1 + p_2$ = Partial Pressure of Subject Gas on Each Side of Membrane

Fig. 119. Gas permeability for polyethylene film. (*Modern Packaging*, **27** [6], 148, 1954.)

were small. Polyethylene films which have been crosslinked by irradiation have a reduced permeability to gases at high-radiation doses, while the temperature dependence was unchanged (see Section 4.7).   The pertinent data are reported in Table LIX.

Gas permeability, according to Szwarc, Stannett, *et al.* (1035), could be expressed as the product of two factors, one characteristic of the film and one of the gas; further involved is an interaction coefficient with a value

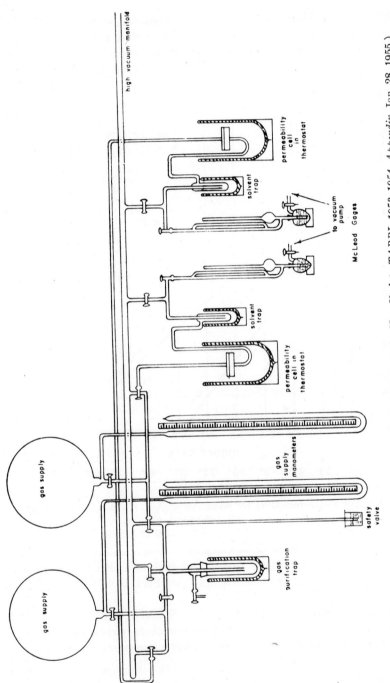

Fig. 120. Gas permeability apparatus. (*Ann. Rept. State Univ. New York to TAPPI, 1953–1954, Appendix*, Jan. 28, 1955.)

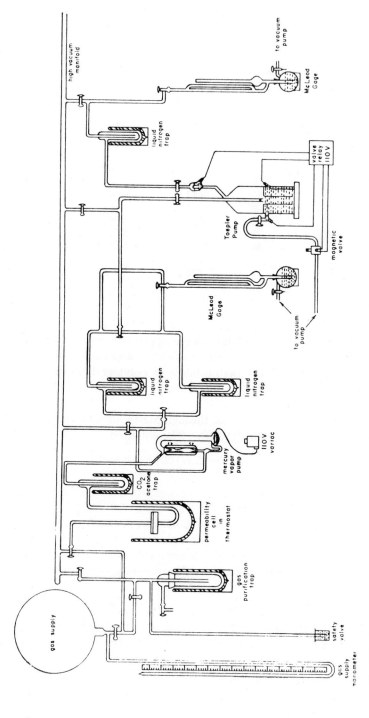

Fig. 121. Gas permeability apparatus (mixed gases). (*Ann. Rept. State Univ. New York to TAPPI, 1953–1954, Appendix*, Jan. 28, 1955.)

TABLE LIX

Permeability Constants for Polyethylene $\times 10^{10}$
(Units cc. s.t.p.-mm./cm.^{2}-sec.-cm. Hg pressure)

Gas	Temp., °C.	Unirradiated	10^7 Roentgens	10^8 Roentgens
Nitrogen	0	2.59	2.67	1.46
	15	7.84	7.72	4.36
	30	21.5	20.1	11.0
	45	54.6	50.6	27.4
Oxygen	0	11.0	..	5.91
	15	27.5	..	15.3
	30	69.4	..	34.8
	45	143	..	73.7
Carbon dioxide	0	54.7	54.6	29.7
	15	130	129	72.7
	30	280	277	152
	45	540	542	287
Methyl bromide	0	501	..	224
	15	975	..	446
	30	1870	..	887
	45	3160	..	1630

Source: See Fig. 121.

close to unity. These calculations were applied to permeability experiments with nitrogen, oxygen, hydrogen sulfide, and carbon dioxide. Additional information on the permeability of polymer films to gases and vapors was presented recently by Waack, Alex, Frisch, Stannett, and Szwarc (1040).

Permeability constants of gases through plastic membranes were correlated by Othmer and Frolich (1009). The equation

$$\log P = [(E^* - \Delta H)/L] \log p + C,$$

where

P = permeability constant,
E^* = activation energy of diffusion, calories per mole,
ΔH = heat of solution, calories per mole,
L = heat of vaporization of reference substance, calories per mole,
p = vapor pressure of reference substance, mm. of Hg or atmospheres, and
C = constant of integration

indicates that if the permeability constant is plotted on logarithmic paper against the vapor pressure of a reference liquid, always taken at the same temperature, a straight line results, the slope of which is given by the value $(E^* - \Delta H)/L$. This has been demonstrated graphically in Figure 122, by using the data of Brubaker and Kammermeyer (715a). In this case,

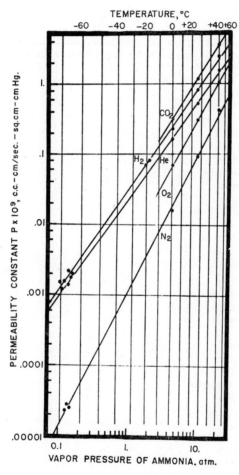

Fig. 122. Logarithms of permeability constant *versus* temperature for various gases through polyethylene. (Temperature scale derived from vapor pressure of ammonia.) (*Ind. Eng. Chem.*, **47**, 1034, 1955.)

the vapor pressure of ammonia was used as the reference substance for determining a temperature scale, because of the relatively low temperatures encountered.

Permeability for Vapors and Various Chemicals and Products

The transmission rates of various polar and nonpolar solvents through unsupported polyethylene films and sheeting are shown in Tables LX, LXI,

TABLE LX

Polyethylene Permeability Values of Some Polar Materials
(Permeability in g./24 hr./100 sq. in. for film 0.001 in. thick at room temperature)

Material	Permeability
Ethylene glycol	0.02
2-Nitro-1-butanol	0.05
Dimethyl phthalate	0.09
Water	0.16
Hydrogen peroxide, 30%	0.33
Formic acid, 85%	0.48
Old Spice Cologne	0.60
n-Octyl alcohol	0.68
Phenol, 94%	0.70
Ethylene chlorohydrin	0.73
Allyl alcohol	0.95
Auvergne Cologne	1.1
n-Butyl alcohol	1.2
Acetic anhydride	1.3
Methyl alcohol	1.6
Ethyl acetoacetate	1.8
Nitroethane	2.0
Nitromethane	2.1
Aniline	2.4
Nitrobenzene	2.6
Glacial acetic acid	2.6
Acetone	7.6
Methyl ethyl ketone	15.0
Ethyl acetate	21.0
Propionaldehyde	25.0
Dimethyl aniline	27.0
Pyridine	29.0
Acetyl chloride	38.0
Monochlorobenzene	38.0
Butyl acetate	40.0
o-Dichlorobenzene	59.0
Ethylene chloride	79.0
Dibutyl ether	200.0
Diethyl ether	410.0
Ethyl bromide	680.0
Chloroform	720.0

Source: *Bakelite Polyethylene for Paper Coatings*, Bakelite Co., p. 8, 1951.

TABLE LXI

Polyethylene Permeability Values of Some Nonpolar Materials
(Permeability in g./24 hr./100 sq. in. for film 0.001 in. thick at room temperature)

Material	Permeability
Kerosene	18
Dioxane	20
Turpentine	61
Styrene	240
Xylene (commercial mixture)	260
Toluene	320
Gasoline (containing tetraethyl lead)	440
Petroleum ether	470
Benzene	490
Carbon tetrachloride	600
Liquid bromine	2100
Carbon disulfide	5200

Source: *Bakelite Polyethylene for Paper Coatings*, Bakelite Co., p. 8, 1951.

TABLE LXII

Polyethylene Permeability Values of Some Common Chemicals
(Permeability in g./24 hr./100 sq. in. for film 0.001 in. thick at room temperature)

Material	Permeability
Xylene sulfonic acid (mixture solid and liquid)	0.045 (gain)
Mineral oil	0.007
Lubricating oil SAE #10	0.009
Oleic acid	0.011
Hydrofluosilicic acid (H_2SiF_6), 26%	0.072
HNO_3, 69%	0.16
Hydrogen peroxide, 30% (not exposed to light)	0.176
Hydrogen peroxide, 30% (exposed to light)	0.352
Camphor (solid)	0.19
Ethyl alcohol, 95%	0.55
HCl, 36%	0.58
Ammonium hydroxide, 26%	1.83

Source: *Bakelite Polyethylene for Paper Coatings*, Bakelite Co., p. 8, 1951.

LXII, and LXIII, reproduced from the trade bulletin of one commercial producer (568). A comparison of transmission rates from liquid phase and vapor phase is shown in Figure 123. Effect of thickness and temperature on permeability are shown in Figures 124 and 125.

Cutler, Kaplan, McLaren, and Mark (532) have investigated the permeability of a 0.0024-cm. film of polyethylene to solvent vapors at 25°C.

at a series of vapor pressures. They demonstrated that the permeability is a straight-line function of the vapor pressure and concluded that it is related qualitatively to the dipole moment and physical structure of the

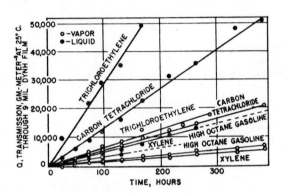

Fig. 123. Comparison of transmission rates from liquid phase and vapor phase. Transmission *versus* time for polyethylene film. (*Bakelite Polyethylene for Paper Coatings*, Bakelite Co., p. 6, 1951.)

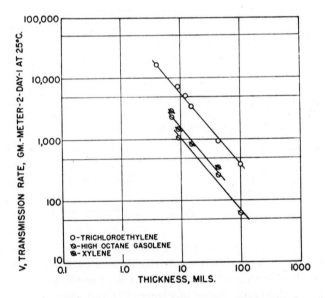

Fig. 124. Transmission rate *versus* thickness for trichloroethylene, high octane gasoline, and xylene through polyethylene DYNH film. (*Bakelite Polyethylene for Paper Coatings*, Bakelite Co., p. 6, 1951.)

TABLE LXIII

Polyethylene Permeability Values of Some Special Commercial Products
(Permeability in g./24 hr./100 sq. in. for film 0.001 in. thick at room temperature)

Material	Permeability
Chlorinated diphenyl oil	negligible
Bath salts (solid)	0.004
Baby oil	0.008
Baby oil, antiseptic	0.027
Naphthenic base oil	0.050
Coiffure lacquer	0.15
Foam shampoo	0.16
Medicinal cream at room temperature	0.16
Medicinal cream at 50°C.	2.5
Hair perfume	0.17
Dental cream	0.18
Imitation maple flavor (alcohol base)	0.20
Hair dressing	0.21
Oil shampoo	0.24
Liquid dentifrice	0.36
After shaving lotion	0.47
Deodorant cologne	0.56
Iodine lotion	0.56
Household air refresher (ethyl alcohol base)	1.8
Mixture of chlorinated diphenyl and chlorinated benzene	4.9
Soil fumigant (chlorinated aliphatic base)	8.0
Rust preventative (pine oil base)	32.0

Source: *Bakelite Polyethylene for Paper Coatings*, Bakelite, Co., p. 8, 1951.

vapor, as well as to the solubility of the vapor in the film.   Quantitative data are shown in Table LXIV.

The loss in weight from 200-ml. bottles of polyethylene of 188 sq. cm. surface area at 35°C. has been determined by Villabona (641).   Results of these tests are shown in Table LXV.

Data for the sorption of water, ethyl alcohol, and acetonitrile by polyethylene and other plastic materials were determined by Cutler and McLaren (725), and diffusion constants were calculated.

Knowledge of the actual shelf-life performance of products in polyethylene bottles is important in the packaging field.   In an extensive study of the behavior of a large number of typical chemicals and products, Pinsky, Nielsen, and Parliman of the Plax Corporation (874,1013), published test methods and data and means for predicting the performance of any specific product in polyethylene containers.   Selected data from this report are presented in Table LXVI.   The weight losses of 67 materials at the various conditions studied in the program are reported.   The permeability (P) factor is expressed in grams per 24 hours per mil thickness per 100 sq. in. at the temperatures specified.

In a study of the effectiveness of p-dichlorobenzene in plastic garment bags, data on the permeability of polyethylene and other plastic films to vapors of p-dichlorobenzene were presented by Arnold (1125).

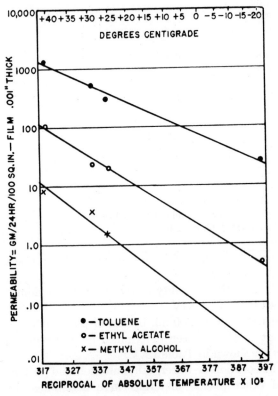

Fig. 125. Effect of temperature on the permeability of organic liquids through polyethylene DYNH film.   (*Bakelite Polyethylene for Paper Coatings*, Bakelite Co., p. 7, 1951.)

Szwarc, Stannett, Meyer, and Rogers (1030,1035), in the course of the permeability work already mentioned, observed an unexpected increase in the permeability constants of certain vapors (methyl bromide, isobutylene) at low temperatures and high pressures (approaching the condensa-

TABLE LXIV

Relationship Between Vapor Pressure and Permeability

Solvent	Vapor pressure, mm. Hg	Permeability, g./sq. m./hr.
Water	4.7	0.021
	22.4	0.108
Propanol	7.0	0.07
	19.0	0.26
Acetone	6.2	0.25
	25.3	0.18
Propionitrile	4.5	0.03
	23.5	0.35
Benzene	4.8	0.09
	21.0	1.16
Hexane	6.0	0.025
	23.0	0.525
Cyclohexane	6.1	0.019
	24.0	0.57
1,2-Dichloroethane	7.7	0.32
	21.2	1.72
trans-Dichloroethylene	5.6	0.23
	25.8	2.10
Nitroethane	4.5	0.11
	19.5	0.70

Source: *Tappi,* **34,** 404 (1951).

TABLE LXV

Permeation of Solvents Through Polyethylene

Compound	Wt. Sample (g.)	Wt. Loss (g./24 Hr.)
Trichloroethylene	42	15
Trichloroethylene	120	19
Trichloroethylene	240	36
Carbon tetrachloride	142	13
Benzene	77	6
Benzene	72	5
Benzene	106	7
Benzene-trichloroethylene (1:1)	115	16
Ligroin	70	3
Petroleum	64	1
Petroleum-acetone (1:1)	93	1

Source: *Rev. Plásticos* (*Madrid*), **3,** 304 (1952).

tion range).   This phenomenon is illustrated in Figure 126.   The effect of changing the pressure is shown in Figure 127.   These results are explained by a "clustering" hypothesis; at temperatures and pressures where the

TABLE LXVI

Weight Loss of Materials in 4-Oz. Boston Round Polyethylene Bottles—Expressed in
P-Factor, 365-Day Loss (g.) and 365-Day Percentage Loss

Test material	Temperature, °F.	Net Contents in g.	365-Day Change in g. Measured	365-Day Change in % Measured	P-factor, g./24 hr.- 100 in.² through 1 mil
Sulfuric acid, 36%	32	148.974	+0.399	+0.268	+0.217
	70	145.261	−1.287	−0.885	−0.631
	100	148.590	−1.204	−0.811	−0.569
	130	138.740	−6.466	−4.705	−3.040
Sulfuric acid, 93%	32	169.503	+2.179	+1.287	+1.027
	70	163.557	+0.239	+0.146	+0.039
	100	167.063	+0.203	+0.121	+0.111
	130	175.550	−0.363(181)	−0.207	−0.348
	165	170.201	−1.142(30)	−0.671	−0.629
Hydrochloric acid, 20%	32	116.608	+0.420	+0.360	+0.233
	70	120.170	−0.271	−0.226	−0.123
	100	117.070	−0.981	−0.838	−0.440
	130	125.443	−5.531	−4.410	−2.630
	165	122.679	−10.220(152)	−8.331	−11.200
Hydrochloric acid, 36%	32	133.721	+0.941	+0.704	....
	70	132.736	−1.581	−1.191	−0.853
	100	132.541	−5.416	−4.086	−3.560
	130	133.573	−17.052	−12.780	−6.920
Nitric acid, 20%	32	127.166	−0.072	−0.057	−0.097
	70	129.474	−0.327	−0.253	−0.161
	100	130.660	−1.355	−1.037	−0.648
	130	125.904	−7.921	−6.300	−3.740
	165	133.219	−26.647(29)[a]	−20.002[a]	−14.750
Nitric acid, 67%	32	157.619	+0.429	+0.272	+0.275
	70	157.655	−0.372	−0.236	−0.170
	100	160.054	−0.240(29)	−0.150	−1.130
	130	164.900	−0.516(10)	−0.313	−9.080
Phosphoric acid	32	154.527	+0.784	+0.507	+0.386
	70	165.680	+0.138	+0.083	+0.003
	100	160.822	−0.004	−0.002	....
	130	173.951	−0.525	−0.302	−0.201
	165	163.657	−1.463(152)	−0.894	−1.548
Fluoboric acid	32	148.087	+0.666	+0.450	+0.308
	70	148.484	−0.029	−0.020	....
	100	150.473	−0.573	−0.381	−0.282
	130	154.019	−3.351	−2.175	−1.570
	165	145.804	−5.178(152)	−3.551	−5.655
Hydrofluoric acid	32	135.589	+0.421	+0.310	+0.181
	70	135.674	−0.418	−0.308	−0.214
	100	132.967	−1.682	−1.265	−0.783

TABLE LXVI (*Continued*)

Test material	Temperature, °F.	Net Contents in g.	365-Day Change in g. Measured	365-Day Change in % Measured	P-factor, g./24 hr.-100 in.² through 1 mil
	130	136.374	−6.192	−4.540	−2.920
	165	136.100	−8.256(126)	−6.066	−9.530
Sodium hydroxide solid	32	120.181	+0.492	+0.409	+0.241
	70	132.028	+0.199	+0.151	+0.090
	100	130.937	+0.162	+0.124	+0.082
	130	143.311	+0.321	+0.224	+0.212
	165	132.595	+0.093(152)	+0.070	+0.139
Sodium hydroxide, 40%	32	151.412	+0.273	+0.180	+0.060
	70	157.666	−0.034	−0.022	....
	100	158.351	−0.568	−0.359	−0.270
	130	148.896	−4.046	−2.720	−1.915
	165	164.368	−5.621(152)	−3.420	−6.420
Aqua ammonia, 10%	32	106.978	−0.968	−0.905	−0.473
	70	107.744	−1.227	−1.139	−0.620
	100	108.751	−3.534	−3.250	−1.803
Aqua Ammonia, 28%	32	101.072	−4.190	−4.146	−2.145
	70	99.305	−4.145	−4.174	−2.090
	100	101.008	−12.280	−12.157	−6.650
Formic acid	32	137.927	−0.357	−0.250	−0.251
	70	137.184	−1.374	−1.002	−0.666
	100	135.961	−5.776	−4.248	−2.790
	130	134.291	−25.219	−18.800	−12.030
	165	137.856	−43.551(146)	−31.592	−51.600
Acetic acid, 56%	32	119.342	−0.519	−0.435	−0.268
	70	119.689	−1.247	−1.042	−0.580
	100	119.917	−4.914	−4.098	−2.265
	130	120.936	−21.056	−17.420	−9.800
	165	119.201	−8.384(29)	−7.033	−50.500
Acetic acid, glacial	32	118.429	−0.569	−0.480	−0.351
	70	118.032	−6.505	−5.511	−3.080
	100	117.791	−28.201	−23.942	−13.550
	130	116.017	−102.365(272)	−88.250	−66.000
	165	118.201	−52.351(29)	−44.290	304.000
Oxalic acid	32	92.534	+0.487	+0.526	+0.360
	70	101.886	+0.122	+0.120	+0.084
	100	97.417	−0.078	−0.080	....
	130	106.446	−0.480	−0.450	−0.205
	165	103.399	−1.127(146)	−1.090	−0.226
Methyl alcohol	32	89.348	−0.507	−0.567	−0.253
	70	90.154	−2.617	−2.903	−1.220
	100	91.075	−11.415	−12.534	−5.350
	130	89.608	−58.536	−65.300	−27.800

Continued

TABLE LXVI (*Continued*)

Test material	Temperature, °F.	Net Contents in g.	365-Day Change in g. Measured	365-Day Change in % Measured	P-factor, g./24 hr.-100 in.² through 1 mil
n-Propyl alcohol	32	85.576	−0.084	−0.098	−0.072
	70	87.663	−1.073	−1.224	−0.495
	100	89.700	−6.376	−7.108	−2.890
	130	91.298	−46.840	−51.300	−22.400
	165	90.725	−53.145(54)	−58.578	−168.000
Allyl alcohol	32	96.828	−0.218	−0.225	−0.161
	70	95.011	−1.460	−1.537	−1.446
	100	91.972	−10.384	−11.290	−4.060
	130	94.061	−53.671	−57.000	−23.030
	165	93.450	−62.706(79)	−67.101	−137.800
n-Butyl alcohol	32	89.555	+0.077	+0.086	....
	70	89.030	−0.969	−1.088	−0.462
	100	90.031	−6.772	−7.522	−3.120
	130	90.312	−51.564	−57.200	−20.380
	165	89.081	−67.715(78)	−76.015	−149.500
sec-Butyl alcohol	32	90.016	−0.960	−0.067	....
	70	90.332	−1.287	−1.425	−0.619
	100	90.098	−9.339	−10.365	−4.350
	130	90.230	−77.900	−86.300	−37.600
	165	89.649	−50.888(31)	−56.764	−278.000
tert-Butyl alcohol	32	89.959	−0.064	−0.071	....
	70	88.900	−0.540	−0.607	−0.260
	100	88.926	−5.121	−5.759	−2.440
	130	88.867	−56.945	−64.000	−27.500
	165	88.172	−8.396(6)	−9.522	−236.500
n-Octyl alcohol	32	93.469	+0.216	+0.231	+0.092
	70	92.923	−1.007	−1.084	−0.498
	100	92.548	−7.222	−7.804	−3.310
	130	93.951	−53.170	−56.700	−25.630
	165	92.857	−34.450(31)	−37.100	−188.500
Phenol	32	117.192	+0.102	+0.087	....
	70	119.721	−1.006	−0.840	−0.484
	100	118.318	−6.975	−5.895	−3.280
	130	117.791	−49.777	−42.300	−23.980
	165	119.623	−98.083(145)	−81.993	−119.000
Ethylene glycol	32	125.846	+0.418	+0.332	+0.193
	70	126.014	+0.157	+0.124	+0.071
	100	125.407	+0.110	+0.088	+0.069
	130	127.617	−0.235	−0.185	....
	165	128.199	−1.110(145)	−0.866	−1.265
Glycerine	32	126.164	+0.218	+0.173	+0.165
	70	130.482	+0.102	+0.078	+0.046
	100	133.158	−0.118	−0.089	−0.051

TABLE LXVI (*Continued*)

Test material	Temperature, °F.	Net Contents in g.	365-Day Change in g. Measured	365-Day Change in % Measured	P-factor, g./24 hr.-100 in.² through 1 mil
	130	144.592	−0.830	−0.574	−0.361
	165	116.455	−1.597(146)	−1.371	−1.620
Diethylene glycol	32	111.359	+0.451	+0.405	+0.206
	70	109.935	+0.172	+0.156	+0.078
	100	111.715	+0.147	+0.132	+0.077
	130	127.257	+0.487	+0.382	. . . .
	165	110.783	−0.713(145)	−0.644	−0.760
Ethylene glycol mono-	32	98.762	+0.141	+0.143	+0.205
butyl ether	70	101.316	−1.417	−1.399	−0.666
	100	99.552	−10.452	−10.499	−4.400
	130	101.198	−73.896	−72.500	−34.900
	165	101.242	−74.483(71)	−73.569	180.300
Ethyl acetate	32	98.553	−4.029	−4.088	−1.903
	70	99.008	−34.981	−35.331	−16.550
	100	99.726	−43.131(92)	−43.250	−83.300
	130	99.817	−95.355(50)	−95.530	−378.000
	165	99.983	−100.083(13)	−100.100	−1703.000
Amyl acetate	32	99.403	−1.143	−1.150	−0.566
	70	96.918	−18.594	−19.185	−8.700
	100	96.365	−81.512	−84.587	−37.700
	130	96.803	−91.466(81)	−94.487	−269.000
	165	98.923	−99.067(30)	−100.146	−1095.000
Dibutyl phthalate	32	115.557	+0.235	+0.203	+0.199
	70	114.342	−0.068	−0.059	. . . .
	100	115.284	−1.703	−1.477	−0.810
	130	118.495	−11.795	−9.950	−5.700
	165	114.859	−23.018(139)	−20.040	−27.750
Dibutyl ether	32	85.657	−24.227	−28.284	−11.250
	70	85.997	−68.494(146)	−79.647	−85.500
	100	84.687	−84.492(64)	−99.770	−374.000
	130	86.552	−48.722(6)	−56.292	−1480.000
	165	83.297	−83.340(6)	−100.052	−3140.000
Formaldehyde	32	124.908	−0.102	−0.082	. . . .
	70	124.883	−1.157	−0.926	−0.534
Butyraldehyde	32	85.315	−1.876	−2.199	−0.890
	70	80.997	−21.253	−26.239	−10.130
	100	86.034	−51.592	−59.967	−41.100
	130	95.078	−74.679(180)	−78.545	−584.000
Benzaldehyde	32	120.059	−0.760	−0.633	−0.369
	70	117.662	−14.182	−12.053	−6.800
	100	116.822	−69.795	−59.745	−32.850
	130	117.670	−94.363(81)	−80.193	−206.500

Continued

TABLE LXVI (*Continued*)

Test material	Temperature, °F.	Net Contents in g.	365-Day Change in g. Measured	365-Day Change in % Measured	P-factor, g./24 hr.- 100 in.² through 1 mil
	165	117.882	−79.766(13)	−67.666	−1060.000
Acetone	32	88.973	−3.430	−3.855	−1.380
	70	89.927	−14.516	−16.142	−6.750
	100	90.142	−68.677	−76.188	−32.450
	130	88.422	−81.044(81)	−91.656	−184.000
Methyl ethyl ketone	32	90.269	−7.586	−8.404	−3.670
	70	89.684	−25.735	−28.694	−12.600
	100	89.233	−61.788(184)	−69.243	−60.000
	130	89.409	−86.574(50)	−96.829	−326.500
	165	89.485	−89.831(12)	−100.387	−1401.000
Diacetone alcohol	32	105.825	−0.098	−0.093	....
	70	105.692	−0.641	−0.606	−0.308
	100	106.707	−4.182	−3.919	−1.960
	130	106.598	−31.535	−29.600	−15.020
	165	106.659	−73.816(138)	−69.207	−92.500
Acetic anhydride	32	122.816	+0.024	+0.020	....
	70	122.096	−1.721	−1.410	−0.809
	100	121.733	−8.705	−7.151	−4.145
	130	122.795	−64.900	−52.900	−29.650
	165	123.762	−45.326(42)	−36.624	−213.000
Turpentine	32	99.461	−6.689	−6.725	−2.480
	70	99.637	−82.028	−82.327	−47.000
	100	98.814	−90.731(70)	−91.820	−287.500
	130	98.286	−47.604(6)	−48.434	−1362.000
	165	99.136	−50.818(1)	−51.261	−8830.000
Camphor	32	66.739	+0.195	+0.292	+0.204
	70	65.164	−0.630	−0.967	−0.293
	100	67.661	−5.456	−8.064	−2.630
	130	67.357	−45.830	−68.100	−21.500
	165	63.736	−54.019(70)	−84.754	−162.200
Dipentene	32	94.683	−31.923	−33.716	−15.130
	70	96.651	−50.633(70)	−52.387	−128.500
	100	97.085	−91.078(70)	−93.813	−501.000
	130	95.061	−69.841(6)	−73.470	−2030.000
	165	95.958	−46.649(1)	−48.614	−8110.000
Aniline	32	116.144	−0.029	−0.025	....
	70	114.615	−3.607	−3.147	−1.712
	100	115.400	−20.450	−17.721	−9.930
	130	116.193	−88.668(272)	−76.250	−59.600
	165	116.876	−90.679(55)	−77.586	−294.000
Acetanilide	32	44.670	+0.169	+0.378	+0.076
	70	45.729	+0.007	+0.015	....
	100	43.328	−0.145	−0.335	−0.057

TABLE LXVI (*Continued*)

Test material	Temperature, °F.	Net Contents in g.	365-Day Change in g. Measured	365-Day Change in % Measured	P-factor, g./24 hr.-100 in.² through 1 mil
	130	43.961	−0.910	−2.070	−0.402
	165	45.821	−2.497(131)	−5.449	−3.410
Nitroethane	32	115.856	−2.003	−1.729	−0.968
	70	115.810	−5.211	−4.500	−2.710
	100	115.945	−23.910	−20.622	−11.410
	130	118.611	−112.820(324)	−95.118	−64.000
	165	114.466	−79.042(50)	−69.053	−290.000
Nitrobenzene	32	133.475	−0.634	−0.475	−0.370
	70	136.294	−10.409	−7.637	−4.930
n-Pentane	32	70.560	−50.775(92)	−71.960	−96.900
	70	70.150	−69.921(31)	−99.674	−526.000
Isopentane	32	69.082	−49.682(184)	−71.917	−47.800
	70	70.974	−70.900(64)	−99.896	−270.000
Pentene-2	32	72.087	−71.591(87)	−99.312	−180.000
	70	72.987	−72.891(31)	−99.868	−695.000
n-Heptane	32	77.239	−50.825(184)	−65.802	−48.600
	70	76.303	−76.151(64)	−99.801	−269.500
	100	79.055	−77.234(22)	−97.697	−850.000
	130	77.669	−71.020(5)	−91.439	−2650.000
	165	76.241	−76.069(2)	−90.770	−8160.000
Decane	32	82.168	−19.978	−24.314	−9.490
	70	83.677	−73.488(247)	−87.823	−71.200
	100	83.541	−78.089(56)	−93.474	−297.000
	130	83.277	−69.339(10)	−83.263	−1220.000
	165	81.439	−81.518(6)	−100.097	−4120.000
Tetradecane	32	87.192	−3.513	−4.029	−1.740
	70	86.703	−30.812	−35.537	−14.600
	100	86.881	−78.971(273)	−90.665	−77.200
	130	90.056	−70.809(31)	−78.628	−404.000
Lubricating oil	32	103.409	+0.267	+0.258	+0.200
	70	103.324	−0.729	−0.706	−0.358
	100	104.182	−7.132	−6.846	−3.520
	130	107.761	−17.823(267)	−16.550	−10.100
	165	102.798	−21.264(64)	−20.685	−451.000
Benzene	32	99.884	−94.517	−94.627	−45.000
	70	98.013	−97.959(62)	−99.945	−440.000
	100	98.678	−98.636(14)	−99.957	−1585.000
	130	99.620	−25.791(1)	−25.889	−4480.000
	165	99.789	−99.870(4)	−100.081	−13670.000
o-Xylene	32	98.096	−73.614	−75.043	−36.100
	70	96.356	−85.693(64)	−88.934	−256.500
	100	98.495	−98.508(31)	−100.013	−1085.000

Continued

TABLE LXVI (*Continued*)

Test material	Temperature, °F.	Net Contents in g.	365-Day Change in g. Measured	365-Day Change in % Measured	P-factor, g./24 hr.-100 in.^{2} through 1 mil
	130	98.055	−94.669(5)	−96.547	−3610.000
	165	98.280	−95.633(1)	−97.307	−16600.000
p-Xylene	32	94.884	−75.998(184)	−80.096	−85.775
	70	95.777	−95.208(64)	−99.406	−486.000
	100	95.077	−94.687(16)	−99.590	−1803.000
	130	96.692	−81.714(3)	−84.510	−4775.000
	165	94.977	−93.918(1)	−98.885	−16320.000
Cyclohexane	32	88.145	−66.256	−75.167	−31.600
	70	86.885	−86.180(64)	−99.189	−251.000
	100	84.262	−83.961(16)	−99.643	−1112.000
	130	89.322	−64.934(3)	−72.697	−3730.000
Chlorobenzene	32	126.376	−120.424	−95.290	−57.800
	70	125.181	−124.997(63)	−99.853	−455.000
	100	116.556	−116.555(21)	−99.999	−1630.000
	130	122.930	−121.539(5)	−98.848	−4410.000
	165	128.872	−121.437(1)	−94.231	−21150.000
Monochloroacetic acid	32	91.625	+0.188	+0.205	+0.117
	70	94.107	−0.633	−0.673	−0.309
	100	96.904	−3.906	−4.027	−1.820
	130	86.202	−29.111	−33.800	−15.050
	165	96.303	−48.348(139)	−50.204	−59.900
Hydrogen peroxide, 3%	32	118.395	−0.135	−0.114	−0.089
	70	115.488	−1.028	−0.890	−0.530
Hydrogen peroxide, 30%	32	131.234	−0.055	−0.042	....
	70	131.203	−3.580	−2.729	−1.745
Silicone oil	32	111.647	+0.227	+0.203	+0.113
	70	110.764	+0.040	+0.036	....
	100	112.322	−0.007	−0.006	+0.015
	130	111.176	−0.011	−0.010	....
	165	110.524	−0.134(130)	−0.121	−0.140
Water	32	112.477	−0.138	−0.123	....
	70	116.237	−0.582	−0.501	−0.279
	100	115.069	−1.757	−1.527	−0.835
	130	113.277	−8.365	−7.390	−3.940
	165	114.928	−13.892(130)	−12.088	−18.400
Ammonium chloride	32	80.948	+0.140	+0.173	+0.060
	70	80.056	+0.005	+0.006	....
	100	82.921	−0.102	−0.123	−0.024
	130	82.142	−0.142	−0.173	....
	165	80.252	−0.232(126)	−0.289	−0.023
Sodium hypochlorite (5% available Cl)	32	123.074	−0.829	−0.674	−0.347
	70	123.570	−0.722	−0.584	−0.347
	100	127.312	−1.907	−1.498	−0.870

TABLE LXVI (*Concluded*)

Test material	Temperature, °F.	Net Contents in g.	365-Day Change in g. Measured	365-Day Change in % Measured	P-factor g./24 hr.- 100 in.² through 1 mil
	130	122.744	−7.989	−6.510	−7.290
	165	127.824	−18.608(44)	−14.558	−20.200
Formamide	70	133.947	+0.031(113)	+0.023	+0.033
	130	133.292	−1.071(113)	−0.802	−1.590

Source: *Modern Packaging*, **27** (10), 145 (1954).
NOTES: Weight changes in grams and percent measured were calculated only for actual length of test.   Where test ran less than 365 days, figures in parentheses indicate number of test days.
Blanks in *P*-factor column indicate that weight loss-time values were too irregular to plot.
[a] High loss probably caused by cracks in bottle wall.

condensation point is approached, the vapor is assumed to pass through the film in the form of clusters of vapor molecules.

Water Vapor Permeability

A comparison of several plastic materials indicates (474) that, next to Saran, polyethylene possesses the lowest water permeability.   At 25°C., expressed as 10^{-8} cm.²-sec.$^{-1}$-atm.$^{-1}$, the following data are given: polyethylene, 16–50; Saran, 0.50–10; paraffin, 21; polyisobutylene, 15–50; pliofilm, 10–250; polystyrene, 700–1,000; polyvinyl acetate, 8,000; cellulose acetate, 8,500–27,000; cellophane, 36,000–130,000.

A scientific analysis of factors affecting water-vapor transmission through thin film was reported by Aiken, Doty, and Mark (172).   A permeability constant (*P*) was calculated as

$$P = P_o e^{-E/RT},$$

wherein R is the gas constant, E is the energy of activation which governs the sensitivity of the permeability constant to temperature, and T is the absolute temperature.

While the permeability constant is independent of the thickness of the film and of the vapor-pressure differential, interpretation of the energies of activation measured for a number of film materials shows that high values of this energy term (high sensitivity to temperature variation) go hand in hand with crystallinity and low values of the permeability constant. In general, plasticizers do not greatly affect the permeability constant, and there appears to be no direct relationship between mechanical behavior and permeability.

A method for calculating the diffusion coefficient of a vapor within a film as a function of concentration has been devised by Rouse (294). Data required are the permeation rates under several vapor-pressure differences and the sorption isotherm. The method also furnishes a means for constructing the gradients of the effective vapor pressure and of the con-

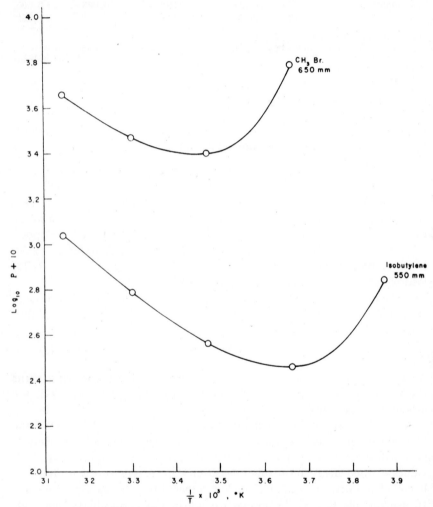

Fig. 126. Permeability *versus* temperature of polyethylene to methyl bromide and isobutylene. (*Ann. Rept. State Univ. New York to TAPPI, 1953–1954*, Appendix, Jan. 28, 1955.)

centration of the vapor within the film through which vapor is passing at a steady state.   Data are presented for water permeation in Figure 128 and for water sorption of polyethylene in Figure 129.   The diffusion coefficient

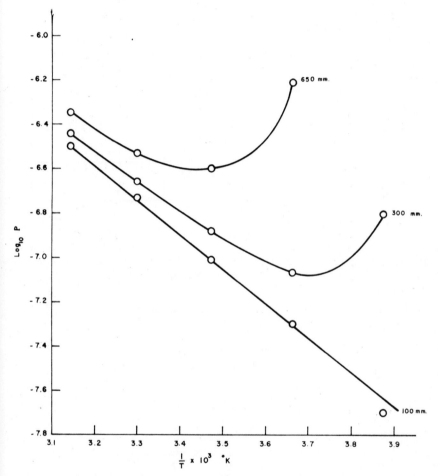

Fig. 127. Temperature dependence of permeability of polyethylene to methyl bromide at various pressures. (*Ann. Rept. State Univ. New York to TAPPI, 1953–1954, Appendix,* Jan. 28, 1955.)

of water vapor is shown as a function of concentrations in Figure 130. Curves representing the vapor pressure and concentration gradients of water in polyethylene are shown in Figure 131.

The relation of moisture permeability to thickness of cast sheeting and of sheeting made by compression molding has been demonstrated by Hahn, Macht, and Fletcher (178) as shown in Figure 132. In these tests,

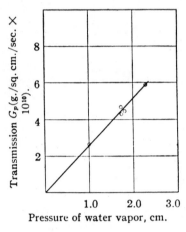

Fig. 128. Transmission of water vapor through polyethylene at 25°C.; film thickness, 0.0139 cm. (*J. Am. Chem. Soc.*, **69**, 1071, 1947.)

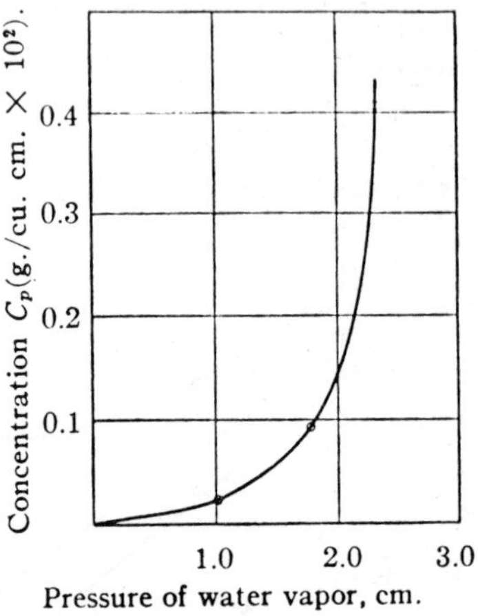

Fig. 129. Sorption of water vapor by polyethylene at 25°C. (*J. Am. Chem. Soc.*, **69**, 1071, 1947.)

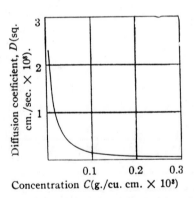

Fig. 130. Diffusion coefficient of water in polyethylene at 25°C. (*J. Am. Chem. Soc.*, **69**, 1071, 1947.)

permeability was measured by the cellophane method of Charch and Scroggie (33). Not only is polyethylene resistant to water vapor, but total contact of one side of the film with liquid water has no effect on rate of transfer.

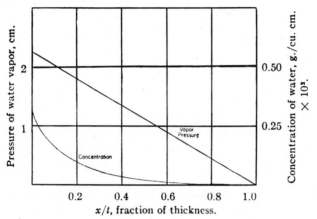

Fig. 131. Gradients of concentration and vapor pressure of water in polyethylene at the steady state at 25°C. (*J. Am. Chem. Soc.*, **69**, 1072, 1947.)

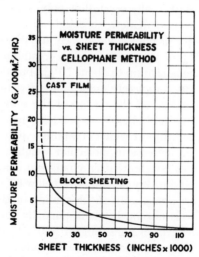

Fig. 132. Relation of moisture permeability of polyethylene to thickness of sheet. (*Ind. Eng. Chem.*, **37**, 531, 1945.)

6.4. Density

With a specific gravity of 0.92 gram per cubic centimeter at 20°C., polyethylene prepared by the conventional high-pressure polymerization process is one of the lightest of all plastic materials. This applies to high molecular weight polyethylenes, to low molecular weight (1,500–5,000) products, and to commercial irradiated polyethylene (Irrathene). Investigations by Sakurada and Nakajima (227) have shown that the density (D) of a liquid (melt) normal paraffin with carbon number (n) at a temperature t is given by

$$1/D_{\text{liquid}} = 1.143 + 0.00089t + 1/(0.500 - 0.00110t)n$$

The experimental values for polyethylene at various temperatures above 100°C. agree well with the values obtained by putting $n = \infty$. The equation also holds for supercooled paraffins. The density of solid normal paraffins at room temperature is given theoretically by

$$1/D_{\text{solid}} = 1.018 + 1.465/n$$

Calculated for $n = \infty$, a density of 0.982 is obtained, as compared with the experimentally determined value of 0.922. The discrepancy is attributed to the fact that about 50% of the solid sample was in the amorphous state. This value does, however, agree well with that observed for the entirely unbranched and totally crystalline polymethylene.

Hunter and Oakes (179) made a thorough study of the effect of temperature on the density of polyethylene. By use of the dilatometer, they found that about 55% of the specimen was crystalline at room temperature and remained unchanged up to about 70°C., but thereafter fell rapidly until the specimen was completely amorphous at a temperature between 100 and 120°C., depending on the nature of the sample. The density of molten polyethylene is only slightly dependent upon average molecular weight, but the temperature at which crystalline material first appears on cooling is raised by an increase in molecular weight. The density of the liquid rapidly becomes constant after change in temperature; between 120 and 60°C., at least one day is required; below 60°C., a constant value is reached after a few hours. By shock-cooling of the liquid, a solid of slightly lower density is obtained, which partially reverts to the density of the slowly cooled form on annealing at 100°C. It is concluded that above 60°C., equilibrium conditions can readily be attained; below 60°C., the ratio of crystalline to amorphous material appears to be frozen, although segmental adjustment with temperature changes continues in the amorphous region. Variation of density with temperature (0–150°C.) is shown in Figure 133 (178).

A relationship for the calculation of crystallinity in polymers from density measurements was derived by Price (561a). At any given temperature,

$X = (V_{lg} - V)/(V_{lg} - V_s)$, where X = volume fraction of crystals in mixture with liquid or glass; V = specific volume of mixture; V_{lg} = specific volume of liquid or glass, whichever is appropriate to the given temperature; and V_s = specific volume of crystals. Using this method, the density data of polyethylene given by Hunter and Oakes (179) were recalculated and compared with those obtained by Raine, Richards, and Ryder (182) from calorimetric data, and with the calculations of Hunter and Oakes. The results of these calculations are shown in Table LXVII.

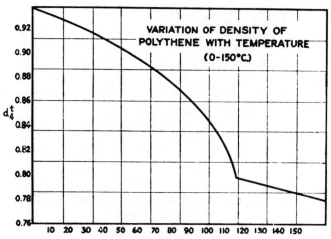

Fig. 133. Variation of density of polyethylene with temperature.
(*Ind. Eng. Chem.*, **37**, 529, 1945.)

Price's method agrees well with the calorimetric method, but yields higher values of X than those of Hunter and Oakes who, according to Price, assumed too low a value of V_s.

TABLE LXVII

Degree of Crystallinity in Polyethylene

Method	Temperature, °C.								
	0	40	60	80	90	100	105	110	115
Price	0.85	0.77	0.72	0.63	0.57	0.48	0.42	0.33	0.14
Hunter and Oakes	0.55	0.55	0.55	0.50	0.45	0.40	0.35	0.25	0.10
Raine *et al.*	..	..	0.70	0.60	0.55	0.45	0.40	0.30	0.15

Source: *J. Chem. Phys.* **19** (7), 473 (1951).

The density of polyethylene increases with pressure. This is demonstrated in Figure 134 [Parks and Richards (413)]. Here, the volume (ml.)

of one gram of polyethylene is plotted as a function of pressure at temperatures between 25 and 160°C.

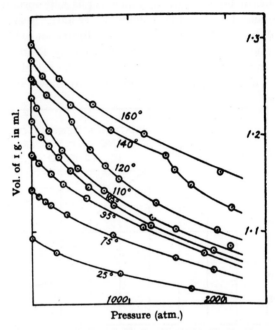

Fig. 134. Volume (ml.) of 1 g. polyethylene at 25–160°C. as a function of pressure, in atmospheres. (*Trans. Faraday Soc.*, **45**, 206, 1949.)

6.5. Specific Heat, Heat of Solution, Heat of Combustion, Thermal Expansion and Thermal Conductivity

The thermal conductivity of polyethylene is low. It is given as 8.3×10^{-4} c.g.s. units by Raine, Richards, and Ryder (182). The specific heat of solid polyethylene at 20°C. was determined by the same authors to be about 0.55 cal./°C./g., which is greater than the specific heat of entirely crystalline short-chain paraffins. As the temperature is increased, the specific heat increases, reaching a value of about 1.0 at 90°C., and 2.0 at 110°C. This relationship is shown in Figure 135. These results indicate a disordering of the structure of the solid beginning below 50°C. and becoming increasingly marked as the temperature is raised, culminating in a relatively sharp change to a liquid structure at about 115°C. These changes resemble those shown by density measurements and are believed due to a decrease in the proportion of long molecules which pass through the crystallites.   The difference between the heat capacity of solid poly-ethylene and the extrapolated heat capacity of liquid polyethylene at the same temperature (heat of fusion) is 43.4 calories per gram at 20°C., de-creasing to 28.7 at 90°C., and 9.6 at 110°C.

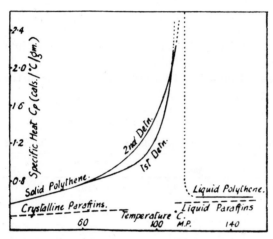

Fig. 135.   Specific heat of polyethylene.   (*Trans. Faraday Soc.*, **41**, 59, 1945.)

Values for the heat of solution in xylene are similar to the heat of fusion at the same temperature.   Experimental values are shown in Table LXVIII.

TABLE LXVIII

Heats of Solution of Polyethylene in Xylene

Sample Number	Molecular Weight[a]	Temperature, °C.	Heat of Soln., cal./g.
1	11,800	78.08	−33.35
		78.95	−33.53
		79.59	−33.09
2	10,000	81.0	−33.2
3	15,600	80.5	−36.8
		90.5	−27.1
		95.0	−25.0

Source: *Trans. Faraday Soc.*, **41**, 61 (1945).
[a] Calculated from the intrinsic viscosity [η] in tetralin at 75°C. using the formula m.w. = 20,000[η].   Molecular weights calculated in this way may not even bear a linear relation to true weight-average molecular weights.

A comparison of these data with the heat of fusion of entirely crystalline paraffins indicates that, at room temperature, the polyethylene sample whose heat capacity was measured was approximately 75% crystalline. The lack of complete reversibility of heat-capacity measurements shows that a thermodynamic equilibrium between crystalline and amorphous regions is not attained instantaneously.

Data for the specific heat of granular, sheeted, annealed, and drawn samples of polyethylene at -20 to $200°C$. were determined by Dole, Hettinger, Larson, and Wethington (599) and are presented in Table LXIX. From the data, changes in enthalpy and entropy between these temperatures have been calculated and an estimate was made of the free energy of the cold-drawing process.

TABLE LXIX

Smoothed Values of the Specific Heat of Polyethylene in cal./g./°C.

$T,°$ C.	Annealed	Granular and Sheet	Drawn
-20	0.420_8	0.419_9	0.409_0
0	0.475_5	0.469_0	0.454_0
20	0.543_3	0.532_0	0.507_0
40	0.625_3	0.607_7	0.576_0
60	0.728_5	0.705_5	0.666_5
80	0.930_5	0.863_0	0.829_5
90	1.09_7	1.03_8	1.01_5
100	1.55_0		
110	1.20_0		
120	0.594_0		
140	0.610_1		
160	0.626_3		
180	0.642_4		
200	0.658_6		

Source: *J. Chem. Phys.*, **20**, 782 (1952).

The heat of combustion of polyethylene was determined by Parks and Mosley (412). Combustion data at $25°C$. are presented in Table LXX. In this table, $-\Delta U_B$ represents the mean values for the energy evolved in the isothermal bomb process per gram at $25°C$., Δ represents the mean deviations of the individual combustions from these values; $-\Delta U_R$ represents the energy evolved in the hypothetical process where the reactants and products are each at one atmosphere; $-\Delta H_R$ represents the heat evolved in the isobaric process at one atmosphere; and $-\Delta H_f^o$ represents the heat of formation of a C_2H_4 unit of polymer from the ele-

TABLE LXX

Combustion Data for Polyethylene at 25.0°C.

Sample	$I(C_2H_4)_{700}$	$II(C_2H_4)_{700}$
No. of combustions	8	2
$-\Delta U_B/m$, cal. per g.	11,095.1	11,093.1
Mean Δ, cal. per g.	± 1.2	± 0.4
$-\Delta U_R$, cal. per C_2H_4 unit	311,162	311,106
$-\Delta H_R$, cal. per C_2H_4 unit	311,755	311,699
$-\Delta H_f^{\circ}$, cal. per C_2H_4 unit	12,983	13,039

Source: *J. Chem. Phys.*, **17**, 692 (1949).

TABLE LXXI

Estimated Crystallization of Polyethylene at 25°C.

Method	Percentage Crystallized
Heat of combustion data	49 to 52
Density measurements	55
Computation from enthalpy data	74
Extrapolation of enthalpy data	61
"Best" estimate	$60(\pm 10)$

Source: *J. Chem. Phys.*, **17**, 693 (1949).

TABLE LXXII

Thermal Expansion Characteristics of Polyethylene

Temperature, °C.	Coeff. Linear Expansion $\times 10^5$	Coeff. Cubical Expansion $\times 10^6$	Sp. Vol. Ratio, $V_E/V_{25°C}$
-35	10.0	300	0.969
-20	13.7	410	0.975
0	18.3	550	0.986
20	23.7	710	0.997
25	24.8	745	1.000
40	29.0	870	1.012
60	33.7	1010	1.031
80	40.3	1210	1.055
100	46.6	1400	1.094
110	51.0	1530	1.130
115	25.0	750	1.142
115–150	25.0	750	. . .
150	25.0	750	1.168

Source: *Ind. Eng. Chem.*, **37**, 526 (1945).

ments, gaseous hydrogen, and graphitic carbon. On the basis of these data, extent of crystallization was calculated in the range of 49 to 52%. Estimated "best" values by comparison with the data of Hunter and Oakes (179), and of Raine, Richards, and Ryder (182) are presented in Table LXXI.

The thermal expansion of polyethylene is quite high ($18 \times 10^{-5}/°C$.); between 120 and 20°C., the volume decrease amounts to about 13%, about half of which takes place during crystallization (178). This property necessitates special consideration in the technique and the design of equipment for molding or extruding the polymer. Care must be taken during cooling to prevent the formation of voids since, like most thermoplastics, the thermal conductivity is low. Thermal expansion characteristics are given in Table LXXII and are presented graphically in Figure 136 (178).

In this connection, reference is also to be made to the elaborate studies by Kovacs (858b) discussed in Section 5.1.

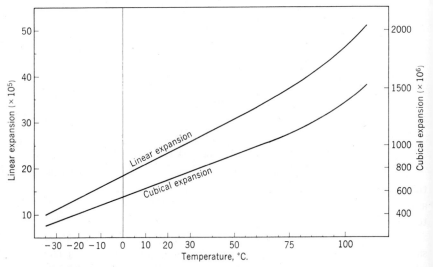

Fig. 136. Coefficients of thermal expansion *versus* temperature. (*Ind. Eng. Chem.*, **37**, 526, 1945.)

6.6 Melting Point

Frith and Tuckett (156a) derived the following relationship for the thermodynamic equilibrium between the crystalline and amorphous phases of polyethylene:

$$\frac{n\Lambda}{RT_m} = n \log \frac{Z-1}{e} + \frac{1}{\theta}$$

where T_m = melting point; Λ = latent heat of fusion of a single link in gram-molecular units; n = number of links between crystal nuclei; Z = average coordination number; θ = fraction of amorphous material in the structure. This equation permits calculation of the melting range of a long-chain polymer in terms of various parameters. Alternatively, it permits calculation of the relative proportions of amorphous and crystalline materials in the structure over a range of temperature. Values of

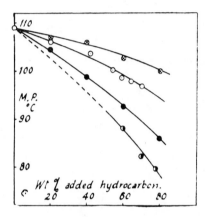

◗ Heptane, M.W. 100.
⊙ Paraffin wax, M.W. 350
● Cetene-2, M.W. 224.
⊘ Degraded polythene,
    M.W. 650.

Fig. 137. Effect of additives on melting point of polyethylene.
(*Trans. Faraday Soc.*, **41**, 134, 1945.)

the crystalline-amorphous equilibrium calculated in this way are in good agreement with values determined experimentally over the same range of temperatures.

Richards (183) pointed out that the melting points of polyethylene samples are normally 20-30°C. below the value expected for a pure linear paraffin of comparable chain length. The melting process extends over a much wider temperature range, and the solid is not entirely crystalline even at room temperature. Samples with the same average molecular weight, as indicated by intrinsic viscosities, can vary as much as 15°C. in melting point. These changes are attributed to variations in molecular weight distribution and in the degree of chain-branching. A study by Staudinger and Berndt (161) was based on similar assumptions (see Sections 5.3, and 6.1). Extending the statistical thermodynamic treatment of

Frith and Tuckett, Richards derived an equation for the variation with temperature of the degree of crystallinity of a long-chain linear paraffin

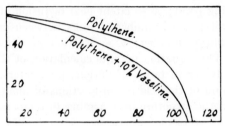

Fig. 138. Effect of vaseline on crystallinity of polythene. (*Trans. Faraday Soc.*, **41**, 135, 1945.) Ordinate: per cent crystallinity; abscissa: temperature, °C.

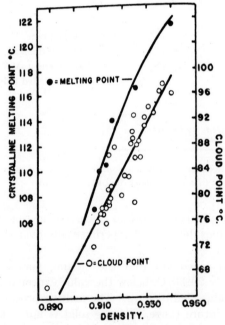

Fig. 139. Crystalline melting point and cloud point *versus* density. (*J. Am. Chem. Soc.*, **75**, 6130, 1953.)

containing various proportions of short-chain paraffinic liquids concentrated in the amorphous regions of the solid. From this equation, a further relationship was derived for change in melting point with the proportion and molecular weights of added liquid.   Melting-point depressions observed when low molecular weight hydrocarbons are added to poly-ethylene are shown in Figure 137.   The observed effect of vaseline on the crystallinity of polyethylene is shown in Figure 138.   The theoretical re-sults were found to be in fair agreement with observed data of melting-point depression by paraffins of various molecular weights.   Theoretically,

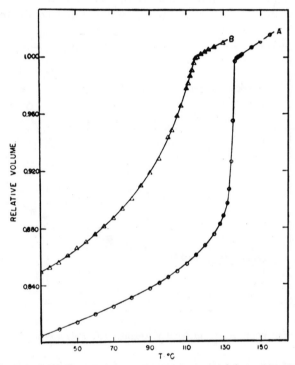

Fig. 140.   Relative volume-temperature curves: curve A for polymethylene O; curve B for polyethylene Δ.   (*J. Am. Chem. Soc.*, **75**, 4093, 1953.)

there should be a connection between the crystallinity and, hence, density of the solid at ordinary temperatures, and the melting point of the samples; this, too, is in accord with observed data.   Richards pointed out further that the presence of side groups might be expected to have an effect similar to that of short molecules; that is, increasing the entropy of the amorphous regions would lead to a more amorphous polymer.   Part of the variability in melting point and crystallinity might be due, therefore, to variations in the degree of chain branching.   This concept has been confirmed and expanded by subsequent studies. A quantitative relationship between crystallinity, as expressed by density, and crystal melting point (also cloud point) is reproduced in Figure 139 from a paper by Sperati, Franta, and Starkweather (772).

The results of a study of the melting temperature of polymethylene and of its volume-temperature behavior were reported by Mandelkern, Hellmann, Brown, Roberts, and Quinn (755). The relative volume of polymethylene (relative to that at 137°C.) was determined dilatometrically

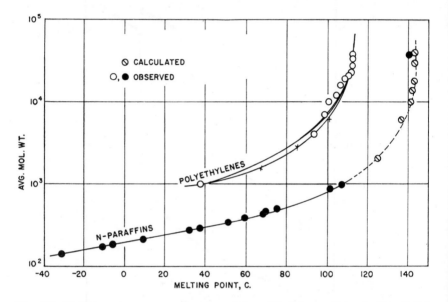

Fig. 141. Melting point *versus* molecular weight. (*J. Polymer Sci.*, **13**, 560, 1954.)

and is plotted in Figure 140 as a function of temperature. A well-defined first-order transition or melting temperature, characterized by the disappearance of the last traces of crystallinity, takes place at 136.5°C., and 70% of the melting occurs in only a three- to four-degree interval. For the branched polyethylene, the melting temperature is lowered to 115°C. and the melting range considerably extended. While the melting temperature for polymethylene is thus found very close to the convergence temperature of 135°C. predicted from an analysis of thermodynamic data for low molecular weight paraffins, other observers, e.g., Buckley and Ray (595), found no melting of polymethylene up to its decomposition point of around 300°C. Mandelkern *et al.* assume that in this case the true melting

TABLE LXXIII

Properties of "Bakelite" Polyethylene Resins

Resin Designation	Molecular Weight[a]	Specific Viscosity Limits[b]	Williams Parallel Plate Flow Height	Description	Transparent Point[c] (Softening Temp.), °C.	Melt Viscosity at 130°C., Poises	Tensile Strength, p.s.i.	Percent Elongation	Yield Point, p.s.i.	50% Brittle Temp. Index, °C.[d]
DXL-1	1,000	......	...	Grease-like	37.5	0.4	...	...	...	...
DXL-4	4,000	0.06–0.09	...	Wax	93	5.2	...	...	...	...
DYGT	7,000	0.15–0.18	...	Soft resin	98	120	615	40	...	−16
DYJT	10,000	0.21–0.24	...	Resinous	100	8×10^2	...	...	...	...
DYLT	12,000	0.26–0.29	...	"	104	3×10^3	910	100	...	−18
DXL-14	14,000	0.32–0.35	...	"	104	14×10^3	...	...	...	...
DXM-16	16,000	...	30–34	"	106	50×10^3	...	...	...	...
DYNF	19,000	...	45–49	"	108	4×10^5	1,200	400	1,450	−55
DYNH	21,000	...	50–59	"	110	1×10^6	1,800	550	1,475	−75
DYNJ	23,000	...	60–69	"	111	1.5×10^6	2,000	550	1,500	Below −75
DXH-28	28,000	...	90–99	"	112	3×10^7	2,400	575	1,600	Below −75
DXH-34	34,000	...	150–159	"	112	1×10^8	3,000	625	1,800	Below −75
DXH-38	38,000	...	190–200	"	112	3×10^8	3,000	625	...	Below −75
Experimental polymethylene	38,000	......	...	"	140	.....	...	...	...	...

Source: *Bakelite Polyethylene for Paper Coatings*, Bakelite Co., p. 5, 1951.

[a] Determined at 130°C. in tetralin. Modified Staudinger equation:

$$M = \frac{K_{em}.\ \log_{10} \eta_r}{C}$$

where M = weight average molecular weight, η_r = relative viscosity, C = base molar concentration of polymer in tetralin at temperature of determination = 4.0 g. per liter at 130°C./14, and $K_{em}.$ = 4.03 × 10⁴ g. per liter of solution at 130°C.

[b] At 70°C., 0.4 gm. resin per 100 cc. solution in methyl cyclohexane.

[c] Transparent point is the temperature at which the resin changes from opaque to transparent, indicating a change from the crystalline to the amorphous state.

[d] Brittleness index is the temperature at which a percentage of the samples do not break on the low temperature brittleness testing equipment, according to ASTM method D746–49T.

point of the polymer was probably obscured by the very high viscosity of the melt. In order to obtain reliable values, heating in the vicinity of the melting temperature must be gradual and should be carried out over a period of several days. Both the branched and linear polymers supercool; the amount of supercooling depending on the cooling rate.

An empirical linear relationship between the melting temperature and the second-order or glassy transition temperature for partially crystalline polymers was established by Boyer (832). Thermodynamic considerations on melting and second-order transitions in high polymers were presented by Münster (866a,1034).

Meyer and van der Wyk (56) have shown that the melting point of the pure normal paraffins increases with increasing chain length according to the empirical relation:

$$1/T_f = a + (b/Z)$$

where T_f = melting point in degrees absolute; $a = 2.395 \times 10^{-3}$ for normal paraffins; $b = 17.1 \times 10^{-3}$ for normal paraffins; Z = the number of carbon-carbon links in the chain. Myers (867) showed (Figure 141) the effect of average molecular weight on the observed and calculated softening or melting temperature of normal paraffins, including the polyethylenes listed in Table LXXIII.

It will be noted that the curve for crystalline paraffins, based on the equation of Meyer and van der Wyk, gives theoretical melting points considerably above those obtained for polyethylene. Agreement between theory and experiment is excellent in the case of pure crystalline paraffins. Relatively high molecular weight polymethylene (approximately 38,000) which is highly crystalline, was observed to have a melting point of 140°C., corresponding quite closely to the theoretical melting point curve. The displacement of the polyethylene curve toward lower melting point values is attributed to the reduction in intermolecular attraction caused by chain-branching and the resulting mixture of crystalline and amorphous structure.

The molecular characteristics which determine the melting points of high-polymer crystals were recently considered by Bunn (937), and it was indicated that the properties of monomeric crystals often throw light on those of the polymers. As the principal factors controlling melting points, molecular cohesion energy (of the whole molecule for monomers, or per chain unit for polymers), molecular flexibility (due to rotation around bonds), and molecular shape effects were considered. Polymethylene and polytetrafluoroethylene were among the polymer series discussed.

6.7. Melt Viscosity

Liquid polyethylene of high molecular weight shows non-Newtonian flow; the viscosity appears to decrease as the pressure and therefore the flow rate increase.   The melt viscosity decreases as the temperature is increased. Viscosity data for a series of commercial polyethylenes of various molecular weights are contained in Table LXXIII, taken from the trade bulletin of one commercial producer of polyethylene (568).

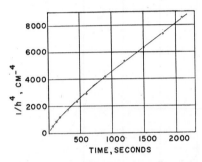

Fig. 142. Typical $1/h^4$ *versus* time curve for polyethylene at 115°C. (*J. Appl. Phys.*, **17**, 463, 1946.)

Fig. 143. Typical $1/h^4$ *versus* time curve for polyethylene at 190°C. (*J. Appl. Phys.*, **17**, 464, 1946.)

Dienes and Klemm (214) established a method for the measurement of the viscosity of high polymers at low rates of shear (in the range of 10^4– 10^9 poises) by means of a parallel plate plastometer.   This is based on the mathematical criterion for separating the viscous portion of the deformation from the "elastic" and "delayed elastic" components.   Experimentally, the plate separation is measured at a given temperature as a function of time.   The theory furnishes a relationship between viscosity, plate separation, applied load, and time, which is also the criterion for predominantly viscous deformation.   This relation, a modified form of Stefan's equation (2), is used to calculate viscosity from experimentally determined data. If the space between the plates is completely filled with the viscous material at all times, i.e., the plates have the same area as the ends of the specimen, the following equation is applied:

$$\frac{1}{h^2} = \frac{4F}{3\pi\,\eta a^4}\,t + C_1$$

If the viscous material does not completely fill the space between the plates, the following relationship exists:

$$\frac{1}{h^4} = \frac{8\pi F}{3\eta V^2}\, t + C_2.$$

In these equations, h = plate separation, F = applied force; t = time; η = viscosity; a = radius of the plates; V = volume (constant, since incompressible); C_1, C_2 = integration constants.

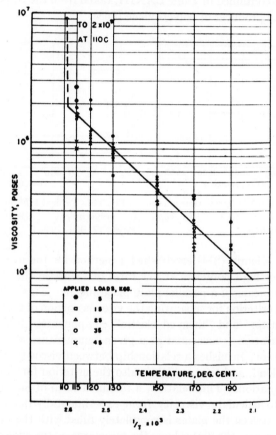

Fig. 144. Viscosity-temperature relation for polyethylene. (*J. Appl. Phys.*, **17**, 464, 1946.)

The viscosity of a polyethylene resin was measured over an 80°C. temperature range at different applied loads. Typical $1/h^4$ *versus* time curves
are shown in Figures 142 and 143, at 115 and 190°C., respectively.

The viscosity-temperature relationship for polyethylene is shown in

Figure 144. Viscosity-temperature characteristics of various molecular weight grades of polyethylene are shown in Figure 145. Since all of these curves have approximately the same slope, it is indicated that the activation energy for viscous flow does not change appreciably over this range of average molecular weights.

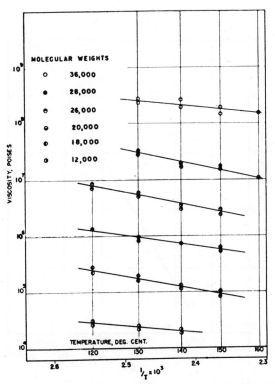

Fig. 145. Viscosity-temperature characteristics of various molecular weight grades of polyethylene. (*J. Appl. Phys.*, **17**, 465, 1946.)

Figure 146 is a plot of log η *versus* the square root of the weight average molecular weight at 130°C. The curve is a straight line, confirming the validity of Flory's relation (93) for polyethylene. According to Flory, the melt viscosity of polymerized linear polyesters varies with the weight average molecular weight and the temperature, according to the equation:

$$\log \eta = D + (B/T) + CM^{1/2}$$

where η is melt viscosity; T = absolute temperature; M = weight average molecular weight (relative), and D, B, and C = constants. Hence, a small change in molecular weight greatly affects the flow behavior.

Parallel-plate viscosity measurements were also carried out on a set of paraffin wax-polyethylene resin mixtures in the 50–100% resin content range. The results, which again confirm Flory's relation, are shown in Figure 147.

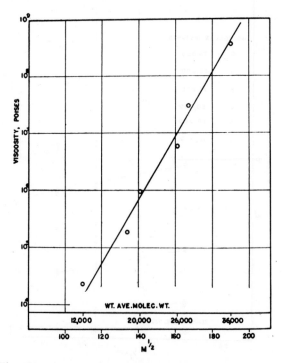

Fig. 146. Viscosity of polyethylene resins as a function of the square root of the weight average molecular weight. Temperature = 130°C. (*J. Appl. Phys.*, **17**, 466, 1946.)

Dienes (285) subsequently published additional studies on the melt-flow properties of thermoplastics, including polyethylene, based on the parallel-plate plastometer.

The flow behavior of molten polyethylene resins, measured with a concentric rotational plastometer which automatically plots the shear strain *versus* time curve for each of a number of stresses, was determined from 130 to 210°C. by Dexter (840b). The rheological behavior of continuously sheared polyethylene was studied by Pollett (1014) in a disc-and-cone rheometer.

As previously demonstrated (Section 5.6), the possibility of characterizing a given sample of polyethylene by a single characteristic value (e.g., grade number), has to be discarded (838a).   The melt-flow properties of polyethylene do not depend on short-chain branching, but are markedly affected by long-chain branching, according to the studies reported by Sper-

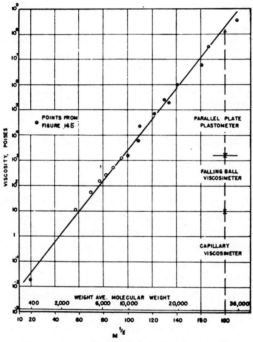

Fig. 147. Viscosity of the polyethylene resins and paraffin wax-polyethylene resin mixtures as a function of the square root of the weight average molecular weight.   Temperature = 130° C.   (*J. Appl. Phys.*, **17**, 468, 1946.)

ati, Franta, and Starkweather (772).   In an attempt to obtain a quantitative picture of fundamental rheological properties, a test for extensibility of molten polyethylene was devised by Billmeyer (708).   If extensibility is defined as the ratio of length at break of molten polymer to the original length, melt extensibility decreases with increasing molecular weight (melt viscosity).   The marked decrease of melt extensibility with increasing long-chain branching index is shown in Figure 148.

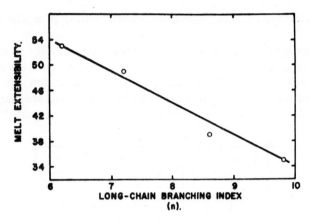

Fig. 148. Effect of long-chain branching on melt extensibility corrected to log melt viscosity = 5.5. (*J. Am. Chem. Soc.*, **75**, 6131, 1953.)

6.8. Light Transmission, Refractive Index, and Birefringence

Transparency of polyethylene is determined by several factors. The following points have been established by Hawkins and Richards (394). More crystalline samples, built from less-branched molecules, are more opaque. Rapid cooling yields a more amorphous sample, which is also more transparent. Absorption by polyethylene of a liquid (benzene, hydrocarbon oil) increases transparency; incorporation of a crystalline paraffin (paraffin wax) decreases the transparency. For samples of the same degree of crystallinity, transparency tends to increase with molecular weight.

The "transparent point," defined as the temperature at which the resin changes from opaque to transparent, indicating the change from crystalline to amorphous states, was determined for a series of commercial polyethylenes, and included in Table LXXIII, taken from the trade bulletin of one commercial producer (568).

Changes in light transmission of polyethylene observed by Hawkins and Richards (394) under rising or falling temperature are related to the growth of spherulites on cooling molten polyethylene and to their decay on increasing the temperature. Figure 149 shows the light transmission of a sample of polyethylene as a function of temperature: (a), on increasing the temperature from 20–120°C., i.e., above the melting point; and (b), on recooling to 20°C. It will be noted that on increasing the temperature, the light transmitted increases steadily at an increasing rate until the sample becomes clear at the melting point, i.e., around 112°C. On cooling from the melt, the specimen becomes very opaque a few degrees below the melting point; then it becomes much more transparent.   Thereafter the light transmission decreases as temperature falls, the transmission-temperature curve approximating to the curve for rising temperature.

The refractive index of polyethylene films has been determined by several investigators.   According to Hahn, Macht, and Fletcher (178), it lies between 1.515 and 1.520 at 20°C., compared to 1.510 for polyisobutylene, 1.523 for natural rubber, and 1.532 for nylon.   Figure 150 shows

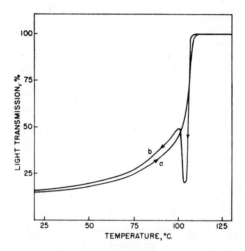

Fig. 149. Light transmission of polyethylene sheet as function of (*a*) rising, and (*b*) falling temperatures. (*J. Polymer Sci.*, **4**, 516, 1949.)

the change in index of refraction with temperature.   The change in this property at 80–100°C. is apparently caused by the disappearance of a certain crystalline phase.   Double refraction also disappears in this temperature range.   Under the polarizing microscope, there is some evidence, however, of persistence of crystalline structure up to about 112°C.   Above 110–115°C., the relation of refractive index to temperature is a straight line, typical of polymers of liquid-like structure.

Bryant (281) calculated the refractive indices of crystalline polyethylene (considered as uniaxial) to be $n_1 = 1.520$ and $n_2 = 1.582$, and the refractive index of amorphous polyethylene to be 1.49.

Baccaredda and Schiavinato (823) studied the refractive indices of five polyethylenes by the immersion method in suitable liquid mixtures.

Powdered samples were prepared from xylene solutions by cooling and by evaporation of the solvent under identical conditions. These, by the way, were the same samples for which densities, degrees of branching, osmotic molecular weights, and μ-values in xylene solutions were determined by Muthana and Mark (407) (see Section 6.1). Under the microscope, the samples appeared to consist of transparent, radial, and weakly birefringent

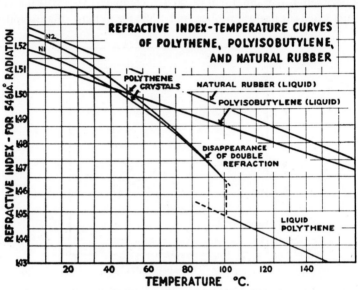

Fig. 150. Effect of temperature on refractive indices of polythene, polyisobutyl-ene, and natural rubber. (*Ind. Eng. Chem.*, **37**, 528, 1945.)

spherulites. Refractive index values were higher than those of the amorphous polyethylene and decreased as the degree of branching increased. This is indicated in Table LXXIV.

TABLE LXXIV

Density and Refractive Index of Polyethylene *versus* Degree of Branching

Sample	Density	Ratio CH_2/CH_3	$Mn \times 10^{-3}$	n_{25}
1	0.91	12	9.91	1.5060
2	0.917	21	26.20	1.5168
3	0.925	22	11.60	1.5152
4	0.929	38	16.66	1.5227
5	0.926	62	38.10	1.5260

Source: *J. Polymer Sci.*, **4**, 527 (1949); **12**, 155 (1954).

The refractive index lowering is ascribed to the change both in molecular structure (branching) and in the ratio between the amounts of amorphous and crystalline materials, the latter depending rigorously on the former when samples are prepared under identical conditions. It is concluded that measurement of the refractive index may be suitable for the empirical determination of the degree of branching in polyethylenes. It appears simpler and more significant than the measurement of the density, since it is relatively independent of the presence of microvoids in the sample.

In a subsequent study, Baccaredda and Schiavinato (822a) determined the refractive indices of polyethylene samples which had been crosslinked by exposure to high-energy radiation in an atomic pile under various conditions. The refractive index, measured by the immersion method, was found to increase with increasing radiation dose, and was not changed by heating the specimens up to 140°C. after exposure to the radiation.

The phenomenon of stress birefringence of polyethylene has been studied by Heller and Oppenheimer (344). They found that stress birefringence shows a steep increase at low elongations followed by an approach to a saturation value, and they were able to correlate, as a linear relationship, permanent stress birefringence with the permanent relaxation of polyethylene under stress. It was further demonstrated that the ability of a polyethylene film to rearrange its structure decreases with the amount of structural anisotropy produced by previous stressing.

More recently, the stress birefringence of polyethylene has been investigated by Peukert (561), who found that the proportionality between elongation and birefringence also applies to limited stresses. High stresses yielded a more pronounced hysteresis. However, cold-drawn specimens showed no reduction of either elongation or birefringence upon removal of the load. The effect of temperatures between 20 and 90°C. on the birefringence was investigated, and an equation was set up for computing the birefringence. A definite reversible orientation corresponds to any given elongation value. Upon removal of the load, the permanent set yields a characteristic optical effect, which leads to the conclusion that within the temperature range under consideration, no slippage occurs between the long molecular chains of the polyethylene.

6.9. Absorption Spectra

Absorption spectra of polyethylenes and their interpretation in terms of molecular structure are discussed in Section 5.4. A few additional papers deserve mention.

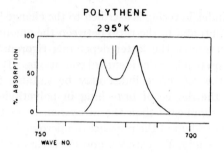

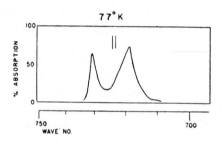

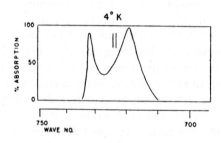

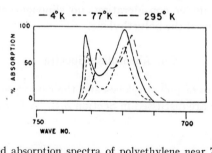

Fig. 151. Infrared absorption spectra of polyethylene near 720 cm.$^{-1}$ with a 1 cm.$^{-1}$ slit width and at 295, 77, and 4°K. (*J. Appl. Phys.*, **20**, 561, 1949.)

Infrared absorption spectra of polyethylene and other polymers were obtained by King, Hainer, and McMahon (397) at 4°K., in the rock salt region, in a specially designed transmission cell containing liquid helium. No unusual changes to alter the absorption occur on cooling.   Some sharpening in resolution occurs, but the widths of most bands in polymers remain broad.   As demonstrated by Figure 151, one component of the doublet at 720 cm.$^{-1}$ in polyethylene becomes very sharp;   its companion remains broad.   The two components are interpreted as CH_2 wagging in *trans*- and *cis*-configurations of the hydrocarbon chain.

Further studies of the infrared spectra of polyethylenes were reported by Fox and Martin (94), Sutherland and Jones (299), Stein and Sutherland (773), and by McCubbin and Sinton (482).   Kellner (396, 544) calculated the vibrations of an infinitely long chain of CH_2 groups as related to the infrared spectrum of polyethylene.   The spectrum of polyethylene was explained as the spectrum of a very long chain of CH_2 groups with one CH_3 group at each end whose presence does not affect the number of possible chain vibrations but leads to the infrared absorption of the otherwise inactive C—C valence vibrations.   An experimental procedure has been described by Elliott, Ambrose, and Temple (341) for measuring dichroism in the infrared spectra of oriented materials, which is particularly applicable to oriented films of polyethylene, as well as, for example, to nylon, polyvinyl alcohol, polyvinyl acetate, and polyvinyl chloride.   Studies of the infrared dichroism of polyethylene and its relationship to crystallinity and orientation were also reported by Nasini and Borello (867a).

Considerable detail in an absorption spectrum of a polyethylene was observed by Rossmann (1020) by the use of thick specimens (0.6 mm.) of polyethylene film in conjunction with a Beckman IR-3 spectrophotometer.

Rugg, Smith, and Atkinson (627) studied the effect of cold-drawing on the infrared band of polyethylene at 13.7 microns.   The spectrum of unstretched and 500% cold-drawn polyethylene was obtained by use of a Perkin-Elmer double-beam spectrophotometer with a polarizer attachment. The unstretched sample showed no orientation;   its absorption doublet at 13.70 and 13.88 μ was unchanged by rotating the plane of polarization. For the cold-drawn sample, with the E-vector at right angles to the direction of stretch, a slight lessening of absorption was noted at 13.70 μ but no change at 13.88 μ.   With the E-vector parallel to the direction of stretch, the 13.70 absorption band practically vanished, while the 13.88 band was greatly reduced.   These data indicate that both absorption bands result from vibrations at right angles to the long-chain axis.   The origin of the 13.70 μ band may be due to crystal size or form, or to the effect of distortion or stress within the crystal.

A comparison of ultraviolet transmission limits of various solid materials, including polyethylene and polyfluoroethylene, is shown in Table LXXV, from a paper by Klevens and Platt (292a).

TABLE LXXV

Ultraviolet Transmission Limits of Solids

Material (source)	Thickness, cm.	Limit, A.
Lithium fluoride	0.6	Below 1350
Fluorite	0.6	Below 1350
Fused quartz	0.03	30–50% at 1650–1570; 5% at 1550; cut-off 1525
	0.4	1600
Fused quartz	0.4	1560
	(Windows on 4 cm. cell)	
Crystal quartz	0.2	Est. 70% at 1750–1650
		Est. 25% at 1550
		Est. 20% at 1525
		Limit at 1520
Artificial sapphire (Al_2O_3)	0.5	1560–1480
Metaphosphate glass	0.5	2050
Polyethylene	0.01	2800–2270
Spinel	0.2	1840
Polyfluoroethylene	0.013	2350–1950
	0.14	2400–2150
Methyl methacrylate	0.20	2600

Source: *J. Am. Chem. Soc.*, **69**, 3056 (1947).

6.10. X-Ray Absorption and Diffraction

The dimensions of the unit cell of polyethylene, determined by x-ray examinations, are compared with those of other high polymers in Table LXXVI (474).

Trillat (488) made use of electron-diffraction patterns in studying the structure of polyethylene and confirmed the existence of identical structures in the hydrocarbon chain contained in macromolecules of polyethylene and of saturated hydrocarbons. Parameters were the same for their orthorhombic crystal structure.

A method for the determination of the amorphous content of polyethylene samples has been developed by Matthews, Peiser, and Richards (404). It is based on a microphotometric comparison of the intensities of the amorphous band and the two strongest crystalline lines on x-ray powder photo-

TABLE LXXVI

The Dimensions of the Unit Cell of Various Crystallized High Polymers

Material	a	b	Fiber Period c
Polyethylene	7.40 A.	4.93 A.	2.53 A.
Polyvinyl alcohol	7.82	5.60	2.52
Polyvinyl chloride	....	....	5.0
Polyvinylidene chloride	13.69	6.30	4.67
Polytetrafluoro ethylene	....	....	2.49–2.60
Polyvinyl acetate	Amorphous		
Polystyrene	Amorphous		
Polyisobutylene	6.94	11.96	18.63
Polybutadiene	....	....	5.0
α-trans-Polyisoprene (α-Gutta percha)	....	....	8.8
β-trans-Polyisoprene (β-Gutta percha)	7.78	11.78	4.72
cis-Polyisoprene (natural rubber)	12.5	8.9	8.1
Polychloroprene (Neoprene)	8.84	10.24	4.79
Butadiene-styrene copolymer	Amorphous		
Butadiene-acrylonitrile copolymer	Amorphous		
Rubber hydrochloride	5.83	10.38	8.95
Polyethylene oxide	....	....	19.5
Polyethylene tetrasulfide (Thiokol A)	8.68	5.03	4.3
Polyhexamethylene adipamide (nylon)	....	....	17.2
Polyethylene terephthalate (Terylene)	5.5	4.1	10.8
Cellulose	8.3	7.9	10.3

Source: R. Houwink, *Elastomers and Plastomers*, Vol. I, 279.   Elsevier Publishing Co., Inc., Houston, Tex., 1950.

graphs obtained from the samples in sheet form.   Figure 152 is an x-ray powder photograph showing that polyethylene is intermediate between entirely crystalline and entirely amorphous paraffins.   Figure 153 illustrates the wide variation in amorphous contents of polyethylene samples at ordinary temperatures.

The results of the measurements indicated that the amorphous contents of the polyethylenes under study varied from below 10% to above 50%, normally being around 25% for commercial grades prepared by the high-pressure, high-temperature polymerization process.   Since the more amorphous samples had a lower density, a quantitative relationship between density and degree of crystallinity was established, as indicated by Figure 154.

An empirical method for calculating x-ray mass absorption coefficients has been developed by Victoreen (424) and applied to polyethylene, polystyrene, and nylon.

Hermans and Weidinger (471), and later Hermans (540), carried out quantitative investigations of x-ray diffraction by various polymers. Crystallinity for polyethylene was found to decrease from 54% at 18°C. to 8% at 115°C.; it was noted that density and heat capacity showed the same trend.

Fig. 152. X-ray powder photographs of (a) a crystalline paraffin, (b) a polyethylene, (c) an amorphous paraffin. (*Acta Cryst.*, **2**, 85, 1949.)

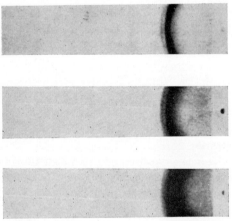

Fig. 153. X-ray powder photographs of three polyethylene samples differing widely in amorphous contents. (*Acta Cryst.*, **2**, 85, 1949.)

Krimm and Tobolsky (549,550), and Krimm (751), in a continuing series of investigations, studied crystalline and amorphous order in high polymers by x-ray determinations. They established that (a), the scattered intensity is proportional to the product of the density (p) and thickness (t) of the sample; (b), equal pt values for two different specimens of the same material implies equal scattering masses in the beam; (c), intensities integrated over all angles scattered by equal masses of the same polymer on amorphous or crystalline states are the same; and (d), the total scattering from different polymers reduced to the same mass of material and corrected for differing scattering factors is the same.   In studying the percentage of crystallinity in polyethylene as a function of temperature and stress, use was made of a Geiger counter x-ray spectrometer.

Arnett, Meibohm, and Smith (460) demonstrated that x-ray diffraction of polyethylene fibers gave small-angle maxima that were discrete inter-

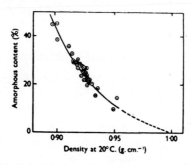

Fig. 154. Relation between amorphous content and density of polyethylene. (*Acta Cryst.*, **2**, 88, 1949.)

ferences not lying in the meridian or in the equator, thus indicating a multi- rather than a unidimensional order.   In further investigations of this phenomenon, Meibohm and Smith (555) showed that the ordering of these structures may be two- or three-dimensional and must extend over larger volumes than the older data would indicate.   The fibers must be given relaxation treatments to form the structures that result in small-angle maxima for other synthetic high-polymer fibers, such as polyamides.   In the case of polyethylene, as noted above, they appear merely upon orientation.

Brown (385) conducted x-ray diffraction studies of the stretching and relaxing of polyethylene.   He found that the orientation of the crystallites, when polyethylene is stretched at 96°, is normal in that, from the onset of stretching, the preferred orientation is the one in which the long-chain axis is parallel to the direction of stretch.   At low extensions, the preference for this orientation is weak, but it progressively becomes stronger as stretching proceeds.   When polyethylene is stretched at room temperature, the crystallite behavior is more complicated.   The first 20% extension produces no preferred orientation of the crystallites.   From 30–200% extension, the preferred orientation is that in which the (011) "axis" is parallel to the direction of stretch, and the long-chain axis therefore inclined to this direction at an angle of 64°.   From 200% extension to the break, i.e., about 600% extension, the tilt of the crystallites in the preferred orientation progressively lessens, almost vanishing at the break. The stress-strain diagram may be interpreted in the light of these findings. The preferred orientation of the crystallites in the region of the shoulder in necked-down polyethylene is also that wherein the (011) "axis" aligns with the stretching direction.   When stretched polyethylene is relaxed by shrinking at elevated temperatures, the crystallites become disoriented, but in a nonrandom manner.

6.11. Electrical Properties

Because polyethylene consists of long, essentially straight chains made up of methylene groups only, and exhibits a high degree of electrical symmetry, it is almost completely nonpolar.   The excellent electrical properties make it outstandingly well suited for the insulation of wires and cables, particularly where high-frequency circuits are involved, as in the field of electronics and telecommunication.   This is especially true since these properties are not appreciably affected by exposure to water or dampness. The polymer is form-stable, tough, and pliable over a wide range of temperatures.   In unmodified form or compounded with auxiliary ingredients, it is readily applied to wire or cable by extrusion in continuous lengths. Another advantage in electrical applications is its comparative immunity to ozone, by which it is considerably less affected than is rubber (162).

Richardson (761) discussed the electrical properties of a large number of high polymers from the standpoint of their use as electrical insulating materials.   Polyethylene, as a nonpolar plastic material, is characterized by extremely uniform dielectric properties over all frequencies and temperatures.   Oxidation, caused by degradation due to solar radiation and other atmospheric influences, introduces polar groups.   This is particularly noticeable in the loss factor.

Data on the electrical properties of polyethylene were published by Myers (159) and by Hahn, Macht, and Fletcher (178), as shown in Tables LXXVII and LXXVIII, respectively.

Further information on the relation of the dielectric strength of polyethylene to thickness is presented in Figure 155, taken from Hahn, Macht,

TABLE LXXVII

Electrical Properties of Polyethylene
(According to Myers)

Property	Value	A.S.T.M. Method of Test
Power factor at 25°C.		
1 Mc.	0.0003	
50 Mc.	0.0003	
Dielectric constant at 25°C.		
1 Mc.	2.3	
50 Mc.	2.29	
Direct current resistivity at 25°C., ohm-cm.	$>10^{15}$	
Surface resistivity, ohms	2×10^{14}	
Dielectric strength, volts per mil		D149–40T
20°C. (0.075 in. thick)	1000–1100	
80°C. (0.075 in. thick)	630	

Source: *Modern Plastics*, **21**, 104 (1944).

TABLE LXXVIII

Electrical Properties of Polyethylene
(According to Hahn *et al.*)

Property	Value	A.S.T.M. Method of Test
Dielectric strength, short-time, volts/mil	475 (0.125 in.)	D149–40T
Volume resistivity, ohm-cm.	10^{15}	D257–38
Dielectric constant		
60 cycles	2.3	D150–42T
10^3 cycles	2.3	D150–42T
10^6 cycles	2.3	D150–42T
10^8 cycles	2.3	. . . . .
Power factor		
60 cycles	<0.0005	D150–42T
10^3 cycles	<0.0005	D150–42T
10^6 cycles	<0.0005	D150–42T
10^8 cycles	<0.0005	. . . . .

Source: *Ind. Eng. Chem.*, **37**, 529 (1945).

and Fletcher (178). The effect of temperature on dielectric constant and power factor is shown in Figure 156, while Figure 157 shows the effect of the milling time of polyethylene, with and without antioxidant, on power factor, all from the same source (compare Section 3.13).

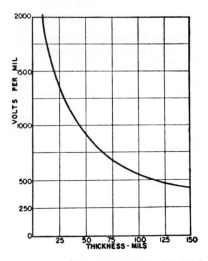

Fig. 155. Relation of dielectric strength of polyethylene to
thickness. (*Ind. Eng. Chem.*, **37**, 531, 1945.)

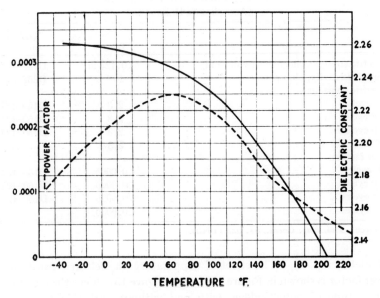

Fig. 156. Effect of temperature on dielectric constant and power factor of
polyethylene. (*Ind. Eng. Chem.*, **37**, 531, 1945.)

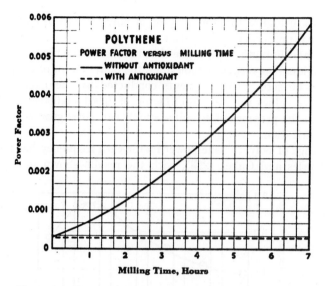

Fig. 157. Effect of milling time of polyethylene on power factor. (*Ind. Eng. Chem.*, **37**, 531, 1945.)

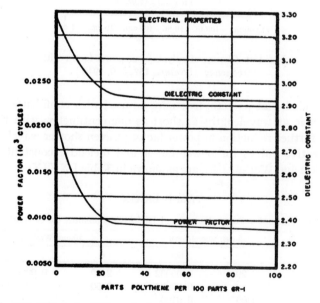

Fig. 158. Effect of addition of polyethylene on power factor and dielectric constant of GR-I. (*Ind. Eng. Chem.*, **37**, 532, 1945.)

As shown in Figure 158, the addition of polyethylene to GR-I improves the electrical properties of the latter.

Jackson and Forsyth (180) argue that because of the nonpolar character of the individual polyethylene molecules, the power factor of the pure material should be zero. Measurements conducted by them on commercial samples gave values for the power factor of 0.0015–0.00030, which they attribute to the presence of a limited number of polar groups formed during polymerization.

The change of polyethylene power factor with frequency has been studied by Powles and Oakes (223), with the results shown in Figure 159.

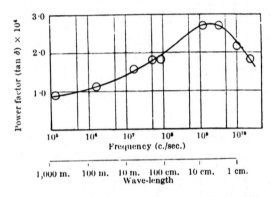

Fig. 159. Change of polyethylene power factor with frequency. (*Nature*, **157**, 840, 1946.)

It is concluded that polyethylene may be used with confidence as a low-loss dielectric at wavelengths as short as one centimeter, with the probability of further reduction in power factor at even shorter wavelengths.

Comparative values for power factor and dielectric constant, according to Dakin and Works (283), are as shown in Table LXXIX.

TABLE LXXIX

Comparative Values for Power Factor and Dielectric Constant for Several Polymers

	3-cm. Wavelength		10-cm. Wavelength	
	ϵ'	tan δ	ϵ'	tan δ
Polyethylene	2.29	0.00032	2.29	0.0002–0.0006
Polystyrene	2.43	0.00036	2.50	0.0003
Nylon	3.09	0.0106		
Silicone 993	2.90	0.0050		

Source: *J. Appl. Phys.*, **18**, 789 (1947).

Power factor-frequency curves for a 2% solution of dioctyl phthalate in polyethylene at a series of temperatures were determined by Plessner and Richards (222) and are shown in Figure 160.   Values of tan δ_{max}. and corresponding frequency (f_{max}.), determined at room temperature for a series of various esters in polyethylene, are summarized in Table LXXX.

An electronic theory of disruptive discharge has been advanced by Fröhlich (288) to account for the phenomena accompanying dielectric breakdown

TABLE LXXX

Values of tan δ_{max}. and f_{max}. for Polyethylene-Ester Mixtures at *ca.* 16°C.

Ester	Concentration, %	tan δ_{max}.	f_{max}. $\times 10^{-7}$
Dibutyl phthalate	0.6	0.0015	8
Dibutyl phthalate	2.0	0.0048	10
Dihexyl phthalate	2.0	0.0050	3.5
Dioctyl phthalate	2.0	0.0054	1.3
Tricresyl phosphate	0.06	0.0006	3
Tricresyl phosphate	2.0	0.0040	1.6
Propyl stearate	6.6	>0.003	>10

Source: *Trans. Faraday Soc.*, **42A**, 209 (1946).

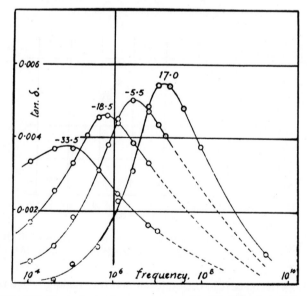

Fig. 160.   Power factor-frequency curve for 2% dioctyl phthalate in polyethylene.   (*Trans. Faraday Soc.*, 42*A*, 208, 1946.)

in solids. More particularly, it may account for the rise of dielectric strength with temperature at low temperatures, and for its decrease at high temperatures. It may also explain why influences tending to increase dielectric strength at low temperatures, such as the admixture of foreign

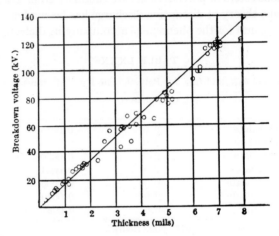

Fig. 161. D.-C. breakdown voltage of Grade 20 Polythene at 20°C. (*Nature*, **159**, 29, 1947.)

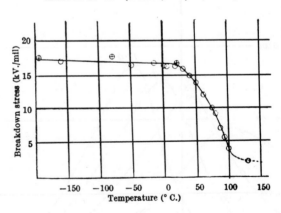

Fig. 162. Variation of breakdown voltage with temperature of Grade 20
Polythene. ⊕, Values obtained by Austen and Pelzer. (*Nature*, **159**, 29, 1947.)

atoms, tend to decrease it in the high-temperature region. Determinations by Oakes (293) on polyethylene show a measure of agreement with this theory which predicts that (a), the electrical strength should be independent of thickness until the latter approaches the electronic mean free path, then should increase with decreasing thickness; (b), below a certain critical temperature, electrical strength should either increase with or be independent of temperature, while above this temperature, it should decrease with increasing temperature.

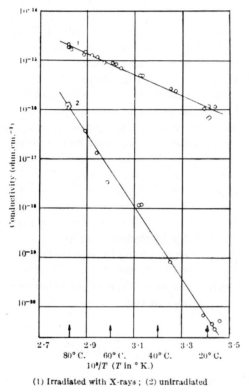

(1) Irradiated with X-rays ; (2) unirradiated

Fig. 163.   Temperature dependence of electrical conductivity induced in polyethylene by x-rays.   (*Nature*, **171**, 1020, 1953.)

As indicated in Figure 161, Oakes found the breakdown voltage for polyethylene specimens varying in thickness from 0.0005–0.008 in. to be an approximately linear function of thickness.   Figure 162 shows the variation of breakdown stress with temperature and indicates that the critical temperature is approximately 25°C.   The agreement between the present results and those obtained by Austen and Pelzer (211) on similar specimens of polyethylene at +20, −80, and −195°C. is considered satisfactory.

More recently, Oakes (410) studied the temperature dependence of the electrical strength of polyethylene, chlorinated polyethylenes, oxidized polyethylenes, polystyrene, polyisobutylene, and polymethyl methacrylate over a range of temperatures from -200 to $+110°C$. The results of this investigation lead to the conclusion that the electrical strength of nonpolar polymers at low temperatures is nearly independent of temperature. At a characteristic temperature (T_c), it falls rapidly with further temperature rise. This temperature is about $40°C$. for polyethylene, $90°C$. for polystyrene, and $-50°C$. for polyisobutylene. The introduction of polar groups into the polyethylene chain produces, as predicted, an increased strength at low temperatures and displaces T_c to a lower temperature. The negative temperature coefficient is not described by the theory in its present form, and it is difficult to establish the position of T_c, since the experimentally determined critical points appear at temperatures at which phase changes or second-order transitions are known to occur.

Studies of the electrical conductivity induced in polyethylene by x-rays, and of the effect of temperature on the induced conductivity, were reported by Fowler and Farmer (732,848) and discussed in terms of electron-trapping mechanisms. The relationship between log (conductivity) and $10^3/T(°K.)$ for the range of 20–$80°C$. is shown in Figure 163 for x-ray irradiated and unirradiated polyethylene samples.

The change in electrical conductivity in polyethylene during γ-irradiation was studied by Mayburg and Lawrence (617). The effect of Co^{60} γ-irradiation on the direct current conductivity, σ, of polyethylene up to an intensity I of 4,000 roentgens per hour at room temperature could be described by the equation

$$\sigma/\sigma_\infty = 1 + (I/I_0)^{3/4},$$

where σ_∞ is the conductivity without radiation [of the order of 10^{-18} (ohm-cm.)$^{-1}$], and I_0 is 20 roentgens/hour. Measurements at liquid nitrogen temperatures gave a 20-fold decrease in the normal conductivity, and a 25-fold decrease in the radiation-induced conductivity below the respective room-temperature values. On the basis of these results, an ionic mechanism for electric conduction in polyethylene, rather than an electronic mechanism, is postulated, whereby the ion contributing most to the conduction may well be the proton.

The change in conductivity of Teflon and polyethylene during γ-irradiation as a function of temperature and dose rate has also been studied more recently by Meyer and Boquet (995). In general, the conductivity of

Teflon was found to be greater than that of polyethylene under γ-irradiation.

6.12. Mechanical Properties

In thin sections, polyethylene made by the conventional, high-pressure, polymerization process is sufficiently pliable to resemble such non-rigid plastics as unplasticized polyvinyl butyral and vinyl copolymers; in

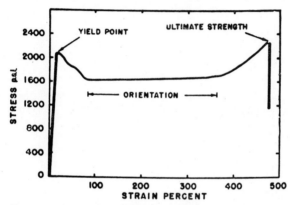

Fig. 164. Tensile properties of polyethylene. (*J. Am. Chem. Soc.*, **75**, 6128, 1953.)

relatively thick sections, it may serve the purposes of a rigid-type plastic. The flexural strength, 1,500–1,700 p.s.i., is comparable to that exhibited by the less rigid plastics.   On the other hand, polyethylene is notably unlike these materials in retaining flexibility at temperatures even as low as −40°C.   Retention of properties at low temperatures is further illustrated by the Izod impact strength test.   At 25°C., a correctly prepared sample will not break in a 4-ft. pound machine, and at −55°C., the impact strength is still 0.4-ft. pound per inch of notch.

The viscoelastic properties of polyethylene were recently characterized by Catsiff, Offenbach, and Tobolsky (1128), and correlated with measurements of crystallinity and birefringence.   Measurements were made on samples of polyethylene from −65 to 80°C. on the glassy state relaxometer (939), and continued up to 105°C. on the Firestone Relaxometer (162a), especially adapted for strip samples (1007).   In agreement with the stress relaxation data, both birefringence and x-ray results indicated a marked decrease in per cent crystallinity and orientation of the stretched samples as the temperature is raised, particularly close to the melting point, but time effects appear to be small.

TABLE LXXXI

Properties of Polyethylene Resins at Room Temperature

Properties	D-40	D-55 (DYNH)	D-70	D-85	D-100	D-130	D-145	Test Method
Molecular weight, average	14–18,000	18–20,000	20–22,000	24–26,000	26–28,000	28–30,000	30–32,000	......
Specific gravity	0.92	0.92	0.92	0.92	0.92	0.92	0.92	......
Stiffness in flexure, p.s.i.								
25°C.	18,000	18,000	18,000	18,000	18,000	18,000	18,000	A.S.T.M. D747–43T
0°C.	30,000	30,000	30,000	30,000	30,000	30,000	30,000	A.S.T.M. D747–43T
−25°C.	66,000	66,000	66,000	66,000	66,000	66,000	66,000	A.S.T.M. D747 (Tentative)
−50°C.	160,000	160,000	160,000	160,000	160,000	160,000	160,000	A.S.T.M. D747 (Tentative)
Yield strength at 25°C., p.s.i.	1,430	1,480	1,490	1,600	1,700	1,830	1,720	A.S.T.M. D412–41
Tensile strength, p.s.i.	1,430	1,825	1,965	2,435	2,965	3,160	3,060	A.S.T.M. D412–41
Compressive strength, p.s.i.	...	3,000	...	...	...	...	...	
Ultimate elongation at 25°C., %	305	560	550	560	580	605	625	A.S.T.M. D412–41
Brittle temperature, °C.	−55	Below −70	Below −70	Below −70	Below −70	Below −70	Below −70	A.S.T.M. D746–43T
Impact strength, ft.-lb./in. of notch	...	>3	...	...	...	...	...	A.S.T.M. D256–43T (A)
Tear strength, p.s.i.	440	500	540	560	580	605	690	A.S.T.M. D624–41T
Abrasion volume loss (standard butyl rubber = 100)	85	55	50	45	40	35	30	142a
Hardness								
Durometer D at 25°C.	52–54	52–54	52–54	52–54	52–54	52–54	52–54	......

Source: *Modern Plastics*, **21** (12), 104 (1944).

Undrawn polyethylene is relatively weak from the standpoint of tensile strength, namely about 1,700 p.s.i. at 500% elongation.   Drawn films and filaments may, however, exhibit tensile strengths from 5,000–15,000 p.s.i.

Mechanical properties of commercial, conventional, high-pressure polyethylenes are given by Myers (159) and shown in Table LXXXI.

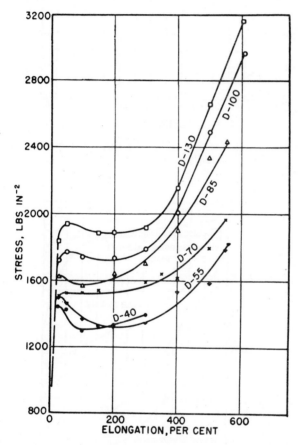

Fig. 165. Stress-strain diagram for polyethylene resins (increasing molecular weight). (*Modern Plastics*, **21**, 104, 1944.)

The stress-strain relationship for a sample of high molecular weight polythylene is best explained by Figure 164, taken from the paper by Sperati, ʼranta, and Starkweather   (772).   It may be seen that, following the nitial, nearly linear deformation, the sample passes through the yield

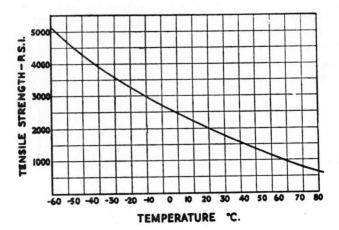

Fig. 166. Effect of temperature on tensile strength of polyethylene. (*Ind. Eng. Chem.*, **37**, 530, 1945.)

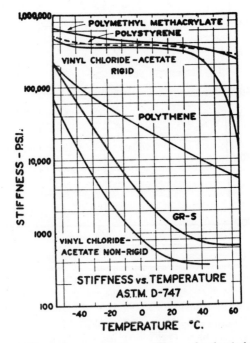

Fig. 167. Effect of temperature on stiffness of polyethylene and other substances. (*Ind. Eng. Chem.*, **37**, 529, 1945.)

point.   A sharp decrease in the tensile stress after the yield point is accompanied by necking-down of the test specimen; cold-drawing with orientation and high elongation follows; finally, the stress increases to the breaking point, denoting the ultimate strength.   Stress-strain curves for the polyethylenes shown in Table LXXXI are presented in Figure 165.

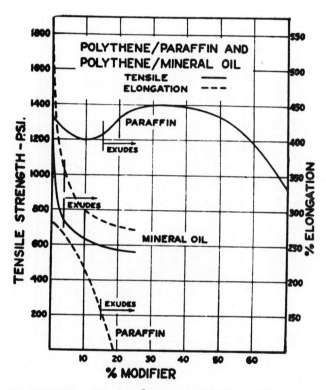

Fig. 168. Effect of modifiers on tensile strength and elongation of
polyethylene. (*Ind. Eng. Chem.*, **37**, 532, 1945.)

The effect of temperature on the tensile strength of polyethylene is demonstrated in Figure 166 from Hahn, Macht, and Fletcher (178).   As shown, the tensile strength, calculated on the original undrawn cross section, varies from about 800 p.s.i. at 70°C. to about 5,000 p.s.i. at −60°C.   The stiffness of polyethylene, in common with that of other well-known plastics, varies considerably with temperature (Figure 167).   Hahn, Macht, and

Fletcher further report the effect of modifiers on tensile strength and elongation (Figure 168) and on rigidity (Figure 169).

The temperature effect in the tensile behavior was recently discussed by Nakamura and Skinner (998). The temperature increases noted in the specimens for various tensile machine crosshead speeds are shown in Table LXXXII.

The changes in specific volume and in dimension of polyethylene under

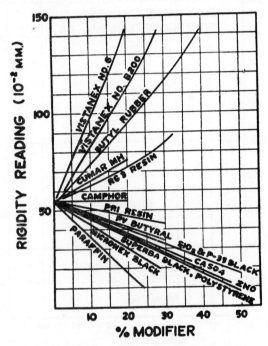

Fig. 169. Effect of modifiers on rigidity of polyethylene. R63 resin is a product of Resinous Products and Chemical Company; PRI is an experimental ether resin. (*Ind. Eng. Chem.*, **37**, 532, 1945.)

TABLE LXXXII

Temperature Rise as a Function of Velocity of Extension

Speed, in./min.	Ave. Temp. Rise, °C.	Max. Temp. Rise, °C.
2	11.0	12.5
5	16.5	19.5
10	18.2	23.0

Source: *J. Polymer Sci.*, **18**, 423 (1955).

tensile stress were measured by Nakamura and Skinner (999) as a function of elongation.

The influence of plasticizers on stiffness over a wide temperature range has been demonstrated by Myers (159) as shown in Figure 170, emphasizing the excellent low-temperature properties of polyethylene. The addition of polyisobutylene, a desirable additive in other respects, was found to in-

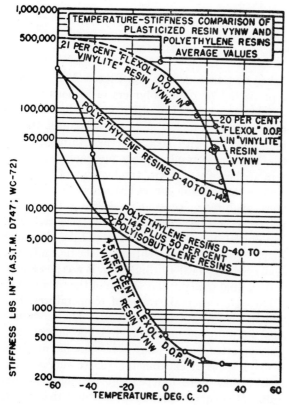

Fig. 170. Temperature-stiffness comparison of plasticized resin VYNW and polyethylene resins. Average values. (*Modern Plastics*, **21,** 105, 1944.)

crease the cold-brittleness temperature of polyethylene and to reduce its puncture resistance in the very low temperature range. The supporting data, as reported by Freeman, Sheridan, and Renfrew (849), are shown in Table LXXXIII.

A comprehensive study of the mechanical properties of polyethylenes

TABLE LXXXIII

Low-Temperature Toughness of Polyethylene-Polyisobutylene Blends

Polyiso-butylene, %	Cold-Brittleness Temperature, °C.	Falling-Ball Puncture Resistance at −20°C., In.-Lb./Mil
0	−71	19
3	−63	21
15	−57	26
30	−46	29
50	−40	23

Source: *Modern Packaging,* **27** (6), 148 (1954).

has been published by Carey, Schulz, and Dienes (465). The fundamental and practical properties of these polymers of various average molecular weights were studied by means of tensile stress-strain and torsional torque-deflection curves. By combining these two techniques, the stiffness characteristics were evaluated with good precision through a wide range of temperatures. From these results, other mechanical properties, such as stress and strain at the "elastic limit," and energy of strain, could in turn be evaluated. The stress-strain curves characteristic of different temperature ranges were analyzed. At −30 to +25°C., there was continuous curvature which could best be described by an exponential type of function, from which an initial tangent modulus could be determined. Below −30°C., the behavior was more conventionally elastic, and a tangent modulus could be evaluated graphically. Similarly, it was possible to calculate a modulus from the initial straight-line section of the torsional torque-deflection curves. Through a common range of temperatures, the tensile and torsional techniques gave equivalent moduli. The modulus-temperature curves of resins of different molecular weights showed on logarithmic scale the familiar inverted S-shape, but were more flat and more extended than those of vinyl resins or elastomers. These curves coincided at low temperatures, i.e., they were independent of molecular weight. With rise in temperature, the curves spread out, and materials of relatively high molecular weight were characterized by correspondingly high moduli. An "elastic limit" is defined as the point on the stress-strain curve where the tangent modulus is 50% of the initial modulus; the corresponding area under the curve is the strain energy. A fundamental relationship which is independent of the temperature and molecular weight, and which is consistent with the exponential nature of the curves, is that the product of the initial modulus and the strain at the elastic limit is proportional to the stress at the elastic limit.

In a later paper, Carey (838) presents additional data on mechanical properties of polyethylene. Tensile strength and final elongation are considered to be of limited significance, while short-time static tests indicate that yield point is a primary criterion for failure.

Moll and Le Fevre (348) described a laboratory apparatus which enables accurate and efficient determination of the relationship between temperature and Young's modulus for a wide variety of plastic materials, including polyethylene, and an equally wide variety of sample sizes. Hillier (541) described a method for obtaining dynamic values of Young's modulus at low frequencies (20–100 cycles per second) by using the forced resonance of a vibrating cantilever. Preliminary results indicate that, for polyethylene, no abrupt changes in the dynamic modulus occur in the complete range of 20 cycles per second to 20 kilocycles per second, at temperatures between 20 and 40°C.

Gohn, Cummings, and Ellis (391) investigated the creep characteristics of compression-molded polyethylene. These are substantially the same for the unmodified polymer or for specimens containing carbon black and an antioxidant. Unlike metals, polyethylene shows high elastic and plastic deformation during the first stage of creep, with the elastic component representing a high proportion of the total creep occurring during this period. As much as 78% of the total elongation is recoverable, whereas with metals little or no recovery is evident upon unloading. Even after 20,000 hours of continuously applied load, a steady creep rate is not attained with polyethylene, although lead-sheathing alloys usually show a steady creep stage after only a few thousand hours under sustained load. Shelf-aging, after molding and prior to starting the creep test, appears to have some effect by increasing the creep strength in the initial period of the test. Artificial weathering for 1,000 hours did not significantly alter the creep characteristics of the compounded polyethylene.

Extensive experiments have been conducted by Weir (569) on the volume changes of a number of polymers at pressures between 1,000 and 10,000 atmospheres. For polyethylenes, the results are in agreement with those reported by Bridgman (338) and shown in Table LXXXIV.

The compressibility of polyethylene and its dependence on pressure was recently calculated by Brandt (935a) from the energy of interaction between —CH_2— groups. The theoretical results were found in good agreement up to 40,000 kg./cm.^{2} with the previously cited experimental data of Bridgman (338), Parks and Richards [(413); see Section 6.4], and Weir (569).

The variation of mechanical properties with molecular weight has been

TABLE LXXXIV

Compressibility of Polyethylenes

Pressure, Kg./Cm.²	Type of Polyethylene		
	Exptl. Mol. Wt. 14,000–16,000	Standard DYNH Mol. Wt. 18,000–20,000	Exptl. Mol. Wt. 36,000–38,000
	Fractional Increase in volume		
0	0.0000	0.0000	0.0000
2,500	0.0553	0.0548	0.0522
5,000	0.0874	0.0897	0.0863
10,000	0.1319	0.1331	0.1300
15,000	0.1621	0.1639	0.1606
20,000	0.1852	0.1876	0.1836
25,000	0.2040	0.2066	0.2024
30,000	0.2194	0.2222	0.2178
35,000	0.2321	0.2351	0.2306
40,000	0.2430	0.2460	0.2416

Source: *J. Research Natl. Bur. Standards*, **46**, 207 (1951).

presented in Table LXXXI. Clarke (177) points out that the physical properties of polyethylene at normal temperatures correlate approximately with the plasticity of the material in the melted state. As the complexity

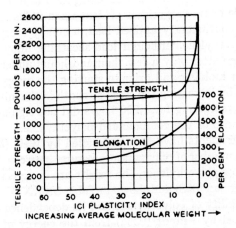

Fig. 171. Tensile strength and elongation *versus* plasticity index. (*Trans. AIEE*, **64**, 920, 1945.)

of the material increases, that is, as the average molecular weight increases, such properties as tensile strength and elongation increase, and the temperature at which the polyethylene becomes brittle under sharp impact is substantially lowered, as shown in Figures 171 and 172, respectively.

Richards (563) has pointed out that, with respect to flexibility at low temperatures, molecular weight is the predominating factor. At the same time, crystallinity and the texture of the polymer have important effects in certain ranges of molecular weight. Generally, if the molecular

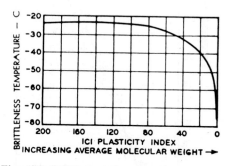

Fig. 172. Brittleness temperature *versus* plasticity index. (*Trans. AIEE*, **64**, 920, 1945.)

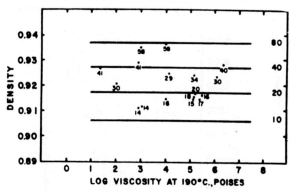

Fig. 173. Stiffness × 10⁻³ p.s.i.   (*J. Am. Chem. Soc.*, **75**, 6129, 1953.)

weight of the polymer is below 20,000, it is improbable that the sample will be flexible below about −35°C. On the other hand, samples of molecular weight above 30,000 are nearly always flexible at −70°C. or below, and samples having molecular weights over 40,000 have been found to have low-temperature brittle points of −140°C. In the intermediate range of molecular weights, the brittle point is very sensitive to crystallinity; as an example, it may be changed from below −70°C. to −25°C. by reducing the

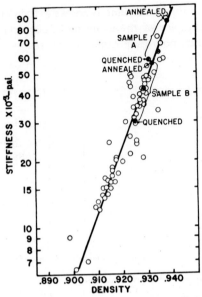

Fig. 174. Log stiffness *versus* density and effect of thermal treatment on stiffness. (*J. Am. Chem. Soc.*, **75**, 6129, 1953.)

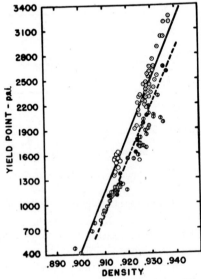

Fig. 175. Yield point *versus* density. (*J. Am. Chem. Soc.*, **75**, 6130, 1953.)

rate of cooling from the melt, thus increasing the degree of crystallinity. Accordingly, two samples of the same molecular weight but of different degrees of chain branching may differ in low-temperature flexibility to a similar extent.

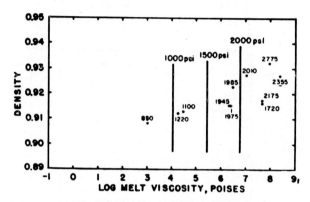

Fig. 176. Ultimate strength, p.s.i.   (*J. Am. Chem. Soc.*, **75**, 6131, 1953.)

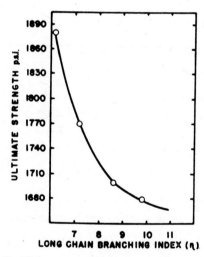

Fig. 177. Ultimate strength *versus* long-chain branching
index.   (*J. Am. Chem. Soc.*, **75**, 6132, 1953.)

The recent attempt by a duPont research team to develop a consistent picture of the relationships between the molecular structure of polyethylene and various physical and mechanical properties has been discussed (Section 5.6). According to Sperati, Franta, and Starkweather (772), stiffness and yield point are controlled primarily by crystallinity, as affected by short-chain branching and measured by density. Ultimate elongation and hardness are related to both density and melt viscosity, and the ultimate strength is determined by molecular weight and the amount of long-chain branching. The equations representing the relationships between

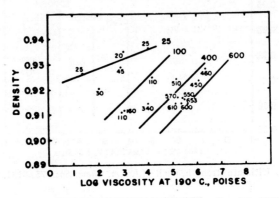

Fig. 178. Ultimate elongation, %. (*J. Am. Chem. Soc.*, **75**, 6132, 1953.)

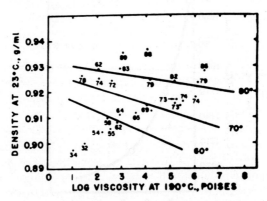

Fig. 179. Hardness, Shore C. (*J. Am. Chem. Soc.*, **75**, 6132, 1953.)

these variables have been discussed in Section 5.6. The experimental data upon which they are based are presented as follows.

Figure 173 shows that the stiffness of various polyethylenes is dependent primarily upon the crystallinity (density) of the sample; at constant density, the stiffness is independent of melt viscosity. In the example presented, the range of viscosities was ten million-fold, and the crystallinities ranged from 40–80%.

Figure 174 shows the plot of log stiffness *versus* density to be a straight line.   The effect of thermal history on the stiffness of two different polyethylenes is illustrated by the solid points on the curve.   Yield point is plotted against density in Figure 175.

The scatter of the observed points is greatly reduced if rigorously controlled conditions are observed in preparing and testing the samples. The solid points and broken lines shown in the figure were determined under such conditions.

Values for density, yield point, and stiffness were the same for a polymer of intermediate crystallinity, made by blending polymers of high and low crystallinity, and for a material of similar crystallinity prepared by direct synthesis.   It is therefore concluded that short-chain branching need not be distributed evenly within the polymer chains, but that an average blending is the effective factor.   Ultimate strength is substantially independent of the density (crystallinity), and primarily dependent on the viscosity of the polymer (Figure 176); it decreases with increasing long-chain branching (Figure 177).

The simultaneous dependence of ultimate elongation on both density and viscosity is illustrated in Figure 178.   Dependence of hardness on both of these factors is shown in Figure 179.

6.13. Adhesion and Frictional Behavior

Borroff and Wake (384a) investigated the factors influencing the load required to strip rubber from foil and fabric surfaces.   Experiments were conducted with chemically treated cotton fabrics in which the mechanical factors, i.e., structure and appearance of the fabric, were maintained constant, and with polyethylene, polystyrene, cellophane, and cellulose acetate sheets.   It was established that the parts played by special factors, such as the polarity of the cloth and the weakening of the cloth under chemical treatment in rubber-to-fabric adhesion, are relatively unimportant.   It was concluded that special influences do, however, play a part, the magnitude of which depends on the presence of polar groups or of groups that can be polarized.

Kraus and Manson (548) studied the adhesion of polyethylene and of polystyrene to steel.   The "specific adhesion," i.e., the total molecular attraction per unit area of interface, was estimated, and the contribution of the London forces was found to be much larger than that of permanent dipoles.   The "effective adhesion," i.e., the adhesion as determined by a physical destruction test, was much lower than the calculated specific adhesion, probably because of flaws, thermal stresses, and deformation under load. Curves of joint failure stress against film thickness of polyethylene or polystyrene at temperatures between $-60°C$. and $+82°C$. were plotted and extrapolated to zero thickness. The extrapolated values represent a lower limit of the specific adhesion. At $25°C$., they were 183 kg./cm.^{2} for polyethylene, and 412 kg./cm.^{2} for polystyrene.

Shooter and Thomas (421) examined the frictional properties of polytetrafluoroethylene, polyethylene, polystyrene, and polymethyl methacrylate with a Bowden-Leben apparatus over the temperature range of 20–200°C. The coefficients of friction increased from tetrafluoroethylene to polymethyl methacrylate in the order stated, and it was concluded that the differences could be accounted for on the basis of polymer structures. At the low rate of sliding used, the frictional heating was insufficient to affect the frictional properties of the polymers appreciably. At higher rates of sliding, sufficient heat was developed to produce marked softening at the rubbing interface, except in the case of tetrafluoroethylene.

In later experiments, Rabinowicz (624) and Shooter and Tabor (631) determined the frictional properties over a range of speeds and loads of polytrifluorochloroethylene, polystyrene, polymethyl methacrylate, nylon, polyethylene terephthalate, polyvinyl chloride, and polyethylene. They concluded that, in general, the behavior of plastics is similar to metals. With metals, cold welding takes place; with plastics, strong adhesion may occur.

More recently, Bowers, Clinton, and Zisman (699,709,710,711,831) also subjected polyethylene and some other high polymers to a series of friction measurements in a modified Bowden-Leben friction-and-wear machine. The static coefficients of friction (μ_s) of some of these high polymers are shown in Table LXXXV; kinetic coefficients of friction (μ_k) of high polymers free from "stick-slip" behavior are summarized in Table LXXXVI. The results showed that the substitution of chlorine for hydrogen in polyethylene caused an increase in friction, and that the substitution of fluorine caused a decrease; the effect of chlorine was found to predominate when both fluorine and chlorine were substituted.

The major component of the frictional force for each plastic, except for polytetrafluoroethylene, is believed to be the force required to shear the bulk plastic. Transfer of plastic occurs for some sliding combinations, and the orientation of the transferred material (polyethylene, polytetrafluoroethylene) during sliding indicates that the possibility of some shearing at the plastic-metal interface cannot be discounted. The particularly low

TABLE LXXXV

Static Coefficient of Friction (μ_s) of Some High Polymers[a]

Polymer	Steel Sliding on Polymer		Polymer Sliding on Steel		Polymer Sliding on Polymer	
	Polished	Abraded	Polished	Abraded	Polished	Abraded
Polyethylene	0.60	0.33	0.60	0.33	0.60	0.33
Polyvinyl chloride	0.90–0.70[b]	0.45[b]	0.45–0.60[b]	0.45–0.50[b]	0.60–0.90[c]	0.45–0.55[b]
Polyvinylidene chloride	1.8–1.0[b]	0.68[b]	1.4–1.6[b]	0.70–0.95[b]	1.3–2.0[b]	0.80–0.95[b]
Polyvinyl fluoride	0.30	...	....	....	....	....
50-50 copolymer of TFE-ethylene[c]	....	0.33	....	....	....	....
Polytetrafluoroethylene	0.15	0.10	....	0.10	....	0.04

Source: PB 111,185 (Naval Research Laboratory Report 4,167), May 19, 1953.
[a] Measured at 0.8 kg. normal load and with a 12.7-mm. diameter slider.
[b] "Stick-slips" occur.
[c] TFE = tetrafluoroethylene.

TABLE LXXXVI
Kinetic Coefficient of Friction (μ_k) of
High Polymers Free from "Stick-Slip" Behavior

Polymer	Steel Sliding on Polymer		Polymer Sliding on Steel		Polymer Sliding on Polymer	
	Polished	Abraded	Polished	Abraded	Polished	Abraded
Polyethylene	0.60–0.50	0.33–0.25	0.60	0.33	0.60	0.33
Polyvinyl fluoride	0.30–0.10	...	..	...	..	..
50-50 copolymer TFE-polyethylene	...	0.33–0.25	..	...	..	..
TFE	0.15–0.08	0.10–0.04	..	0.10–0.04	..	0.04

Source: PB 111,185 (Naval Research Laboratory Report 4,167), May 19, 1953.

coefficient of friction for polytetrafluoroethylene is presented as evidence that shearing in depth must be only a minor component of the frictional force for this plastic.

The frictional measurements of thin films of the polymers on steel showed that the frictional force was always much less than for a bulk piece. A good approximation of μ_s for very thin films could be calculated by multiplying μ_s for the bulk plastic by the ratio of the yield pressure of the plastic to the yield pressure of the substratum. Ease of material trans-

fer combined with low shear strength was found to be confined to polyethylene and polytetrafluoroethylene; the additional properties of low
adhesion and heat stability make the latter more suitable for many applications as a solid lubricant.

A study of the coefficient of friction, the shear strength, and the indenta-
tion hardness of polyethylene and other polymeric materials was carried
out by King and Tabor (748) over the temperature range of -100 to
$+80°C$.

The effect of speed on the kinetic friction of polyethylene and other
plastics on ice was studied by Niven (1136a). Compard with Teflon and
Bakelite, polyethylene was found to have a relatively high kinetic friction
value.

6.14. Propagation of Sound Velocity

Rama Rao (121) studied data on the velocity of sound and density in
liquids and found that the following relation between these quantities
exists:

$$v^{1/3}M/d = R$$

where

  v = velocity of sound in the liquid;
  M = molecular weight;
  d = density;
  R = constant independent of temperature.

For members of homologous series, plotting the constant (R) against the
molecular weight leads to the equation

$$R = \alpha M + \beta$$

where α is a general constant, and β a characteristic constant for any one
homologous series. The difference in R for successive members of homologous series is a constant independent of the series, and R is an additive
function of the chemical structure. A subsequent study by Natta and Baccaredda (349) indicated that the ratio of the ultrasonic velocity to the density of various polymers is related to the form of the molecules. In particular, it is known that this ratio increases in compounds with a rigid, straight
paraffin chain with increasing molecular weight, from 1.69 at 20°C. for
low molecular weight hydrocarbons, to 1.92 for high molecular weight
polyethylenes. In crosslinked compounds with ethyl and methyl groups,
this ratio is practically a constant for all compounds up to a molecular
weight of 15,000. In general, the compressibility is higher for polymers

with frequent and large crosslinkages than for compounds with little or no crosslinking.   It was later demonstrated by Natta and Baccaredda (408, 409) that the molecular ultrasonic velocity is an additive property for compounds with low molecular weight, given by the sum of the velocities of the individual radicals.   Branching reduces the velocity only moderately. For high molecular weight and unbranched chain compounds, the sound velocity can be calculated from the molar ultrasonic velocity.   In the case of branched polymers, the ratio between the experimental and the calculated velocities, termed "form-factor," can be used to a certain extent to determine number and size of the branches.   This factor is one (or somewhat higher) for unbranched or little-branched compounds of high molecular weight, such as paraffins, polyethylenes, polyethylene oxides, and nylon.   It is less than one for higher branched compounds; 0.90 for natural rubber; 0.79–0.80 for polyisobutylenes. This method appears to be only of limited value in the study and characterization of polyethylenes.

6.15. Low Molecular Weight Polyethylenes

The properties of some commercial polyethylenes of low molecular weight, recommended primarily in coating applications, are summarized in Table LXXXVII, taken from a trade bulletin (883) of one producer.

TABLE LXXXVII

Physical Properties of A-C Polyethylenes

Grade[a]	Average Molecular Weight	Melting Point, °C.	Hardness	Specific Gravity	Viscosity at 140°C.
6	2,000	97–102	0.3–0.5	0.92	185 sec. Furol
7	2,000	102–106	0.2–0.3	0.92	250 sec. Furol
615	5,000	102–104	0.3–0.4	0.92	4,000 cps.
617	1,500	88–90	2.0–2.5	0.92	69 sec. Furol

Source: Semet-Solvay Div., Allied Chemical and Dye Corp., New York, 1954.
[a] The dielectric constant for grades 6, 7, and 615 is 2.5 (60 to 10^6 cycles).

Another manufacturer is promoting a hard, waxlike, near-white, slightly translucent polyethylene of low molecular weight (A-Wachs, BASF), for use in blends with other waxes, in shoe pastes, floor polishes, and similar applications.   The product is microcrystalline and rather tough, with a melting point of 103–105°C. and specific gravity of 0.91.

The preparation of low molecular weight, wax-like, saturated polyethylenes by heating high molecular weight polyethylenes in the presence of hydrogen and hydrogenation catalysts to temperatures between 300 and

600°C. is claimed by Hopff and Eilbracht in Ger. 922,618 (1054), and in Brit. 728,551 (1070), both to BASF.

Two grades of low molecular weight polyethylenes (2,000–6,000), the one modified to be usable for water-emulsion polishes (Epolene "E"; also Section 8.12); the other, a hard and tough wax designed for paste polishes and other applications (Epolene "N"), has been recently described in the commercial trade bulletin of still another producer (952, 1122b).

Low molecular weight polyethylenes may accelerate heat-bodying of drying oils [U.S. 2,739,975 (1152)].

6.16. Irradiated Polyethylenes

The changes occurring in polyethylene during irradiation have been described in Section 4.7. Because development has been rapid, most of the applications for irradiated polyethylene are still in the experimental stage. The present status of this field has been summarized recently by Goodwin (959), by Bockhoff and Neumann (933,933a), and by Goodwin and Wetzel (960). The latter paper includes a discussion of the advantages of irradiated conventional polyethylenes over unirradiated high-density polyethylenes in electrical applications.

The following information is taken from the trade bulletin of one manufacturer of irradiated polyethylene (821). It is pointed out that the properties of irradiated polyethylene depend strongly on the electron dose level, and that the most marked property improvements are increased heat resistance and stiffness. Typical properties of Agilene-HT, a commercial irradiated polyethylene, are shown in Table LXXXVIII.

TABLE LXXXVIII

Typical Properties of Agilene-HT

Property	A.S.T.M. Designation	Value
Tensile strength	D412–51T	1,800–2,100 p.s.i.
Elongation	D412–51T	600%
Stiffness	D747–50	45,000 p.s.i.
Specific gravity	D792–50	0.92
Shore hardness "D"	D676–49T	48
Impact strength Izod	D256–47T	Did not break
Water absorption	. . . . .	Negligible
Dielectric constant (60 cycles to 100 megacycles)	D150–47T	2.3
Power factor (60 cycles to 100 megacycles)	D150–47T	0.0005

Source: *Properties and Applications of Agilene-HT*, American Agile Corp., 1954.

Irradiated polyethylene produced commercially in film form by another manufacturer (851) (GE Irrathene 101) is claimed not to melt or flow under light load and at temperatures as high as 177°C. Resistance to cracking under stress in soaps, detergents, acids, solvents, and other corrosive media is claimed to be outstanding. Typical physical properties of GE Irrathene 101 are given in Table LXXXIX; typical electrical properties in Table XC; resistance to stress cracking is shown in Table XCI.

The addition of fillers to polyethylene has been generally found to degrade the product and lead to stiff and brittle materials. However, a highly loaded, carbon black filled polyethylene which has been crosslinked by high energy irradiation (GE Vulkene 107-E) was recently described (923b) as having good low-temperature flexibility and heat aging characteristics, and resistance to sunlight and chemicals. Parts from this new material must be fabricated before irradiation. According to Szwarc (1141c) carbon black particles act as radical traps and as bridges linking many molecules. Degradation is thus prevented, and the new links formed tend to make the polymer mechanically stronger.

TABLE LXXXIX

Typical Physical Properties of GE Irrathene 101

Tensile strength, p.s.i.	1,800–2,200
Modulus of elasticity, p.s.i.	18,000–20,000
Ultimate elongation	500–600%
Hardness (Rockwell)	R11
Specific gravity	0.92
Water absorption	Negligible
Flammability	Slow burning
Chemical resistance	Excellent resistance to acids or alkalis
Solvent resistance	Good below 60°C. Badly swollen by hydrocarbons and chlorinated compounds above 60–100°C.
Resistance to sunlight	Must be protected from sunlight.

Source: General Electric Co., Chemical Division, 1954.

Irradiation of polyethylene for a small fraction of the time required to effect appreciable changes in mechanical properties is claimed by Charlesby in Brit. 732,047 [United Kingdom Atomic Energy Authority (1075)] to develop a resistance to the solvent action of organic solvents. Moreover, polyethylene which has a marked melting point before treatment no longer melts and flows but may still soften at elevated temperatures.

The influence of irradiation on the permeability for gases of polyethylene films has been discussed in Section 6.3.

A process for irradiating polyethylene film to ensure acceptable adhesion of printing inks to the treated film is described in Section 8.18.

TABLE XC

Typical Electrical Properties of GE Irrathene 101

Dielectric strength (5 mil film)	
Short time 25°C.	2,500 volts/mil
50°	2,300
Step-by-step 25°C.	1,800
50°	1,800
Power factor	
60 cycle	<0.0005
1 mc.	<0.0005
10,000 mc.	<0.0005
Dielectric constant	
60 cycle	2.3
1 mc.	2.3
10,000 mc.	2.3
Insulation resistance 80–100 mil	>20 × 10⁶ megohms

Source: General Electric Co., Chemical Division, 1954.

TABLE XCI

Environmental Stress Cracking of GE Irrathene 101

Corrosive Medium	Days to Crack,[a] 25°C.	
	Polyethylene	GE Irrathene 101
Acetic acid	1	OK after 100 days
Cyclohexanone	3	"
Chlorobenzene	20	"
Triton X-100 (10%)	3	"
Triton X-100 (100%)	3	"
Acetone	2	"
Toluene	22–100	"
Ligroin	30	"
Silicone oil	1	"
Carbon tetrachloride	50	"
Methanol	1–3	"
Linseed oil	70	"

Source: General Electric Co., Chemical Division, 1954.
[a] Test described in Sections 7.2 and 7.11 (533).

6.17. Chlorinated Polyethylenes

Chlorination processess and some properties of chlorinated polyethylenes are discussed in Sections 4.4, 5.4, and 5.5.

The thermoplastic polymers formed by progressive substitution chlorination of polyethylene were used by Oakes and Richards (221a) for a study of the relationships between structure and properties of polymers. A continuous series of chlorinated polyethylenes with increasing chlorine content (to over 70%, i.e., to approximately one chlorine atom per molecular atom), but with the same carbon skeleton, was investigated.   In addition, polymers of the same chlorine content and the same chain length, but prepared under different chlorination procedures, were compared.   The hot-process series was made by chlorination of a solution of polyethylene in carbon tetrachloride at 65–70°C.   The cold-process series was made by chlorinating a suspension of the same, but finely divided, polyethylene in carbon

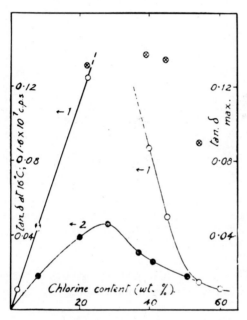

Fig. 180. Power factor as a function of chlorine content.   (a) Power factor (tan δ at 16°C. and 1.6 × 10⁶ cps.) of (1) hot-process chlorinated polythenes, (2) cold-process chlorinated polythenes, as a function of chlorine content (tan δ for original polythene = 0.00025.)   (b) Peak power factor (tan δ_max) for hot-process samples ⊗.   (0–25% Cl from variable frequency measurements at room temperature; 40–54% from variable temperature measurements at 1.3 × 10⁵ cps.)   (*Trans. Faraday Soc.*, **42A**, 200, 1946.)

tetrachloride at 30–40°C.   The power factor as a function of chlorine content for hot-process and cold-process chlorinated polyethylenes was found to vary, as shown in Figure 180.

The increase of the average dipole-orientation relaxation time with increase in chlorine content is in accord with a change from a flexible or rubbery to a rigid state.   The breadth of the relaxation time distribution (α is unity for a single relaxation time, and zero for an infinitely wide distribution) increases at room temperature as the chlorine content rises.   These relationships are shown in Figure 181.

A comparison of dipole moments (Tables XCII and XCIII) suggests the presence of the chlorine in —CCl₂— groups or on adjacent carbon atoms as

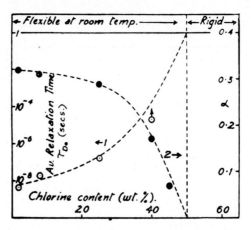

Fig. 181. Influence of chlorine content on: (1) Average electrical relaxation time τ_{Do} at room temperature (16°C.).   (2) Parameter α measuring breadth of relaxation time distribution at 16°C. ($\alpha = 1$ for a single relaxation time.)   (*Trans. Faraday Soc.*, **42A**, 202, 1946.)

—CHCl—CHCl—, or —CHCl—CHCl₂— groups in the chlorinated polyethylenes, the effective average moment being reduced by dipole interaction.

TABLE XCII

Average Dipole Moments per C—Cl Link, Calculated from Power Factor-Frequency Curves

Sample	Average Dipole Moment, Debye units
2% hot-process	1.56
8% hot-process	1.44
25% hot-process	1.38
8% cold-process	1.02
Neoprene	1.99, 2.15
Plasticized polyvinyl chloride	2.1–2.8

Source: *Trans. Faraday Soc.*, **42A**, 203 (1946).

The difference in electrical properties between the hot-process and the cold-process chlorinated polyethylenes, and the higher softening points of

TABLE XCIII

Dipole Moments of Simple Chlorinated Paraffins

Type	Material	Dipole Moment	Dipole Moment per C—Cl Link
Single CHCl group	CH_3Cl	1.56–2.0	1.56–2.0
	C_2H_5Cl	1.90–2.05	1.98–2.05
	$CH_3 \cdot CHCl \cdot CH_3$	2.04–2.18	2.04–2.18
	$C_3H_7 \cdot CHCl \cdot C_3H_7$	2.0 –2.04	2.0 –2.04
Single CCl₂ group	CH_2Cl_2	1.48–1.62	0.74–0.81
	$CH_3 \cdot CHCl_2$	1.8 –2.05	0.90–1.02
	$C_2H_5 \cdot CHCl_2$	2.06	1.03
	$CH_3 \cdot CCl_2 \cdot CH_3$	2.0 –2.18	1.0 –1.09
Adjacent CHCl groups	$CH_3 \cdot CHCl \cdot CH_2Cl$	1.85	0.92
Adjacent CHCl and CCl₂ groups	$CH_2Cl \cdot CHCl_2$	1.15–1.55	0.57–0.77

Source: *Trans. Faraday Soc.*, **42A**, 203 (1946).

the latter, are explained by different distribution of the chlorine atoms along the carbon-carbon chain, as shown in the following formulas:

Hot chlorination:

—CHCl—CHCl—CH₂—CHCl—CH₂—CH₂—CCl₂—CH₂—CHCl—CH₂—CHCl—

Cold chlorination:

—CH₂—CH₂—CH₂—CH₂—CH₂—CH₂—CCl₂—CHCl—CCl₂—CH₂—CH₂—CHCl—

   Crystallite of original   Amorphous region of
     polyethylene   original polyethylene

This study essentially confirms the concept that changes in the chemical structure of a polymer, such as the introduction of polar groups or of bulky side chains, may be expected to lead to changes in the properties of the individual molecule, such as the readiness with which it can coil and uncoil by rotation about the bonds connecting the atoms of the main chain. Changes in the intermolecular forces would also be anticipated.   An increase in the concentration of a polar side group may in general be expected to increase intermolecular forces and to decrease molecular flexibility, and hence to increase both mechanical and electrical relaxation times and their associated activation energies.

6.18. Chlorosulfonated Polyethylene

A chlorosulfonated polyethylene, claimed to meet many of the requirements for wire and cable insulations and jackets, is made by treating polyethylene with chlorine and sulfur dioxide (compare Section 4.5). The chlorine is substituted along the hydrocarbon chain, and the sulfur is combined with chlorine and attached to the chain as sulfonyl chloride (SO_2Cl) groups. There is approximately one chlorine atom for every six or seven carbon atoms, and one sulfonyl chloride group for every hundred carbon atoms. Substitution is believed to be random. Since the regularity of the polyethylene structure is broken up by substitution, the material can no longer crystallize, and the product is a soft, elastic material at room temperature.

As pointed out by Keeley and Roche (856), "Hypalon," duPont's chlorosulfonated polyethylene, is an elastomer and requires the incorporation of vulcanizing agents and activators for curing. In properly compounded "Hypalon," the tensile strength may range up to 3,000 p.s.i., the elongation at break from 200–500%, and the hardness (Durometer Shore A) from 60–95. Given a light cure, the water pickup of properly compounded "Hypalon" is less than 20 milligrams per square inch after immersion in tap water for seven days at 70°C. Only minor increases in volume and weight are noted after soaking in boiling water. The electrical properties of "Hypalon" are intermediate between those of natural rubber and neoprene, as shown in Table XCIV. The heat resistance of properly compounded "Hypalon" (Table XCV) is noteworthy and should permit intermittent use at temperatures as high as 150°C. Resistance to ozone cracking, abrasion, heat, sunlight, and weather is claimed to be excellent, as is colorability. An extensive survey of properties, processing, and methods of compounding is contained in duPont "Hypalon" trade bulletins (e.g., 951), and is also presented by Schlicht (881). The performance at high temperature of Hypalon and Neoprene has been compared by Smook (1027a).

Gelation reactions of chlorosulfonated polyethylene solutions were studied by Busse and Billmeyer (836). Results obtained with a gelation test, together with some confirmatory infrared experiments, indicated that chlorosulfonated polyethylene can react in the following ways: (a), primary aliphatic amines react at low temperatures to form sulfonamide links; (b), primary aliphatic amines react at higher temperatures with removal of chlorine from the chain and subsequent formation of crosslinks; and (c), tertiary amines, urea, ammonium hydroxide, and ethers react through the sulfonyl chloride group. Reactions with sodium sulfide, thiourea, thiuram sulfide, and rubber vulcanization accelerators do not directly involve the sulfonyl chloride group, but may be activated by this group. These compounds may then react through unsaturated or active sites re-

TABLE XCIV

Electrical Properties of "Hypalon"

DC Resistivity, ohm-cm.	1×10^{14}
Specific inductive capacity, 1000 cps.	6
Power factor, 1000 cps., %	2.1
Dielectric strength (0.075-in. slab), volts/mil	551
Surface resistivity, ohms	1×10^{13}
Specific insulation resistance (K at 60°F.)/1000 ft.	22,000
Insulation resistance of $^3/_{64}$-inch insulation over #14 AWG at 60°F.	
megohms/1,000 ft.	5,600
Specific inductive capacity after immersion in 70°C. water	
Increase after 14 days' immersion over 1-day value, %	3
Increase after 14 days' immersion over 7-day value, %	1
Electrical properties at 125°C.	
DC resistivity, ohm-cm.	2.3×10^{11}
Specific inductive capacity, 1000 cps.	5.3
Power factor, 1000 cps, %	3.6
Dielectric strength, volts/mil ("short time")	500

Source: *Wire and Wire Products*, **29**, 637 (1954).

sulting when a sulfonyl chloride leaves the chain.   Reaction with sulfuric acid and potassium hydroxide may take place through active hydrogen atoms on the chain.

A process for the preparation of a vulcanized chlorosulfonated polyethylene by reaction with aromatic primary diamines is claimed by Mc-

TABLE XCV

Heat Resistance of "Hypalon" Compositions

Oven Aged at 257°F. (125°C.)	Original	7 Days	28 Days	42 Days	60 Days
Tensile strength, p.s.i.	1560	2060	2185	2125	1710
Elongation at break, %	555	325	290	160	95

Oven Aged at 302°F. (150°C.)	Original	1 Day	2 Days	5 Days
Tensile strength, p.s.i.	1560	1975	2225	2450
Elongation at break, %	555	365	330	230

Source: *Wire and Wire Products*, **29**, 637 (1954).

Alevy in U. S. 2,723,257 [duPont (1099)].   Blends of chlorosulfonated polyethylene with a polyvinyl acetal are described in U. S. 2,693,459 to Fisk [duPont (912a)]; with natural and synthetic rubbers and elastomers in U. S. 2,729,608 to Strain [duPont (1143)].

6.19. Commercial High-Density Polyethylenes

Properties

References were made in previous sections to the properties noted in highly unbranched, highly crystalline, high-density polyethylenes (e.g., Section 3.8) and in the entirely unbranched polymethylene (e.g., Section 1.1). While these references dealt largely with experimental samples, mention was also made in several instances of the recently introduced commercial high-density polyethylenes (e.g., Section 1.6). Their preparation is described in Section 3.5, while Section 5.7 summarizes what has become known to date in respect to the molecular structure of these polyethylenes. There are three products to be considered, Phillips polyethylene (Marlex), I.C.I. high-density polyethylene (Alkathene HD), and Ziegler polyethylene. The latter is being manufactured by different companies under various trade marks, e.g., Hostalen (Hoechst), Super Dylan (Koppers Co.), Hi-fax (Hercules Powder Co.), and RCH-Polyethylenes (Ruhrchemie AG.).

The following presentation of the properties of these polyethylenes, their processing and handling, as well as uses and applications, is based on a few publications only.

A general discussion of Phillips and Ziegler high-density polyethylenes is contained in papers by Neumann and Bockhoff (1006), Campbell (938), and in two consecutive articles in *Modern Plastics* (927a,927b). Branched and linear polyethylenes are compared with each other and with polystyrene in a paper by Goggin, Thayer, and Cheney (1131) of Dow. In particular, data for Phillips Marlex are given in the trade bulletin of the manufacturer (1012)*. For the Ziegler polyethylenes, reference must be made to papers by Ziegler and co-workers (1044,1046), Grams and Gaube (961), Schulz and Mehnert (1024), Krause (987), and Sollenberger (1029). Additional information is contained in trade bulletins, describing Hoechst "Hostalen" (953), Koppers "Super Dylan" (982), and Ruhrchemie "RCH-Polyethylene" (1021,919b). The latter polyethylene is supplied in the molecular weight range of 100,000 to 1,000,000.

The I.C.I. high-density polyethylene (Alkathene HD) is reported (1120) to be made by a modification of the I.C.I. conventional high-pressure process. The properties of this new material lie closer to the Ziegler-Phillips low-pressure products than to the conventional, low-density, high-pressure polyethylene.

Similar to low-density polyethylenes, the Phillips and Ziegler high-density polyethylenes are practically odorless and tasteless, and nonpoisonous. They are resistant toward acids (including hydrofluoric acid) and

---

* And also in a paper recently presented by Jones and Boeke (1133a).

alkalis, but are attacked by concentrated oxidizing acids, and by halogens. Resistance towards organic solvents is increased, and the degree of swelling in these media decreases. Most solvents which dissolve high-pressure polyethylenes may only swell the high-density polyethylenes under the same conditions. Boiling benzene, for example, dissolves the low-density polyethylenes but only swells the high-density polyethylenes. Aliphatic and aromatic hydrocarbons, and halogenated hydrocarbons behave similarly. The resistance toward solvents tends to increase with increasing molecular weight of the polymer (1021).

While molten polyethylene, by its very nature, is noncorrosive toward metals, a highly reactive organo-metallic catalyst may, under certain circumstances, leave a residue in the polymer which presents corrosion problems. A process for the purification of these polymers is described by Roelen and Geiser in German Patent Application No. R 13922 [Ruhrchemie (1148a)]. The polymer obtained in the polymerization reaction is freed from the organic solvent by filtration (weight of cake, 1 kg.), and treated at 100°C. for 30 minutes with saturated steam. The polymer is then slurried in 10% nitric acid (10 kg.) containing 0.5% of a wetting agent and stirred at 60–80°C. for 4 hours. The product is washed with water until free of acid, and dried under a stream of warm nitrogen.

Where removal of the catalyst residue is difficult, corrosion of fabrication equipment, particularly the steel of injection molds, may be avoided by the incorporation of a proper stabilizer in the resin (1131).

The tendency of high-density polyethylenes toward environmental cracking in various active media is greatly reduced in comparison to that of low-density polyethylenes, and is mostly limited to the lower molecular weight types when subjected to extreme stresses.

Resistance towards oxygen and weathering appears to be good, but actual data have to date not been published. Aging through light and heat may be inhibited in high-density polyethylenes by adding stabilizers, as is customary with low-density polyethylenes. In both cases, finely divided carbon black is particularly effective, not only against the action of light but also against thermal degradation in the dark.

Reduced permeability to gases (factor, approximately $1/_3$) has been reported for the high-density polyethylenes; similar observations were made in respect to vapors and liquids.

The melting point, indicated by complete disappearance of crystalline structure (see Section 7.6), is higher for the high-density polyethylenes than for low-density polyethylene. The same applies to the softening point, characterized as the temperature at which flow is noted under a

TABLE XCVI

Comparison of Properties of Commercial Polyethylenes
(Compiled by R. F. Kratz, Jr.)

PART A. GENERAL COMPARISON

Property	Units	ASTM Test Method	Low-Density (High-Pressure) Polyethylenes	High-Density Polyethylenes			Polystyrene	Modified Polystyrene (High Impact)	Polyvinyl Chloride
				Phillips Marlex 50	Ziegler Types	I.C.I. (High Pressure)			
Mechanical properties									
Elastic modulus in tension	lb./sq.in.	D638-52T	14,000–35,000		50,000–100,000		400,000–600,000	180,000–450,000	500,000–600,000
Yield point	lb./sq.in.	D638-52T	1,200–1,800		2,800–3,500			ca. 3,500	
Tensile strength	lb./sq.in.	D638-52T	1,200–2,500	3,800	2,800–5,500	ca. 2900[c]	5,000–9,500	3,500–6,500	5,000–9,000
Total elongation	percent	D638-52T	400–650	400	100–800	ca. 200[c]	1.0–3.6	22–30	5.0–15.0
Stiffness in flexure	lb./sq.in.	D747-50	11,000–27,000	140,000	50,000–125,000	50,000		250,000–280,000	450,000
Impact strength, Izod	ft.-lb./in.	D256-54T	no break	3.0	1–5		0.3–0.6	1.0–11.0	0.4–20
Impact strength, unnotched	ft.-lb./in.	[a]	no break		>30		2–6	10–90	0.6–0.9
Tear strength	lb./mil	D1004-49T	ca. 0.50	1.0	1.0–2.8				
Physical characteristics									
Specific gravity, 23/23C.	relative to water	D792-50	0.91–0.92	0.96	0.93–0.95	0.940	1.04–1.065	0.98–1.10	1.35–1.55
Crystallinity	percent	[b]	40–60	93	65–85		nil	nil	very low
Crystal size	Angstroms	[b]	180–190	390	200–350				<100
Hardness	Rockwell	D785-51	R9–R11 (Shore D 45–55)	(Shore D 68–70)	R32–R43 (Shore D 63–74)		M65–M90	M30–M70; R50–R100	M25–M45 (Shore D 70–100)
Refractive index	n_D	D542-50	1.51–1.53		1.526–1.534		1.585–1.60		1.54–1.55
Water vapor permeability	cm.²/sec.-atm. $\times 10^{-8}$		40–60		15–30		700		100–200
Gas permeability O_2	cm.²/sec.-atm. $\times 10^{-8}$		1.8–2.1	0.5	0.5				
Gas permeability H_2	cm.²/sec.-atm. $\times 10^{-8}$		5–6	1.5	1.4	1.5			
Gas permeability CO_2	cm.²/sec.-atm. $\times 10^{-8}$		8–11	1.6	1.8				

Property	Units							
Melt index	g./10 min.	D1238–52T	0.2–30	0.6–0.8	0.1–4.0	0.7	0.4	....
Melting point of crystallite	°C.	[b]	108–120	126–135	126–135	....	....	....
Brittleness temperature	°C.	D746–55T	−80 – −55	<−118	<−140 – −100	<−70	....	....
Deformation under load	percent	D621–51	....	....	Method A: 7–10 Method B: 0.05–0.40	0.5–2.5	4–6	0.6–0.9
Heat distortion temperature (66 psi)	°F.	D648–45T	105–120	165–175	135–145	170–210[d]	150–200[d]	140–170[d]
Flammability	in./min.	D635–44	1.0–1.5	1.04	0.9–1.1	0.5–1.0	1.0–1.2	self-extinguishing
Heat capacity	cal./°C.-gm.		0.5–0.55		0.55	0.32	0.30–0.35	0.20–0.28
Thermal conductivity	cal./cm.-sec./°C. $\times 10^{-4}$	C177–45	6–8		ca. 10	1.9–3.3	1.0–3.0	3.0–7.0
Dielectric strength (short-time)	v./mil	D149–55T	430–570	510	500–700	400–700	300–600	425–1300
Dielectric constant (10^6 cycles)		D150–54T	2.3–2.4	2.35	2.2–2.3	2.40–2.70	2.4–3.8	2.8–3.0
Dissipation Factor (tan δ, 10^6 cycles)		D150–54T	0.0003–0.0009	0.0001–0.0003	0.0002–0.0001	0.0001–0.0005	0.0004–0.02	0.006–0.014
Specific resistance	ohm-cm.	D257–54T	$>10^{15}$	$>6\times10^{15}$	$>10^{15}$	ca. 10^{18}	$>10^{12}$	$>10^{16}$

PART B. DEPENDENCE OF PROPERTIES OF HIGH-DENSITY POLYETHYLENES (RUHRCHEMIE) ON MOLECULAR WEIGHT

Property	Units	RCH-Polyethylene[e]		
		100	500	1000
Mechanical properties				
Yield point	lb./sq.in.	3300	3300	3300
Tensile strength	lb./sq.in.	5400	5800	6700
Total elongation	percent	1300	800	450
Hardness	Shore D	70	72	74

Property	Units	RCH-Polyethylene[e]		
		100	500	1000
Thermal properties				
Softening temperature[f]	°C.	130	140	150
Highest use temperature[g]	°C.	125	130	135
Brittle temperature	°C.	−100	<−140	<−140

Sources: In addition to sources quoted in the bibliography (568,702,749,843a,953,961,982,983,984,987,1000,1009,1012,1021,1024,1120,1131,1132,1133a), the following publications were used in the compilation of the table: Koppers Technical Bulletin C-4-105,; "Properties of 15 Popular Modern Rigid Plastics,; Chemical Division, Koppers Co., Inc., Pittsburgh, Pa.; *Modern Plastics*, Encyclopedia Issue, September, 1955; *Styron Formulation 475*, Technical Data, The Dow Chemical Company, Midland, Michigan.
[a] Method similar to ASTM D256–54T, but specimen not notched.
[b] Polarizing microscope technique.
[c] Extension rate: 20 in./min.
[d] Fiber stress of 264 p.s.i.
[e] Numbers are indicated by Ruhrchemie to represent viscosity-average molecular weights × 1/1000.
[f] Flow at very low load.
[g] No load.

small load. This temperature increases somewhat with the molecular weight, e.g., 130°C. for 100,000; 140°C. for 500,000; and 150°C. for 1,000,-000. The highest temperatures at which these materials may still be used are somewhat below these values, e.g., 125, 130, and 135°C., respectively. The considerable superiority of the high-density polyethylenes over the low-density polyethylenes in respect to heat stability is obvious.

The "reduced viscosity" (η_{red}) is used by Grams and Gaube to characterize the degree of polymerization of a polyethylene. It is measured in a solution (0.5%) of the polymer in tetrahydronaphthalene at an elevated temperature (120°C. for high-density polyethylenes, 75°C. for low-density polyethylenes) and calculated from the following equation: $\eta_{red} = (1/c) \cdot [(\eta - \eta_0)/\eta_0]$ (η = viscosity of the solution; η_0 = viscosity of the solvent; c = concentration of the solution, %).

High-density polyethylene possesses a considerably lower melt-viscosity than a low-density polyethylene of the same reduced viscosity. Further, a relatively small increase in reduced viscosity causes only a small increase in the melt viscosity of high-density polyethylenes, but raises considerably the melt viscosity of low-density polyethylenes. This behavior, as is pointed out by Grams and Gaube, is of great practical importance since it permits the processing of high-density polyethylenes of relatively high molecular weights.

While the high crystallinity of the high-density polyethylenes is the cause of their remarkable mechanical strength, a very high degree of crystallinity (density above 0.955) combined with very low reduced viscosity (below 1.5) can cause the polymer to be brittle. However, no brittleness will be observed even in a very highly crystalline polymer if the reduced viscosity is sufficiently high. Polyethylene samples which fall in this safe range will not become brittle through after-crystallization, noted on shock-cooled samples by storage at temperatures from 60°C. to the crystal melting point (compare Section 5.1).

The optical properties of the high-density polyethylenes are also influenced by their high crystallinity, causing objects such as films made from this polymer to be less transparent than similar objects made from low-density polyethylene under comparable conditions. Objects made from high-density polyethylenes may be given an improved surface with good gloss, unlike the waxy finish of ordinary polyethylene.

Property data of the commercial high-density polyethylenes are computed in Table XCVI, and an attempt is made to compare these with values reported for commercial low-density polyethylenes, polystyrene, a high-impact-type polystyrene, and polyvinyl chloride.

Processing and Handling

The high-density polyethylenes, in spite of their toughness, rigidity, and high heat resistance, may be processed by the same conventional equipment in use for low-density polyethylenes, although somewhat higher processing temperatures are required. Specifically, a Ziegler-type polyethylene (Super Dylan) is reported to require about 50°F. more heat than ordinary polyethylene, and 30–50°F. less than many of the well-known, rubber-modified polystyrenes.

The processing of high-density polyethylenes may thus be carried out on presses, extruders, injection molding machines, also by deep-drawing, blowing, flame-spraying, whirl-sintering, centrifugal-casting, and press-sintering. Polyethylenes which are normally produced in the form of a powder (Ziegler types) are particularly suited to be used as such in the four last-mentioned processes. Especially recommended for these applications are high molecular weight resins, e.g., RCH-Polyethylenes (Ruhrchemie AG). Specifically, press-sintering of polyethylene applies the methods used in powder metallurgy to form porous products of high strength and elasticity by pre-pressing and subsequent heat treatment. Depending on their density, the products may resemble cork, leather, wood, or ivory. They may contain fillers and be subjected to further treatments common to the metal industry, such as forging, forming, deep-drawing, or machining. The fabrication of porous products by this process is described in Belg. 540,316 to Ruhrchemie (1083a).

A number of machines, e.g., double-worm extruders, are capable of converting the polyethylene powder directly to molded objects. Two extruders can also be lined up together, whereby the first accomplishes the preliminary softening of the material, while the second gives the final shape. The first extruder can be replaced by a heated kneader. As is the case with polyvinyl chloride, the separation of the process into a preliminary softening and a final forming of shape is advantageous, particularly since the first step removes a certain amount of air and causes preliminary compression of the material. Fine dispersion of additives such as stabilizers, pigments, dyes is guaranteed only if they are added during the initial softening stage.

Where pellets are required granulation may, for example, be carried out by extrusion of a band or strand of the polymer, and cutting it into pellets of the desired shape and size.

Uses and Applications

Properties, such as high heat resistance, rigidity, chemical resistance, resistance to penetration, low-temperature toughness, high tensile strength, and ease of processing recommend the high-density polyethylenes for many applications.

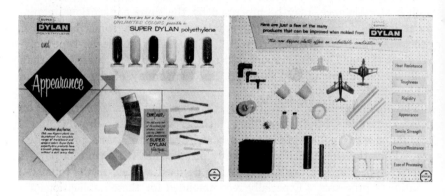

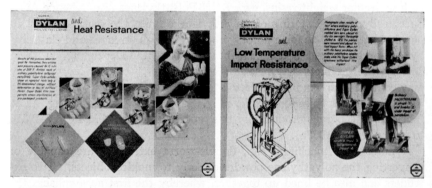

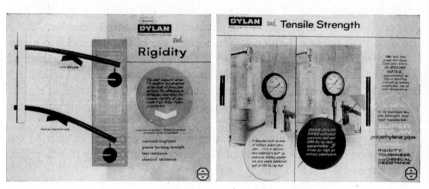

Fig. 182. Properties and applications of "Super Dylan." (*Bulletin C-5-216, "Super Dylan,"* Koppers Co., Inc., 1955.)

Properties and applications of one commercial high-density polyethylene are shown in Figure 182.

Pipes for water lines made of polyethylene do not corrode or form scale or other deposits on the inside, and are resistant to frost, since they tolerate the expansion of water on freezing.   They may be bent, welded, and joined. When made of high-density polyethylenes, they exhibit remarkable bursting strength at ordinary temperature, but caution is required in the case of warm water installations.   However, a pipe made of high-density polyethylene is claimed to have the same bursting strength in boiling water as displayed at room temperature by a pipe made of low-density polyethylene.

A greatly reduced tendency towards environmental cracking combined with increased heat resistance are advantages for the use of high-density polyethylenes as insulating materials for wires and cables.

Where the use of high-density polyethylenes as films is concerned, their lower transparency may be a disadvantage.   Decreased permeability towards gases and chemicals, non-blocking characteristics, good slip properties, and the fact that such films may be sterilized are, however, distinct advantages in their application for packaging purposes.

A high degree of crystallinity and orientability, combined with flexibility at low temperatures, suggest the application of high-density polyethylenes in the field of fibers.

Injection molded articles from high-density polyethylenes are interesting because they are stiff, form-stable, boil resistant, and may be colored. Bottles and hollow objects may be made with thin walls, and can be sterilized.

Coatings and linings made of high-density polyethylenes are remarkably hard and heat resistant.

Irradiation of Marlex, as previously observed with low-density polyethylene, causes crosslinking, accompanied by an increase in tensile strength, hardness, and density; the product becomes finally insoluble and infusible. The fact that the thermal properties of the polymer can be further improved by irradiation is taken as an indication that the use of high-density polyethylene can be widened by this treatment in applications such as film, fibers, and wire coating.   This is further borne out by a recent news release on Hyrad, an irradiated polyethylene developed by Sequoia Process Co.   In this process, Ziegler polyethylene is claimed (1121b) to yield a better product than ordinary polyethylene. (Compare Section 8.18.)

VII. ANALYSIS AND TESTING OF POLYETHYLENES

Frequent references were made previously, particularly in Chapters V and VI, to test methods used by various authors in the determination of certain properties of polyethylene. The present chapter, following essentially the order of presentation used in Chapter VI, is intended to add a few details not previously mentioned and to summarize the subject.

The testing of polyethylene is complicated by its crystallinity, which expresses itself as a tendency to orientation. As emphasized in Chapters V and VI, the crystalline nature of the material must constantly be kept in mind and related to the thermal history of the sample. Thus, test specimens prepared with a minimum of orientation, such as by compression molding, will test differently from those prepared by injection, extrusion, or blowing, where orientation takes place. Furthermore, the rate of cooling molten polyethylene will affect the crystallinity and therefore the density of the polymer (179). Annealing, as has been demonstrated, leads to a product of maximum crystallinity, of increased hardness and brittleness, and of high density; rapid cooling of the melt and quenching result in a softer, more flexible, less opaque product of lower density and crystallinity.

Therefore, the preparation of test specimens by compression molding at 160°C. is recommended (772), and should be followed by cooling in the press. An additional treatment in some cases, involving heating the sample for one hour in boiling water, is indicated.

Pertinent information on the analysis of polyethylene is presented in a recent book by Thinius (634).

7.1. Composition, Solubility, Compatibility, and Chemical Resistance

The chemical analysis of polymers and copolymers of ethylene for carbon, hydrogen, and any other elements built into the polymer chain, and also for ash and impurities, may be carried out by the customary analytical procedures. The properties of polyethylene may be influenced significantly by small amounts of oxygen present in the chain. For its determination, the methods developed by Zimmermann (83), Schütze (81), and Unterzaucher (103), and recently improved by Hinkel and Raymond (736) can be used.

The solubility of polyethylene is determined by heating the sample in hydrocarbons (toluene, xylene, decalin, tetralin) above its melting point. Cloud temperatures may be measured on cooling the solutions, as shown by Myers (867) and discussed in Section 6.1. Sperati, Franta, and Starkweather (772) define "cloud point" as the temperature of formation of a second phase in a 1% solution of polyethylene in refined paraffin (m.p. 56–57°C.).

Any gel content of the polyethylene, caused by crosslinking during the polymerization reaction or through aftertreatment, e.g., irradiation, will be detected as an insoluble residue in these solubility tests. Gel in polyethylene, while simulating a higher average molecular weight of the polymer, causes the occurrence of inordinately low tensile elongations. It also tends to show up as "fish eyes" in films, blown articles, and thin molded sections. The extent of gel formation may be determined (841) by weighing the polyethylene in a stainless-steel wire basket (200 mesh) before and after extraction with boiling toluene.

The extent of unsaturation in polyethylene can be deduced from the increase in weight of a polyethylene film exposed to bromine vapor in the dark. One molecule of bromine is absorbed for every double bond. Based on methods developed by Becker (3) and Rossmann (27), the use of this procedure has been described by Dole, Keeling, and Rose (841).

Test methods and means for predicting the performance of any specific product in polyethylene containers have been suggested by Pinsky, Nielsen, and Parliman of Plax Corp. (874). They reported studies on the permeability of polyethylene *per se*, as well as chemical and physical effects on a large number of chemicals in polyethylene bottles.

7.2. Environmental Cracking

Several tests for determining the cracking sensitivity of polyethylene have been published. De Coste, Malm, and Wallder (533) have described a qualitative laboratory test suitable for studying environmental cracking, which gives results that correlate reasonably well with those obtained on cable sheath. Essentially, a razor slit is introduced into a molded specimen low in residual stress; then the sample is bent with the slit outside and inserted into a test tube filled with a cracking agent, such as a detergent. Tests are generally carried out at 50°C., the condition of the sample being examined at regular intervals. Test specimen and apparatus for determining crack resistance are shown in Figure 183.   The appearance of the stressed specimen before and after cracking is illustrated in Figure 184.

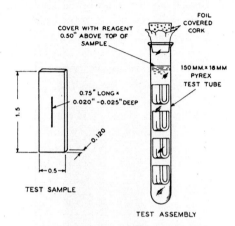

Fig. 183. Test specimen and apparatus for determining crack resistance. (*Ind. Eng. Chem.*, **43**, 117, 1951.)

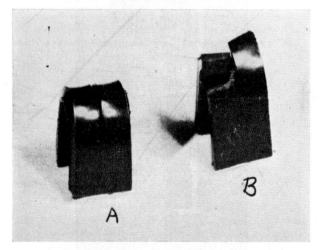

Fig. 184. Appearance of stressed specimen: *A*, before cracking; *B*,
after cracking. (*Ind. Eng. Chem.*, **43**, 117, 1951.)

The proposed (1955) ASTM test method for environmental-cracking of polyethylene plastics, essentially based on the above work by De Coste, Malm, and Wallder, is quoted in Section 7.11.

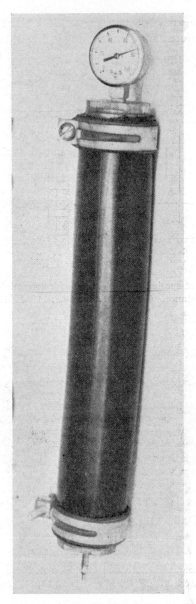

Fig. 185. Pipe specimen. (*ASTM Bull.*, **178**, 47, 1951.)

With the assumption that environmental-cracking is caused by internal bi- or polyaxial stresses, an optical method was developed by Kortsch (750,858a,985) and applied to the quantitative evaluation of internal stresses in insulation for cables.   Internal stress and birefringence being related, refractive indices were determined with polarized light at 36 points of a thin cross section of the cable sheath.   Differences were clearly noted, and the method was found to be well reproducible.

Two creep test methods for the determination of the cracking sensitivity of polyethylene have been described by Ellis and Cummings (534).   One

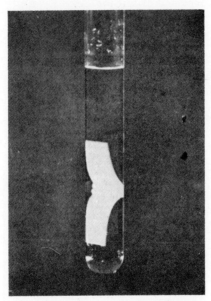

Fig. 186. Stress cracking test according to Agile Method 17-W.
(*Modern Plastics*, **32** [2], 150, 1954.)

method, using strip-tension specimens, is particularly applicable to the evaluation of materials in an experimental program.   The other method, using internal pressure in a pipe sample (Figure 185), is applicable to polymers manufactured in the form of tubes.   The methods of stressing result in polyaxial or biaxial stresses required for cracking to take place.   In the pipe sample, no artificial notching is needed, and the biaxial stress can be calculated.   In these tests, crack resistance was found to increase with plasticity number and, therefore, with increase in average molecular weight range.   For a given stress condition and environment, there appeared to be a threshold value of stress and strain for the occurrence of cracking.

In the presence of certain active environments, polyethylene welds, particularly when under stress, may undergo embrittlement leading to complete failure of the weld. A test for the evaluation of possible stress cracking environments is given in Agile test method 17-W (828) and shown in Figure 186, taken from a paper by Bockhoff and Neumann (827). A welded-corner specimen is forced under stress into a test tube into which the test reagent is introduced; if no failure occurs within 60 days, the welded polyethylene may be considered safe for use.

7.3. Deterioration by Weathering and Corrosion

Protecting polyethylene intended for outdoor use is of the utmost importance to manufacturers of plastic pipe, as well as to the wire and cable industry. Methods to investigate the influence of weathering on poly-

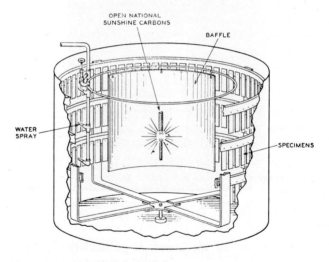

Fig. 187. Modified X-1-A Accelerated Weathering Unit. (*Ind. Eng. Chem.*, **42**, 2320, 1950.)

ethylene by accelerated aging (by determining the low-temperature brittleness of the polymer) have been developed by Wallder, Clarke, De Coste, and Howard (491). An accelerated-weathering unit is shown in Figure 187.

Tests to determine the oxidative degradation of polyethylene and to evaluate the stabilizing effect of antioxidants, particularly by following the change of the electrical properties (power factor, dielectric constant) during milling of the polymer at 160°C. for up to 6 hours, have been discussed by Biggs and Hawkins (707).

In connection with these test methods, reference is also made to Chapter III with respect to the results obtained with them.

7.4. Permeability

The sorption of reagents by polyethylene is determined by the weight increase (mg.) of a specimen 2.0″ × 0.50″ × 0.060″ after immersion in the test reagent for 7 days at 50°C. (772).

Various types of apparatus are known for the determination of the permeability of membranes to gases and vapors, a number of which have been applied to the study of polyethylene permeability (Section 6.3). A preferred form of apparatus usually comprises a gas cell which is divided into two chambers by a membrane. One of the chambers contains the gas or vapor to be studied; the other chamber is either filled with an arbitrary gas or is evacuated. The permeability constant (Q) is related to the diffusion constant (D) and the solubility coefficient (S), by the equation $Q = DS$. Both D and S have to be determined separately. Several methods of carrying out such measurements have been described in the literature (474). Particular reference is to be made to a direct method described by Edwards (1130), whereby the positive gas pressure is applied to one side of the membrane in a simple cell. The gas permeating the specimen displaces liquid from a graduated capillary tube, permitting a direct measurement of the volume. The method requires only a minimum of equipment or skill and is relatively rapid, since the passage of only a small amount of gas is required to establish the permeability with a suitable degree of accuracy.

For the determination of the water-vapor permeability of polyethylene and other cable sheath materials, Heering, Puell, and Drewitz (343a) have described a simple method whereby the cable sheath is used to form a closed vessel without interference of any metallic parts.

Reference to a method to measure the grease resistance of polyethylene film (292b) was made in Section 6.1.

7.5. Density

Since the density of a polyethylene sample is indicative of its degree of crystallinity, density determinations of high accuracy are essential in testing polyethylene. Of equal accuracy, the use of the density gradient tube appears preferable to the flotation method in the determination of poly-

ethylene densities (179,722).   In addition to being less time consuming, it
also eliminates the manipulations required in pycnometer measurements.
The density-gradient method makes use of Fick's principle: if two miscible
liquids are layered over one another, and the bottom layer is of greater

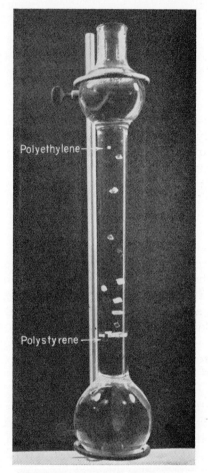

Fig. 188. Density-gradient tube.   (*J. Polymer Sci.*, **1**, 249, 1946.)

specific gravity, a linear density gradient develops in the region of the
juncture of the two.   Figure 188 shows the relative position of two samples
of polyethylene and polystyrene in a typical density-gradient tube.   The
small size of the samples is to be noted (212).   Rapid methods of construct-

ing density gradient tubes were recently described by Tung and Taylor (1038) and by Mills (1135b).

Early applications of this principle by Linderstrøm-Lang et al. (54,68, 96,119) were for the determination of specific gravities of liquids used in the micro-estimation of enzyme activity and determination of densities of D_2O–H_2O systems.   Subsequent investigators [Boyer, Spencer, and Wiley (212)] made use of the density-gradient tube for obtaining crystallization rate data, for determining variations in composition of copolymers, and for measuring rates of polymerization.   Anfinsen (210) also gives a description of the apparatus and its application to the measurement of D_2O–H_2O densities.

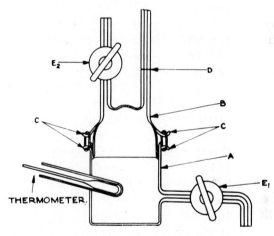

Fig. 189. Dilatometer for density measurements.   (*A.E.R.E Report M/R 1401— 1954 Appendix* [*Declassified*], Dept. of Atomic Energy, Harwell, Berks., England.)

Tessler, Woodberry, and Mark (228) have used the gradient tube in a study of inhomogeneities in natural and synthetic fibers.   Low and Richards (615) have applied this principle to the determination of crystal densities.   Mention has been made recently of the use of the density-gradient column in the control laboratories of commercial producers of polyethylene (810,935).   This method is presently under consideration by the ASTM.

For recording changes in density, the dilatometer shown n Figure 189 has been proposed by Ross (879).   It consists of a lower vessel (A) with two side tubes.   One of these holds a thermometer, the bulb of which is surrounded by a small quantity of mercury; the other side tube has a stopcock (E_1) to allow mercury to be removed from the vessel or the level to be

adjusted.   The lid (B) of the dilatometer, which can be removed for loading the specimen, carries a 25-cm. long, precision-bore tube (variation in
bore $\pm 0.5\%$) and a second tube with a stopcock (E_2) for the introduction of
mercury.   The volume of the vessel up to the mark (D) is nearly 25 ml.
The hooks (C) on lid and vessel are used to hold the halves together by metal
springs.

7.6. Melting Point and Heat Resistance

The melting point of a polyethylene sample is determined as the temperature at which crystallinity suddenly disappears between crossed Nicols
on a hot-stage microscope (772).   Kantor and Osthoff (740) obtained by
thermal analyses the melting points of polymethylenes prepared by the
catalytic decomposition of diazomethane (Section 1.1).   A copper-con-
stantan thermocouple and a recording potentiometer were used.

A dilatometric method of determining the first-order transition or melting
temperature of polymethylene and polyethylene was described by Mandelkern, Hellmann, Brown, Roberts, and Quinn (755; see Section 6.6).   In
visual observation of the melting point, the true melting point of the polymer may be obscured by the very high viscosity of the melt.   At any rate,
heating in the vicinity of the melting temperature must be gradual and
should, according to these authors, occur over a period of several days.

The measurement of the heat resistance of polyethylene is becoming increasingly important.   One procedure for examining this property is
measurement of the Zero Strength Time (ZST) as reported by Kaufman,
Kroncke, and Gianotta (855) for testing Kel-F (polychlorotrifluoroethylene).   The ZST represents the time required for a standard sample under
a low stress to break at a specified temperature.   This test was devised to
replace a similar test, the No Strength Temperature (NST), which measured the temperature attained at break of a similar specimen under the influence of a slow, constant temperature increase.   Kaufman (1134) reported recently that the log ZST varied directly with the number-average
molecular weight of polyethylene film.   He also observed that the re-
producibility of the test was remarkably good, notwithstanding a variation
of film thickness of up to 1%.

7.7. Viscosimetry and Rheometry

Viscosimetric methods applied to the determination of molecular weights
and the subject of melt viscosity of polyethylene have been discussed in
Section 5.3.   Additional information on the viscoelasticity of polyethylene

is contained in Section 6.7.   On the subject of viscosimetry and rheometry in general, reference is made to a treatise by Umstätter (640) where the design and performance of numerous absolute viscosimeters and accessory equipment are described.

The instrument most widely used for the determination of the melt flow of polyethylene (ASTM Designation: D 1238–52T) is the melt indexer

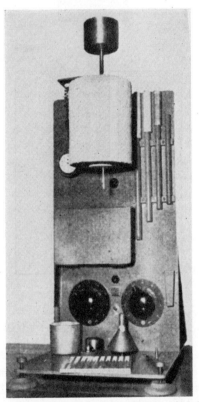

Fig. 190. Over-all view of melt indexer. (*Modern Plastics*, **31** [2], 146 (1953).)

described by Tordella and Jolly (774).   This extrusion plastometer is pictured in Figure 190.   It consists of a steel cylinder thermostatically controlled at two temperatures, a piston fitted to the cylinder, two weights, and one orifice.   A sketch of the cylinder in cross section is shown in Figure 191, while Figure 192 shows details, also in cross section, of piston and orifice

A rheometer, designed to be operable at temperatures and shear rates comparable to those found during injection molding and extrusion, has recently been described by Karam, Cleereman, and Williams (974). A schematic diagram of the "caplastometer" is presented in Figure 193.

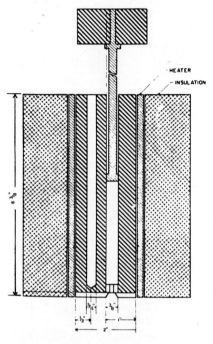

Fig. 191. Cylinder of melt indexer. (*Modern Plastics*, **31** [2], 146, 1953.)

For the measurement of the viscosity of high polymers at low rates of shear, an improved parallel-plate plastometer has been described by Dienes and Klemm (214). This plastometer is shown in front elevation in Figure 194. The instrument is comprised of two parallel plates, both either 4.00 or 1.125 inches in diameter, the upper (1) movable, the lower (2) stationary. The upper plate is attached to the vertical shaft (3) which is aligned and guided in the low-friction ball-bearing assembly illustrated (4). The test load is applied by means of the beam (5), mounted at the upper end of the shaft (3), and the two movable weights (6 and 7). The dial indicator (9), which makes contact with the loading shaft, is fastened to the frame of the plastometer and indicates the plate separation at any instant. A hand-

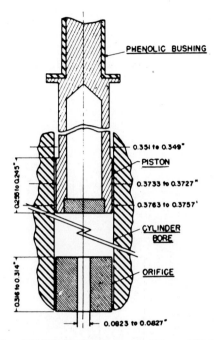

Fig. 192. Detail of piston and orifice. (*Modern Plastics*, **31** [2], 146, 1953.)

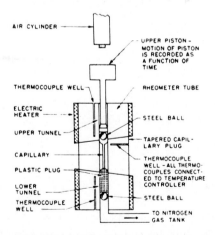

Fig. 193. Schematic diagram of caplastometer.
(Pressure of tank can be regulated from 0 to 2200 p. s. i.)
(*Modern Plastics*, **32** [7] 130, 1955.)

operated rack and pinion mechanism (8) on the left side of the oven permits the application of the test force without opening the oven door. The plastometer is supported by three legs, fitted with leveling screws, which project through the bottom of the oven. The performance of this instrument and results obtained by it in the study of polyethylene are discussed in Section 6.7.

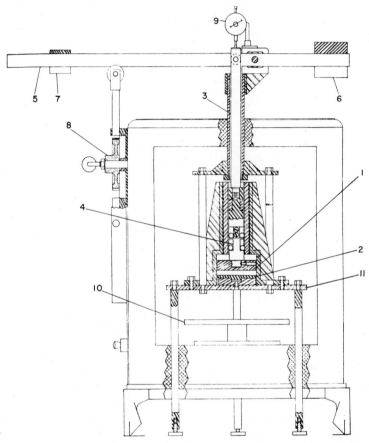

Fig. 194. Parallel plate plastometer. (*J. Appl. Phys.*, **17,** 458, 1946.)

A concentric cylinder rotational plastometer which automatically plots the shear strain *versus* time curve for each of a number of shear stresses is described by Dexter (840b). A plastometer for the continuous determination of the extrusion characteristics of thermoplastic materials, particularly polyethylene, is the subject of the recent French 1,103,975 to I.C.I. (1102).

7.8. Refractive Index

Refractive index values are considered by Baccaredda and Schiavinato (823; see Section 6.8) to be easier to measure and to be more significant than density values in the determination of the degree of branching in polyethylene.   When using the immersion method in suitable liquid mixtures, the refractive index is affected only by those microvoids of a size not larger than the wavelength of the light used.   Literature references to other methods of measuring the refractive index of polyethylenes are presented in the same paper.

7.9. Blocking

Blocking, defined as that degree of cohesion or adhesion between layers of film or sheet which prevents their being satisfactorily used, is a characteristic noted in polyethylene.

Currently, TAPPI (T 477 m-47) and ASTM (D 884–48) have qualitative methods by which block resistance is measured by evaluating the ease with which one can separate or peel apart blocked film.   The film is then graded as blocked, slightly blocked, considerably blocked, or completely blocked.

A quantitative method to determine the force required for separating plastic film was devised by Umminger (639a).   An improved apparatus to carry out such measurements was recently described by Voigt (1039).

7.10. Resinographic Methods

Microscopy, although occasionally proposed, is too seldom used in the study of plastic materials and in the control of their properties.   In a brief survey of this subject, a description of the application of the microtome for the study of plastics by Vieweg and Klein (122a) deserves mention.   Swelling phenomena in plastics were studied by Vieweg and Schneider (122b) by the use of polarized light.   A paper by Rochow (418) on the resinography of synthetic resins includes a study of polyethylene and contains considerable information on this particular method.   A progress report on the microscopic examination of plastic materials was published in 1950 by Vieweg and Moll (490a).   Recently, a paper by Claver and Merz (946) on microscopic studies of heterogeneous polymeric systems dealt with phase and electron microscope investigations of polyethylene films and styrene-rubber polyblends.

The texture of some crystalline synthetic polymers, including polyethylene, was studied by electron microscopy by Cooper, Keller, and Waring (724a). The measurement of the scattering of light by solid polymers as a means of determining their structure was proposed by Stein and Keane (1031) and applied, in particular, to polyethylene film by Stein, Keane, and Norris (1134a,1137).

Widely used is the microscopic study of dispersions of carbon black in polyethylene since, for maximum weather protection, the carbon black must be dispersed in the resin in a way which will allow full use of its small particle size. As described by Wallder, Clarke, DeCoste, and Howard [see Section 3.12 (491)], a sample of the polyethylene-carbon black mix is hot pressed between microscopic slides to form a thin film (0.001 in. or less), and examined by transmitted light under a magnification of 100 diameters for degree of dispersion and particle size. This and other methods are presently investigated for their potential inclusion among the ASTM standards methods.

7.11. ASTM Test Methods

A tentative standard for polyethylene molding and extrusion materials has been adopted by the American Society for Testing Materials under ASTM Designation: D 1248–52T. The properties enumerated in these standards are to be determined in accordance with the ASTM methods, quoted as follows:

(a) Conditioning Test Specimens. For those tests where conditioning is required, the molded test specimens of polyethylene shall be conditioned in accordance with Procedure B of the Tentative Methods of Conditioning Plastics and Electrical Insulating Materials for Testing (ASTM Designation: D 618).

(b) Test Conditions. Tests shall be conducted in the standard laboratory atmosphere of $23 \pm 1.1°C$. ($73.4 \pm 2°F$.) and $50 \pm 2\%$ relative humidity, unless otherwise specified in the testing methods or in these specifications.

(c) Sieve Analysis. Standard Methods of Testing Molding Powders Used in Manufacturing Molded Electrical Insulators (ASTM Designation: D 392).

(d) Specific Gravity. Method B of the Standard Methods of Test for Specific Gravity of Plastics (ASTM Designation: D 792).

(e) Melt Index. Tentative Methods of Test for Measuring Flow Rates of Thermoplastics by Extrusion Plastometer (ASTM Designation: D 1238).

(f) Tensile Strength and Ultimate Elongation. Tentative Methods of Tension Testing of Vulcanized Rubber (ASTM Designation: D 412).

(g) Brittleness Temperature. Tentative Method of Test for Brittleness Temperature of Plastics and Elastomers by Impact (ASTM Designation: D 746).

(h) Dissipation Factor and Dielectric Constant.   Tentative Methods of Test for Power Factor and Dielectric Constant of Electrical Insulating Materials (ASTM Designation: D 150), with the following exceptions:

(1) Preconditioning.   The material to be tested for dissipation factor and dielectric constant shall be preconditioned by processing approximately 400 g. for from $2^1/_2$ to 3 hr. in a two-roll laboratory rubber mill, having rolls 8 in. in diameter and 16 in. long, turning at the rate of 25 to 30 r.p.m., at a temperature of 160° ± 5°C., with the distance between the rolls so adjusted that the charge will maintain a uniform rolling bank.   Any other size two-roll laboratory rubber mill may be used, provided the charge is adequate to maintain a uniform rolling bank on the rolls and to furnish sufficient material for test specimens.

(2) Purpose of Milling Procedure.   The purpose of the milling procedure described in item (1) is to ascertain whether a suitable type or concentration of antioxidant has been included in the materials designated Grade 4 and Grade 5.   Due to the time-consuming nature of this preconditioning procedure, the frequency with which it is applied shall be as established by sound statistical quality control practices by the individual manufacturer.   However, the specified electrical tests shall be performed on every batch or "run," using the normal conditioning procedure (a).

Naturally, other specifications and methods for testing plastics have been developed by the American Society for Testing Materials (822) and may be applied to polyethylene whenever suitable.

An ASTM test method for environmental stress-cracking of ethylene plastics (see Section 7.2) has been recently proposed (1955) and is quoted below:

Scope

1. This is a method of test for determining the susceptibility of ethylene plastics to environmental stress-cracking.   Under certain conditions of stress and in the presence of environments such as soaps, wetting agents, oils and detergents, ethylene plastics may exhibit mechanical failure by cracking.

The method consists of exposing bent specimens of the plastic having a controlled imperfection on one surface to the action of a surface active agent.   The time required for cracking to take place is observed.

Significance

2. This method establishes the time at which 50% of the specimens in test fail when subjected to the conditions herein specified.   The cracking obtained with the test reagent is indicative of what may be expected from a wide variety of surface active agents, soaps and organic substances which are not absorbed appreciably by the polymer.

Stress-cracking is a property that is highly dependent on the nature and level of the stresses applied.   Under the conditions of the test, high local multiaxial stresses are developed through the introduction of a controlled imperfection.   Stress-cracking has been found to occur most readily under such conditions.

Where stress concentrations are low, as in thin-wall sections, cracking may not occur even in the presence of a cracking reagent.   Information from this test is not intended for direct application to engineering problems but should be considered primarily for ranking ethylene plastics in the order of their susceptibility to cracking. In this sense the method serves as a classification test for ethylene plastics. Differences in stress-crack time less than $\pm 10\%$ are not considered significant.

Definitions

3. (a) Stress-Crack. A fracture of the surface of a material resulting from a complex stress less than its short-time tensile strength with or without an environment which contributes to failure.

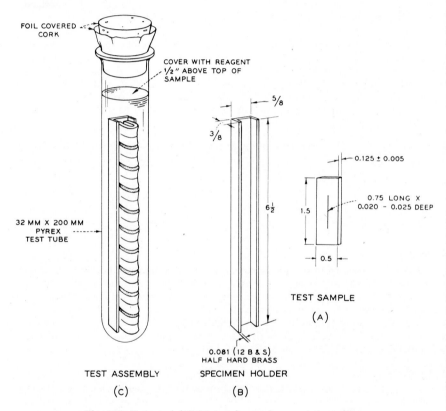

Fig. 195. Proposed ASTM test for environmental cracking.

(b) Stress-Crack Failure. For purposes of this test, any crack visible to the unaided eye shall be interpreted as a failure. Extension of the controlled imperfection shall not be construed as a failure.

Note: Cracks generally develop at the controlled imperfection and run to the outer edge of the specimen approximately at right angles to it. The cracks need not extend completely through the specimen to constitute failure.

(c) Stress-Crack Time. The time required for 5 out of 10 specimens to show stress-crack failures when tested in the specified manner.   The symbol F_{50} shall be used to represent the stress-crack time.

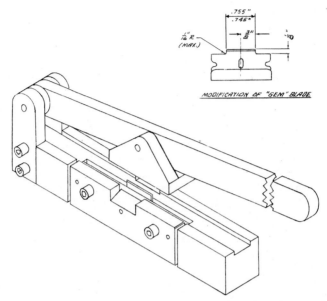

Fig. 196. Proposed ASTM test for environmental cracking (nicking jig).

Apparatus

4. (a) Blanking Die. A suitable rectangular die for cutting specimens 1.5 ± 0.1 by 0.50 ± 0.02 in.

(b) Jig. A jig for making a controlled imperfection 0.750 ± 0.005-in. long and 0.020 –0.025-in. deep, parallel to the long edges of the specimen and centered on one of the broad faces.   The jig shown in Figure 196 shall be used.

Note: Drawings of this jig may be obtained from ASTM Headquarters.

(c) Specimen Holders. Lengths of half hard brass channel having the dimensions shown in (B) of Figure 195 shall be used.   Any burrs present on the inside of the channel should be removed.

(d) Test Tubes. Pyrex glass tubes nominally 200-mm. long with an outside diameter of 32 mm.

(e) Corks. No. 15.

(f) Aluminum foil, approximately 0.005-in. thick in which to wrap the corks.

(g) Constant Temperature Bath. A constant temperature liquid bath maintained at 50.0 ± 0.5°C.

(h) Test Tube Rack. A rack to hold test tubes immersed to reagent level.

Reagent

5. (a) Igepal CO-630 (Antarox A230) obtained from General Dyestuff Corp., New York.

Note: This is an alkyl aryl polyethylene glycol. The reagent should be stored in closed metal or glass containers because it is somewhat hygroscopic.

(b) Fresh reagent shall be used for each determination.

Note: Where there is reasonable assurance that no degradation or contamination of the reagent has occurred, it may be reused.

Specimen Preparation

6. (a) Specimens shall be die-cut from smooth pressed sheet having a thickness of 0.125 ± 0.005 in. The sheet may be pressed from granules or pellets, or from plaques of milled material.

Note: The purpose of milling is to obtain a more uniform specimen. Milling shall be performed for no longer than 10 min. at the lowest temperature possible for each resin.

A molding procedure shall be used that will assure dense uniform sheets, essentially free of internal stresses. The dimensions of the die-cut specimens shall be 1.5 ± 0.1 in. by 0.50 ± 0.02 in., and the die shall be such that clean cuts are made. One specimen from each sheet shall be placed on a polished plate coated with Teflon or in a petri dish containing $1/8$ in. of talc and set in an air oven at 130°C. for 30 min. If shrinkage is less than 5% in the lengthwise direction, the molded sheet can be considered strain-free.

Conditioning

7. Test specimens shall be submerged in boiling water for 30 min. They shall then be conditioned for at least 24 hr. at 23 ± 1.1°C. (73.4 ± 2°F.) as defined in A.S.T.M. Designation D618–53. The test specimens shall not be bent and shall not be treated with the reagent until immediately prior to the test.

Procedure

8. (a) Each specimen shall be given a controlled imperfection on one surface as shown in (A) of Figure 195. A sharp blade mounted in the jig shown in Figure 196 shall be used for making this imperfection. The blade should be replaced whenever there is any question of it having become dull or damaged. In no case should it be used for more than 1,000 specimens.

(b) The test specimen is bent in a loop with the controlled imperfection on the outside and inserted in the specimen holder as shown in (B) of Figure 195 so that the ends of the specimen touch the bottom of the channel. The bend should be no more than necessary just to allow the specimen to slide into the holder. Nine more specimens are inserted in a similar manner. The samples should be evenly spaced in the holder so that no two specimens touch each other.

(c) Within 10 min. of the time the first specimen is introduced into the holder, the holder shall be inserted in the test tube. The tube is then filled to approximately 0.5 in. above the top specimen with reagent that has been adjusted to a temperature of 23 ± 1.1°C. The tube is then stoppered with a foil-wrapped cork and immediately placed in the constant temperature bath at 50.0 ± 0.5°C. The controlled imperfections should not be touching the test tube during the test.

Note: The heat capacity and the heat input capacity of the bath should be high enough so that the temperature does not drop below 49.5°C. when the samples are added.

(d) The test specimens are inspected 0.5, 1, 2, 4, 24, and 48 hr. after the loaded test tube is inserted in the bath, and the total number of failures at each inspection is recorded.   Longer or shorter periods may be used where necessary.   Inspections may be discontinued after 70% of the specimens have failed.

Calculation

9. (a) The number of failures is plotted *versus* the logarithm of time, and the best straight line is drawn through these points.

(b) The stress-crack time, F_{50}, shall be the time in hours taken from the curve at 5 failures.

Report

10. The report shall include the following:
    (1) Stress-crack time, F_{50}.
    (2) Plot of total failures *versus* the logarithm of time.
    (3) Complete identification of material tested.
    (4) Date of test.
    (5) Name of observer.

The following references are cited in the proposed test:
Carey (464a); DeCoste, Malm and Wallder (533); and Hopkins, Baker, and Howard (473).

7.12. Miscellaneous Tests

A paper by Boyd (935) discusses quality control of vinyl and polyethylene insulating and jacketing materials.   It is pointed out that the properties desired in the ultimate application of the material, as well as those additional properties needed by the extruder of the material, must be established

TABLE XCVII

Desired Properties of Polyethylene Materials

Finished Extrusion	Fabrication
Tensile strength	Extrudibility
Ultimate elongation	Contamination
Brittle temperature	Bulk factor
Melt index	
Dissipation factor	
Dielectric constant	
Dielectric strength	

Source: *Rubber Age*, **78,** 882 (1955).

prior to the time any quality control system can be developed.   These particular properties are detailed in Table XCVII.   This list of properties can be simplified, along with the primary control point relative to each general group of properties, as shown in Table XCVIII.

TABLE XCVIII

Simplified List of Desired Properties of Polyethylene Materials

General Property	Primary Control Point
Mechanical	Raw materials
Electrical	Raw materials
Extrusion	Raw materials—process

Source: *Rubber Age*, **78**, 882 (1955).

The mechanical properties of a polyethylene compound of this nature are almost completely controlled, therefore, by the mechanical properties of the polymer, and specifications for raw materials must be established which limit the basic variables.   As a primary control, the melt index is advocated;   secondary controls are also maintained for tensile strength, ultimate elongation, and brittle temperature.   Dielectric properties are of great importance in this particular material.   Electrical controls involving the precise measurement of dissipation factor and dielectric constant should be maintained on the basic polymer and on the finished product.   As a whole, however, a successful quality control system should operate mainly on raw materials and processing rather than on the finished product, which should receive only a minimal degree of inspection or quality-assurance testing.

The wall thickness of an extruded polyethylene sheath can be determined, according to Eppler (845), from the electrical capacitance between the inner metallic element and the outer surface.

A ball-drop technique to provide an independent measure of polyethylene film toughness has been proposed by Supnik and Adams (1141b).

A discussion on the use of plastic pipes, particularly in the gas industry, and test methods adapted to this special application, are detailed in a paper by Bunnell (834).   Light weight, ease of installation, simplified installation techniques, lower cost compared to copper, and freedom from corrosion problems are enumerated as the chief advantages.   However, for general use, the establishment of reliable standards for materials, practical installation techniques, and simplified testing and inspecting procedures are required.   In the final analysis, the safety record of plastic pipe compared to steel, iron, and copper may well be the decisive factor.

The odor of polyethylene samples may be determined in osmoscopes of the types described by Baylis (24a) and by Fair (28a).   A critical review of techniques applied in olfactometry was presented by Wenzel (355a) in 1948.   Recently, the Elsberg Olfactometer, an instrument designed to detect brain tumors on the olfactory nerve tract, was modified by Clausen (945) at the General Mills Laboratories to be used for the detection of odors given off by polyethylene bag lining.   The apparatus and techniques for treating samples to be tested for odors are described.

VIII. PROCESSING AND HANDLING OF POLYETHYLENES

The methods of processing applicable to polyethylene are dependent on the mechanical properties of the polymer and on their changes with temperature. These, in turn, are influenced by the size and the size distribution of the macromolecules, which depend upon polymerization conditions. The presence of a large portion of a low molecular weight polymer may be undesirable for some uses, while the presence of very large molecules makes the polymer rather difficult to process. A further characteristic property of polyethylene is its crystallinity, which results in the rigidity of the polymers. Orientation in polyethylene can generally be destroyed by heating above the melting point. Nevertheless, extrusion of very high molecular weight polyethylene causes some orientation of the molecules even above the melting point. The tendency of polyethylene to oxidize when heated in air must be considered in all processing steps. It can, however, be almost completely avoided by the incorporation of antioxidants.

Polyethylene is generally supplied in the form of granules, either as such, or compounded with an antioxidant or pigment. It is usually packaged in polyethylene-lined paper bags, or in fiber drums containing polyethylene liners. Polyethylene can be homogenized on the mill and blended with other additives. Panels and other molded articles can be formed in the press. As with all moldings, the fact that polyethylene exhibits considerable shrinkage (linear, 3.5%; cubical, 11%) has to be kept in mind. Slow and even cooling is advisable, and lowering of the pressure during cooling should be prevented by appropriate mold design. Tubes, filaments, wire covers, and films can be extruded. Certain difficulties may still be encountered because of the relatively low viscosity of the molten plastic. Blending with polyisobutylene is helpful in increasing the viscosity of the melt. High rates of injection molding can be realized, but premature flowing of the material must be prevented by careful mold design. The production of containers such as bottles, ampoules, and toys is effected by a variation of the film-blowing process, similar to glass blowing. Compression molding and shaping of the preformed sheet is also practiced. Polyethylene can be machined readily with wood-working tools if the temperature is kept low.   Polyethylene pipes or sheets may be welded with a stream of hot nitrogen and a filler rod of the same plastic.   Various materials can be coated with polyethylene by covering them with a plastic film of polyethylene or by applying a solution or dispersion of polyethylene, or by using the polymer in the form of a powder.   A flame-spray process has been developed for dealing with larger surfaces.   Centrifugal casting of tubes has been described, whereby granules of the polymer are rotated at high speed in a metal cylinder and heated to fusion.   Whirl-sintering and press-sintering are particularly applicable to the processing of the Ziegler-type polyethylenes (see Section 6.19).

A process for fabrication of filaments, films, coatings, tubing, and other shapes has been described (902c) whereby the polyethylene is swelled with organic solvents which can dissolve the polymer only under heat at a temperature below the solution temperature.   The polyethylene is then freed from excess solvent and subsequently fused together and formed at elevated temperatures, but below the softening point of the polyethylene used as starting material.

Polyethylene is easily bonded under heat by all of the common methods. In using high-frequency heating techniques, a polar intermediate layer has to be heated in contact with the polyethylene pieces to be sealed.

The methods of processing polyethylene are compared by Schaupp (880) with those in use for polystyrene and plasticized cellulose acetate.   Valuable recommendations as to methods of fabrication are contained in the technical bulletins of polyethylene manufacturers.   Information on the molding of polyethylene in general has been presented in a paper by Persak (414).

Useful instructions on high-pressure polyethylene manufacturing procedures are contained in a recent article in *Modern Plastics* (817).   From this paper, the section on molding techniques and mold design is quoted:

Working with polyethylene, molders should evaluate the relative importance of the various factors involved in molding the material—mold shrinkage, flash, quality of surface, ease of ejection from the mold, and cycle.   A consideration of these points will determine optimum mold temperature, cylinder temperature, and injection pressure.

Molding (cylinder) Temperature.   Polyethylene can be molded at cylinder temperatures from 300–500°F.   In some cases, however, depending upon the end results desired, temperatures can run as low as 250°F. and as high as 600°F.   A molding temperature of 450–500°F., coupled with a high mold temperature, is recommended to obtain maximum low-temperature flexibility and to minimize orientation in the molded item.   High cylinder temperature minimizes shrinkage and improves surface finish. Low cylinder temperature results in less tendency to flash and makes possible easier ejection and reduced cycle.

Mold Temperature.   A mold temperature of 110–130°F. is suggested for maximum gloss.   To obtain minimum cycle time, a lower temperature is recommended.   A low mold temperature and cylinder temperature may be advisable for minimum cycle time and low unit cost, where conditions warrant use of the lower temperatures.

Mold Design.   The use of a well designed, well machined mold will greatly reduce flashing—a difficulty that is sometimes encountered when molding polyethylene.

Molds should be designed to permit both halves to be cored for circulating fluids, so that temperature can be controlled at the cavity surfaces.   This temperature may range from 70–130°F.   Molding of dissimilar articles in one mold and the use of unbalanced mold layouts should be avoided.

Wall Thickness.   Wall sections as thin as 0.025 inch can be molded, depending upon the size of the molding.   The design of the knockout should take into consideration the flexibility of the plastic in such thin sections.   It is generally better to pull or blow a thin-walled piece from the mold, since pushing it may cause buckling.   Cavities should be adequately vented to facilitate molding at the lowest injection pressures.   Sticking in the mold of complicated shapes often can be overcome by etching or vapor-blasting the surface of the mold.

Shrinkage.   Shrinkage of the piece of polyethylene in the mold is generally from 2–3% (20–30 mils per inch), depending upon the molding conditions and thickness of the molded piece.   Thin sections show less shrinkage than thick sections.   Shrinkage increases as mold temperature increases.   As a rough approximation, an increase of 20°F. in mold temperature increases shrinkage by 0.002 inch per inch.   Shrinkage can be reduced by higher cylinder temperatures, higher plunger pressure, and longer plunger dwell.

Short dwells are recommended to minimize sticking in the cavity.   Care should be taken, however, to prevent dwells that are too short, resulting in shrink voids.

Gates.   A gate measuring 0.015 by 0.040 inch or larger is recommended for best results.   Gates as small as 0.005–0.010 by $^3/_{32}$–$^7/_{32}$ inch have been tried out and result in higher gloss in the molded piece, although usually making mold fill-out difficult and promoting the appearance of sink marks in the piece.

Fillers.   Materials that serve as fillers can be used in quantities up to 40%.   Calcium carbonate and clay have been used.   Filled compounds require up to 35% higher injection pressure.   Stiffness has been increased up to 100% by the use of 40% filler.

Hot-runner Molds.   Polyethylene is probably the most suitable of the thermoplastics for use in hot-runner molds (usually operated at about 280°F.), eliminating the recycling of sprues and runners.

Injection Machine Ratings.   Since polyethylene has the lowest specific gravity of all moldable plastics, 0.92, machine ratings will be lower than for heavier plastics, e.g., 1-oz. machine rating for polystyrene compares with 0.88 for polyethylene.

A recent book by Haim and Neumann on the welding of polyethylene (853) goes considerably beyond the subject implied by the title (*Manual for Plastic Welding: Polyethylene*) and represents a source of important information in concise form.

Processing conditions particularly suited for the recently marketed high-density polyethylenes were outlined in Section 6.19.

As a safety precaution, adequate ventilation to ensure removal of vapors formed during the processing of polyethylene is essential. Since polyethylene is insoluble in water and aqueous solutions, it may be safely used for the manufacture of articles which come into contact with food. However, under certain circumstances, the taste and smell of foods can be adversely affected. Such problems can best be solved on the basis of practical experiments in each instance. This applies particularly to food containing fats, alcohols, essential oils, or other aromatic matter. Toxicity of some polyethylene additives is discussed by Wilson and McCormick (890a).

The explosion characteristics of polyethylene dust are presented in Table XCVIIIa (554).

TABLE XCVIIIa

Explosion Characteristics of Polyethylene Dust

Ignition temperature of dust cloud	450°C.
Minimum spark energy required for ignition of dust cloud	80 millijoules
Minimum explosives concentration	0.025 oz./cu. ft.
Maximum explosion pressure	83 p.s.i.
Rate of pressure rise (p.s.i./sec.), average	400
Rate of pressure rise (p.s.i./sec.), maximum	1,250
Limiting oxygen percentage to prevent ignition of dust cloud by electric sparks	15

Source: L. S. Marks, *Mechanical Engineers' Handbook*, Fifth Edition, McGraw-Hill Book Co., New York, 1951.

8.1. Comminuting, Refining, and Pelletizing

Comminuting

Conventional grinding methods, when applied to the softer grades of polyethylene, result in the formation of long, fibrous particles. These are not only difficult to screen, but are also quite unsuited for a number of uses, e.g., in the flame gun. Polyethylene may be prepared in powdered form without resultant brittleness by a process described by Wilson in Brit. 571,814 to Telegraph Construction and Maintenance (198). The resin is dissolved at an elevated temperature in a solvent in which it is substantially insoluble at relatively low temperatures. Upon cooling the solution, the polymer precipitates in finely divided form. As an example, when petroleum ether and polyethylene are heated under reflux to 70°C., agitated until solution is complete, and then allowed to cool, finely divided polyethylene precipitates. This may subsequently be readily separated and dried. A similar method was proposed by Scheermesser and Spindler in Fr. 1,042,310 (804), and in Brit. 718,815 (913a).

The addition of 10% methanol to the softer grades of polyethylene has been proposed by Jarrett in U. S. 2,451,743 (375) and in Brit. 579,769 (254), both to I.C.I., to render the resin sufficiently brittle to be worked readily in a Banbury mixer.   U. S. 2,534,079 of Strain and Peterson to duPont (523) relates to the recovery of hydrolyzed ethylene-vinyl ester copolymers in granular form.   The copolymers contain 50–80% of ethylene, and the ester portion is at least 50% hydrolyzed.   By this method, solutions of the hydrolyzed copolymers are comminuted by a jet of steam and kept in a state of turbulence until the solvent content of the polymer is reduced below the level at which agglomeration occurs.   The steam jet may first strike a dilute starch solution, by which the droplets of polymer solution and ultimately the polymer become coated with starch, further reducing their tendency to agglomerate.   The products are dropped into an agitated vessel containing 0.5% starch solution at 94°C.; the resultant slurry is filtered, and the products washed and dried.

According to Fr. 966,283 (518) to Société Nouvelle de Métallisation, polymeric materials such as polyethylenes or nylon are ground to a fine powder against a coarse grinding wheel, turning with a peripheral speed of 600–1,000 meters per minute.   The plastic is applied with a pressure of from 0.50–2.50 g. per square mm.   For polyethylene, the speed is 800 meters per minute, and the pressure 1.25 g. per square mm.   The plastic being ground is cooled during the grinding process by a jet of compressed air.

Two U. S. patents to Union Carbide relate to the pulverization of polyethylene.   In the earlier of these, U.S. 2,582,327 to Haine (647), high molecular weight polyethylene is charged to a Banbury mixer and subjected to a pressure of 40–60 p.s.i.   After $4^{1}/_{2}$ minutes, the softening point of the polymer is exceeded, owing to frictional heat within the mixer; water, which acts as a coolant and lubricant, is added, and the pressure of the mixture alternately released and applied.   Small, discrete, feathery polymer particles are obtained.   Shrinkage of the particles by relief of internal stresses below the softening point is brought about by remixing under pressure.   The coarser portion of the polymer may then be subjected to a re-treatment if desired.   Plastics which are difficult to pulverize, such as polyethylene and ethyl cellulose, may be powdered mechanically under refrigeration, according to U. S. 2,609,150 to Bludeau (664).   The precooled resin is chilled below the brittle point by a spray of liquid refrigerant and then subjected to impact.

The use of a Banbury-type mixer in a closed chamber under positive pressure to convert polyethylene into a powder is proposed in Austral. 6302/55 to Monsanto (1053).   Dry-pulverizing polyethylene between a pair of closely spaced rolls in a hammer mill, roller mill, rod mill, or similar grinding equipment is described in Brit. 740,054 to Montecatini (1100).

Refining

Polymers of ethylene produced by the conventional, high-pressure process are generally nonuniform in structure. When extruded into thin sheets, they exhibit translucent or opaque spots which, because of their physical appearance, have come to be known as "fisheyes." For the most part, they represent gel particles of polyethylene which were crosslinked during polymerization or by subsequent partial overheating during processing. The elimination of these "fisheyes" is a major problem because they are not only unsightly but also tend to weaken or disrupt the films prepared from polyethylene. Several methods of refining polyethylene have been described.

According to U. S. 2,480,615 to Strain and Osgood [duPont (455)], polyethylene free from graininess when coated on wire or fabricated into sheets may be obtained by subjecting the polymer to high shearing stresses at temperatures between 100 and 250°C. The shearing apparatus extrudes the polymer past a cylindrical rotating head positioned at the end of an Archimedes screw. The head has a peripheral speed between 60 and 700 feet per minute, and a clearance factor of not less than 40. (*Note:* the clearance factor is defined as the length of the head times the reciprocal of the clearance between the outer face and the inner wall of the extruder.)

According to Austral. 6303/55 [Monsanto (1053a)], polyethylene may be refined by intense mixing in a Banbury-type mixer under a pressure of 20–30 p.s.i. for no more than 2 minutes, and then continuing the mixing under a pressure of no more than 5 p.s.i., while the walls of the mixer are cooled by circulation of water (10°C.).

Another method of refining polyethylene, described by BASF in German Patent Application No. B 25 064 (1096), consists of forcing the polymer through narrow slits at a temperature range between the transformation point and the melting point, but below the melting point at relative velocities of the contact surfaces, or at flow velocities of the polyethylene at which it will not melt during the treatment. Rolls in sets of two, three, or four may be used for the process; these are cooled because of the frictional heat. In such roll systems, it is possible to reduce the number of required passes by increasing the differences between the peripheral speeds of the rolls.

Pelletizing

The granulation of polyethylene is discussed in a recent paper by Kennaway (981). An early method consisted of chipping strips or pieces of the resin between a set of rotating knives and a fixed anvil; the disintegrated material produced was random in shape and size.   In a later method, aimed at achieving a more uniform product, the resin was cut into cubes. Another method of producing granules is to extrude laces which, when cooled, can be cut into little cylinders (so-called "spaghetti" cutting). The most recent method, disclosed in patent applications of Evans, Farr Gilmour, Kennaway, and I.C.I., consists of cutting the extruded laces while still molten ("Caviare Cut"). Uniformity of the spheroids, free flow, high packing density, and freedom from dust are the advantages claimed for polyethylene granulated by this method.

8.2. Compounding and Coloring

Lack of polarity renders polyethylene inert to solvents at room temperature and incompatible with plasticizers. This lack of compatibility is so pronounced that even molten mixtures of polyethylenes of widely different molecular weights show tendencies to separate on cooling. For specific data on the compatibility of polyethylene with various materials, reference is made to Section 6.1.

The incorporation of modifiers such as polyisobutylene, of antioxidants, or of pigments before fabrication may be carried out on open rolls, in internal mixers, or in extruders. It is frequently more advantageous to feed concentrates of the additive in polyethylene rather than the undiluted additive. In milling polyethylene, a fairly narrow temperature range must be maintained. At higher temperatures, the tendency of the polymer to stick becomes disturbing; at lower temperatures, milling cannot be carried out.

Carbon Blacks

As long ago as 1857, Hancock (1) showed that rubber colored black deteriorated less quickly under the action of sunlight than did white rubber. Since then, it has come to be a truism of the industry that black compounds age better than nonblacks. Quite recently, Newton and Wake (484) established that nonblack, rubber-coated fabrics are less resistant to embrittlement by exposure to sunlight than are black coatings. Protection apparently is afforded by the presence, in dispersed form, of a relatively small amount of carbon black in the rubber composition. This is assumed to be due to the light-absorbing or screening properties of the carbon black. It would be logical to suppose that this property could also be extended to other thermoplastic materials which are subjected to light-catalyzed oxidation reactions.

The application of dispersed carbon blacks to compounding polyethylene insulating compositions was first described by Habgood in patents assigned to I.C.I. (123,150,168). Compositions suitable for sheathing telephone and telegraph cables are prepared by milling one or more carbon blacks of small particle size into polyethylene of molecular weight of 10,000–50,000. Milling is carried out at the customary (elevated) temperatures. Any of the common blacks, acetylene, channel, or lamp black, are suitable in the process of the invention.

Dannenberg, Jordan, and Stokes (467) published the results of an inquiry into the effect of mechanical aggregation on the dispersion characteristics of carbon black. The media investigated were water, news ink vehicle, natural rubber, low-temperature GR-S, butyl rubber, a butadiene-acrylonitrile copolymer, and polyethylene. With regard to polyethylene, it was found that well-dispersed, high-color channel blacks of small particle size, in concentrations of about 3 parts per 100, resulted in polyethylene compositions having maximum weathering qualities. It was also established that degree of dispersion of the black is critical. At such low concentrations, the presence of large aggregates seriously reduces the resistance to weathering of the resultant composition. It was further established that the dry density of the black has an appreciable effect on the degree of dispersion obtainable. Since dry density is an indirect measure of the degree of dry aggregation, this correlation is hardly surprising. This is especially true considering the difficulty of mechanically dispersing blacks uniformly through a polyethylene batch. In this series of experiments, care was taken to control closely the temperature of mixing and to maintain maximum shearing conditions throughout. In this way, it was found possible to ensure the necessary degree of dispersion in the final product, using normal commercial varieties of densified blacks.

It is of interest to note that the Acheson Dispersed Pigment Company (unit of Acheson Industries, Inc.) is currently marketing a carbon black-polyethylene dispersion recommended for use in extruding black polyethylene pipe (693). The dispersion is provided in a granular, dust-free form, and is stated to contain approximately 25% of colloidal carbon black.

A highly loaded, carbon black filled, irradiated polyethylene (GE Vulkene 107-E) was discussed in Section 6.16. There, reference is also made to a paper by Szwarc (1141c) providing a uniform explanation of various phenomena observed in polymers containing carbon black as a filler.

Fillers

Midwinter and Richards, in patents assigned to I.C.I. (307,433), claim that the toughness and softening point of polyethylene compositions may be increased by the incorporation therein of finely divided, activated calcium carbonate as a filler. From 10–60% of filler may be used, but about

TABLE XCIX

Property Changes in Polyethylene Caused by Fillers

	Unfilled polyethylene	Polyethylene—60% Clay—40%
50% brittle temp. index, °C.	−90	−15
Tensile strength, p.s.i.	1,950	1,800
(ASTM D638–46T)		
Ultimate elongation, %	150	45
(ASTM D638–46T)		
Dielectric strength, v./mil		
(ASTM D149–44)		
At 25°C.	1,000	980
At 80°C.	630	530
Power factor, 25°C.		
(ASTM D150–47T)		
At 1 mc.	0.0003	0.004
At 50 mc.	0.0003	0.009
Dielectric constant at 1 mc.		
(ASTM D150–47T)		
At 25°C.	2.3	2.9
Water absorption, %		
(ASTM D570–42)	<0.01	<0.1
Tear resistance, lb./in.		
(ASTM D624–48)	500	275

Source: *Ind. Eng. Chem.*, **42**, 848 (1950).

30% is preferred. The calcium carbonate should not exceed 0.1μ in particle size. The polyethylene must exhibit a melt viscosity in excess of 60,000 poises, preferably 1,300,000 poises at 190°C. Mixing is conducted on conventional rolls at about 170°C. Sheets pressed from the preferred composition are stated to be flexible at temperatures as low as −40°C., and to exhibit toughness and other qualities superior to the same grade of polyethylene alone.

Bostwick and Carey (462) evaluated in more general terms the effectiveness of incorporating inorganic fillers as stiffening agents in polyethylene compositions. Barium sulfate, precipitated calcium carbonate, ground calcium carbonate (two grades), carbon black, clay, magnesium chloride, and three grades of silicon dioxide were tested. They found that the fillers did not materially influence processing and injection-molding character-istics of the compositions. All of the materials tested did, however, re-duce mold shrinkage very appreciably.

In the case of 60%-polyethylene, 40%-clay, or 40%-calcium carbonate compositions, this reduction was consistently of the order of 50%. At the same time, the presence of any of the fillers evaluated resulted in deg-radation of the physical and electrical properties of the polyethylene. Tensile strength, tear resistance, and ultimate elongation were seriously decreased. Concurrently, the dielectric constant and power factor were increased. Furthermore, water absorption and specific gravity were in-creased for all of the fillers tested. Values typical of property changes caused by the addition of fillers are presented in Table XCIX.

Elastomers

The milling, extruding, mixing, and calendering of natural and synthetic rubbers and rubber compositions with polyethylene, polyvinyl chloride, etc., has been studied in a general way by Penn (181) in an attempt to correlate the molecular changes which take place with the changes in physical properties.

The basic patents relating to polyethylene-rubber compositions are those issued to I.C.I. Thus, Brit. 514,687 (89) and equivalent Fr. 853,754 (107), relate to compositions comprised of 5–95% polyethylene and a natural rubber or synthetic rubber, with or without other ingredients. According to Brit. 544,359 (140), plastic and adhesive compositions, useful for bonding polyethylene to other materials such as metals, are obtained by incorporating together one to two parts of polyethylene and one part of a cyclo-rubber. Canadian 430,775 (200), assigned by Latham to C.I.L., relates to ethylene polymers blended with a polymer of butadiene; iso-prene; polyisobutylene; polymerized 2-chloro-1,3-butadiene; chlorinated-, hydrochlorinated-, or hydrogenated rubber; balata or gutta percha. In-creased softening point and notch bend resistance and improved flexibility in the final product are claimed to result.

The relatively early (1940) Brit. 517,649 to Brislee, Quale, and Chapman [British Insulated Cables (104)] describes an electrical condenser in which the dielectric consists of a thin sheet of a material formed from a mixture of polyethylene and polyisobutylene, containing 5–40% of the latter.

U. S. 2,615,857 (668) by Clarke, assigned to Bell Telephone Laboratories, relates to gels of polyethylene and polyisobutylene which are of value in the potting of electrical apparatus.   For example, a composition of 7.5% polyethylene (molecular weight 12,000), 92% polyisobutylene (molecular weight 3,000), and 0.5% trimethyldihydroquinoline (antioxidant) is mixed together at 130–135°C.   Variations of this basic formula containing 5–35% polyethylene are stated to give satisfactory gels.

U. S. 2,628,203 to van Gilder and Harney [Standard Oil (783)] discloses solutions of rubbery polymers from particles of uniform diameter.   Thus, polyethylene, polyisobutylene, and copolymers of butadiene, styrene, acrylonitrile, and isoprene having uniform particles of not over $1/4$ inch are dissolved in wax by agitating at a temperature above the melting point of the wax.

U. S. 2,339,958 (163) assigned by Sparks to Jasco, Inc., claims compositions suitable for food-wrapping sheets comprised of polyethylene (75–20 parts), polyisobutylene (25–80 parts), and, optionally, a wax such as paraffin (1–25 parts).   These compositions are thermoplastic at 75–130°C., substantially transparent in thin films, essentially insoluble in water and aqueous solutions, and generally compatible.

Polyvinyl Compounds

Child and Habgood patents, Brit. 542,140 (130) and Can. 425,816 (187), to I.C.I. and to C.I.L., respectively, relate to polyethylene mixed with polyvinylisobutyl ether (20–50%), for example in an open rolling mill.

U. S. 2,448,666 (370), assigned by Fletcher and Renfrew to duPont, describes compositions for coating on semirigid surfaces.   These are prepared from polyvinyl butyral (50 parts) and polyethylene (50 parts).   The film is applied by spreading as a thin layer of the powdered material on wood, pressing at 200 p.s.i. and 160°C. for 5 minutes, and cooling.   The wood has a highly polished, waxlike surface with excellent adhesion of the coating to the wood.   Polyethylene alone gives good finish, but is without adhesion to the wood.

U. S. 2,388,169 (204), assigned to duPont by McAlevy, Strain, and Chance, concerns a process for obtaining vulcanized elastomers from a copolymer of ethylene and an organic acid ester of vinyl alcohol.   The ester may be vinyl acetate, propionate, butyrate, acrylate, methacrylate, or the higher straight- and branched-chain vinyl esters of the aliphatic organic acids generally.   The copolymer is first pyrolyzed at 250–400°C., and the pyrolyzate compounded with sulfur (0.25–15.0%), accelerators (0.1–15.0%), metal oxides of Group 2 of the Periodic Table (1–30%), and reinforcing agents (up to 60%), and cured with or without pressure.

Carboxylic Acid Esters

Two Alderson patents [U. S. 2,405,933 (259) and Brit. 590,055 (321)], assigned to duPont, describe polyethylene compositions suitable for the production of films. These are stated to be flexible, free from pinholes, and otherwise especially suited for use as a moisture-proof wrapping foil. The compositions are prepared by milling and calendering a mixture of polyethylene or polyethylene copolymer, a carboxylic acid ester, and a naturally-occurring fatty acid glyceride. The ester is derived from a carboxylic acid of at least 14 carbon atoms and an alcohol having preferably 11 to 18 carbon atoms. Examples cited for such esters are undecyl stearate, dodecyl stearate, myricyl linoleate, and lauryl palmitate. Preferred fatty acid glycerides include palm, coconut, and linseed oils. Relative proportions of ingredients (parts by weight) are polyethylene (or polyethylene copolymer) 100, carboxylic acid ester 1, and fatty acid glyceride 0.5. The composition is milled on hot rolls and calendered at 130–140°C.

U. S. 2,462,331 to Myers, assigned to Bakelite (427) relates to the use of carboxylic acid esters as polyethylene lubricants. These result in ready release of the polyethylene composition from rolls at temperatures considerably above the adhesion temperature of unmodified polyethylene, i.e., substantially above 100°C. The esters are derived from polyhydric alcohols and metal salts of monocarboxylic fatty acids having from 12–24 carbon atoms. The proportion of ester present is from 0.2–0.5% of the polyethylene.

Urea-Aldehyde Condensation Products

In two patents (Brit. 578,643 and U. S. 2,436,080), assigned to duPont (248, 361), Smith has described molding powders comprised of a urea-aldehyde resin blended with an ethylene copolymer. According to this invention, approximately 1,520 parts of A-stage urea-formaldehyde resin are mixed with 1,300 parts of hydrolyzed vinyl acetate-ethylene copolymer, and 0.5% β-bromohydrocinnamic acid and 0.7% aluminum stearate are added. By varying the ratios of ingredients, the final products may be molding powders or adhesives. Articles molded from these are stated to exhibit improved water-resistance and impact strength over cellulose-filled urea resins.

Flame-Retarding Additives

Flame-retardant polyethylene with mechanical properties similar to the uncompounded polymer may be prepared by blending polyethylene with antimony trioxide and a chlorinated hydrocarbon, whereby the flame-retarding properties of antimony trioxide are used in conjunction with the plasticizing and flame-retardant properties of the chlorinated paraffin wax.   Antimony trioxide, if used alone, would have to be added in such quantities as to make the polymer hard and brittle.   Flame-retardant compositions are claimed in U. S. 2,480,298 by Happoldt [duPont (454b)], discussed in Section 4.8, and by Rugar in Brit. 652,669 [Diamond Alkali (573a)].

Flame-retardant plastics, in general, and flame-retardant polyethylene, in particular, were discussed by Rugar (763a), and by Cooke (724b). Flame-retardant polyethylene, if properly compounded is easily process-able; does not drip and spread fire; has good high frequency electrical proper-ties; is resistant to cracking; has satisfactory abrasion resistance; and does not exhibit cold flow.   It has been evaluated for neon sign cable, cable for coal mines, nonmigratory cable sheaths for radar use, and other applications where a flame-retardant material approximating polyethylene in all other respects is required [e.g., Brit. 713,174 to Rome Cable Corp. (906f)].

Rivals to flame-retardant polyethylene are, besides mineral insulations, polytetrafluoroethylene, polychlorotrifluoroethylene, polyvinyl chloride, and chlorinated polyethylene.

Coloring Polyethylene

The major problems in the application of colors (including carbon blacks) to polyethylene are dispersion of the colorant in the formulation and per-formance of the colorant after dispersion.   A description of the processing operations and a list of colorants recommended for polyethylene have been published by Goodwin (852) and reprinted by Stoeckhert (1033).   As indi-cated by Figure 197, the simplest method of coloring polyethylene is by dry blending, either directly or by preparing a dry-blend master batch.   The use of wetting agents to improve distribution of the colorant on the resin is recommended.   Dispersing the colorant in a vehicle which is compatible with polyethylene improves the quality of the colored formulation.   The dispersion, used as a master batch, is diluted with natural resin and given additional processing in a Banbury mixer or an extruder.   Not only ap-pearance but also the degree of resistance to weathering of the colored polyethylene can be improved by the degree of dispersion of colorant in the polyethylene.

A process whereby mixtures of aqueous pastes of pigments and aqueous dispersions of polymers of unsaturated esters (e.g., polyvinyl acetate, poly-

vinyl propionate), from which the water has been removed, are used for
the coloring of polyethylene and other thermoplastic resins by blending is
described by Hirsekorn and Fischer in German Patent Application No.
B 30 786 [BASF(1098)]. For good color effect, and in order to maintain

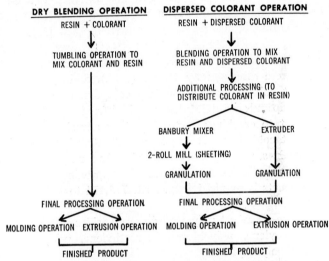

Fig. 197. Flow chart of processing operations for coloring polyethylene. (*Modern Plastics*, **31** [12], 105 (1954).)

the mechanical properties of the polymer, good compatibility between the
color blend and polymer is essential. Polyethylene color concentrates and
blends are commercially available.

8.3. Extrusion Molding

Polyethylene can be fabricated in conventional extrusion equipment.
Wire and cable covering is applied by extrusion methods, and a variety of
electrical conductors are insulated by polyethylene in this manner. Film,
tubing, rods, tapes, and monofilaments are other forms of polyethylene
made by the extrusion process.

British 570,139 and U. S. 2,384,224, both to Williams [I.C.I. (196,197)]
describe a process whereby coated wires or insulated electric cables may be
made free from voids by extrusion-coating with a composition containing
a substantial proportion of polyethylene. The coated material is then
subjected to drastic cooling by compressed air, water, or other fluid medium
under a pressure sufficient to prevent the formation of voids. Gradual
cooling of a polyethylene covered wire is recommended by Tunnicliff and
Barlow in U. S. 2,732,592 [Brit. Insul. Callender's Cables (1146a)].

Minor improvements in machines designed for the extrusion of rubber mixes and for synthetic plastic compositions of the polyethylene type are described in Brit. 560,476 to Griffiths and Henley's Telegraph Works (165).

An extrusion method for forming films and bands of polyethylene has been described by Perrin, Paton, and Williams in Brit. 474,426 (63), and in French 832,174 (74), both to I.C.I.   The polymer is shaped by extruding above the softening temperature, then solidified and rolled or cut into

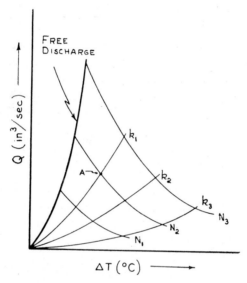

Fig. 198. Typical performance diagram for adiabatic melt extrusion.   (Q is extrusion rate, and ΔT is temperature rise of the molten plastic.)   (*Rubber World*, **130** [A], 513 (1954).)

thin strips or sheets.   Alternatively, shaping may be effected by passing the polyethylene through a pair of rollers, one of which is maintained at a temperature above the softening point of the polymer, while the other is kept cold.   The polymer may also be applied as a powder or as a solution to the surface of a solid or of a heavy liquid, such as mercury, and heated to a temperature sufficiently high to form a continuous film.

British 561,373 to duPont (166) describes the extrusion of polyethylene onto a moving support, such as a revolving drum, which is maintained at a temperature below the melting point of the polymer.   Heat is applied to the molten film during its passage from the slot orifice to the support.

The screw extrusion of thermoplastic materials has been studied by

Atkinson and Owen (701). In polyethylene extrusion, the generated pressure was found to increase with screw depth at constant pitch. There is a limiting average depth beyond which output falls off rapidly, and on a constant-pitch, diminishing-depth screw, the compression ratio must not be such that the final depth is below a given value. The method for applying compression ratio is considered more significant than the compression ratio itself. Compression ratio achieved by decreasing depth at constant pitch is preferable to a constant depth of diminishing pitch.

Based on a mathematical analysis of the adiabatic operation of melt extruders, Bernhardt and McKelvey (825,826) applied adiabatic techniques to polyethylene extrusion. For adiabatic melt extruders, the theory permits calculation of the relation between pressure, temperature, extrusion rate, screw speed, and the screw and die constants. This is illustrated in Figure 198, a typical theoretical-performance diagram for an adiabatic melt extruder, where the ordinate is the extrusion rate, and the abscissa is the temperature rise of the molten plastic. The free discharge (heavy line) shows how extrusion rate and temperature increase with screw speed. The light lines radiating from the origin demonstrate this relation for extrusion through dies of various resistances. The lines intersecting the free discharge line connect points of equal screw speed, indicating the change of extrusion rate and temperature with resistance at a given speed. It is demonstrated that polyethylene extrusion under near-adiabatic conditions can be obtained in practice. Further, the adiabatic melt-extrusion theory can serve as a semiquantitative guide to the design of extruders with mostly mechanical power as well as for analysis of the performance of existing extruders.

A quantitative study of the advantages obtained by preheating polyethylene before extrusion was presented by Wilton and Marrow (1142a).

8.4. Injection Molding

Injection molding in standard equipment is the most economical method for molding polyethylene. A detailed description of an injection molding machine especially suited for use with polyethylene is given in Brit. 567,375 to Shipton and Hill (186). In general, the temperature of the heating cylinder should be between 175 and 260°C. in order to ensure adequate softening. The temperature of the mold itself is rather critical and must be sufficiently below the softening point to permit the molded article to harden in a reasonable time. On the other hand, too cold a mold will result in strains developing in the article from too rapid cooling, and may also interfere with the maintenance of adequate pressure upon the article as it cools. Good results are usually secured with a mold temperature of about 60°C., provided the channels connecting the heating cylinder with the mold cavity are large enough to prevent premature hardening of their contents, with resultant failure to transmit pressure.

According to Brit. 499,333 issued to Fawcett, Gibson, Perrin, Paton, Williams, and I.C.I. (84), polyethylene may be injection molded from a chamber heated above the softening temperature (for example at 120°C., in the case of very small amounts) through a nozzle into a mold which may be cold, i.e., at room temperature, for compact shapes, but heated at the side remote from the nozzle for long articles. Because of the high linear contraction on solidification, the mold should be 5% oversize, on a linear basis.

8.5. Injection-Extrusion Molding

A method particularly developed for the manufacture of polyethylene articles of large size has been described by Ferguson (156). It combines the screw feed of the extrusion technique with the molding arrangement of injection practice. A screw feed forces the hot mass into a mold at a pressure of 200–400 p.s.i. By providing a small clearance between screw and barrel, these pressures can be sustained without rupturing the mold during cooling. Owing to the low pressures involved, the accurate positioning of small inserts and wires can easily be ensured. Other advantages include the automatic exclusion of air bubbles by action of the screw feed on the material; the elimination of heavy molds, since the low pressures can be handled by light-weight molds, which may make small production runs economically feasible; and the reduction in size of the machine required to produce relatively large moldings.

8.6. Film Manufacture

Polyethylene film may be produced by extrusion and by calendering methods. While both processes are capable of yielding products of equally good properties, the extrusion method is more widely employed. U. S. 2,586,820 to Hemperly and Smith [Union Carbide and Carbon (651)] describes the production of polyethylene films, 0.001-inch thick, by calendering. Small amounts of antioxidant and release agent are added on a mill, and the resin is transferred to a calender operating at 140–150°C. The film leaves the calender at a thickness of 0.004 inch and is stretched above its softening temperature within a few inches of the take-off point to 0.001 inch and at once quenched in water. Stretching is accomplished by higher speed take-off rolls. The resulting film undergoes only slight shrinkage on heating at 100°C.

In the extrusion process, flat stock is obtained when linear dies are used. With circular dies, tubing is obtained which may be used *per se* or split to form flat sheets. By continuously inflating the extruded tubing (extrusion blowing) a uniform, sausagelike tube of thin polyethylene is formed (Figure 199).

Fig. 199. Extrusion blowing of polyethylene. (Copyright, Du Pont Magazine, May-June, 1949.)

Haine and Land (604) have discussed the effect of extruder variables on properties and output of polyethylene film. Compound extrusion and output rate, die-orifice clearance, hot-stretch distance, and bath temperature were found to have little effect on specular gloss, light transmission, and haze of polyethylene, within the operating limits studied. Blocking may be substantially reduced when hot film is extruded into a water bath at temperatures of 85–90°C. The usable extruder capacity is limited by the stretchability of the hot extruded film and the appearance of the finished film.   Low compound temperatures were found to result in nerviness and poor stretchability immediately after exit from the die.   The take-off assembly for the extruded thin film of polyethylene used in these experiments is shown in Figure 200.

A nomograph recommended for use in estimating extruder film output rate, when film thickness and width and extruder delivery rate in pounds per hour are known, is reproduced in Figure 201 from the article by Haine and Land.

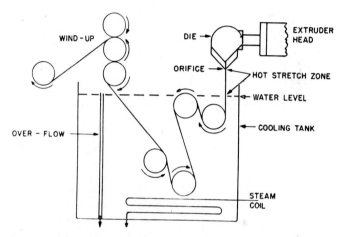

Fig. 200. Take-off assembly for extruded thin film of polyethylene. (*Modern Plastics*, **29** [6], 110 (1952).)

The problem of producing thin films of polyethylene and other plastic materials for packaging purposes has recently been discussed by Romanowski (763) on the basis of practical works experience and the technical equipment used.   Further processing of the extruded tubing by cutting, welding, and printing is mentioned.

According to patents assigned to duPont, casting polyethylene to form flexible, tear-resistant, waterproof, and moisture-impermeable films which retain their toughness at low temperatures may be carried out by two processes.   In one process described by Ingersoll in U. S. 2,431,042 (330), a molten film of polyethylene is formed on a smooth metal sheet, cooled until maximum haze formation occurs, then heated until the haze disappears, recooled, and stripped from the support.   The other process, described by Peters in U. S. 2,405,977 (262) and Brit. 579,022 (250), involves casting polyethylene above its melting point from a solution, preferably xylene, upon a rotating drum or spreader, the temperature of which is below the melting point of the polymer. The solvent is evaporated by the circulation of hot air above the surface, and the film, prior to the time of its crystallization, i.e., haze formation, is quenched with a nonsolvent cooling liquid, preferably water, at 0–10°C., and stripped from the support. This time interval does not vary with the temperature if quenching takes place

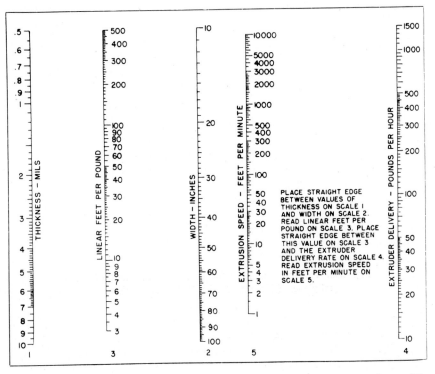

Fig. 201. Nomograph for polyethylene flat film production. (*Modern Plastics*, **29** [6], 118 (1952).)

from 7–75°C. below the melting point of the polyethylene. It decreases with increased rate of solvent evaporation, and is increased by incorporation into the casting solution of a modifying agent, e.g., 1% of a salt of a long-chain carboxylic or sulfonic acid.

Ellis (286) has devised a method for the preparation of films of polyethylene, particularly suited for use in electron microscopy. Approximately 75 ml. of a solution of 0.2 g. polyethylene in 100 ml. xylene is placed in a wide-mouthed bottle.   A microscope slide is half-immersed in the solution and a stopper inserted while the bottle is heated at 100°C. until the solution is clear.   The film is removed from the slide and floated on water at 50°C., from which it can be lifted by a mesh and allowed to dry in the usual manner.   The film is said to show a clear structure which does not interfere in most applications.

Unsupported films of polymers of tetrafluoroethylene and its copolymers with ethylene or other unsaturated compounds may be prepared according to U. S. 2,520,173 to Sanders [duPont (514)] by spreading a film from a suspension of the polymer on a metal sheet, evaporating the suspending medium, subjecting the coated metal sheet to a high temperature to sinter or coalesce the polymer particles, and immersing the sheet in a bath to dissolve the metal.   In an example, an unsupported film was prepared from a copolymer of ethylene (25%) and tetrafluoroethylene (75%), suspended in dimethyl phthalate.   This method may be modified for continuous production of thin films, where thin aluminum foil is coated with polymer suspensoid, passed through a zone heated to 93°C. to evaporate the water, through a zone at 371°C. to coalesce the particles, through an amalgamating bath to increase the reactivity of the aluminum foil with solvent, through a 10% aqueous sodium hydroxide bath at 60–93°C. to dissolve the aluminum, and finally through a water bath to remove the sodium hydroxide from the continuous unsupported polymer film.

The formation of films of polyethylene by precipitation is described by Myles and Bache in U. S. 2,210,771 to I.C.I. (110).   A hot, concentrated solution of polyethylene in an organic solvent or solvent mixture is passed into a liquid, such as butanol or propanol, which is immiscible with the solvent and has little or no solvent power for the polymer.   The temperature should be sufficiently high to ensure precipitation of the polyethylene in a coherent form; that is, the temperature of both polymer solution and precipitating bath must necessarily be above 70°C., preferably between 90 and 96°C.

By a process described in U. S. 2,535,373 to Shearer and Martin [American Viscose (524)], films and sheets of polyethylene and other thermoplastic materials may be formed by molding thermoplastic fibers of these polymers at temperatures below the melting point of the fibers so that they are softened and yet do not flow.   They are then allowed to cool while under pressure.   The fibers are transformed into a continuous transparent or translucent mass with retention of their individual surfaces which are not discernible under ordinary conditions, unless subjected to mechanical working.

A special orientation treatment of polyethylene films is described by Bryant in U. S. Patent Application No. 691,180 to duPont (571). By this method, a film 0.2-mm. thick of solid polymer of high molecular weight is cold-drawn at room temperature in one direction to produce substantial molecular orientation, then redrawn in a direction 30 to 90° removed from the original direction to result in a tensile strength 50–100% greater than that obtained from a single drawing operation. The continuous production of molecularly oriented polyethylene films without the customary preliminary production of molecularly unoriented films is claimed by Bright in U. S. 2,631,954 to the Kendall Company (787). Elastomers, preferably not more than 12% by weight of the total polymer, may be blended by milling to increase the elasticity and flexibility. Typical compounds are crude rubber, isoprene, and polyisobutylene. The apparatus comprises heated nip rolls and a chilled quench roll, which are operated at differential surface speeds to give a particular surface film. These films have relatively low softening points and a tendency to swell in hydrocarbon solvents, and are claimed to be particularly receptive to adhesives and therefore useful in the preparation of coated films and laminates.

A method of improving gloss, clarity, and transparency of polyethylene film by quenching is described in Brit. 694,870 to Plax (800b).

The properties of polyethylene films may be improved according to U. S. 2,499,756 to Jacobson [duPont (504)] by the addition of various quantities of a paraffin hydrocarbon with a melting point above 120°C. Improvement in clarity of extruded polyethylene film by compounding with 2% each of carnauba wax and di-2-ethylhexylphthalate is claimed by Fuller in U. S. 2,499,486 to Visking (503).

Uniform distribution of sulfur or phosphorus sulfide (0.01–1%) in polyethylene is claimed by Goldrick and Marks in U. S. 2,480,297 to duPont (454a) to improve transparency and surface characteristics of polyethylene products, particularly films.

The tendency of polyethylene compositions, e.g., films, sheeting, filaments, and coatings, to accumulate electrostatic charges can be reduced, according to Lee and MacLeod in U. S. 2,525,691 to I.C.I. (519), by incorporating either a condensation product of ethylene oxide and a water-insoluble fatty acid or alcohol, or a saturated aliphatic alcohol containing more than 12, but not more than 32 carbon atoms. Similarly, Brit. 731,728 to I.C.I. (1074) claims that polyethylene compositions with improved surface characteristics, particularly improved slip and a reduced tendency to accumulate electrostatic charges, may be obtained by the incorporation of a condensation product of ethylene oxide with an alkyl or cycloalkyl substituted phenolic compound. These alkylaryl polyglycol ethers preferably contain 8–14 ethylene oxide groups. (Compare also "Blocking" in Section 7.9.)

As to the use of proper release agents, silicones when used on commercial band sealers were found by the Bakelite Co. (1123) to cause stress cracking when exposed film packages are tightly packed in a carton. Sticking without silicone lubrication may be prevented by coating the bands with tetrafluoroethylene, or a silicone elastomer; impregnated glass fabric may be used as the separating agent. Also, under certain precautions, metal bands may be used without lubrication.

Destaticizers for polyethylene (Electrosols D and M) are produced by Alframine Corp. (1124). An addition of 0.5–1.5% of these compounds to the powder or pellets is claimed to prevent sheets from clinging together and to retard dust collection. In addition, good mold or extrusion release, improved elasticity, increased resilience, and greater clarity in transparent sheets are obtained. Similar effects are claimed (1124a) for Arquad 18, a quaternary ammonium salt produced by Armour Corp.

8.7. Manufacture of Filaments and Fibers

Monofilaments extruded from polyethylene are particularly interesting since their tensile strength can be greatly increased by cold drawing. For example, a tensile strength of 2,500 p.s.i. can be increased to 23,000 p.s.i. through orientation by cold-drawing. Tensile strengths of 34,000 p.s.i. can be reached by the use of higher molecular weight resins. Annealing the drawn monofilament serves to "set" the strength. A shrinkage of 7–9% at 66°C. occurs with one-stage annealing; two-stage annealing reduces the average shrinkage to 1.5–2% at 66°C., and to 3–4% at 74°C. Fabrics made from these monofilaments by weaving, knitting, or other usual procedures show excellent wear resistance (see Chapter 9.2).

Early I.C.I. patents (62,73) relate to the manufacture of threads, yarns, and fabric from polyethylene. These describe a process which comprises extruding or drawing a solid ethylene polymer in fluid form under such conditions that the material solidifies immediately upon attenuation. The material to be spun may be molten, or it may be in the form of a hot, concentrated solution in a volatile organic solvent, for example, benzene. The threads may be woven into fabrics or cut into staple fibers, twisted, and pulled into yarn or twist, and woven. When fully oriented, the threads show considerable elasticity. When stretched by 3%, they recover 75% of the stretch within two seconds. The tensile strength increases with the molecular weight of the initial material, as shown in Table C. In a modifi-

TABLE C

Dependence of Tensile Strength of Polyethylene Threads on Molecular Weight of
Polymer

Molecular weight	Tensile strength, kg./mm.^{2}
6,000	3.5
10,500	8.5
15,000	10.0
21,000	21.0

Source: Brit. 472,051, Sept. 16, 1937, Perrin, N. W., Paton, J. F., Williams, E. G., and Imperial Chemicals Industries, Ltd.

cation of this method described by Loasby in Can. 456,913 to I.C.I. (446), molten polyethylene is extruded through a spinneret at a temperature between 200 and 350°C., and a viscosity of from 200–2,000 poises. It is then passed into a chamber, the upper end of which is vertically offset from the spinneret about 1.5 inches and through which a current of cooling gas flows. The cooled filaments are cold-drawn by passing between feed rolls of successively greater speeds and around a snubbing pin between the rolls, and then collected on a winding roll.

A process for orienting staple fibers of polyethylene along the fiber axis by cold-stretching is described by Perrin, Paton, and Williams in U. S. 2,210,774 to I.C.I. (111).

British 568,890 to duPont (190) relates to a process according to which polyethylene is heated to a temperature less than 85°C. above the melting point, in the absence of oxygen, and extruded at a temperature of from 200–450°C. into a bath of cooling liquid, collected by pinch rolls running at a greater rate than the extrusion so as to cold-draw the material under tension, and finally collected on a bobbin.

The manufacture of elastic filaments is described by Richards in Brit. 575,296 (230) and in Can. 456,914 (447), both to I.C.I. A molten filament from polyethylene having a molecular weight of 15,000–30,000 is extruded continuously from a spinneret at a temperature of 150–320°C., solidifying within a small fraction of a second. Tension is applied to the length of molten and solidified filament at a linear rate at least three times the linear rate of molten filament formation. The ratio of the linear rates of windup and filament formation are controlled by the rate of feed of polyethylene and the rate of driving the windup roll.

A process for obtaining improved fibers of hydrolyzed ethylene-vinyl ester copolymers by wet-spinning into an aqueous solution of monosodium dihydrogen phosphate is described by Dietrich in U. S. 2,467,196 to duPont

(435).   The process comprises adding to the aqueous solution of the copolymer from 2–10% of a water-soluble compound, such as a lower aliphatic
alcohol, a thiol, an amine, or thioglycolic acid.   As an example, spinning
solutions containing from 2–10% ethanol have fewer gel particles and yield
fibers of higher tenacity than corresponding solutions without the ethanol.
The tenacity is also claimed to be improved by the addition of 0.005–0.050%
of a cationic surface-active agent to the coagulating bath.

A process to reduce the shrinkage of polyethylene fibers is described by
Ingersoll in U. S. 2,325,060 (153) and in Brit. 564,584 (169), both to duPont.
This is accomplished by heat-setting the previously oriented threads, while
preventing contraction at a temperature above the desired initial shrinkage
temperature, but below the melting point of the solid, until there is no
further reduction in tension.   The material is then shrunk in the relaxed
condition at a temperature at least as high as the desired shrinkage temperature, but below the temperature of the heat-setting treatment.   During
heat-setting, the filament may be extruded by drawing to slightly less than
the break elongation.   In an example, polyethylene of a molecular weight
of 20,000 and a melting point of 110°C. is wound on a bobbin and treated
in aqueous sodium chloride solution at 108°C. for 5 minutes (heat-setting).
The yarn is then skeined and allowed to relax for 5 minutes in water at
92°C. (shrinking).   The improvement in the shrinkage characteristics of
the yarn without substantial decrease in its tenacity is shown in Table CI.

TABLE CI

Improvement in Shrinkage Characteristics of Polyethylene Fiber

	Shrinkage at 90°C., %	Initial shrinkage (°C.)	Tenacity,[a] g./d.—o.d.	Elongation, %
Original yarn	38	40	3.2	10
After heat-setting	6	70	2.9	27
After shrinking	0	95	2.2	40

Source: Brit. 564,584, Oct. 4, 1944, p. 4, Ingersoll, H. G., and E. I. duPont de Nemours & Co.

[a] Grams per denier, based on original dimensions of yarn.

A different process for accomplishing the same purpose, which may be
applied to nylon, Vinyon, and Vinylite, as well as to polyethylene, is described in U. S. 2,441,209 to Rose [All-American Aviation (365)].   The
fibers are treated with a mixture containing shellac (80%), glycerol (10%),
and a pitch solution (10%; made up of about 33% pitch and 67% alcohol
solvent).   After immersion for 24 hours, the fibers are allowed to dry.

The dried fibers have absorbed and retain about 20% by weight of the treating composition.

8.8. Blow Molding

Equipment developed in Great Britain for the blow molding of polyethylene bottles has been described in a recent article (680).   As in conventional processes used for blowing glassware, the bottle is blown from a parison, i.e., a cylindrical tube closed at one end.   The parison is injection molded in polyethylene around a long tube, the nozzle of which is fitted with a valve.   While still hot and plastic, the parison with the tube still inside it is transferred to a mold corresponding to the shape of the finished bottle.   Air is blown into the parison through the tube and the polyethylene is forced out against the walls of the mold, where it is allowed to cool for a few seconds.   The mold is then opened and the finished bottle removed.   The whole cycle requires about 30 seconds, measured from the beginning of the injection molding cycle to the time the bottle is withdrawn.

The extrusion-blowing of polyethylene to obtain film as a lay-flat tube was described in Section 8.6.

8.9. Compression Molding

Several patents were issued to I.C.I. on a process for compression molding of polyethylene developed by Renfrew, Davison, and Dunbar (88,106, 124).   The process consists of heating the polymer to a temperature at least 10°C. above its melting point in a mold under pressure, cooling the mold, and increasing the pressure during cooling.   Since the coefficient of thermal expansion of polyethylene is relatively high, it necessitates consideration in the design of equipment, and development of molding techniques.   Compression molds of the flash type do not, in general, give satisfactory results, since they are unable to maintain pressure upon the material as it cools and shrinks after the land surfaces have been brought together.   Good results are obtained with molds of the positive type, in which the pressure upon the article is maintained or even increased during its cooling shrinkage.   Cooling in the mold, particularly if the article is of thin section, must be relatively slow in order to minimize strains which tend to develop by reason of the high coefficient of expansion.   To be molded properly, uncompounded polyethylene must be heated to at least 120°C., but the use of temperatures greater than about 160°C. will cause the molded article to adhere to the mold.   If necessary, this adherence can be prevented, or at least reduced, by coating the surface of the mold cavity with a lubricant.

8.10. Casting

Polyethylenes with lower molecular weights, i.e., lower softening points and lower melt viscosities, are used in hot melts and potting compounds. The casting process is carried out at atmospheric pressure.

Difficulties encountered during the molding of polyethylene shapes due to the fact that polyethylene forms relatively thin liquid melts, that considerable shrinkage takes place during solidification, and that decomposition under heat may cause the formation of bubbles within the shapes, may be overcome by a process described in German Patent Application No. B 199 by BASF (575). By this method, the polyethylene is molded *in vacuo* in the molten state without application of pressure. An appropriate procedure consists in placing powdery polyethylene in a mold, setting this under vacuum, e.g., by transfer to a vacuum cabinet, and heating the mold to temperatures above the melting point of polyethylene, e.g., to about 150°C. The melting may be effected in the mold for the desired shape, or the melt may be poured into this mold under vacuum.   Since shapes to be processed without pressure are much simpler in structure than those designed for pressure-molding, the shrinkage attendant upon cooling of the melt can easily be taken into account and compensated.

8.11. Foaming

Polyethylene can be produced in the form of a porous, spongy foam. A method of making this cellular product, described by Johnston in U. S. 2,256,483 to duPont (128), consists in incorporating a gas in the molten polyethylene and cooling the resulting froth to a resilient, porous solid. In the preferred procedure, the gas is allowed to expand in the molten polymer by reduction in pressure during the extrusion process. Varying the shape of the extrusion nozzle permits shaping the froth into any desired form prior to cooling.   The process is illustrated in Figure 202.

In Can. 521,294 to duPont (1146b), Hahn describes a process for the production of expanded polyethylene by adding to polyethylene sodium bicarbonate (0.5–1.75 parts by weight per 100 parts of polyethylene) and mineral oil (0.1–9 parts by weight per part of sodium bicarbonate), heating the mixture under pressure, and releasing the pressure at the elevated temperature.

A description of the preparation of "Bakelite" Cellular Polyethylene has been published in a paper by Higgins (969).   An intimate dispersion of a chemical blowing agent in polyethylene is prepared.   The blowing agent is a thermally sensitive chemical compound which liberates gas at a

specific temperature under controlled conditions. The cellular polyethylene can be handled in an extruder, where the flowing agent liberates
gas by the application of heat. Sufficient pressure is maintained in the
barrel, head, and die to prevent expansion of the liberated gas before it
emerges from the die. By proper adjustment, a product with a smooth
surface, a uniform bubble size, and a unicellular structure is obtained

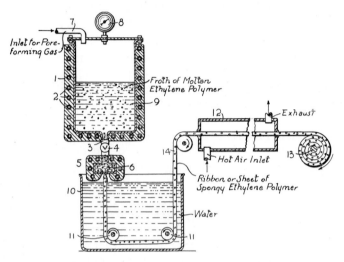

Fig. 202. Preparation of polyethylene foam. (1) Steel pressure chamber. (2)
Electrical resistance coils (external heating). (3) Short tube. (4) Valve. (5) Extrusion box (heated). (6) Slit opening. (7) Inlet for gas. (8) Pressure gauge. (9)
Froth of molten polymer. (10) Tank with cold water. (11) Rollers. (12) Drying
oven. (13) Windup. (U. S. 2,256,483, Sept. 23, 1941, Johnston, F. L. (E. I. duPont
de Nemours & Co.).)

Reed (1017) pointed out that different batches of polyethylene may require different heating times on expansion with blowing agents, because of
slight changes in mobility due to molecular variations in the range 10,000–
50,000.

The excellent insulating properties of polyethylene which make it useful
as a sheathing material for cables and telephone wires are little impaired on
100% expansion of the polymer. The best method claimed to manufacture such cable, which is much lighter in weight, is by coaxial extrusion of
core and expanded sheath.

8.12. Emulsification

The preparation of polyethylene emulsions by emulsion polymerization of ethylene was described in Section 3.4.

Several methods have also been developed for preparing stable aqueous emulsions of polyethylene useful for impregnating textiles, by emulsifying the polymer subsequent to its preparation.   According to Gomm in U. S. 2,313,144 to I.C.I. (149), hot water is added to a hot solution of the polymer in an organic solvent immiscible with water and containing a dispersing agent, and the organic solvent is then volatilized.   According to Alvarado and Dorough in U. S. 2,290,794 to duPont (141), the incorporation of a dispersing agent, a protective colloid, and water is sufficient for these purposes.

Scheermesser and Spindler, in Fr. 1,050,223 (894) and in Ger. 910,964 (901), describe the preparation of an aqueous dispersion of polyethylene by agitating the polymer in water in the presence of an emulsifying agent, which can subsequently be removed from the dispersion by distillation. A water-dispersible polyethylene is described by the same inventors in Fr. 1,055,561 (896).   In this process, polyethylene is dissolved in an organic solvent at elevated temperatures.   The gel obtained on cooling this solution can be separated and subsequently dispersed in water.   A modification of this method is described in Fr. 1,059,221 (897), while the use of these emulsions as coatings or paint bases is the subject of Fr. 1,063,919 (900).

Partially oxidized, low molecular weight (2,000) polyethylenes are claimed by the Semet-Solvay Petrochemical Division, Allied Chemical and Dye Corp., to possess good emulsification properties and to give films on glass which have excellent transparency (883).   As described in the trade bulletin cited, the low molecular weight polyethylene, alone or mixed with carnauba or similar waxes, is melted; oleic acid, stearic acid, or coconut oil soaps, followed by morpholine or ethanolamines, are added. The resultant hot mixture is added to hot water with agitation and allowed to cool.

Another low molecular weight (2,000–6,000) polyethylene, emulsifiable, it is claimed, because of the presence of free acid groups in the polymer molecule, has been recently brought on the market by Eastman Chemical Products, Inc.   Properties, emulsification procedures, and applications are described in the trade bulletin of the manufacturer (952).

8.13. Coating Processes

Cloth or paper surfaces may be given the desirable properties of poly-

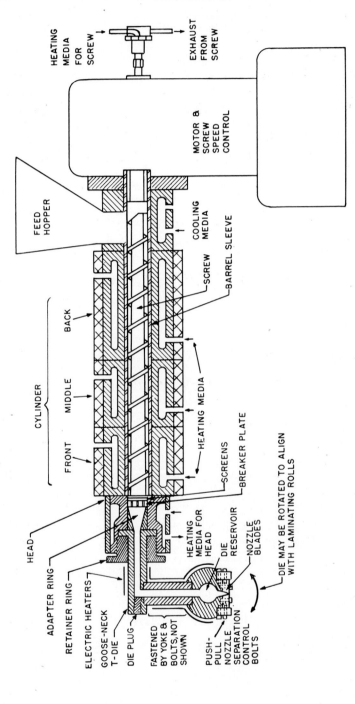

Fig. 203. Extrusion of polyethylene flat film for lamination to paper. (*Bakelite Polyethylene for Paper Coatings*, Bakelite Co., p. 19, 1951)

ethylene, such as chemical resistance, insolubility, and low moisture-vapor transmission, by application of one of the following procedures:

(a) For solution coating, low molecular weight polyethylene resins are dissolved in hot aromatic hydrocarbons and applied in conventional coating equipment. However, the temperature of the entire system must be kept above 90°C. to prevent premature gelling of the solution of the resin.

(b) For hot-melt coating, higher or lower molecular weight polyethylenes, or mixtures of the latter with paraffin waxes, are melted and applied by conventional roller or knife coaters. Oxidation of the polyethylene is

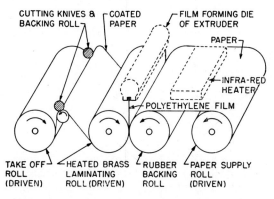

Fig. 204. Extrusion-lamination of polyethylene film to paper. (*Bakelite Polyethylene for Paper Coatings*, Bakelite Co., p. 22, 1951.)

minimized by avoiding exposure to the air and by the addition of antioxidants.

(c) By the relatively new extrusion-lamination method, one of the more widely used techniques for coating paper, a higher molecular weight grade of polyethylene is extruded through a linear die and the resultant film immediately laminated to paper by the use of chilled rolls. Detailed information on this method is contained in the technical bulletin of one commercial producer of the resin (568). Figures 203 and 204 are reproduced from this source. The former is a schematic diagram of a plastic extruder designed to produce continuous quantities of given cross-sectional designs. Besides thin films, wire insulation and jackets, garden hoses, tubing, and monofilaments are made in this equipment. The immediate application of the polyethylene film leaving the die of the extruder to the paper is shown in Figure 204.

Railing claims in U. S. 2,663,652 [duPont (806a)] that tough, continuous, adherent polyethylene films can be produced on metallic and other surfaces by mixing a finely divided, high boiling (150–300°C.) but volatile material which is a solvent for polyethylene at temperatures above 120°C. (e.g., naphthalene, diphenyl, dibenzyl, acenaphthene, paradichlorobenzene, dichloronaphthalenes) with powdered polyethylene, and applying this mixture in the form of a powder to the surface to be coated; subsequent baking removes substantially all the solvent. Application of polyethylene powder to a preheated metal surface by mechanical means only is described by Heisler, Heisler, and Starr in U. S. 2,737,461 (1148b).

Sheets or films of regenerated cellulose may be coated with polyethylene by a process described by Morf in U. S. 2,726,171 [duPont (1104)] by first contacting the film with a solution of an acetate of Al, Fe, Cu, Ni, Cr, or Co.

8.14. Flame-Spraying

Flame-spraying processes make use of finely and uniformly ground, polyethylene powder, medium-to-high molecular weight, containing an antioxidant and sprayed through a flame to form a continuous coating on a target. An oxyacetylene or propane gun system is generally used. Modifications are chiefly to prevent decomposition in the flame, improve adhesion, and increase toughness and impact resistance. The powdered material passes through the flame in milliseconds, too fast for actual melting to take place before contact with the object being sprayed. The repeated passing of the flame over the powder on the surface, and the heat of the object sprayed, combine to melt the powder into a continuous, nonporous coating. The surface to be coated is generally prepared by blast-cleaning.

The earliest patent relating to the flame-spraying of polyethylene is Brit. 551,339 to Glint, Taylor, and I.C.I. (148). Metal, cloth, wood, paper, brick, and cement surfaces can be given a continuous, adherent, protective coating by this process. Powdered polyethylene suitable for use in the process may be prepared, according to U. S. 2,451,743 to Jarrett [I.C.I. (375)], by treating the softer grades of polyethylene with a lower aliphatic alcohol, disintegrating the embrittled polyethylene mechanically in a closed space, and drying the resultant powder. A flame-spray gun to be used with polyethylene has been described by Powers and Bludeau in U. S. 2,643,955 [Union Carbide (798a)].

Other patents dealing with the flame-spraying of polyethylene are Swiss 269,269 to Schaerer (517) and Brit. 573,264 to Williams and I.C.I. (207). According to the latter patent, coatings are produced by flame-spraying a blend of polyethylene and polyisobutylene (10–40%). The addition of diethylene glycol stearate as a fluxing aid to polyethylene is claimed by Deniston in U. S. 2,676,932 to the Commonwealth Engineering Co. of Ohio (899).   Better adhesion of the polyethylene coating to the metal surface may be achieved according to Powers in U. S. 2,718,473 [Union Carbide (1094)] by the addition of 0.5–2% of titanium dioxide (anatase) to the powdered stream of polyethylene.

A number of articles have appeared in the literature relating to flame spraying, particularly with polyethylene.   DeLong and Peterson (388)

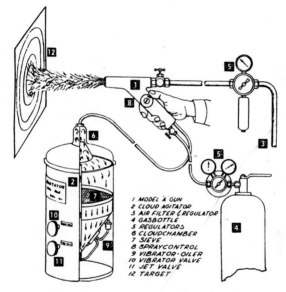

Fig. 205. Flame-spraying gun and associated equipment.   Uniform flow of air-powder mixture to the gun is provided by the special feeder shown at lower left.   (*Modern Plastics*, **27** [10], 85 (1950).)

have described a torch specially developed for applying adherent, corrosion-resistant polyethylene coatings on steel.   Blake (461) has discussed some aspects of flame-spraying by the powder process.   A special apparatus is described in which air at 60 p.s.i. is used at the rate of about 10 cubic feet per minute.   Fuel gas consumption is 20 cubic feet per hour of propane, or 40 cubic feet per hour of acetylene.   The rate of powder application is dependent upon the material employed, but only about two-thirds of the through-put is deposited.

Design and operating techniques for a polyethylene flame-spray assembly are described by Neumann (483,1005). A flame-spraying gun and associated equipment are shown in Figure 205. Tests have established that flame-sprayed polyethylene has essentially the same physical characteristics and resistance to chemical attack as molded or extruded material. Typical data are listed in Tables CII and CIII. Proper pretreatment of the surfaces

TABLE CII

Physical Characteristics of Flame-Sprayed Polyethylene

Sp. gravity		0.92–0.94
Refractive index	n_D^{25}	1.52
Tensile strength	p.s.i.	2,300–3,100
Elongation	%	200–600
Flexural strength	p.s.i.	1,500–1,700
Impact strength	ft.-lb./in. notch	3
Specific heat	cal./°C./g.	0.55
Thermal expansion	10^{-5}/°C.	64
Thermal conductivity	cal./sec./cm./°C./cm.	7×10^{-4}
Resistance to heat (continuous)	°C.	80
Flammability	in./min.	1.1–1.4
Softening point	°C.	100–115
Hardness	Rockwell	R.25-R.35
Effect of light		Unaffected
Water absorption	24-hr. immersion	Nil
Moisture vapor permeability	mg./sq. in./day	1
Dielectric strength	v./mil, short time on films 3–15 mils thick	1,000–1,500
Dielectric constant	from 1–100Mc/s	2.3
Power factor	from 1–100 Mc/s	0.0005
Volume resistivity	ohms/cm.^{3}	3×10^{17}

Source: *Modern Plastics*, **27** (10), 85 (1950).

to be sprayed is essential for successful operation. A 60-mil thick flame-sprayed coat of polyethylene is claimed to have excellent adhesiveness to sand-blasted steel. The thickness of coatings can be determined by a magnetic thickness tester, and the porosity measured with a high-frequency tester. Flame-spraying stable emulsions does not give good coatings.

Stoeckhert (486a) has further discussed the factors involved in flame-spraying thermoplastics, especially polyethylene. Special techniques for flame-spraying polyethylene have been outlined by Gemmer (538). Thus, excessively high flame temperatures are avoided by using air instead of oxygen. The formation of pores is largely prevented by the addition of materials, such as polyisobutylene, which are amorphous even at room

TABLE CIII

Resistance of Flame-Sprayed Polyethylene to Chemical Attack

	At room Temperature	At 60°C. (140°F.)		At room Temperature	At 60°C. (140°F.)
Acetic acid, 10%	*	*	Hydrogen peroxide, 30%	*	0
Acetic acid, 100%	0	—	Hydrogen peroxide, 90%	*	—
Acetone	0	—	Iodine	—	—
Ammonia	*	*	Lactic acid, 10%	*	*
Ammonium carbonate	*	*	Lactic acid, 90%	*	*
Aniline	*	—	Methyl bromide	*	
Beer	*		Milk	*	
Benzene	—	—	Mineral oil	0	—
Bromine (vapors or liquid)	—	—	Nitric acid, 10%	*	*
Calcium hydroxide	*	*	Nitric acid, 30 to 50%	*	*
Carbonic acid	*	*	Nitric acid, 70%	*	*
Carbon tetrachloride	—	—	Nitric acid, 95%	0	—
Caustic potash up to 50%	*	*	Petrol	—	—
Caustic potash, 50% and over	*	*	Phosphoric acid, 30%	*	*
Caustic soda, up to 50%	*	*	Phosphoric acid, 90%	*	—
Caustic soda, 50% and over	*	*	Photographic developer	*	*
Chlorine	—	—	Potassium chloride (saturated)	*	*
Chromic acid	*	*	Potassium dichromate, 40%	*	*
Cider	*		Silver nitrate, 10%	*	*
Citric acid (cold saturated)	*	*	Sodium carbonate, diluted	*	*
Copper sulfate	*	*	Sodium carbonate (saturated)	*	*
Cyclohexanone	—	—	Sodium chloride (saturated)	*	*
Dibutyl phthalate	*		Sodium sulfate	*	*
Di-ethylene glycol	*	0	Sulfuric acid, 10%	*	*
Distilled water	*	*	Sulfuric acid, 70%	*	0
Ethylene dichloride	—	—	Sulfuric acid, 98%	0	—
Gin	—		Sulfurous acid	*	*
Glycerol, 50%	*	*	Tallow	*	*
Formaldehyde	*		Tannic acid	*	*
Formic acid, 100%	*	*	Tanning extracts	*	*
Formic acid, up to 50%	*	*	Trichloroethylene	—	—
Hydrobromic acid, 50%	*	*	Vegetable and animal oils	—	—
Hydrochloric acid, 10%	*	*	Vinegar	*	*
Hydrochloric acid, more than 35%	*	*	Whiskey	—	
Hydrofluoric acid, 40%	*	*	Wine	—	
Hydrofluoric acid, 75%	*	*	Xylene	—	—
Hydrofluosilicic acid	*	*	Yeast	*	
			Zinc chloride	*	*
			Zinc sulfate	*	*

Source: *Modern Plastics*, **27** (10), 88 (1950).
Legend: *satisfactory; 0 slightly attacked;—unsatisfactory; blank spaces indicate that data not yet available.

temperatures. Close temperature control must be maintained at all times to avoid overheating, and the advisability of preparing the surface by sandblasting prior to coating is emphasized. Goldberg (539) reviewed the history of flame-spraying and described in some detail both guns and powder containers used for applying flame-sprayed coatings.

Work recently completed on the first phase of a research project for the United States Atomic Energy Commission has resulted in the development of a satisfactory system for applying flame-sprayed polyethylene linings or coatings to porous as well as to nonporous surfaces. The immediate problem, according to a report by Wiese (890), was lining the concrete wall of a decontamination cell which could be washed with nitric acid, if necessary. The research also involved the development of techniques for application of flame-sprayed polyethylene to other materials of a porous and nonporous nature. For porous surfaces, the system includes application of a resin sizing, a coating of a resin cement, an intermediate layer of a mixture of silicon dioxide and polyethylene, and an outer layer of flame-sprayed pure polyethylene. For nonporous surfaces, the sizing operation was omitted. Compare also U. S. 2,716,075 to Wiese [United States Atomic Energy Commission (1088)].

The flame-spraying of steel, metals, and plastics is treated in the recent book by Fritz (956).

8.15. Whirl-Sintering

Closely related to the process of flame-spraying is that of whirl- or cyclone-sintering, a recent German invention (Wirbelsintern). Both methods serve to apply a protective, abrasion resistant and insulating coating of plastics to metals and other bases. A description and comparison of both methods is given by Gemmer (957,958).

Whirl-sintering consists essentially of dipping sanded and preheated objects into a fluidized bed of the finely divided plastic material. This fluidized bed is obtained by forcing a gas under pressure through the porous bottom of the container holding the polyethylene powder. Heated objects dipped into this "powder bath" become evenly covered with fused polyethylene. The desired thickness of the plastic coat can be obtained by properly adjusting such variables as temperature of the object to be coated, and duration of immersion.

The use of blends of the finely ground polyethylene with powdered metals is claimed (926d) to offer additional advantages in this process.

Equipment to carry out whirl-sintering has been developed, and objects of any desired shape, including pieces as long as 9 ft., can be treated.   Annealing of the coated objects is required to prevent the formation of pores and cracks caused by crystallization of the polyethylene when the cooling is carried out too fast.

Flame-spraying, as well as whirl-sintering, is particularly applicable to the high-density (Ziegler) polyethylenes, both in view of their properties and the fact that they are obtained directly as fine powders (see Section 6.19).

8.16. Uniting Molded Articles

The coalescence behavior of polyethylene and other polymers was studied and compared by Meissner and Merrill (405).   In general, high polymers known to exhibit first- and second-order transition temperatures also exhibit a critical temperature below which coalescence rates between flat

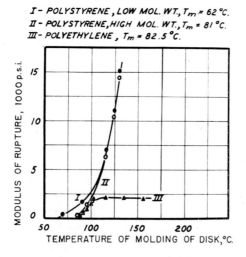

Fig. 206. Effect of molding temperature on disk strength.   (Disks molded under 140 p.s.i. pressure for $1/2$ hr.)   (*Modern Plastics*, **26** [8], 106 (1949).)

smooth surfaces of the polymers become vanishingly small even under high pressures.   The development of more effective coalescence above the transition temperature is attributed to the enhanced mobility of the molecular segments.   In other tests, the granulated resins were charged into a cylindrical steel mold and pressure was applied when the desired temperature was reached.   The rupture strength of these disks (molded at 140 p.s.i.

for one-half hour) was determined at room temperature. As indicated in Figure 206, the effect of molding temperature on disk strength was different for polyethylene, for polystyrene, and for other plastic materials. This unusual behavior is shown by the fact that polyethylene disk strength above 80°C. was independent of molding pressure between 140 and 10,000 p.s.i. No disks could be formed, regardless of pressure, in the interval from −68 to +80°C., evidently due to softness of the material. At −68°C., polyethylene undergoes another second-order transition. Below this temperature, disks could be made, but only under high molding pressures, presumably due to the hardness of the granules. These disks, however, exfoliated into powder when allowed to warm to room temperature, because of the development of internal stresses.

Joining

According to a process described by Romeyn and Ferrell in U.S. 2,-520,737 to U. S. Rubber (516), thick sheets of polyethylene can be obtained by lapping the sheets and heating the materials at the interface to a temperature of not less than 5°C. below, nor more than 15°C. above, the melting point of the polyethylene, while subjecting the joint to mechanical pressure. Spacers may be placed between the press platens to control the amount of flow and the thickness of the material at the joint.

Polyethylene can be machined and molded much like metal. It has been common practice, therefore, to use threaded fittings and molded flanges for joints in polyethylene pipe. Because of its plastic properties, this pipe has also been joined to metallic materials by banding. When these methods are impractical or inconvenient, excellent connections may be made with lap-joint flanges. Pledger and Ryan (875) discuss a simple and effective method for forming integral lap-joint flanges on polyethylene pipe. These are especially useful when joining polyethylene to tanks with flanged connections, or to thin-walled stainless steel pipe which cannot be threaded. To be used with lap-joint flanges, polyethylene pipe must have an integral flange. Although polyethylene can be worked easily after immersion in boiling water, such flanges are difficult to form with conventional tools. A flaring tool, similar to that used for flaring copper tubing, has been developed which can form flanges on polyethylene pipe easily, quickly, and at low cost. In operation, the plug with a threaded stud is inserted in the tube and clamped. The end of the pipe is then submerged in boiling water to soften it. Next, the lap-joint flange is slipped over the pipe and the flarer is placed on the stud and screwed into the pipe. Finally, the as-

sembly is quenched in cold water and the tool removed.   Where exception-
ally good joints are required, lap-joint flanges are best suited, since they
combine mechanical strength with resistance to leakage.

Fig. 207. Impulse-type heat sealer.   Nichrome element on lower jaw of this impulse-
type heat sealer for polyethylene film prevents sticking by rapidly dissipating the burst
of heat during 1-sec. pressure cycle.   The dial provides a current setting for various
gauges of film.   Lower photograph is a side view of the control box, showing cam and
microswitch which control the timing of high-amperage impulse; rheostat controls
the input voltage of the transformer. (Photos courtesy Wrap-ade Machine Co.)
(*Modern Packaging*, 133, Dec., 1949.)

Welding

Articles made of polyethylene with a molecular weight above 6,000 may be united autogeneously according to Brit. 567,360 to duPont (185) by bringing them into contact with each other and applying a flame to the contiguous surfaces. This hot-gas welding technique is particularly useful in the fabrication of very large or complicated articles. According to Freeth (216), polyethylene can be flame-welded by directing a hot (300°C.) blast of nitrogen onto the joint and using a filler rod of polyethylene. In

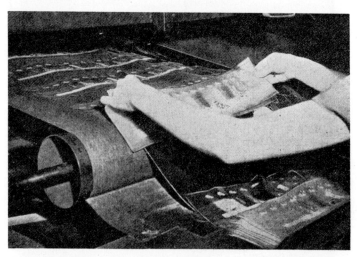

Fig. 208. Flame-sealing of bags. Bags travel through flame-sealing machine at rate of 27 ft. per minute and are here shown being removed, ready to be packed for shipment. (*Modern Packaging*, 135, Dec. 1949.)

this way, large containers, pipes three or four feet in diameter, T-pieces, and flanged pipes, can readily be constructed.

Foils of polyethylene may be welded, according to Ger. 811,506 to Meixner and Loch [Norvin Kunststoff-G.m.b.H. (580)], by using gas flames and metallic or glass bodies as direct heat carriers. This procedure is especially adapted to the manufacture of polyethylene bags and similar closed film packages. Attention is also drawn to several articles dealing with the manufacture of polyethylene bags and special problems arising therefrom (689,730) and to a paper by Kerhoas (747) relating to the use of infrared heating elements for welding polyethylene in such applications.

The sealing of polyethylene films in a high-frequency electric field is described by Zoubek in U. S. 2,667,437 to Swift and Co. (895a); the use of temperature-controlled platens is proposed by Bedford in U. S. 2,679,469 to Ciba (902).

New methods of heat-sealing, flame-sealing, welding, and induction-bonding polyethylene have been discussed by Ryan (419).   In each instance, the method to be used is determined by the particular application and production requirements.   An impulse-type heat sealer is shown in Figure 207.   Flame-sealing the ends of sections of polyethylene tubing to

Fig. 209. Gas-welding of polyethylene.   Hot-jet torch, used in gas welding of thicker sections of polyethylene. Process is similar to metal welding, except that the filler rod is polyethylene containing up to 12% polyisobutylene.   Nitrogen gas is fed through the electrically heated torch at a pressure of 30 p.s.i.   (*Modern Packaging*, **22** [12], 136, 1949.)

form bags is illustrated in Figure 208.   Gas-welding thicker sections of polyethylene with a hot-jet torch is shown in Figure 209.   Figure 210 pictures induction-bonding of polyethylene bottles.

The subject of polyethylene welding is treated in some detail in the recent manual by Heim and Neumann (853).   Quality control for welded polyethylene is outlined by Neumann and Bockhoff (827) who sponsor a complete examination of a weld by a combination of three tests specific for each application: a spark test for porosity; a radioactive negative; and a test for detrimental environmental effects.   A bag-making machine which welds together by a hot knife two layers of polyethylene at the sides has been introduced by the G. T. Schjeldahl Co. (1124b).

Fig. 210. Induction bonding of polyethylene bottles. Induction bonding of base to body of injection-molded polyethylene bottle is accomplished by inserting a ring of small-gauge metal wire around base. *Above*, base and ring are pressed in place. Weld is accomplished (*below*) by bringing bottle assembly under work coil of induction heater. Ring in base becomes heated by induced eddy currents; under slight pressure, molten plastic adjacent to ring intermixes. (*Modern Packaging*, 137, Dec., 1949.)

The articles by Haim (964), Neumann (1005), and Bosworth (934a) summarize the present status of the welding of plastic materials.

Adhesives

The chemical inertness of polyethylene makes the application of conventional adhesives difficult. Robert DeCoudres and Myers, in U. S. 2,622,056 to Union Carbide (676), describe special adhesive compositions for bonding polyethylene. These are prepared by compounding halogenated aromatic hydrocarbons with the polyethylene resin itself at elevated temperatures. Preferred chlorinated aromatic hydrocarbons include chlorinated biphenyls with a halogen content of 60–65% by weight, chlorinated naphthalene with a halogen content of 30–65%, and chlorinated benzene with a halogen content of 60–70%. Suitable polyethylene resins are those having molecular weights within the range of 15,000–20,000. The adhesives are prepared by milling at 100–105°C., or by open-kettle brushing, dipping, or troweling, or by surface distribution of the granulated polymer at room temperature followed by heating.   For example, polyethylene resin (1 part) and chlorinated biphenyl (60% chlorine content, 3 parts), were mixed for 2 hours at 180°C.   After cooling and grinding, the adhesive was heated to 190°C. and spread on metal plates heated to 190°C. To each plate a polyethylene sheet was applied and pressed.   Plates of steel, lead, stainless steel, aluminum, brass, copper, galvanized steel, chromium, and cast iron gave satisfactory bonds.

Another adhesive composition for polyethylene, described by Davis, Durette, and Johnson in U. S. 2,656,297 to B. B. Chemical Co. (803), consists of polyethylene and a synthetic rubber copolymer of isobutylene and a small proportion of a diene. A composition claimed by Heller in Can. 518,479 to duPont (1101) consists of an organic solvent, a rubber dispersed therein, and a tackifier. Another polyethylene glue consisting of 40% beeswax and 60% rosin is proposed in Fr. 1,107,800 to Spécialités Alimentaires Bourguignonnes (1144).

The adhesion of polyethylene to aluminum foil, cellophane, Mylar, and steel can be improved by precoating these materials with titanium organics such as tetrabutyl titanate, or tetraisopropyl titanate, which deposit a film of TiO_2 on hydrolysis. These adhesion promoters and their applications were recently developed by duPont (923a).

A flexible adhesive for polyethylene, Polygriptex, which can be applied by conventional labeling machines and by brushing and spraying, has recently been brought on the market by Adhesive Products Corp.   A peelable adhesive for polyethylene (No. 991 Rubbatex) is being advertised by Rubba Inc.

Oxidation of Surface

Similar to treatments used in improving the printing properties of polyethylene (see Section 8.19), methods to modify the polyethylene surface by oxidation to increase adhesion have been developed. Brown and Angel, in Brit. 713,634 [Venesta, Ltd. (906a)], heat polyethylene in the presence of oxygen to render it adherent to metal foil. The heat-treated polyethylene may be extruded as a film and oriented before or during application to the metal foil.

A method for bonding polyethylene to copper is described by Foord in U. S. 2,551,591 to International Electric Corp. (576). It is claimed that polyethylene adheres strongly to copper without void formation if, prior to pressing or extrusion of the plastic on the metal, the latter is oxidized to the pink stage. For example, copper foil is oxidized and then rolled and heated with polyethylene foil to result in a laminated structure free from voids and not easily stripped.

The formation of a thin coating of polyethylene on the metal surface, oxidizing the thin coating by baking it above its melting point, and bonding the main body of the polyethylene by heat to the thin coating of oxidized polyethylene is described in Austral. 7295/55 to I.C.I. (1062).

Treatment of a polyethylene surface with ultraviolet light to improve the bonding properties is claimed in Austral. 6949/55 to British Cellophane (1061).

· A method of joining a metal to polyethylene is described by Lasak in U. S. 2,697,058 to General Electric (916). A layer of polyethylene is flame-sprayed onto the surface of the heated metal, the polyethylene member is pressed against the coated, hot-metal surface, and the joined members allowed to cool.

Bonding to Rubber

A water-resistant, permanent bond between polyethylene and vulcanized rubber is claimed by Peters in U. S. 2,635,975 to Bell Telephone Laboratories (792) to result from inserting one or more intermediate layers consisting of polyethylene and of rubber, and up to 50% (based on the combined weights) of an acid carbon black having a mean particle diameter of 5 mμ. The rubber may be natural rubber, neoprene, or other vulcanizable synthetic rubber or elastomer. The rubber (preferably neoprene) may be vulcanized with an intermediate layer containing polyethylene (60 parts), neoprene (40 parts), and carbon black (10 parts), and heat-sealed to the polyethylene.   Where it is desired not to use carbon black, three or four layers differing from each other by less than 15 parts polyethylene, based on the total weight, are required.   Carbon black, when used, is thoroughly milled with polyethylene and the mixture is blended with rubber.   Bonding of polyethylene to a metal such as brass or copper can be accomplished by using any one of the foregoing systems, and by vulcanizing the rubber layer to the metal.

Butyl rubber may be bonded to polyethylene according to Olson in U. S. 2,711,985 [U. S. Rubber (1076)] by incorporating polyethylene in the surface of the rubber article while still in the uncured state, curing the rubber article while holding it in contact with the polyethylene article, and applying heat and pressure to the assembly.

A process for bonding a polyethylene film to a fibrous web is described in U. S. 2,714,571 by Irion and Prindle [Dobeckmun Co. (1082)].   Here, a film of molten polyethylene is extruded on a fibrous web and pressed into it by passing it through rolls, followed by reheating and cooling.

8.17. Surface Treatment

Surface curing of molded or extruded polyethylene articles, especially coatings on wire, can be carried out by a method described in Brit. 619,905 to duPont (431).   It is proposed to dissolve an organic compound capable of generating free radicals on heating (e.g., peroxides, peracids, hydrazine derivatives), immerse the polyethylene article in this solution at elevated temperature, and cure the treated article in a mold or press by the application of heat, preferably under pressure.   As an example, polyethylene films can be made substantially insoluble and less thermoplastic by immersing for 1–15 minutes in a 13% solution of benzoyl peroxide at 60°C., removing the film from the bath, and heating for a few minutes at 120–145°C. in a press or oven.

Polyethylene is mentioned in Brit. 581,751 to duPont (270) among other plastic materials which may be coated with polysilicic acid ester solutions, with or without a modifying polymer, to improve surface characteristics, such as scratch resistance, and to decrease tackiness and dust-collecting tendencies.   A preferred composition consists of partially hydrolyzed tetraethyl silicate and partially hydrolyzed polyvinyl acetate or polyvinyl butyral.   The former has high scratch and weather resistance, while the latter exhibits improved adhesion and flexibility and less tendency to craze.

Certain alkylaryl polyglycol ethers applied as aqueous solutions to the surface of polyethylene films, filaments, fibers, and coatings, are claimed by Banigan in U. S. 2,519,013 to duPont (512) to act both as an antistatic and as a slip-promoting agent, without detracting from the flexibility, strength, moisture-proofness, chemical resistance, and heat-sealability of the polymer (compare also Section 8.7).

A process for the preparation and application of a polyethylene dispersion to a polyethylene surface so that it will withstand the adhesive tape test has been described by Jenett in U. S. 2,628,172, assigned to Emhart Manufacturing Co. (781). The polyethylene dispersion is formed at an elevated temperature as a clear solution by adding 10–30% by weight of an initially solid polyethylene to an organic liquid medium containing 30–90% of xylene and 70–10% of petroleum naphtha. The solution is simultaneously agitated and cooled at a rate not greater than 3°C. per minute to form a stable finely divided polyethylene dispersion, flowable at room temperature. The polyethylene surface to which the polyethylene dispersion has been applied is heated to volatilize the solvent.

8.18. Irradiation

The improvements brought about by the irradiation of polyethylene, and the commercial products obtained by these processes, have been discussed in Sections 4.7, 6.3, and 6.16. An additional application is described in the following Section 8.18. The present status of this field has been summarized by Bockhoff and Neumann of American Agile (933) and by Goodwin of General Electric (959).

Meikle and Graham [Sequoia Process (1135c; cf. 1121b)] recently described "Hyrad," an irradiated "special formulation" of polyethylene indefinitely stable at 150°C. (cf. Section 6.19).

8.19. Printing

Inks

The chemical inertness of polyethylene, which is of great advantage in many applications, is also the cause of difficulty in applying inks and adhesives to polyethylene film. For this reason, a number of ink formulations have been proposed for such use. An ink designed for printing on polyethylene is prepared according to Loukomsky in U. S. 2,628,208 (785) by melting polyethylene (molecular weight, 10,000), aromatic hydrocarbons (boiling range, 140–200°C.), xylene, methyl isopropyl ketone, cyclohexanone, polyvinyl acetate–chloride copolymer, and phthalocyanine blue.

Printing is carried out on the polyethylene surface at room temperature, followed by a two-second exposure to a temperature of 77°C. The ketone is thereby volatilized, and a phase reversal of the ink dispersion takes place. In addition, the less volatile hydrocarbon is volatilized, and the polyethylene present in the ink is melted and bonded to the surface. This ink is not removable by the stripping test.

An ink developed for use in rotogravure, screen printing, hand painting, or as a surface lacquer for polyethylene is reported by Lane (475) to consist of polyethylene, polyisobutylene, Vulcafar Red 2RS, tetrahydronaphthalene, and trichloroethylene. Tetrahydronaphthalene alone gave slightly better adhesion, but addition of trichloroethylene gave faster drying. U. S. 2,612,480 to May [Sun Chemical (666)] proposes an ink obtained by milling polyethylene, paraffin wax, natural or synthetic rubber, and pigment, and dispersing the mixture in an aromatic hydrocarbon solvent, preferably xylene. The ink film fuses to the polyethylene-base film by heating at 82–104°C. Water may be incorporated into the ink to give an emulsion-type ink of increased viscosity.

Writing, rotogravure, intaglio, printing, or lithographic inks for printing on plastics such as polyethylene are described in U. S. 2,618,574 to Pavlic [duPont (671)]. These are prepared from chlorinated or chlorosulfonated polymers of ethylene, preferably in toluene as the solvent.

An ink containing infrared absorbing, heat generating material is used by Hoover according to U. S. 2,715,363 [A. B. Dick Co. (1087)] for printing on polyethylene. Radiations having a high intensity of infrared are claimed to build up a heat pattern in the inked areas which softens the underlying portion of the polyethylene and achieves anchorage of the ink image.

An overprint varnish designed to protect printed surfaces of polyethylene film has been recently developed (819). The coating is stated to have excellent abrasion resistance, good flexibility, and to be nonblocking. It may be applied with regular aniline coating equipment. A similar process is claimed in Austral. 7788/55 to British Cellophane (1066). The use of solutions of hydroxyl groups containing polyesters and polyisocyanates for the printing or lacquering of polyethylene is described by Gerlich in Ger. 931,216 [BASF (1083)].

Liberty (862) points out that the largest obstacle to better printing on polyethylene is the lack of a method to dry the ink completely, thus eliminating offset and increasing printing speeds. The best drying results were obtained by combining blown hot air with either the open gas flame or reflected heat (see Figure 211). An extreme improvement in the degree of drying was observed in all experiments where crust formation was retarded with bottom heating. Another printing problem is the need for high heats to form an instantaneous deep crust of ink on polyethylene film. It is now

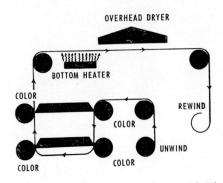

Fig. 211. Suggested set-up for printing on polyethylene film. (*Modern Plastics*, **32** [2], 137, 1954.)

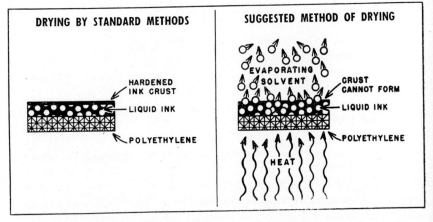

Fig. 212. Comparison of ink drying processes on polyethylene. Application of heat to bottom of film prevents crust formation at top of ink, facilitates solvent evaporation. (*Modern Plastics*, **32** [2], 137 (1954).)

believed that instantaneous deep crusting could be achieved by passing the film over large chill drums and simultaneously applying the maximum possible heat. A comparison of the drying process by standard methods and by the proposed method is illustrated in Figure 212.

Modification of Surface

A different approach to the problem of printing on polyethylene led to attempts to change the printing qualities of the polyethylene surface itself. Chlorination in the vapor phase under the influence of light could be developed to a commercial process.   Oxidation of the surface with chromic acid and other oxidizing solutions (e.g., a permanganate) resulted in appreciable improvement, according to Horton in U. S. 2,668,134 and U. S. Re. 24,062 [Plax (895b,1093)], and Austral. 7789/55 [Cellophane Ltd.

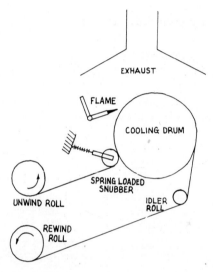

Fig. 213. Schematic drawing of typical installation for treating film and lay-flat tubing by the Kreidl Process. (*Plastics Technology,* 1 [1], 33, 1955.)

(1067)].   Treatment of the polyethylene surface with ozone and a gaseous accelerator (halogen–hydrogen halide) is claimed by Wolinski in U. S. 2,715,075 (1084); with ozone and nitrous oxide, in U. S. 2,715,076 (1085) with nitrous oxide, in U. S. 2,715,077 (1086).   All three patents, assigned to duPont, specify treatment temperatures in the range of 150–325°C.

Physical rather than chemical means to render polyethylene printable were applied by Kreidl.   The process is described in U. S. 2,632,921 (788a), Ger. 844,348 (662a), and by Kreidl and Hartmann (988).   As shown in Figure 213, the process is characterized by exposure of the surface of the polyethylene article to a high temperature, while the bulk of the material is kept at a low temperature. The change occurring in the surface is gradual, depending mainly on time and temperature. Accordingly, treatment can be effected either by short exposure to high temperatures, or longer exposure to moderate temperatures. Hot combustion gases, hot air, exposure to an open flame or to an electric heating element, can be used to accomplish the desired effect, which is claimed to be permanent. Some or all of the following three factors may be responsible for the increased affinity of the polyethylene surface for ink: oxidation, decrease in surface orientation, and change in distribution and perhaps total percentage of crystallinity. However, the recently marketed highly crystalline, high-density polyethylenes are claimed to possess better printability than the less crystalline, conventional high-pressure, polymerized products, when no after-treatment is given.

Another method to render the surface of polyethylene compatible with printing inks was developed by the Traver Corp. The treatment is accomplished by passing the polyethylene through an electrical field of such a nature that an extremely rapid electron bombardment of the surface takes place. The treatment is said to be permanent and very uniform, since a high degree of electrical control is assured. Top film speeds appear to be in the same range for this and for the Kreidl process; i.e., approximately 300–360 feet per minute. The Modern Plastic Machinery Corp. is the manufacturer of equipment embodying this technique.

Increased ink adhesion, faster press runs, and lower printing costs are claimed for Cheslene-TF, a polyethylene film developed by Chester Packaging Products Corp. and based on a new surface-treating process (700).

These methods of treatment of polyethylene to improve ink reactivity namely chlorination, differential heat treatment, oxidation, and electronic treatment were recently discussed and critically compared by Irving (971). An evaluation of existing methods by which polyethylene surfaces can be prepared for ink adhesion has also been presented by Bloyer (932a).

A method for the improvement of the printing and bonding properties of polyethylene by γ-irradiation with a cobalt-60 source has been proposed by Chapman and Colombo (942,943) of the Brookhaven National Laboratory. The treatment is said to be uniform, modifying both sides of the polyethylene simultaneously due to the penetration of the γ-rays. Improved adhesion is believed to be due to the oxidation of the surface molecules and not to unsaturation or reorientation of the molecules. The presence of carbonyl groups was established by infrared analysis, and rubbing of the surface of the irradiated film with organic solvents was found to destroy its retentive power for ink completely. Similar conclusions were drawn by Rossmann (1139), who applied two forms of treatment to a poly-ethylene film: a Tesla coil discharge at atmospheric pressure, and a glow discharge at reduced pressure.

8.20. Processing and Compounding of Chlorosulfonated Polyethylene

The properties of "Hypalon," duPont's chlorosulfonated polyethylene, were discussed in Sections 4.5 and 6.18.   As outlined by Keeley and Roche (856), Drogin (727), and McCune (993), milling and Banbury mixing are both applicable, the latter requiring only short cycles because the polymer need not be broken down before the incorporation of pigments.   "Hypa-lon" can be extruded on wire and cured by customary processes.   Com-pounding includes the incorporation of vulcanizing agents and accelera-tors.   The addition of carbon black is not required in order to develop maximum tensile strength.   However, heating chlorosulfonated poly-ethylene in the presence of channel black is claimed by Youngquist, Smook, and Brooks in U. S. 2,659,707 to duPont (806) to effect curing of the poly-mer.

Scorching during milling, calendering, and extrusion of chlorosulfonated polyethylene may be prevented, according to U. S. 2,630,425 to Rodman [duPont (786)], by keeping its moisture content below 0.5–0.75%; a tight cure is subsequently obtained by increasing the moisture content.   The reduction in moisture may be accomplished by drying the compounding ingredients or by the addition of dehydration agents such as CaO, $CaCl_2$, or silica gel.   The subsequent increase in moisture content may be effected by the addition of water, hydrated salts, glycols, sugars, or alkanolamines.

A process for bonding rubber to chlorosulfonated polyethylene is de-scribed by Strain and Crim in U. S. 2,711,986 [duPont (1077)].

IX. USES AND APPLICATIONS OF POLYETHYLENES

Numerous articles deal with the manifold uses of polyethylene. Most recently, Bockhoff and Roth (934) discussed the application of polyethylene to chemical engineering construction, and they related its properties to manufacturing variables and end uses. As the conclusion, it was felt by these authors that polyethylene fabrications offer a satisfactory and long-lasting solution to many of the particularly annoying corrosion problems encountered with other construction materials. The utilization of polyethylene in the field of chemical engineering, it is pointed out, will be even greater as more process engineers become acquainted with the unique adaptability of this material to their particular needs. The application of polyethylene in industrial batteries (Exide Industrial Division of Electric Storage Battery Co.) and in pumps designed for corrosive chemicals (Vanton Pump and Equipment Corp.) are examples of this trend. Also, the uses for polyethylene in building construction are increasing (919a,928a,1123a).

Uses and applications for which the recently developed high-density polyethylenes appear particularly suited have been described in Section 6.19. The following references are, therefore, limited essentially to the conventional high-pressure polymerized polyethylenes.

9.1. Film

Demand for polyethylene in the form of film has consistently increased ever since it became commercially available. A fundamental reason has been that the demand has far outstripped the supply, and as quickly as new production became available, a greater percentage was diverted to this assured market than might otherwise have been the case. There are presently at least 35 producers of polyethylene film, and competition consequently has become keener. This has led to increased efforts to exploit present markets and to develop new fields of application. As an example of the former, only 10–15% of the 75 billion pounds of fresh produce sold in the United States in 1953 was prepackaged. Current developments are aimed at securing a greater share of this market and broadening the base by adapting polyethylene film to the prepackaging of more varieties of produce, e.g., lettuce and pears.   The use of polyethylene as artificial shells for eggs, eliminating breakage loss and reducing spoilage, has been recently developed by Darrah (949) at Cornell University.

Apart from its use as a packaging material, polyethylene film is finding new applications based upon its unique physical properties.   As a tarpaulin material, it is used for covering machinery and for painters' drop cloths. As a barrier membrane, it is being applied as a protective underground sheath around poured basements.   As a lining material, it is being successfully applied to trench silos and irrigation ditches, and in the home to upholstery and garment bags.   The packaging of metallic sodium in polyethylene-lined containers is described in U. S. 2,712,384 [Corneil to duPont (1078)].

The possibilities of polyethylene film as a packaging material, especially for foodstuffs, was recognized early.   In this country, the Visking Corporation pioneered in the development of thin-walled film, extruded as a seamless tube.   Commercial-scale production was begun in 1945, and since that time at least 34 additional producers of polyethylene film have entered the field.

For food-packaging purposes, molten polyethylene is extruded through a circular or a flat-slot die to result in a seamless tube or in a single-thickness film.   As in the case of other film-forming materials, e.g., cellophane, extrusion through a circular die may be conducted to result in a polyethylene film oriented in both transverse and longitudinal directions.   Flat-slot die extrusion, on the other hand, yields films oriented chiefly longitudinally. As would be anticipated, films oriented in both directions exhibit substantially higher tear strength and improved durability compared with those oriented only in the longitudinal direction.   Since the product is to be used for packaging sensitive foodstuffs, it is preferable to omit plasticizers, stabilizers, or other additives from the polyethylene extrusion melt. At the same time pigments and opacifiers can be and often are added to impart color and enhanced opacity to the extruded film, without otherwise affecting its physical properties.

Commercial polyethylene film for food packaging is available as single-thickness film in widths up to 120 inches and thickness from 1–20 mils. Seamless tubing is sold in the same range of widths and thicknesses.   The film has a density of only 0.92 and a very high yield factor of about 30,000 square inches per pound (1-mil film).   Physical properties of typical commercial film at different temperatures are illustrated in Table CIV (886).

In addition to adequate initial physical properties, polyethylene exhibits highly desirable aging characteristics.   This is of obvious practical im-

TABLE CIV

Typical Commercial Food-Packaging Polyethylene Film

Physical Properties	Tempera- ture, °F.	Direction	
		Longitudinal	Transverse
Tensile strength, p.s.i.	77	2480	1600
	32	2990	2050
	0	3430	2525
Elongation, %	77	230	185
	32	100	55
	0	70	45
Tear strength, g./mil thickness	77	180	125
	32	45	290
	0	30	260
Impact puncture resistance, in.-oz./in. tear	77	90	50
	0	60	55

Source: *Modern Packaging*, **27** (5), 155 (1954).

portance to the wholesaler and to the retail merchant.   Typical physical properties for polyethylene film stored for a period of 5 years are presented on a comparative basis in Table CV.

TABLE CV

Effect of Aging on Tensile and Tear Properties of Polyethylene Film

Property	Direction on Film	Test 1, Oct., '48	Test 2, Feb., '50	Test 3, Feb., '51	Test 4, Aug., '53
Tensile strength, p.s.i.	Long.	3,624	3,049	3,563	3,708
	Trans.	1,419	1,720	1,799	1,539
Elongation, %	Long.	196	225	178	230
	Trans.	152	864	464	650
Tear strength, g./mil	Long.	153	228	250	196
	Trans.	109	108	119	80

Source: *Modern Packaging*, **27** (5), 155 (1954).

In the field of packaging and wrapping, a plastic film may be desired which is as impermeable as possible to gases or vapors, particularly moisture, loss of which would cause a deterioration of the qualities of the wrapped product.   On the other hand, it may be desirable to have a membrane which is permeable or selectively permeable to a single gas; thus, the transmission of oxygen through the film to the wrapped material may be desirable in order to kill anaerobic bacteria.   The permeability of polyethylene film to water vapor (relatively low) and to oxygen (relatively high), as compared to the permeability of other currently available films (see Section 6.3), makes polyethylene a highly desirable and inexpensive packaging material. Typical data of interest in the field of food packaging are given in Table CVI. These rates are inversely proportional to the thickness of the film.

TABLE CVI

Gas Transmission of Polyethylene Film

Gas	Gas Transmission, ml./100 sq. in./24 hr./mil (25°C.)
Nitrogen	180
Oxygen	550
Helium	1,225
Freon "12"	1,690
Hydrogen	1,960
Carbon dioxide	2,900
Sulfur dioxide	6,200
Ethylene oxide	29,300
Methyl bromide	79,100

Source: *Modern Packaging,* **27** (5), 155 (1954).

However, as indicated previously (Section 6.19), the permeability of a high-density polyethylene for gases, liquids, and moisture vapor is considerably lower than that of conventional low-density polyethylene.

For practical packaging purposes, polyethylene film is commonly fabricated into plain or gusseted bags. Film thicknesses of the order of $1^{1}/_{2}$–4 mils are ordinarily preferred. Fabricating for the most part is done with high-speed automatic bag machines, capable of handling rolls either of film or of tubing, and of turning out bags of any desired size. The bags are heat-sealed, using any of the standard techniques, such as hot-wire, rotating band, heated roller, flame-sealing, and electronic welding. Adhesive sealing has not yet been undertaken successfully. Laminating and spot-gluing polyethylene to dissimilar surfaces are standard procedures for special purposes, but the latex-type adhesives used have not been adapted to the high-speed machine operations of bag fabrication. Solvent-sealing is, of course, not considered feasible. While bag closure may be, and is, effected in any of the usual ways, the re-use value of polyethylene often dictates a temporary, nondestructive closure.

Printing on polyethylene film presents special problems inherent in the nature of the film (see Section 8.7) which, to some extent, have been overcome. It is usually considered advantageous to print polyethylene film continuously on rolls of tubing or single-thickness film prior to fabricating into bags.

The various uses for polyethylene film (shrinkable film, elastic film, balloon film, black film for outdoor use), and the outlook for future improvements, were discussed recently by Henderson (968).

9.2. Fibers and Filaments

Polyethylene fiber (see Section 8.7) may be used in upholstery, shoe and handbag fabrics, for novelty shrinkage effects, for braiding, draperies, protective fabrics, clothing, filter cloth, tow targets, novelty yarns, braided laces and cords, ropes, edging, threads, surgical dressing, electrical insulation material, and as fusible interliners in semistiff collars.   It can be wound, warped, woven, knitted, and finished.

Polyethylene monofilaments, as well as fabrics and articles woven thereof, are made in the United States by Dawbarn Brothers, Inc., Firestone Plastics Co., Reeves Brothers, Inc. (Reevon), The National Plastic Products Co. (Wynene I), and by the United States Rubber Co. (Trilok); in England, by Courtaulds Ltd. (Courlene).   For general information on these products and their comparison with other fiber-forming materials, reference is made to the "1955 Synthetic-Fiber Table" by London (990).

The properties of Reevon polyethylene monofilaments are shown in Table CVII (1018).   Equivalent deniers, counts, and yards per pound are

TABLE CVII

Properties of Reevon Polyethylene Monofilaments

Melting point: 240 to 255°F.
Softening point: 225 to 240°F. (lower under pressure or stress)
Decomposition: Above 600°F. (no deterioration when heated to melting point)
Odorless (no plasticizer incorporated)
Nontoxic
Slow burning
Specific gravity: 0.90–0.92
Tensile strength oriented: 2.0 to 3.0 grams/denier or 22,000 to 30,000 lbs./sq. in.
Elongation to break: Unoriented 500 to 700%; oriented regular 40%, special 20 to 100% adjustable
Color: Natural clear, pigmented in wide range of light-fast colors
Cross section of filaments: round, elliptical, special shapes

---

Source: *Reevon Bulletin*, Reeves Brothers, Inc., 1955.

compared in Table CVIII.   The chemical resistance of these filaments is essentially the same as previously described for conventional high-pressure polymerized polyethylene (see Section 6.1).

In the preparation of filaments, polymer granules are melted in an extrusion head.   A number of monofilaments issue from a jet at the face of

TABLE CVIII

Reeves Polyethylene Monofilaments

Diameter, Inch	Denier Range	Average Yield, Yd./Lb.
0.003/0.005[a]	50/100	60,000
0.008	250/300	17,000
0.010	400/450	10,000
0.012	550/600	7,500
0.015	900/950	4,600
0.020	1,600/1,800	2,600
0.023	2,000/2,400	2,000
0.030	3,500/4,000	1,200
0.036	5,000/5,800	800

Source: *Reevon Bulletin*, Reeves Brothers, Inc., 1955.
[a] Supplied as multifilament: 4, 6, 8, or 12-ply.

the extrusion head and are quenched to lower the temperature and aid solidification. The monofils are then suitably drawn to give the necessary

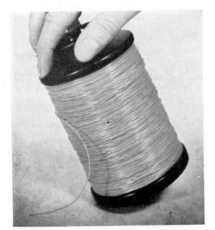

Fig. 214. Courlene monofil. (Courtaulds, Ltd., "*Courlene*," 1955.)

Fig. 215. Fancy weave—green and black monofil (*magnification* × 5). (Courtaulds, Ltd., "*Courlene*," 1955.)

mechanical properties for use as a textile, and finally they are collected on bobbins. As examples of Courlene, a spool with the monofil, a fancy weave, and the method of cutting Courlene fabric with a hot knife are shown in Figures 214, 215, and 216 (948).

The United States Rubber Co. has recently (919b,923d,928b)introduced a fabric (Trilok) which is woven on a regular loom out of polyethylene and conventional textile yarns such as wool, cotton, silk, rayon, or nylon.   In this fabric, the polyethylene yarn runs lengthwise, while the conventional yarns run both lengthwise and crosswise.   When the fabric is immersed in boiling water, the prestretched polyethylene shrinks considerably more (55%) than the other yarns (8–12%), and a three dimensional design, determined by the weaving pattern, results.   Use of this fabric for automotive and furniture upholstery is visualized, where its cushioning effect is claimed to offer unusual comfort.

Fig. 216. Cutting Courlene fabric with a hot knife.   (Courtaulds, Ltd., "*Courlene*," 1955.)

Curled ribbons of polyethylene may be used as a tower-packing material. Harshaw Tellerette (965) was designed by the Harshaw Chemical Co. for diffusional operations based on the principle of holdup of liquid in interstitial spaces rather than the holdup on the wetted surface of conventional packing.

9.3. Tube and Pipe

Historically, one of the major markets for polyethylene has been the production of industrial piping, although applications within this field have been and are still relatively limited.   Until recently, cold-water supply systems, irrigation and farm-watering systems, and deep-well piping have been the chief consumers of polyethylene pipe.   A substantial outlet has been developed by the use of polyethylene for mine pipe and for installation in freezing plants, food and beverage plants, golf courses, skating rinks, and as radiant heating coils.   Some use has been made of this piping for the transmission of natural gas and crude petroleum products and for effluent drainage.   Further developments along these and related lines are inevitable.   At the same time, the physical properties of polyethylene are such as to restrict its applications as piping within quite well-defined limits of temperature and physical environment.

For at least some of these applications, polyethylene is far superior to the materials it has supplanted.   For example, Shearon (630) describes the use of polyethylene as a coal-mine piping.   At least one case has been reported in which 2,000 feet of 2-inch steel pipe had to be replaced after every 8 hours of service.   Polyethylene installed in its place was still in excellent condition after more than $2^1/_2$ years.

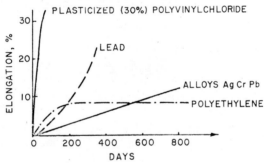

Fig. 217. Deformation under load (36 kg./cm.^{2}) of different materials.
Source: *Chim. et. Ind.* (*Supp. Mensuel., Génie Chim.*), **73**, 63, 1955.

More than 50% of the plastic pipe manufactured in the United States is made of polyethylene, according to a series of articles by Reis (1019) on the industrial application of plastic pipe.   The superiority of polyethylene over other construction materials, which makes it particularly suitable for use in piping, is demonstrated in Figure 217.

The steady growth of the use of plastics for the manufacture of pipe, and the part taken by polyethylene, has been recently discussed (923); pertinent data are presented in Figure 218.   The same article quotes a plastic pipe comparison in respect to cost and properties from a paper by Seymour (1026), and shows several of the specialized uses of polyethylene pipe.   These are reproduced in Table CIX and shown in Figure 219.

Devoted to the discussion of the use of plastic pipe, particularly for underground structures, is a paper by Seymour (1027), which presents data on the physical properties of pipe made of polyethylene and other plastic materials, together with extensive information on their chemical resistance.

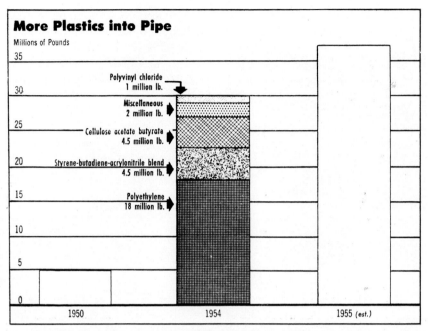

Fig. 218. Use of plastics for the manufacture of pipe. (*Chem. Eng. News,* **33,** 3062 (1955).)

TABLE CIX

Plastic Pipe Comparison
(Relative index values rated from 0–10 with 10 being the most desirable)

	Poly-ethylene	Cellulose Acetate Butyrate	Styrene-Butadiene-Acrylo-nitrile	Polyvinyl Chloride (High Impact)	Cast Iron
Relative cost	10	6	6	6	10
Relative resistance to					
Temperature	2	3	7	5	10
Impact	10	5	10	10	3
Soil	10	10	10	10	7
Natural gas	10	10	10	10	10
Artificial gas	4	5	7	10	10
Salts	10	10	10	10	4
Caustic	10	3	9	10	10
Petroleum crudes	8	6	8	10	5
Hydrochloric acid	10	1	10	10	2
Total	84	59	87	91	71

Source: *Ind. Eng. Chem.,* **47,** 1338 (1955).

Fig. 219. Specialized uses of polyethylene pipe: sluice mining operations (top left), insulated raceways on telegraph poles (top right), chemical plant (bottom left), and coal mine drainage (bottom right). (*Ind. Eng. Chem.*, **47**, 1338 (1955).)

Seymour proposes specifications for an ideal pipeline, and he covers some of the essential engineering characteristics of correctly used plastic pipes.

The most important published work on the problems involved in the application of polyethylene piping to the supply and distribution of potable water has been carried out in Great Britain (425,553,598).   The British Government has indicated awareness of its importance and inherent possibilities by the publication of appropriate materials specifications. The current standards are identified as British Standards 1972:1953 and 1973:1953 "Polythene Tube for Cold Water Services" (713,778).

A discussion of the favorable results of an extensive study by the National Sanitation Foundation at the School of Public Health, University of Michigan, on the suitability of plastics, including polyethylene, in pipes for drinking water was recently presented by Tiedeman (1141d).

In the United States, cast polyethylene pipe is commercially available in the standard sizes indicated in Table CX (887).

TABLE CX

Standard Cast Polyethylene Pipe

Outside Diameter, Inches	Inside Diameter, Inches	Weight, Lb./Ft.
2.75	2.375	0.605
3.0	2.625	0.690
3.625	3.250	0.810
4.0	3.625	0.910
4.75	4.375	1.080
5.625	5.250	1.280
5.75	5.250	1.730
6.625	6.125	2.000
8.50	8.000	2.650
10.25	9.750	3.200
12.50	12.000	3.850
14.50	14.000	4.500
17.50	17.000	5.750
20.50	20.000	6.500

Source: See Table CXI.

Dimensions and tolerances for the 10 sizes of flexible standard-wall polyethylene pipe are given in Table CXI.

The British have also been active in the application of polyethylene pipe for effluent drainage.   Here it has found favor especially as a replacement for stoneware spigot-and-socket pipelines, since it avoids the necessity for

TABLE CXI

Dimensions and Tolerances

Nominal Size, Inches	Inside Diameter of Pipe		Wall Thickness of Pipe		Weight of Pipe	
	Diameter, Inches	Tolerances, Inch	Thickness, Inch	Tolerance, Inch	Minimum, Lb./100 Ft.	Nominal, Lb./100 Ft.
$^1/_2$	0.622	+0.010, −0.010	0.109	±0.006	9.1	10
$^3/_4$	0.824	+0.010, −0.015	0.113	±0.006	12.2	13
1	1.049	+0.010, −0.020	0.133	±0.007	18.0	20
$1^1/_4$	1.380	+0.010, −0.020	0.140	±0.007	24.6	27
$1^1/_2$	1.610	+0.015, −0.020	0.145	±0.008	29.3	32
2	2.067	+0.015, −0.020	0.154	±0.008	39.7	43
$2^1/_2$	2.469	+0.015, −0.025	0.203	±0.009	63.4	68
3	3.068	+0.015, −0.030	0.216	±0.010	82.8	89
4	4.026	+0.015, −0.035	0.237	±0.012	117.5	127
6	6.056	+0.020, −0.035	0.280	±0.015	206.7	223

Source: United States Department of Commerce, "Commercial Standard CS 197–54, Dimensions and Tolerances for Flexible Standard Wall Polyethylene Pipe," Oct. 15, 1954.

TABLE CXIIA

Comparison of Physical Properties of Plastic Tubing and Piping Materials

No.		Styrene Butadiene Polymers[a]	Boron Silicate Glass	Glass Lining	Glass Fiber Reinforced Plaster
1	Specific gravity	1.07	2.23	....	1.8
2	Max. tensile strength, p.s.i.	5,500	....	....	41,000
3	Impact strength, ft.-lb./in. notch Izod	5	....	....	15–34
4	Operating temp. range or maximum, °F.	170	250[b]	550	−60 to +275
5	Working pressure, p.s.i.	60–150	20–50	150	....
6	Maximum pressure, p.s.i.	....	....	150–2,000	600[d]
7	Dielectric constant	2.9	4.6	....	3.6–4.0
8	Thermal expansion, in./in./°F.	3.4×10^{-5}	0.18×10^{-5}	0.65×10^{-5}	....
9	Thermal conductivity, Btu./hr./ft.²/ °F./in.	1.0	8.1	....	....
10	Sizes available, in.	0.5–2.0[c]	1.0–6.0	1.0–6.0	0.25–12.0
11	Lengths available, ft.	10 and 21	to 10	10–20	30
12	Joint method				
	Threaded	x		x	x
	Slipsleeve and bond		x		x
	Flange	x	x	x	x
	Heat weld		x		
	Solvent weld				
13	Fittings	Std.	Std.	Std.	Std.
14	Rigidity	Rigid	Rigid	Rigid	Rigid

(*See opposite page*)

making tight and corrosion-resistant joints. In carrying out the actual installation (846), 30–40 feet of polyethylene pipe of the required diameter is welded together and carefully rolled into a prepared trench. The welding of succeeding sections is carried out in place. When completed, the pipeline is filled with water and immediately surrounded by concrete. The trench is refilled after the concrete has set. As an added advantage, the system can be coupled to polyethylene-lined sumps, catch-pits and manholes, resulting, in effect, in a completely jointless polyethylene effluent system.

A comparison between conventional high-pressure polymerized polyethylene and other commercially available plastic tubing and piping materials is presented in Table CXIIA and B. It is understood that these data do not include custom-blended tubing for medical and other specialty uses.

TABLE CXIIB

Comparison of Physical Properties
of Plastic Tubing and Piping Materials

No.	Polyvinylidene Chloride Tubing	Piping	Lining	Low-Density Polyethylene Tubing	Piping	P.V.C. (filled) (Unplasticized)	Cellulose Acetate Butyrate	Phenol-HCHO Asbestos
1	1.68–1.75	1.45–1.55		1.12		1.34–1.38	1.20	1.7
2	4,000–8,000	2,000–2,500		1,400–2,000		8,000–9,000	6,000	2,250–4,500
3	2–8		2–8	32		0.2–0.6	1.5–3	0.476
4	175		−40 to +194	−70 to +140		158	150	265
5	50		500	60 to 170	25 to 100	....	100	65 (4 in. and smaller)
6	....		1,000	....	....	....	500	650 (4 in. and smaller)
7	3–5		3–5	....	....	3.2–3.4	3.5–6.4	5.8
8	28.4×10^{-5}	....		32.4×10^{-5}		4.4×10^{-5}	6.1×10^{-5} to 9.4×10^{-5}	1.8×10^{-5}
9	1.77×10^{-4}		1.77×10^{-4}	2.30		2.4×10^{-4}	3.22×10^{-4} to 6.45×10^{-4}	1.7×10^{-2} to 5.1×10^{-2}
10	0.125–0.75	1–4	1.0–6.0	0.25–1.0	0.5–6.0	0.5–2	0.5–6	0.5–12
11	2.5	10	10	Coils to 500	400	4 and 10	20 and 30	Up to 10^6
12		x	x				x	x
					x			
		x	x		x			
							x	
13		Std.	Std.		Std.		Std.	Std.
14	Flex.	Semi-Flex.	Rigid	Flex.	Flex.	Rigid	Rigid	Rigid

Source: *Chem. Eng. News*, **30**, 316 (1952).
[a] Copolymers of styrene and butadiene with acrylonitrile.
[b] Up to 500°F. when insulated from thermal shock.
[c] 3- and 4-in. available March, 1952; 6-in. available June, 1952.
[d] Nonwoven glass mat; woven cloth pipe has bursting strength up to 4,500.

The particular advantages in the use of the recently developed highly crystalline polyethylenes in the manufacture of pipes, in view of their increased bursting strength, have been discussed in Section 6.19.

9.4. Molded Polyethylene

Next to polyethylene film, injection moldings have exhibited the fastest growth. It has been estimated conservatively that by the year of 1960, if not before, the total volume of all plastic housewares will have reached 80–90 million pounds. Polyethylene should participate in this market to the extent of at least 50%.

9.5. Wire, Tape, and Cable

The substantial decline in 1954 in the consumption of polyethylene for electrical purposes has been attributed to the cutback in United States Army orders for wire of this type, e.g., assault wire. At the same time, further loss is not anticipated since civilian requirements for telephone wire and special-purpose insulation wiring is expected to continue a steady growth pattern.

During World War II, the bulk of the polyethylene produced was used for insulating cables, particularly high-frequency types. Since that time, improvements on these have been worked out, and new types of polyethylene-based insulating compositions and devices have been developed.

A paper by Hancock (470) deals with the application of plastics in the manufacture of cables. The use of polyisobutylene in admixture with polyethylene to provide an improved cable dielectric has been described by Wilson (570). A blend of Alkathene Grade 2 with $12^1/_2\%$ polyisobutylene is claimed to produce an insulating material almost ideal with respect to strength and resistance to environmental-cracking. The use of low molecular weight polyethylenes (A-C Polyethylenes, see Section 6.15) as processing aids for natural rubber and synthetic elastomers is proposed by the Semet-Solvay Petrochemicals Division, Allied Chemical & Dye Corporation.

Insulating Tape

British 585,934 to Telegraph Construction and Maintenance (314) describes an adhesive insulating tape which is resistant to prolonged aging, adheres to porcelain and polyethylene, and possesses insulating properties for high-frequency electrical apparatus. The tape has a backing of polyethylene or a mixture of polyethylene and polyisobutylene, and an ad-

hesive substance on one or both faces of the backing consisting of polyisobutylene, which may be a mixture of polymers of different molecular
weights.

Oriented polyethylene pressure-sensitive tape and film are described by
Miller (556) as being exceptional electrical insulating materials for splicing
all types of cables in the field at high voltages and high frequencies.   Large
pipes in a cooling tower protected with this polyethylene tape are shown in
Figure 220.

Fig. 220.   Large pipes in a cooling tower are protected with polyethylene tape.   (*Modern
Plastics*, **28** [5], 74, 1951.)

Recently, there became commercially available in the United States another self-bonding, polyethylene-base insulating tape of a very similar type
(694).   In application, it is wrapped snugly around the pipe or cable to be
insulated, and the end pressed firmly in place.   Within a short time, the
"plastic memory" of the polyethylene causes the tape to contract to such an
extent that it is fused into a solid homogeneous mass which cannot be un-
wound.   It is especially recommended for wire and cable splicing, insulating
motors, harnessing, coil wrapping, taping bus bars and television antenna
leads, and sealing conduit joints.

The practical aspects of polyethylene tape for pipe coating have been
discussed at some length by Parker (1010).   The author describes a full-
scale field test made under actual service conditions.   The polyethylene
tape used was an oriented polyethylene film, 8 mils thick, manufactured as a

pressure-sensitive tape with an adhesive mass of 4 mils. A section of 8-inch gas line 12.12 miles in length was wrapped with 8-inch tape and an outer, unbonded wrap of tar-saturated asbestos pipe line felt. The remainder of the line, 52.88 miles in length, was coated with a conventional system. This consisted of a coal-tar primer, followed by a $^3/_{32}$-inch coat of coal-tar enamel with a bonded outer wrap of glass-reinforced felt. Coating conductances calculated from the field data are presented in Table CXIII. Data for Test 1 were measured about 6 weeks after the line had

TABLE CXIII

Coating Conductances of Polyethylene Tapes

	Tape Section	Coal-Tar Section
Test 1		
Total current drained, ma	76	110
Average driving voltage, mv	472	169
Input resistance, ohms	6.22	1.54
ohm-sq. ft.	889,000	318,000
micromhos/sq. ft.	1.13	3.15
Test 2		
Total current drained, ma	38	120
Average driving voltage, mv	236	159
Input resistance, ohms	6.22	1.38
micromhos/sq. ft.	1.13	3.52

Source: *Petroleum Engr.*, D-28–D-30 (Jan. 1955).

been buried. Test 2 was made some 100 days after Test 1. Several conclusions are drawn from these data. For example, the very low conductance values would imply lower cathodic protection costs, due to lower total current requirements. Again, almost complete freedom from possible interference effects with other structures is assured because of the extremely low current densities involved. A more speculative point, but one which may indicate the direction of future developments in the applications of cathodic protection systems, is also considered. That is, the very low current demands may make attractive the installation of constant-potential rather than the conventional constant-current system. This is made possible by the high resistance of the part of the circuit lying between the pipe metal and the earth. Since this resistance is so large, it could conceivably be made the controlling factor in the circuit by the installation of a current source of low potential but of intrinsically high current capacity. Any significant damage to the coating, then, would automatically be followed by an increase in the current supplied, so as to maintain pipe-to-soil potential virtually constant.

Cable

In an article published in 1952 (643), Wallder of the Bell Telephone Laboratories has discussed at some length the use of polyethylene as a cable sheath in the light of difficulties encountered in field use.   Protection against weathering is, of course, one problem, but an equally serious one may be environmental stress-cracking when the polyethylene is subjected to such unfavorable media as soaps, alcohols, and wetting agents.

A method of preventing cracking in extruded polyethylene cable sheaths, which have been wound into coils and stored for a longer period of time, based on the application of heat during unwinding to relieve internal stresses created by distortion of the age-hardened sheath, is described by Henning in U. S. 2,695,769 to Western Electric (914).

In the field of commercial installations, one of the most important, tonnage-wise, is that of submarine cables.   It has recently (811) been pointed out that for nearly one hundred years gutta percha and balata monopolized this cable-insulating field.   Now, however, all new submarine cables are insulated with polyethylene.   Polyethylene has a higher softening point than gutta percha, and a greater resistance to water absorption and diffusion.   Polyethylene is much more inert, is harder, stronger, and has a lower density.   In terms of economics, polyethylene is considerably the cheaper of the two.

It is estimated (809) that approximately 1,400 tons of polyethylene will be used in the fabrication of a transatlantic cable system presently (1955) being laid to link the United Kingdom, Canada, and the United States. The system consists of two cables, one for each direction of transmission, between Oban, Scotland and Clarenville, Newfoundland.   Each will be about 2,250 miles long, and will join a cable 380 miles long running from Clarenville to Sydney Mines on the mainland.   A very hard grade of polyethylene is being used, with 5% butyl rubber incorporated; the outer diameter of the insulating core is 0.620 inches.

Another submarine installation is currently being fabricated and laid for the United States Air Force Missile Test Center at Cape Canaveral, Florida (807,813).   Essentially, this is comprised of coaxial telephone cable insulated with a high molecular weight polyethylene composition.   The total length of the installation has not been published, but it is known to extend from the launching area at Cape Canaveral past the British West Indies at least as far as Puerto Rico.

An electric cable with an aluminum cover and a protective coating of polyethylene applied by the flame-spraying process is described in Brit. 678,896 to Felten und Guilleaume Carlswerk (665a).   A composition consisting of an insulating oil, polyethylene, and a micro-crystalline petroleum wax is proposed in Brit. 715,193 to Dussek Brothers and Company (906c) for the impregnation of fibrous material for the insulation of the conductors of cables or condensers.

9.6. Coating

Polyethylene has made steady advances as a coating material ever since its commercial inception. In particular, polyethylene as a coating on cellophane is believed to hold real promise of future development. It exhibits the sum of the desirable qualities found uniquely in each material. Accordingly, it should find increasing acceptance in those applications where this combination of properties is of importance. For example, low gas-transmission rate coupled with toughness, grease resistance, printability, clarity, and capacity for heat-sealing recommend it for packaging meats, liquid products such as fruit juices, and vacuum-packed foods [e.g., Mahaffy in U. S. 2,714,557 to duPont (1081)].

The addition of polyethylene to coating compositions increases their abrasion resistance, as shown by Gowing, Langdon, and Selby in U. S. 2,518,462 to duPont (511a), but also results in a reduction of the gloss of the coating. This may be overcome according to U. S. 2,655,489 of Lawson [duPont (801a)] by incorporating a liquid alkyl polysiloxane.

Beater-sizing of paper by aqueous dispersions of polyethylene is proposed by O'Flynn and Pye in U. S. 2,739,058 [duPont (1149)].

9.7. Containers

The rate of growth of the polyethylene bottle industry has decreased but, characteristically, sales have grown from about 30 million units in 1949 to 350 million units in 1954. The relatively slow rate of growth has been attributed to several factors, not the least of which is competition from the much cheaper glass containers. Other sources of competition have also been far from negligible. For example, it is estimated that at least 200 million metal or glass aerosol units were delivered in 1954. It is understood that nylon and melamine containers of this type are being currently developed. It must be anticipated that these will be brought to successful commercial completion and will further divide the aerosol market, at the very least. Another factor which has hampered the more rapid application of the polyethylene bottle has been the long test period necessary in each separate instance in order to establish the suitability of the container to the product to be packaged. At the same time, the immediate commercial acceptance of the polyethylene bottle in some special applications gives reason for optimism.   As an example, the octagonal polyethylene nursing bottle is believed to have sold nearly 20 million units in 1954.   In furtherance of this, optimism is also felt with regard to the development of polyethylene cosmetic jars, detergent containers, and similar applications.   It is also believed that collapsible tubes and nozzles of polyethylene, that permit spraying, brushing, or drop-by-drop dispensing, are certain of eventual development.

Containers claimed to retain compression strength under high humidity are made by St. Regis Paper Co. (1119) by "sandwiching" a layer of foam polyethylene between two layers of Kraft paper.

Carboys and Drums

Polyethylene carboys were first introduced early in 1952 in $6^1/_2$- and 13-gallon capacities.   There are reported to be more than two hundred commercial users who have adopted this type of blow-molded and bottle-shaped package for some of their products.   The two-piece, square-shaped polyethylene carboy was announced in January, 1953 (691).   Both types have been fully approved by the Interstate Commerce Commission under recommendations of the Bureau of Explosives.

Use of polyethylene carboys was pioneered by the General Chemical Division, Allied Chemical and Dye Corp.   General Chemical introduced the bottle-shaped carboy for packaging hydrofluoric acid, and then extended its application to other Baker and Adamson fine chemicals.   With a wall thickness of $1/_{10}$ inch and equipped with a cylindrical outer jacket of four-ply, phenolic-bonded, water-resistant plywood, the package has proved virtually unbreakable in normal service.   Additional advantages were found in an estimated 20% saving in transportation costs of the filled carboys, and a 60% saving in shipping costs of empties.

The square polyethylene carboy was originally developed for Tennessee Products and Chemicals Corp. for the shipment of hydrochloric acid.   It has a uniform wall thickness of $1/_8$ inch, and a capacity of 15 gallons.   It is encased in a $3/_4$-inch wooden box, reinforced with triple-coated, acid-resistant steel strapping.   Because of its cubical shape, it lends itself to palletized shipment and to stacking five or more containers high.

A more recent development in polyethylene shipping containers is the steel-covered, molded polyethylene drum (690).   Presently available in 5-, 15-, 30-, and 55-gallon round sizes and a 5-gallon cube shape, the drum container is molded in one piece with side-wall thickness of $1/_{16}$ inch and $3/_{32}$ inch top and bottom.   The containers have two openings like standard drums, threaded to receive $3/_4$-inch and 2-inch polyethylene plugs.   Outer surfaces of the flanges are threaded to fit metal or plastic screw caps of 43- and 83-mm. diameter. The drum sizes are dimensioned to fit into standard fiber, steel, or plywood jackets. The 5-gallon cube is adapted to be shipped in a standard corrugated carton.

As pointed out by Pruett (1016), the polyethylene carboys and the poly-

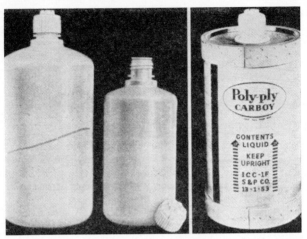

Fig. 221. Polyethylene carboys. (*Ind. Eng. Chem.*, **47,** 1196 (1955).)

Fig. 222. Thirty-gallon polyethylene drum. (*Ind. Eng. Chem.*, **47,** 1196 (1955).)

ethylene drums combine the chemical resistance, flexibility, toughness, and other desirable properties of polyethylene with the ruggedness and strength of overpack containers, such as wooden boxes and plywood and steel drums. Specifications for these containers are presented. The $6^1/_2$- and 13-gallon polyethylene carboys, bare and encased in plywood drums, are shown in Figure 221; a 30-gallon molded polyethylene drum, bare and encased in a plywood drum, and partially inserted in an ICC-6J steel drum, is pictured in Figure 222.

Based on tests and on the recommendations of the Manufacturing Chemists' Association, the Bureau of Explosives proposed to the Interstate Commerce Commission that special test permits be issued upon the request of interested shippers to authorize the temporary use of the containers. A number of these special permits were issued, and many thousands of these polyethylene drums encased in ICC-6J open-head steel drums are now being used for shipment of certain regulatory products.

9.8. Closures

Polyethylene as a closure material is only beginning to be exploited. A significant innovation was reported in April, 1954, with the announcement (815) that the world's largest single user of collapsible tubes, the Colgate-Palmolive Company, was changing from rigid plastic to polyethylene for molded, threaded caps on toothpaste tubes. The change was made primarily to eliminate the problem of loose caps and loose liners, and to achieve a more efficient valve seat. The engineering problems involved in this development are illustrative of the special difficulties presented by polyethylene in such applications. For example, because of the resiliency of the caps, a buttress-type thread had to be designed to give a broader bearing surface, and thread tolerances were required to be held to 0–0.003 inch.

Another polyethylene closure which has attracted attention is a dispensing spout for lighter fuel (816). In this application, the polyethylene spout is provided with an integral closure of the same material which seals securely and cannot be lost. In eliminating the screw-capped lead spout, the polyethylene dispenser also eliminates the former requirement of cutting or piercing the nozzle prior to dispensing fluid from the container. In essence, the closure consists of two parts—an outer housing, circular at the bottom and shaped into a hollow rectangular extension at the top, and a circular flow disk integral with a pierced spout. Held tighly in the groove by the resiliency of the polyethylene, the spout may be swung to either end of the opening to shut off the flow of liquid, or to a central position when fluid is to be dispensed. This arrangement is so effective that, under pressure test, the can will rupture at the seams before the spout will leak. From design and engineering standpoints, it is doubtful whether any other plastic exhibits the physical properties and chemical inertness required for this special application.

9.9. Large Fabricated Structures

The application of polyethylene to the fabrication of large structures is favored most frequently in those instances where lightness in weight and corrosion resistance are decisive factors. For such applications, use is made of polyethylene sheets, blocks, or centrifugally cast tubing. Sheets of polyethylene are commercially available in widths from 48–72 inches and thicknesses of $1/4$ to 1 inch; blocks usually measure 12 by 12 inches in length and breadth, and from 2–4 inches in thickness. Standard cast polyethylene tubing is currently available in 2.375–20.000 inches inside diameter (2.75–20.50 inches o.d.) and corresponding weights of 0.605–6.500 pounds per foot (see Table CX). With these basic components, fabricated structures of nearly any size and shape can be constructed by the hot-gas welding technique. Examples of such structures are exhaust ducts, mixing tanks, electroplating and glass-etching vats, and similar applications in the fields of food processing, paper manufacture, bleaching and dyeing, and in the manufacture of light bulbs, television tubes, and rayon and other textiles.

9.10. Surgical Applications

Interest in polyethylene for surgical applications started around the year 1947, as indicated by reports on experimental and clinical studies with polyethylene film (290,292), and attention is being drawn to some of the physical properties of polyethylene which make it of potential value in the field of surgery (291). Early (292) as well as later (353,356,402,565) publications caution against the possible presence in polyethylene of irritating chemical additives, such as dicetyl phosphate, a stripping agent incorporated in the polyethylene during certain methods of manufacture.

Reports generally agree that pure polyethylene is well tolerated by living tissue (343,565) without causing a fibrous tissue reaction, or giving rise to tumors, or revealing evidence of carcinogenic stimulus (356). However, Oppenheimer, Oppenheimer, and Stout (621) found that every tested plastic film (cellophane, polyethylene, polyvinyl chloride) produced sarcomas in rats when imbedded subcutaneously. The suggestion that the tumor is caused by some impurity in the film is rendered less likely by these authors' findings that cellophane, thoroughly extracted with alcohol, is at least as carcinogenic as the original film, while pure polyethylene, without additives, produces about the same percentage of tumors as the commercial film. Oppenheimer *et al.*, on the other hand, point out that there is no reported instance in which the embedding has resulted in a malignant tumor in man.

According to a subsequent publication by Oppenheimer, Oppenheimer, Stout, and Danishefsky (758), a considerably higher percentage (45.4%) of malignant tumors was obtained by embedding cellophane B than with commercial polyethylene (12.4%) or pure polyethylene (18.4%), as indi-

TABLE CXIV

Tumors Obtained by Embedding Plastics Subcutaneously

Completed Experiments			
		Malignant Tumors Produced	
Material	Animals	No.	%
Cellophane A	Rats	15/42	35.7
Cellophane A	Mice	8/35	22.8
Cellophane A	Mice (black)	1/22	
Cellophane B	Rats	20/44	45.4
Polyethylene A	Rats	10/80	12.5
Pure polyethylene	Rats	7/38	18.4
Pure polyethylene	Mice	3/29	10.3
Polyvinyl chloride	Rats	17/44	38.6
Glass coverslip	Rats	1/50	

Experiments Still in Progress			
Material	Animals	Malignant Tumors Produced	Animals Still Alive
Cellophane C	Rats	11	16
Pure polyethylene			
perforated	Rats	1	30
textile	Rats	1	31
Silastic	Rats	12	3
Teflon	Rats	4	15
Nylon	Rats	4	21
Dacron	Rats	3	29
Dacron perforated	Rats	1	30
Polystyrene	Rats	2	22

Source: *Science*, **118**, 305 (1953).

cated in Table CXIV.   Although there is thus far no proven instance in the literature of a maligant tumor induced in man by embedding a plastic, it must be remembered that if it takes one to two years for a malignant tumor to appear in a rodent, it may take 10 to 15 years for a similar result in a human being.

Based on these studies, Druckrey and Schmaehl (842,843) attempted an explanation for the carcinogenic properties of a material as chemically inert as polyethylene. Of interest is the prediction of Fitzhugh (730a) that ionic polymerization should give resins of low carcinogenicity.

In a recent publication, Oppenheimer, Oppenheimer, Danishefsky, Stout, and Eirich (1008) consider it as fairly certain that the carcinogenic activity of films of polyethylene and other polymers (cellophane, Dacron, polyvinyl chloride, Silastic, Pliofilm, nylon, polymethyl methacrylate, polystyrene, Saran, Ivalon, Kel-F, Teflon, silk) when imbedded subcutaneously is not caused by impurities but is inherent in the polymer itself. Experiments with tagged polymers have shown that they are degraded and metabolized in the body, at least in the rat. The amount of breakdown is extremely minute, and no metabolites have as yet been identified. The possibility of an interaction between the polymer or its degradation products and some basic cell constituent of the organism may be considered, and the carcinogenic activity of the polymer may arise in at least two ways. Either the degradation products of the polymer are carcinogenic, or the creation of reactive centers in the polymer itself, as a result of the degradation, may impair the metabolism of the adjacent cell.

Generally, successful use of polyethylene tubing has been reported for intravenous therapy in infants (335), for resection of the trachea of dogs (339), in urological surgery (342), and as insertions in the pulmonary vein and in the left ventricle of cats (345). The use of polyethylene tubes in the reparative surgery of injuries to arteries (387,390) has also been described.

However, complications from the use of polyethylene tubing as a means of administering continuous or prolonged intravenous infusions were noted (353), and it has been conjectured that these tissue reactions may be due to the presence of dicetyl phosphate, or to degradation products resulting from extrusion of the polyethylene at elevated temperatures. According to another report (395), polyethylene tubes used in the experimental surgery of the ureter proved unsuitable because of their relatively rapid obstruction by urinary deposits.

Polyethylene tubing was shown by Bellamy and Watt (383) to be entirely without deactivating effect on penicillin; by contrast, penicillin in contact with rubber tubing for 24 hours suffers loss in potency amounting to as much as 20%. This destructive activity was found to be related to the kind and quantity of accelerator in the vulcanizate, some mixes deactivating to the extent of as much as 90%.

Polyethylene tubing for continuous spinal anesthesia has been described by Kirchof and Boals (545); such tubing is small enough to pass through an 18-gauge spinal needle and will admit a 26-gauge hypodermic needle.

Polyethylene film was used in the treatment of craniosynostosis (346), of hernia (352), as fillings for the artificially created, unnatural extrapleural spaces in 21 cases of pulmonary tuberculosis (386), and tested as prosthesis to replace the lung after pneumonectomy (392,422,469).

A polyethylene substitute for the upper two-thirds of the shaft of the femur of a 12-year-old boy was found adequate (420), while a polyethylene cup used in arthroplasty of the hip proved unsuitable (559).

As to plastic surgery, fine polyethylene "hair" has been recommended as a substitute for fat to build out facial contours (423).

X. STATISTICAL SUMMARY

10.1. Consumption

The consumption of plastics in the United States has risen from an estimated 60,000 tons in 1938 to 1,600,000 tons in 1955. For purposes of comparison, shipments of steel ingots and castings have increased from 31.6 to 117.1 million tons in the same period. It is apparent that plastics have assumed a position of major importance in the national economy. The spectacular nature of this growth is illustrated graphically in Figure 223, which

TABLE CXV

Consumption of Plastics and Competitive Materials
(Millions of short tons)

Year	Plastics[a]	Leather[b]	Rubber[c]	Wood[d]	Steel[e]
1938	0.06	0.85	0.625	27.7	31.6
1939	0.09	1.03	0.855	32.5	52.6
1940	0.12	0.97	0.942	38.0	64.2
1941	0.21	1.28	1.156	44.0	80.5
1942	0.21	1.35	0.727	54.0	83.2
1943	0.28	1.20	0.873	47.5	86.7
1944	0.32	1.16	1.077	43.7	88.5
1945	0.34	1.14	1.165	40.0	79.5
1946	0.43	1.10	1.472	42.2	66.1
1947	0.51	1.16	1.580	42.8	84.4
1948	0.55	1.06	1.490	46.1	88.4
1949	0.53	0.95	1.357	43.3	77.7
1950	0.82	1.01	1.750	53.5	96.7
1951	0.92	0.90	1.746	48.9	105.1
1952	0.86	0.93	1.726	51.0	102.1
1953	1.08	0.72	1.900	47.2	111.5
1954	1.09	0.74	1.659	..	118.6
1955	1.60	0.77	1.837	..	117.1

[a] Plastics includes all synthetic and cellulosic plastics and resins except those used in protective coatings, as production intended for end use. Data are on a dry-weight basis.
[b] Leather was estimated from number of cattle hides using a factor of 60 lb./hide.
[c] Rubber includes natural, synthetic, and reclaimed rubber.
[d] Wood was estimated from board feet consumed, using a factor of 2.57 lb./board foot.
[e] Steel includes ingots and castings only.
Sources: United States Tariff Commission Reports; *Survey of Current Business;* *Chemical Economics Handbook*, Stanford Research Institute.

shows consumption of plastics and "competitive" materials for the years 1938 to 1954. Supporting data are presented in Table CXV.

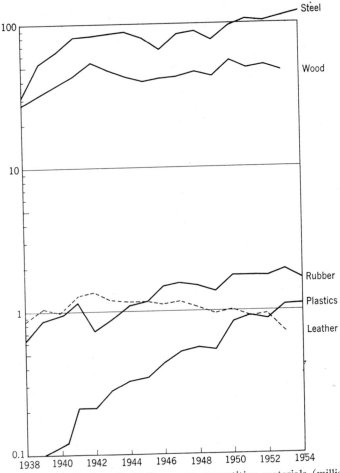

Fig. 223. Consumption of plastics *versus* competitive materials (millions of short tons). (United States Tariff Commission Reports; *Chemical Economics Handbook*, Stanford Research Institute.)

10.2. Production

The domestic production of thermoplastic, thermosetting, and cellulosic resins and plastics for the years 1938 to 1954 are presented graphically in Figure 224 and tabulated in Table CXVI.

Figure 225 illustrates changes in production of the major thermoplastics, polystyrene, polyvinyls, polymethacrylates, coumarone-indenes, and polyethylene from 1938 to 1954. To show the comparative growth rate of

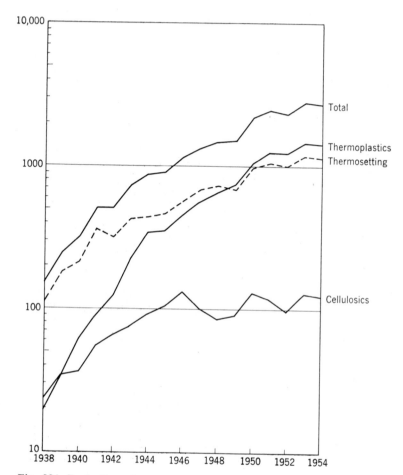

Fig. 224. Production of synthetic resins and plastics (millions of pounds). (United States Tariff Commission Reports; *Chemical Economics Handbook*, Stanford Research Institute.)

polyethylene more clearly, Figure 226 plots annual production of this polymer and of all other thermoplastics for the same years. The data supporting both Figures are set out in Table CXVII.

TABLE CXVI

Production of Synthetic Resins and Plastics[a]
(Millions of pounds)

Year	Thermoplastics[b]	Thermosetting	Cellulosics	Total
1938	19.2	111.2	23.7	154.1
1939	33.5	179.8	34.2	247.2
1940	62.4	214.4	36.8	313.6
1941	90.4	361.8	55.4	507.6
1942	124.3	315.7	67.4	507.4
1943	225.3	428.6	76.4	730.3
1944	339.2	443.2	92.0	874.4
1945	357.7	460.3	103.8	921.8
1946	462.3	562.4	133.4	1158.2
1947	567.5	684.6	100.4	1352.5
1948	665.0	728.5	85.6	1479.1
1949	743.4	682.9	90.7	1517.0
1950	1059.6	979.8	129.6	2169.0
1951	1259.9	1066.6	117.0	2443.5
1952	1243.9	1003.9	98.1	2345.9
1953	1474.4	1190.0	129.0	2793.4
1954	1436.6	1160.0	123.2	2719.8
1955	2087.1	1220.3	144.8	3452.2

[a] All data are on a net resin-content basis except "Cellulosics," which include plasti-cizers and fillers. Data for 1948–1955 were corrected to this basis on the assumption that for these years data for phenolic and other tar-acid resins used for molding include 50% fillers, and that data for all other non-cellulosics do not include fillers.
[b] Thermoplastics estimated by subtracting "Thermosetting (except alkyds)" and "Alkyd Resins" from "Total Synthetic Plastics" reported by the Tariff Commission.
Sources: United States Tariff Commission Reports; *Chemical Economics Handbook*, Stanford Research Institute.

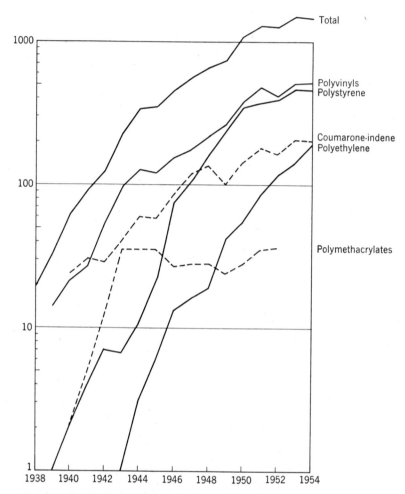

Fig. 225. Production of thermoplastics (millions of pounds). (United States Tariff Commission Reports; *Chemical Economics Handbook,* Stanford Research Institute; *Modern Plastics,* **32** [5], 84 (1955).)

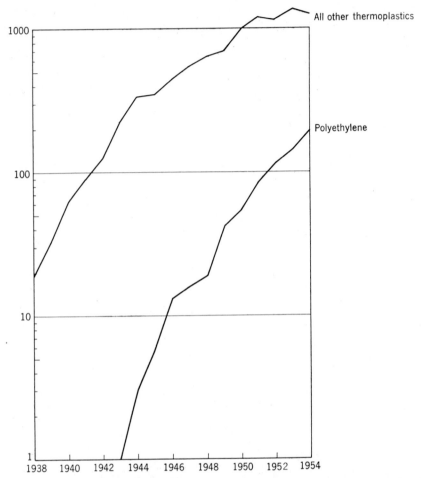

Fig. 226. Production of polyethylene *versus* all other thermoplastics (millions of pounds). (United States Tariff Commission Reports; *Chemical Economics Handbook*, Stanford Research Institute; *Modern Plastics* **32** [5], 84 (1955).)

TABLE CXVII

Production of Thermoplastics
(Millions of pounds)

Year	Poly-ethylene[a]	Poly-meth-acrylates[a]	Coumarone-Indene[a]	Poly-vinyls	Poly-styrene[b]	Total[c]
1938	0	0	...	...	0	19.2
1939	0	1	...	14.2	1.0	33.5
1940	0	2	24	22.5	2.0	62.4
1941	0	5	30	27.0	4.0	90.4
1942	0	12	29	52.2	7.0	124.3
1943	1	35	40	95.6	6.7	225.3
1944	3	35	59	126.9	10.6	339.2
1945	6	35	58	122.7	22.0	357.7
1946	13	27	86	155.6	73.0	462.3
1947	16	28	120	177.4	104.9	567.5
1948	19	28	135	218.2	162.7	665.0
1949	42	24	101	267.7	237.2	743.4
1950	55	28	143	381.0	340.4	1059.6
1951	85	35	177	475.8	372.6	1259.9
1952	115	36	166	420.1	397.8	1243.9
1953	144	..	206.6	515.8	468.5	1474.4
1954	195	..	202.9	516.8	463.5	1436.6
1955	375	..	259.6	698.1	616.6	2087.1

[a] Polyethylene, polymethacrylates, and coumarone-indene (in part) estimated from reports in the technical literature.
[b] Polystyrene data include only thermoplastic styrene resins.
[c] Total obtained by subtracting "Thermosetting" and "Alkyd Resins" from "Total Synthetic Plastics" reported by the Tariff Commission.
Sources: United States Tariff Commission Reports; *Chemical Economics Handbook*, Stanford Research Institute; *Modern Plastics*, **32** (5), 84 (1955); **33** (5), 75 (1956); **33** (7), 196 (1956).

10.3. Uses

As consumption of synthetic resins and plastics in the United States has increased, the end-use pattern has changed as new applications and improved processing techniques have been developed. Figure 227 shows a plot of major uses as percentage of total consumption for the period of 1938 to 1954. The major changes which have occurred during this period are evident. Supporting data are presented in Table CXVIII. Similar data for polyethylene are set forth separately in Table CXIX, and are illustrated graphically in Figure 228. In this case, only estimated data are available for the years 1953 and 1954. These are supplemented by what is believed to be a realistic forecast of end uses when total consumption has reached 600 million pounds per year.

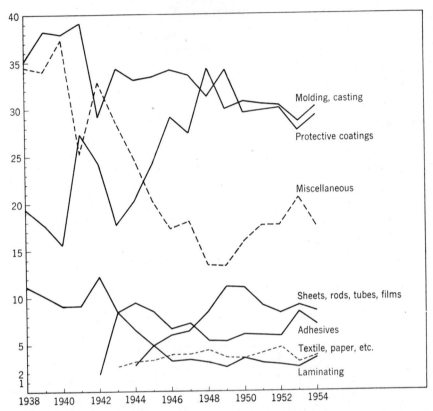

Fig. 227. Consumption pattern.   Uses of all plastics and resins as percentage of total consumption.   (United States Tariff Commission Reports; *Chemical Economics Handbook*, Stanford Research Institute.)

TABLE CXVIII

Consumption Pattern

(Uses of all plastics and resins as percentage of total consumption)

Year	Molding, Casting	Laminating	Adhesives	Protective Coatings	Textile, Paper and Leather	Sheets, Rods, Tubes, Films	Miscellaneous	Total
1938	19.4	11.1	..	35.1	..	..	34.4	100.0
1939	17.8	10.1	..	38.2	..	..	33.9	100.0
1940	15.6	9.1	..	38.0	..	..	37.3	100.0
1941	27.2	9.1	..	38.5	..	..	25.2	100.0
1942	24.2	12.1	1.7	29.2	..	..	32.8	100.0
1943	17.7	8.5	8.3	34.2	2.7	..	28.6	100.0
1944	20.2	6.5	9.4	33.2	3.2	2.8	24.7	100.0
1945	24.2	4.9	8.5	33.5	3.4	5.4	20.1	100.0
1946	29.0	3.2	6.6	34.1	3.9	5.9	17.2	100.0
1947	27.4	3.4	7.2	33.6	4.0	6.4	18.0	100.0
1948	34.0	3.1	5.4	31.3	4.4	8.4	13.4	100.0
1949	30.0	2.6	5.3	34.1	3.6	11.1	13.3	100.0
1950	30.7	3.5	6.0	29.5	3.5	11.0	15.8	100.0
1951	30.4	3.0	5.9	29.8	4.2	9.1	17.6	100.0
1952	30.3	2.9	5.9	30.3	4.7	8.3	17.6	100.0
1953	28.6	2.6	8.4	27.7	3.2	9.0	20.5	100.0
1954	30.3	3.5	7.1	29.3	3.8	8.5	17.5	100.0

Sources: United States Tariff Commission Report; *Chemical Economics Handbook,* Stanford Research Institute.

TABLE CXIX

Consumption Pattern

(Uses of polyethylene as percentage of total consumption)

End Use	Consumption		
	1953	1954	19..
Film	32	36	33
Wire and cable	22	15	14
Pipe	17	17	15
Injection molding	14	16	26
Paper and film coating	10	12	7
Bottles and jars	5	4	5

Source: *Modern Plastics,* **32** (5), 83 (1955).

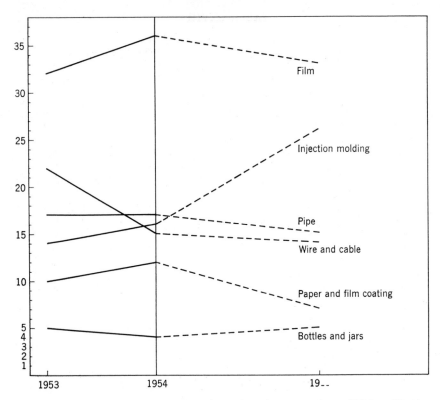

Fig. 228. Uses of polyethylene as percentage of total consumption. (*Modern Plastics,* **32** [5], 83 (1955).)

10.4. Producers

Domestic producers of polyethylene are listed in Table CXX; foreign producers, in Table CXXI.

TABLE CXX

Domestic Producers of Polyethylene

Company and Locations	Announced Cost ($ millions)	Announced Capacity (million lb./yr.)
Allied Chemical and Dye Corp.		
Tonawanda, N. Y.	10	20
Dow Chemical Co.		
Freeport, Tex.	12	32–35
E. I. du Pont de Nemours and Co.		
Beaumont, Tex.	Production of "Hypalon" only	
Belle, W. Va.	..	25
Orange, Tex.	..	100
Hercules Powder Co., Inc.		
Parlin, N. J.	10	30
M. W. Kellogg Co.		
Pasadena, Tex.	..	25–30
Koppers Company, Inc.		
Port Arthur, Tex.	..	20
Woodbridge, N. J.	..	10
Koppers Co., Inc.-Brea Chemicals Co.		
Long Beach, Calif.	..	50
Monsanto Chemical Co.		
Texas City, Tex.	..	99
National Petro-Chemicals		
Tuscola, Ill.	..	26
Phillips Chemical Co.		
Pasadena, Tex.	..	110
Sweeny, Tex.	..	120
Spencer Chemical Co.		
Orange, Tex.	25	45
Texas Eastman Corp.		
Longview, Tex.	10	30
Union Carbide and Carbon Chemicals Corp.		
Seadrift, Tex.	43	60
South Charleston, W. Va.	..	70
Texas City, Tex.	..	60
Torrance, Calif.	36	60

TABLE CXXI

Foreign Producers of Polyethylene

Country, Producer, and Location	Announced Capacity (million lb./yr.)
Argentina	
Iudustrias Quimicas Duperial S.A.	
Buenos Aires	0.55+
Brazil	
W. R. Grace and Co.–Farbwerke Hoechst AG.	
Sao Paulo	...
Union Carbide do Brazil	
Santos	...
Canada	
Canadian Industries, Ltd.	
Edmonton, Alberta	25
Carbide and Carbon Chemicals, Ltd.	
Montreal East, Quebec	...
France	
Ethylene-Plastique S.A.	
Carling (Lorraine)	...
Mazingarbe (Pas de Calais)	4
Houillèries du Bassin du Nord et du Pas de Calais	
Douai (Pas de Calais)	...
Germany	
Badische Anilin-u. Soda-Fabrik-AG.	
Ludwigshafen	...
Deutsche Shell–Badische Anilin-u. Soda-Fabrik-AG.	
Cologne	20
Kohle-Oel Chemie AG.	
Gelsenkirchen	24
Rheinische Olefinwerke AG.	
Wesseling	25
Great Britain	
Carbide and Carbon Chemicals, Ltd.	
Grangemouth	26
Imperial Chemical Industries, Ltd.	
Wilton	60
Italy	
Montecatini	
Ferrara	8
Japan	
Mitsui Petro-Chemical Industry Co.	
Iwakuni	7.5
Sumitomo Chemical Co.	
Niihama City	20
Netherlands	
Staatsmijnen in Limburg	...
Spain	
Union Quimica de Norte de Espana	4

A list of trademarks of commercial polyethylenes and polyethylene products is given in Table CXXII.

TABLE CXXII

Trademarks of Some Commercial Polyethylenes and Polyethylene Products

Allied Chemical Dye Corp.	
Semet-Solvay Petrochemical Division	A-C Polyethylene
American Agile Corp.	Agilene; Agaline; Agilene HT
Anchor Plastics Co.	Aeroflex; Super Aeroflex
Badische Anilin-u. Soda-Fabrik-AG.	Lupolen; A-Wachs BASF
Brea Chemicals Co.	Brea Polyethylene
Catalin Corp. of America	Molding Compound 15-5
Chester Packaging Products Corp.	Cheslene-TF
Dawbarn Brothers, Inc.	Polyethylene Fiber
Dow Chemical Co.	Dow Polyethylene
Durathene Corp.	Durathene
Dynamit AG., Troisdorf	Trolon
Eastman Chemical Products, Inc.	Epolene; Tenite Polyethylene
E. I. duPont de Nemours & Co.	Alathon; Rulan; Hypalon
Extruders, Inc.	Polyflex
Farbwerke Hoechst AG.	Hostalen
Fiberfil Corp.	Polyethylene and Fiberglass
Firestone Plastics Co.	Polyethylene Fiber
General Electric Co.	G-E Irrathene; G-E Vulkene
Gering Products, Inc.	Gering Polyethylene; Stretch
Harshaw Chemical Co.	Harshaw Tellerette
Hercules Powder Co.	Hi-fax
Imperial Chemical Industries, Ltd.	Alkathene HD
Kendall Co., Polyken Sales Div.	Polyken
Koppers Company, Inc.	Dylan; Super Dylan
Luminous Resins, Inc.	Paulite
Lurie Plastics, Inc.	Luraplast P
Monsanto Chemicals, Ltd.	Orizon
Montecatini	Fertene; Rotene
H. Muehlstein and Co., Inc.	Super Modulene
National Plastic Products Co.	Wynene I
Nobel Francaise	Socarex
Olin Mathieson Chemical Corp.	Olin Polyethylene
Palo Laboratory Supplies, Inc.	Nalgene; Nalgene HH
Papeteries Léon Riquet	Papiethylene
Phillips Chemical Co.	Marlex
Plastic Molded Parts, Inc.	Poly-Plugs
Plax Corp.	Plaxpak
Reeves Bros., Inc.	Reevon
Ruhrchemie, A.G.	RCH-Polyethylene
Sequoia Process Co.	Hyrad
Société Éthylène-Plastique	Plastylene
Spencer Chemical Co.	Poly-Eth
Texas Eastman Corp.	Tenite

(Table continued)

TABLE CXXII (*Concluded*)

Union Carbide and Carbon Corp.	Bakelite Polyethylene; Poly-
Bakelite Division	ethylene DXM-103
U. S. Industrial Chemicals Co.	
National Distillers Products Division	Petrothene
U. S. Rubber Co.	Trilok
Visking Corp.	Visqueen
Wathelet Cie.	Polyethylene

REFERENCES

[1] Hancock, Thomas, *Personal Narrative of Thomas Hancock*, Longman, Brown Green, Longmans and Roberts, London, 1857, p. 27.

[2] Stefan, M. J., *Akad. Wiss. Wien, Math.-Natur. Klasse. Abt. 2*, **69**, 713 (1874).

[3] Becker, P., *Analyst*, **20**, 49 (1895).

[4] Thiele, J., and Heuser, K., *Ann.*, **290**, 1 (1896).

[5] Losanitsch, S. M., and Jovitschitsch, M. Z., *Ber.*, **30**, 138 (1897).

[6] von Pechmann, H., *Ber.*, **31**, 2643 (1898).

[7] Bamberger, E., and Tschirner, F., *Ber.*, **33**, 955 (1900).

[8] Losanitsch, S. M., and Jovitschitsch, M. Z., *Ber.*, **40**, 4664 (1907).

[9] Losanitsch, S. M., and Jovitschitsch, M. Z., *Monatsh.*, **29**, 5, 753 (1908).

[10] Ipatieff, V. N., *J. Russ. Phys. Chem. Soc.*, **43**, 1420 (1911).

[11] Brit. 11,635, May 11, 1914, Matthew, F. E., and Elder, H. M.

[12] Chalmers, W., *J. Am. Chem. Soc.*, **65**, 90 (1926).

[13] Demyanov, N. V., and Pryanishnikov, N. D., *J. Russ. Phys. Chem. Soc.*, **58**, 462 (1926).

[14] Treadwell, W. D., and Tauber, E. L., *Helv. Chim. Acta*, **2**, 601 (1919).

[15] Menzies, A. W., and Wright, S. L., Jr., *J. Am. Chem. Soc.*, **43**, 2314 (1921).

[16] Taylor, H. S., *Proc. Am. Phil. Soc.*, **65**, 90 (1926).

[17] Lind, S. C., Bardwell, D. C., and Perry, I. H., *J. Am. Chem. Soc.*, **48**, 1556 (1926).

[18] Demyanov, N. V., and Pryanishnikov, N. D., *Ber.*, **61**, 1358 (1928).

[19] Pryanishnikov, N. D., *Ber.*, **61**, 1358 (1928).

[20] Carothers, W. H., Hill, J. W., Kirby, J. E., and Jacobson, R. A., *J. Am. Chem. Soc.*, **52**, 5279 (1930).

[21] Pease, R. N., *J. Am. Chem. Soc.*, **53**, 613 (1931).

[21a] Friedrich, M. E. P., and Marvel, C. S., *J. Am. Chem. Soc.*, **52**, 376 (1930).

[22] Herzog, R. O., and Spurlin, H. M., *Z. physik. Chem. Bodenstein-Festband*, 239 (1931).

[23] Ger. 505,265, Sept. 21, 1931, Hofmann, F., and Otto, M.

[24] Ger. 512,959, Sept. 23, 1931, Hofmann, F., and Otto, M.

[24a] Baylis, J. R., *Waterworks and Sewage*, **79**, 425 (1932).

[25] Chalmers, W., *Can. J. Research*, **7**, 113 (1932).

[26] Pease, R. N., *J. Am. Chem. Soc.*, **54**, 1876 (1932).

[27] Rossmann, E., *Ber.*, **65B**, 1847 (1932).

[28] de Saint-Aunay, R. V., *Chimie & industrie*, **29**, 1011 (1933).

[28a] Fair, G. M., *J. New Engl. Water Works Assoc.*, **47**, 248 (1933).

[29] Fawcett, E. W., and Gibson, R. O., *J. Chem. Soc.*, **1934**, 386.

[30] Baladin, A. A., Eidus, Y. T., and Zalogin, N. G., *Compt. rend. acad. sci. U. R. S. S.*, **IV**, No. 3, 132 (1934).

[31] Storch, H. H., *J. Am. Chem. Soc.*, **56**, 374–378 (1934).

[32] U. S. 1,981,819, Nov. 20, 1934, Wiezevich, P. J., and Whiteley, J. M., (Standard Oil Co.).

[33] Charch, W. H., and Scroggie, A. G., *Paper Trade J.*, **33** (Oct. 3, 1935).

[34] Eyring, H., *J. Chem. Phys.*, **3**, 107 (1935).

[35] Gee, G., *Trans. Faraday Soc.*, **31**, 969 (1935).

[36] Ipatieff, V. N., and Pines, H., *Ind. Eng. Chem.*, **27**, 1364 (1935).

[37] Kistiakowsky, G. B., *J. Am. Chem. Soc.*, **57**, 65, 876 (1935).

[38] Koch, H., and Ibing, G., *Brennstoff-Chem.*, **16**, 141 (1935).

[39] Staudinger, H., and Frost, W., *Ber.*, **68**, 2351 (1935).

[40] Storch, H. H., *J. Am. Chem. Soc.*, **57**, 2598–2601 (1935).

[41] Desparmet, E., *Bull. soc. chim. France*, **3** (5), 2047–2055 (1936).

[42] Gee, G., *Trans. Faraday Soc.*, **32**, 656–666 (1936).

[43] Ipatieff, V. N., and Grosse, A. V., *J. Am. Chem. Soc.*, **58**, 915 (1936).

[44] Kistiakowsky, G. B., *J. Am. Chem. Soc.*, **58**, 137–146 (1936).

[45] Malishev, B. W., *Petroleum Z.*, **2** (19), 1–3 (1936).

[46] Mark, H., and Raff, R., *Z. physik. Chem.*, **B31**, 275 (1936).

[47] Schulz, G. V., and Husemann, E., *Z. physik. Chem.*, **B34**, 187 (1936).

[48] Szukiewich, W., *Roczniki chemji*, **13**, 245 (1936).

[49] Staudinger, H., *Trans. Faraday Soc.*, **32**, 97–121 (1936).

[50] Brit. 453,850, Sept. 18, 1936, Imperial Chemical Industries, Ltd., and Goldstein, R. F.

[51] U. S. 2,000,964, May 14, 1934, Lenher, S. (E. I. duPont de Nemours and Co.).

[52] Burk, R. E., Thompson, H. E., Weith, A. J., and Williams, I., *Polymerization and its Applications in the Field of Rubber, Synthetic Resins and Petroleum*, Reinhold Publishing Co., New York, 1937.

[53] Flory, P. J., *J. Am. Chem. Soc.*, **59**, 241 (1937).

[54] Linderstrøm-Lang, K., *Nature*, **139**, 713 (1937).

[55] Melville, H., *Proc. Roy. Soc. (London)*, **A163**, 511 (1937).

[56] Meyer, K. H., and van der Wyk, A. J. A., *Helv. Chim. Acta*, **20**, 1313 (1937).

[57] Taylor, H. S., and Jungers, J. C., *Trans. Faraday Soc.*, **33**, 1353–1360 (1937).

[58] U. S. 2,089,524, Aug. 10, 1937, Abrams, A.

[59] French 817,374, Sept. 1, 1937, Imperial Chemical Industries, Ltd.

[60] Brit. 471,590, Sept. 6, 1937, Fawcett, E. W., Gibson, R. O., Perrin, M. W., Paton, J. G., Williams, E. G., and Imperial Chemical Industries, Ltd.

[61] Ger. 650,038, Sept. 9, 1937, Mark, H., and Ruppel, W., (I. G. Farbenindustrie, A-G.).

[62] Brit. 472,051, Sept. 16, 1937, Perrin, M. W., Paton, J. F., Williams, E. G., and Imperial Chemical Industries, Ltd.

[63] Brit. 474,426, Oct. 29, 1937, Perrin, M. W., Paton, J. G., Williams, E. G., and Imperial Chemical Industries, Ltd.

[64] Eidus, Y. T., *Bull. acad. sci. (U.R.S.S.), Classe sci. math. nat., Sér. chim.* **1938**, 737–751.

[65] Eirich, F., *Oesterreich. Chem. Ztg.*, **41**, 251 (1938).

[66] Hall, F. C., and Nash, A. W., *J. Inst. Petroleum Tech.*, **24**, 471–495 (1938).

[67] Joris, G. G., and Jungers, J. C., *Bull. soc. chim. Belg.*, **47**, 135–147 (1938).

[68] Linderstrøm-Lang, K., and Lanz, H., *Compt. rend. trav. lab. Carlsberg, Sér. chim.*, **21**, 315 (1938).

[69] Russell, F. R., and Hottel, H. C., *Ind. Eng. Chem.*, **30**, 183–189 (1938).

[70] Schulz, G. V., Dinglinger, A., and Husemann, E., *Z. physik. Chem.*, **B39**, 246 (1938).

[71] Snow, R. D., and Frey, F. E., *Ind. Eng. Chem.*, **30**, 176 (1938).

[71a] Brit. 481,515, March 1, 1938, Fawcett, E. W., and Imperial Chemical Industries, Ltd.

[72] Brit. 492,322, Sept. 19, 1938, Fawcett, E. W., and Imperial Chemical Industries, Ltd.

[73] French 48,915, Sept. 21, 1938, Addn. French 817,374, Imperial Chemical Industries, Ltd.

[74] French 832,174, Sept. 22, 1938, Imperial Chemical Industries, Ltd.

[75] Brit. 497,643, Dec. 22, 1938, Perrin, M. W., Fawcett, E. W., Paton, J. G., Williams, E. G., and Imperial Chemical Industries, Ltd.

[76] Barrer, R. M., *Trans. Faraday Soc.*, **35**, 628–643 (1939).

[77] Bunn, C. W., *Trans. Faraday Soc.*, **35**, 482–491 (1939).

[78] Cuthbertson, A. C., Gee, G., and Rideal, E., *Proc. Roy. Soc.* (*London*), **A170**, 300 (1939).

[79] Jahn, F. P., *J. Am. Chem. Soc.*, **61**, 798–800 (1939).

[80] Schulz, G. V., and Husemann, E., *Z. physik. Chem.*, **B43**, 385 (1939).

[81] Schütze, M., *Z. anal. Chem.*, **118**, 245 (1939).

[82] Velikovskii, A. S., Podolskaya, F. I., and Polonskaya, S. I., *Petroleum Neftyanoe Khoz.*, **20** (9), 41–43 (1939).

[83] Zimmermann, W., *Z. anal. Chem.*, **118**, 258 (1939).

[84] Brit. 499,333, Jan. 23, 1939, Addn. Brit. 471,590, Fawcett, E. W., Gibson, R. O., Perrin, M. W., Paton, J. G., Williams, E. G., and Imperial Chemical Industries, Ltd.

[85] French 836,988, Jan. 31, 1939, Imperial Chemical Industries, Ltd.

[86] U. S. 2,153,553, April 11, 1939, Fawcett, E. W., Gibson, R. O., and Perrin, M. W., (Imperial Chemical Industries, Ltd.)

[87] Brit. 507,323, June 9, 1939, Scott, T. R., Field, M. C., and Standard Telephone and Cables, Ltd.

[88] Brit. 513,742, Oct. 20, 1939, Renfrew, A., Davison, J. W., and Imperial Chemical Industries, Ltd.

[89] Brit. 514,687, Nov. 19, 1939, Williams, E. G. (Imperial Chemical Industries, Ltd.).

[90] U. S. 2,183,503, Dec. 12, 1939, McAlevy, A. (E. I. duPont de Nemours and Co.).

[91] Barrer, R. M., *Trans. Faraday Soc.*, **36**, 644–648 (1940).

[92] Burnham, H. D., and Pease, R. N., *J. Am. Chem. Soc.*, **62**, 453 (1940).

[93] Flory, P. J., *J. Am. Chem. Soc.*, **62**, 1057 (1940).

[94] Fox, J. J., and Martin, A. E., *Proc. Roy. Soc.* (*London*), **A175**, 208–233 (1940).

[95] Hessels, W. J., van Krevelen, D. W., and Waterman, H. I., *Rec. trav. chim.*, **59**, 696–702 (1940).

[96] Jacobsen, C. F., and Linderstrøm-Lang, K., *Acta Physiol. Scand.*, **2**, 149 (1940).

[97] Jungers, J. C., and Yeddanapalli, L. M., *Trans. Faraday Soc.*, **36**, 483–493 (1940).

[98] Konaka, Y., *J. Soc. Chem. Ind.* (*Japan*), **43**, suppl. 330, 363 (1940).

[99] Mark, H., *J. Phys. Chem.*, **44**, 764 (1940).

[100] Pichler, H., and Buffleb, H., *Brennstoff-Chem.*, **21**, 257 (1940).

[101] Romm, F. S., *J. Gen. Chem.* (*U.S.S.R.*), **10**, 1782–1792 (1940).

[102] Steacie, E. W. R., and Potvin, R., *Can. J. Research*, **18B**, 47–54 (1940).

[103] Unterzaucher, J., *Ber.*, **73B**, 391 (1940).

[104] Brit. 517,649, Feb. 5, 1940, Brislee, F. J., Quale, J. C., and Chapman, H. B., (British Insulated Cables, Ltd.).

[105] U. S. 2,192,931, March 12, 1940, Paton, J. G., and Williams, E. G., (Imperial Chemical Industries, Ltd.).

[106] Brit. 518,916, March 12, 1940, Dunbar, D., and Imperial Chemical Industries, Ltd.

[107] French, 853,754, March 28, 1940, Imperial Chemical Industries, Ltd.

[108] Can. 388,355, April 30, 1940, Fawcett, E. W., Gibson, R. O., Perrin, M. W., Paton, J. G., Williams, E. G., and Imperial Chemical Industries, Ltd.

[109] U. S. 2,200,429, May 7, 1940, Perrin, M. W., Fawcett, E. W., and Williams, E. G. (Imperial Chemical Industries, Ltd.).

[110] U. S. 2,210,771, Aug. 6, 1940, Myles, J. R., and Bache, L. L. (Imperial Chemical Industries, Ltd.).

[111] U. S. 2,210,774, Aug. 6, 1940, Perrin, M. W., Paton, J. G., and Williams, E. G. (Imperial Chemical Industries, Ltd.).

[112] U. S. 2,212,155, Aug. 20, 1940, Ellis, L. M. (E. I. duPont de Nemours and Co.).

[113] U. S. 2,212,786, Aug. 27, 1940, McQueen, D. M. (E. I. duPont de Nemours and Co.).

[114] U. S. 2,220,930, Nov. 12, 1940, Kraus, C. A. (Standard Oil Development Co.).

[115] Beeck, O., and Rust, F. F., J. Chem. Phys., 9, 480–483 (1941).

[116] Flory, P. J., J. Chem. Phys., 9, 660 (1941).

[117] Huggins, L. M., J. Chem. Phys., 9, 440 (1941).

[118] Mark, H., J. Appl. Phys., 12, 41 (1941).

[119] Linderstrøm-Lang, K., Jacobsen, O., and Johansen, G., Compt. rend. trav. lab. Carlsberg, Sér. chim., 23, 17 (1941).

[120] Mark, H., and Raff, R., High Polymeric Reactions, Interscience Publishers, New York, N. Y., 1941.

[121] Rao, M. R., J. Chem. Phys., 9, 682 (1941).

[122] Schulz, G. V., Z. Elektrochem., 47, 265 (1941).

[122a] Vieweg, R., and Klein, J., Kunststoffe, 31, 11–13 (1941).

[122b] Vieweg, R., and Schneider, W., Kunststoffe, 31, 417 (1941).

[123] Brit. 532,665, Jan. 29, 1941, Habgood, B. J., and Imperial Chemical Industries, Ltd.

[124] U. S. 2,232,475, Feb. 18, 1941, Renfrew, A., and Davison, J. W., (Imperial Chemical Industries, Ltd.).

[125] Russ. 59,036, Feb. 28, 1941, Dintses, A. I., and Postnov, N. I.

[126] Brit. 536,102, May 2, 1941, E. I. duPont de Nemours and Co.

[127] French 865,102, June 2, 1941, I. G. Farbenindustrie A.-G.

[128] U. S. 2,256,483, Sept. 23, 1941, Johnston, F. L. (E. I. duPont de Nemours and Co.).

[129] U. S. 2,261,757, Nov. 4, 1941, Fawcett, E. W. (Imperial Chemical Industries, Ltd.).

[130] Brit. 542,140, Dec. 30, 1941, Child, C. L., Habgood, B. J., and Imperial Chemical Industries, Ltd.

[131] Burnham, H. D., and Pease, R. N., J. Am. Chem. Soc., 64, 1404–1410 (1942).

[132] Flory, P. J., J. Chem. Phys., 10, 51 (1942).

[133] Freund, E. H., and Mark, H., Rayon Textile Monthly, 23, 515–517, 605–606 (1942).

[134] Gallaway, W. S., and Barker, E. F., J. Chem. Phys., 10, 88 (1942).

[135] Gee, G., Trans. Faraday Soc., 38, 276 (1942).

[136] Habeeb, H., Le Roy, D. J., and Steacie, E. W. R., J. Chem. Phys., 10, 261–267 (1942).

[137] Huggins, L. M., J. Am. Chem. Soc., 64, 1712 (1942).

[138] Michels, A., and Geldermans, M., *Physica*, **9** (10), 967–973 (1942).

[139] Steacie, E. W. R., and Le Roy, D. J., *J. Chem. Phys.*, **10**, 22–34 (1942).

[140] Brit. 544,359, April 9, 1942, Child, C. L., Clarke, R. B. F. F., Habgood, B. J., and Imperial Chemical Industries, Ltd.

[141] U. S. 2,290,794, July 21, 1942, Alvarado, A. M., and Dorough, G. L. (E. I. duPont de Nemours and Co.).

[142] U. S. 2,301,356, Nov. 10, 1942, Arnold, H. W., Brubaker, M. M., and Dorough, G. L. (E. I. duPont de Nemours and Co.).

[142a] Duggan, F. W., *Product Eng.*, **14**, 44 (1943).

[143] Flory, P. J., *J. Am. Chem. Soc.*, **65**, 372 (1943).

[144] Fuoss, R. M., and Mead, D. J., *J. Phys. Chem.*, **47**, 59 (1943).

[145] Imperial Chemical Industries, Ltd., Plastics Tech. Bull. No. 5, "*Alkathene*" *Brand of Polyethylene*, November, 1943.

[146] Kolsky, H., and Shearman, A. C., *Proc. Phys. Soc.* (*London*), **55**, 383–395 (1943).

[147] Umstatter, H., *Kolloid-Z.*, **102**, 232 (1943).

[148] Brit. 551,339, Feb. 18, 1943, Glint, C. F., Taylor, H., and Imperial Chemical Industries, Ltd.

[149] U. S. 2,313,144, March 9, 1943, Gomm, A. S. (Imperial Chemical Industries, Ltd.).

[150] U. S. 2,316,418, April 13, 1943, Habgood, B. J. (Imperial Chemical Industries, Ltd.).

[151] U. S. 2,316,481, April 13, 1943, Whittaker, D. (Imperial Chemical Industries, Ltd.).

[152] Ger. 737,960, July 1, 1943, Hopff, H., Goebel, S., and Rautenstrauch, C. W. (I. G. Farbenindustrie A.-G.).

[153] U. S. 2,325,060, July 27, 1943, Ingersoll, H. G. (E. I. duPont de Nemours and Co.).

[154] U. S. 2,334,195, Nov. 16, 1943, Hopff, H., and Goebel, S. (General Aniline and Film Co.).

[155] Ger. 745,425, Dec. 2, 1943, Hopff, H., and Goebel, S. (I. G. Farbenindustrie A.-G.).

[156] Ferguson, A. D., *Brit. Plastics*, **16**, 430–432 (1944).

[156a] Frith, E. M., and Tuckett, R. F., *Trans. Faraday Soc.*, **40**, 251 (1944).

[157] Funahashi, H., *J. Soc. Chem. Ind.* (*Japan*), **47**, 800–813 (1944).

[158] Irwin, H. H., *India Rubber World*, **111**, 65–66 (1944).

[159] Myers, C. S., *Modern Plastics*, **21**, 103 (1944).

[160] Reitlinger, S. A., *J. Gen. Chem.* (*U.S.S.R.*), **14**, 420–427 (1944).

[161] Staudinger, H., and Berndt, F., Unpublished paper: "The Determination of Molecular Weights of Paraffins and Polyethylenes," 1944.

[162] Swallow, J. C., *Endeavour*, **3**, 26–31 (1944).

[162a] Tobolsky, A. V., Prettyman, I. B., and Dillon, J. H., *J. Appl. Phys.*, **15**, 380 (1944).

[163] U. S. 2,339,958, Jan. 25, 1944, Sparks, W. J. (Jasco, Inc.).

[164] U. S. 2,342,400, Feb. 22, 1944, Hopff, H., Goebel, S., and Rautenstrauch, C. W.

[165] Brit. 560,476, April 5, 1944, W. T. Henley's Telegraph Works Co., Ltd., and Griffiths, F. T.

[166] Brit. 561,373, May 17, 1944, E. I. duPont de Nemours and Co.

[167] U. S. 2,351,120, June 13, 1944, Hanford, W. E. (E. I. duPont de Nemours and Co.).

[168] Can. 422,336, Aug. 29, 1944, Habgood, B. J. (Canadian Industries, Ltd.).

[169] Brit. 564,584, Oct. 4, 1944, Ingersoll, H. G., and E. I. duPont de Nemours and Co.

[170] U. S. 2,360,673, Oct. 17, 1944, Hanford, W. E. (E. I. duPont de Nemours and Co.).

[171] U. S. 2,364,410, Dec. 5, 1944, Whittaker, D. (Imperial Chemical Industries, Ltd.).

[172] Aiken, W. H., Doty, P. M., and Mark, H., *Modern Packaging*, **45** (12), 137–140, 166, 168 (1945).

[173] Allen, P. C., *Plastics (London)*, **9**, 68–69, 72–73 (1945).

[174] Bunn, C. W., and Alcock, T. C., *Trans. Faraday Soc.*, **41**, 317–325 (1945).

[175] Charlesby, A., *Proc. Phys. Soc. (London)*, **57**, 496–509 (1945).

[176] Charlesby, A., *Proc. Phys. Soc. (London)*, **57**, 510–518 (1945).

[177] Clarke, W. J., *Trans. A.I.E.E.*, **64**, 919–922 (1945).

[178] Hahn, F. C., Macht, M. L., and Fletcher, D. A., *Ind. Eng. Chem.*, **37**, 526–533 (1945).

[179] Hunter, E., and Oakes, W. G., *Trans. Faraday Soc.*, **41**, 49–56 (1945).

[180] Jackson, W., and Forsyth, J. S. A., *J. Inst. Elec. Engrs. (London)*, **92**, I. 214 (1945)

[181] Penn, W. S., *India-Rubber J.*, **109**, 741–742, 744, 773–774, 777 (1945).

[182] Raine, H. C., Richards, R. B., and Ryder, H., *Trans. Faraday Soc.*, **41**, 56–64 (1945).

[183] Richards, R. B., *Trans. Faraday Soc.*, **41**, 127–137 (1945).

[184] Thompson, H. W., and Torkington, P., *Proc. Roy. Soc. (London)*, **A184**, 3–20 (1945).

[185] Brit. 567,360, Feb. 12, 1945, E. I. duPont de Nemours and Co.

[186] Brit. 567,375, Feb. 12, 1945, Shipton, E., and Hill, W. N.

[187] Can. 425,816, Feb. 27, 1945, Child, C. L., and Habgood, B. J. (Canadian Industries, Ltd.).

[188] U. S. 2,372,001, March 20, 1945, Joyce, R. M., Jr. (E. I. duPont de Nemours and Co.).

[189] U. S. 2,373,561 April 10, 1945, Hanford, W. E., (E. I. duPont de Nemours and Co.).

[190] Brit. 568,890, April 25, 1945, E. I. duPont de Nemours and Co.

[191] Brit. 569,043, May 2, 1945, Richards, R. B., and Imperial Chemical Industries, Ltd.

[192] U. S. 2,377,753, June 5, 1945, Brubaker, M. M. (E. I. duPont de Nemours and Co.).

[193] U. S. 2,377,779, June 5, 1945, Hanford, W. E., Roland, J. R., and Young, H. S. (E. I. duPont de Nemours and Co.).

[194] Brit. 569,927, June 14, 1945, E. I. duPont de Nemours and Co.

[195] U. S. 2,378,629, June 19, 1945, Hanford, W. E. (E. I. duPont de Nemours and Co.).

[196] Brit. 570,139, June 25, 1945, Williams, E. G., and Imperial Chemical Industries, Ltd.

[197] U. S. 2,384,224, Sept. 4, 1945, Williams, E. G. (Imperial Chemical Industries, Ltd.).

[198] Brit. 571,814, Sept. 11, 1945, Wilson, H. F., and Telegraph Construction and Maintenance Co., Ltd.

[199] Brit. 571,943, Sept. 17, 1945, Baird, W., Forsyth, J. S. A., and Imperial Chemical Industries, Ltd.

[200] Can. 430,775, Oct. 23, 1945, Latham, G. H. (Canadian Industries, Ltd.).

[201] U. S. 2,387,755, Oct. 30, 1945, Hanford, W. E. (E. I. duPont de Nemours and Co.).

[202] U. S. 2,388,138, Oct. 30, 1945, Greenewalt, C. H. (E. I. duPont de Nemours and Co.).

[203] U. S. 2,388,160, Oct. 30, 1945, Krase, N. W. (E. I. duPont de Nemours and Co.).

[204] U. S. 2,388,169, Oct. 30, 1945, McAlvey, A., Strain, D. E., and Chance, F. S. (E. I. duPont de Nemours and Co.).

[205] U. S. 2,388,178, Oct. 30, 1945, Peterson, M. D. (E. I. duPont de Nemours and Co.).

[206] U. S. 2,388,225, Oct. 30, 1945, Brooks, R. E., Peterson, M. D., and Weber, A. G. (E. I. duPont de Nemours and Co.).

[207] Brit. 573,264, Nov. 13, 1945, Williams, J. H., and Imperial Chemical Industries, Ltd.

[208] U. S. 2,391,218, Dec. 18, 1945, Bacon, R. G. R., and Richards, R. B. (Imperial Chemical Industries, Ltd.).

[209] Brit. 574,031, Dec. 18, 1945, Hunter, E., Richards, R. B. and Imperial Chemical Industries, Ltd.

[210] Anfinsen, C., *Preparation and Measurement of Isotopic Tracers—A Symposium Prepared for the Isotope Research Group*, J. W. Edwards, Ann Arbor, Michigan, 1946, pp. 61–65.

[211] Austen, A. E. W., and Pelzer, H., *J. Inst. Elec. Engrs. (London)*, **93**, Pt. 1, 525–532 (1946).

[212] Boyer, R. F., Spencer, R. S., and Wiley, R. M., *J. Polymer Sci.*, **1**, 249 (1946).

[213] Davis, D. W., *Paper Trade J.*, **123** (9), 33–40 (1946).

[214] Dienes, G. J., and Klemm, J., *J. Applied Phys.*, **17**, 458–471 (1946).

[215] Freeth, F. A., *Brit. Plastics*, **18**, 444–447 (1946).

[216] Freeth, F. A., *Engineering*, **162** (4215), 388–389 (1946).

[217] Hopff, H. and Goebel, S., *Modern Plastics*, **23** (9), 141–145, 188, 190, 192 (1946).

[218] Hopff, H. and Kern, K., *Modern Plastics*, **23** (10), 153–160, 206, 208, 210, 212, 214, 216, 218, 220 (1946).

[219] Kodama, S., Tahara, H., and Taniguchi, I., *Rev. Phys. Chem. Japan, Shinkichi Horiba Commen. Vol.*, 50–57 (1946).

[220] Kume, T., *Rev. Phys. Chem. Japan, Shinkichi Horiba Commen. Vol.*, 98–107 (1946).

[221] Michels, A., Geldermans, M., and de Groot, S. R., *Physica*, **12** (2/3), 105–117 (1946).

[221a] Oakes, W. G., and Richards, R. B., *Trans. Faraday Soc.*, **42**, 197–205 (1946).

[221b] Petrocarbon, Ltd., *Petroleum Times*, **50**, 1078–1081 (1946).

[222] Plessner, K. W., and Richards, R. B., *Trans. Faraday Soc.*, **42**, 206–213 (1946).

[223] Powles, J. G., and Oakes, W. G., *Nature*, **157**, 840–841 (1946).

[224] Pratt, A. W., and Foskitt, N. L., *Trans. A.I.Ch.E.*, **42**, 149–163 (1946).

[225] Randolph, A. F., in *Colloid Chemistry*, Vol. VI, J. Alexander, ed., Reinhold Publishing Co., New York, 1946, pp. 976–983.

[226] Richards, R. B., *Trans. Faraday Soc.*, **42**, 10–28 (1946).

[22'] Sakurada, I., and Nakajima, A., *Chem. High Polymers (Japan)*, **3**, 91–95 (1946).

[228] Tessler, S., Woodberry, N. T., and Mark. H., *J. Polymer Sci.*, **1**, 437 (1946).

[229] Zimm, B. H., and Myerson, I., *J. Am. Chem. Soc.*, **68**, 911 (1946).

[230] Brit. 575,296, Feb. 12, 1946, Richards, R. B., and Imperial Chemical Industries, Ltd.

[231] U. S. 2,394,960, Feb. 12, 1946, Young, H. S. (E. I. duPont de Nemours and Co.).

[232] U. S. 2,395,327, Feb. 19, 1946, Hanford, W. E. (E. I. duPont de Nemours and Co.).

[233] U. S. 2,395,347, Feb. 16, 1946, Sharkey, W. H. (E. I. duPont de Nemours and Co.).

[234] U. S. 2,395,381, Feb. 19, 1946, Squires, L. (E. I. duPont de Nemours and Co.).

[235] Brit. 575,689, Feb. 28, 1946, E. I. duPont de Nemours and Co.

[236] U. S. 2,396,677, March 19, 1946, Brubaker, M. M. (E. I. duPont de Nemours and Co.).

[237] U. S. 2,396,785, March 19, 1946, Hanford, W. E. (E. I. duPont de Nemours and Co.).

[238] U. S. 2,396,920, March 19, 1946, Larson, A. T. (E. I. duPont de Nemours and Co.).

[239] U. S. 2,397,260, March 26, 1946, Hanford, W. E., and Roland, J. R. (E. I. duPont de Nemours and Co.)

[240] U. S. 2,398,426, April 16, 1946, Hanford, W. E. (E. I. duPont de Nemours and Co.).

[241] Brit. 576,830, April 23, 1946, E. I. duPont de Nemours and Co.

[242] U. S. 2,398,803, April 23, 1946, Myles, J. R., and Jones, F. S. B. (Imperial Chemical Industries, Ltd.).

[243] U. S. 2,398,926, April 23, 1946, Dorough, G. L. (E. I. duPont de Nemours and Co.).

[244] U. S. 2,399,653, May 7, 1946, Roland, J. R. (E. I. duPont de Nemours and Co.).

[245] U. S. 2,402,136, June 18, 1946, Hanford, W. E. (E. I. duPont de Nemours and Co.).

[246] U. S. 2,403,464 July 9, 1946, Smith, A. F. (E. I. duPont de Nemours and Co.).

[247] Brit. 578,584, July 4, 1946, E. I. duPont de Nemours and Co.

[248] Brit. 578,643, July 5, 1946, E. I. duPont de Nemours and Co.

[249] Brit. 578,992, July 19, 1946, E. I. duPont de Nemours and Co.

[250] Brit. 579,022, July 19, 1946, E. I. duPont de Nemours and Co.

[251] Brit. 579,023, July 19, 1946, E. I. duPont de Nemours and Co.

[252] Brit. 579,666, Aug. 12, 1946, Forsyth, J. S. A., and Imperial Chemical Industries, Ltd.

[253] Brit. 579,676, Aug. 12, 1946, Forsyth, J. S. A., and Imperial Chemical Industries, Ltd.

[254] Brit. 579,769, Aug. 15, 1946, Jarrett, K. B., and Imperial Chemical Industries, Ltd.

[255] Brit. 579,881, Aug. 20, 1946, E. I. duPont de Nemours and Co.

[256] Brit. 579,882, Aug. 20, 1946, E. I. duPont de Nemours and Co.

[257] Brit. 579,883, Aug. 20, 1946, E. I. duPont de Nemours & Co.

[258] Brit. 579,938, Aug. 21, 1946, Forsyth, J. S. A., and Imperial Chemical Industries, Ltd.

[259] U. S. 2,405,933, Aug. 20, 1946, Alderson, W. L., Jr. (E. I. duPont de Nemours and Co.).

[260] U. S. 2,405,962, Aug. 20, 1946, Larson, A. T., and Krase, N. W. (E. I. duPont de Nemours and Co.).

[261] U. S. 2,405,971, Aug. 20, 1946, McAlevy, A. (E. I. duPont de Nemours and Co.).

[262] U. S. 2,405,977, Aug. 20, 1946, Peters, F. T. (E. I. duPont de Nemours and Co.).

[263] U. S. 2,046,039, Aug. 20, 1946, Roedel, M. J. (E. I. duPont de Nemours and Co.).

[264] U. S. 2,407,181, Sept. 3, 1946, Scott, S. L. (E. I. duPont de Nemours and Co.).

[265] Brit. 580,416, Sept. 6, 1946, E. I. duPont de Nemours and Co.

[266] Brit. 581,279, Oct. 7, 1946, Whittaker, D., Forsyth, J. S. A., and Imperial Chemical Industries, Ltd.

[267] Brit. 581,717, Oct. 22, 1946, Myles, J. R., Whittaker, D., and Imperial Chemical Industries, Ltd.

[268] U. S. 2,409,679, Oct. 22, 1946, Hanford, W. E. and Roland, J. R. (E. I. duPont de Nemours and Co.).

[269] U. S. 2,409,996, Oct. 22, 1946, Roedel, M. J. (E. I. duPont de Nemours and Co.).

[270] Brit. 581,751, Oct. 23, 1946, E. I. duPont de Nemours and Co.

[271] Brit. 582,093, Nov. 5, 1946, Imperial Chemical Industries, Ltd.

[272] Brit. 582,334, Nov. 13, 1946, Imperial Chemical Industries, Ltd.

[273] U. S. 2,411,474, Nov. 19, 1946, Stevenson, H. B. (E. I. duPont de Nemours and Co.).

[274] Brit. 582,663, Nov. 25, 1946, Imperial Chemical Industries, Ltd.

[275] Brit. 582,890, Dec. 2, 1946, Imperial Chemical Industries, Ltd.

[276] Brit. 583,166, Dec. 11, 1946, Bacon, R. G. R., Richards, R. B., and Imperial Chemical Industries, Ltd.

[277] Brit. 583,178, Dec. 11, 1946, Forsyth, J. S. A., and Imperial Chemical Industries, Ltd.

[278] Brit. 583,181, Dec. 11, 1946, E. I. duPont de Nemours and Co.

[279] Brit. 583,419, Dec. 18, 1946, E. I. duPont de Nemours and Co.

[280] Aiken, W. H., *Plastics (Chicago)*, **7** (2), 34–36, 58 (1947).

[281] Bryant, W. M. D., *J. Polymer Science*, **2**, 547–564 (1947).

[282] Cherepow, F. H., *Paper Trade J.*, **125** (19), 110, 112, 114, 116, 118 (1947).

[283] Dakin, T. W., and Works, C. N., *J. Applied Phys.*, **18**, 789–796 (1947).

[284] Dennis, N., and Taylor, A. W. C., *German Acetylene Chemical Industry*, BIOS Final Report No. 1058 (1947).

[285] Dienes, G. J., *J. Colloid Science*, **2**, 131–161 (1947).

[286] Ellis, S. G., *J. Applied Phys.*, **18**, 846–847 (1947).

[287] Flory, P. J., *J. Am. Chem. Soc.*, **69**, 2893 (1947).

[288] Fröhlich, H., *Proc. Roy. Soc. (London)*, **A188**, 521–532 (1947).

[289] Houwink, R., *Verfkroniek*, **20**, 172–176 (1947).

[290] Hunter, B. M., Grindlay, J. H., and Craig, W. M., *Proc. Staff Meetings Mayo Clinic*, **22** (20) 453–456 (1947).

[291] Ingraham, F. D., Alexander, E., Jr., and Matson, D. D., *J.A.M.A.*, **135** (2), 82–87 (1947).

[292] Ingraham, F. D., Alexander, E., Jr., and Matson, D. D., *New England J. Med.*, **236**, 362–368 (1947).

[292a] Klevens, H. B., and Platt, J. R., *J. Am. Chem. Soc.*, **69**, 3055 (1947).

[292b] Lavers, C. G., *Can. J. Research*, **25F**, 1 (1947).

[293] Oakes, W. G., *Nature*, **159**, 29–30 (1947).

[294] Rouse, P. E., Jr., *J. Am. Chem. Soc.*, **69**, 1068–1073 (1947).

[295] Schutt, H. C., *Chem. Eng. Progress*, **43**, 103–116 (1947).

[296] Sergeys, F. J., *The Thermal Cracking of Ethane—Oppau Process*, FIAT Final Report No. 1294 (1947).

[297] Simril, V. L., *J. Polymer Science*, **2**, 142–156 (1947).

[298] Steiner, H. F., *J. Inst. Petroleum*, **33**, 410 (1947).

[299] Sutherland, G. B. B. M., and Jones, A. V., *Nature*, **160**, 567–568 (1947).

[300] Tani, H., *Chem. High Polymers (Japan)*, **4**, 82–89 (1947).

[301] Tani, H., *Mem. Inst. Sci. Ind. Research Osaka Univ.*, **5**, 119–125 (1947).

[302] Tani, H., Mori, S., and Horie, S., *Chem. High Polymers (Japan)*, **4**, 126–134 (1947).

[303] Tani, H., Mori, S., and Horie, S., *Chem. High Polymers (Japan)*, **4**, 151–157 (1947).

[304] Tani, H., and Sato, C., *Mem. Inst. Sci. Ind. Research Osaka Univ.*, **5**, 126–142 (1947).

[305] Brit. 584,309, Jan. 13, 1947, Imperial Chemical Industries, Ltd.

[306] Brit. 584,324, Jan. 13, 1947, Richards, R. B., Myles, J. R., and Whittaker, D. (Imperial Chemical Industries, Ltd.).

[307] Brit. 584,620, Jan. 20, 1947, Midwinter, E. L., Richards, R. B., and Imperial Chemical Industries, Ltd.

[308] Brit. 584,794, Jan. 27, 1947, E. I. duPont de Nemours and Co.

[309] Brit. 585,396, Feb. 6, 1947, E. I. duPont de Nemours and Co.

[310] Brit. 585,504, Feb. 7, 1947, E. I. duPont de Nemours and Co.

[311] U. S. 2,416,069, Feb. 18, 1947, Scott, S. L. (E. I. duPont de Nemours and Co.).

[312] Brit. 585,711, Feb. 20, 1947, E. I. duPont de Nemours and Co.

[313] Brit. 585,814, Feb. 25, 1947, Imperial Chemical Industries, Ltd.

[314] Brit. 585,934, Feb. 28, 1947, Dean, J. N., and Telegraph Construction & Maintenance Co., Ltd.

[315] Brit. 585,969, March 3, 1947, E. I. duPont de Nemours and Co.

[316] Brit. 586,826, April 1, 1947, The Resinous Products and Chemical Co.

[317] Brit. 587,378, April 23, 1947, Hunter, E., Feachem, C. G. P., Richards, R. B., and Imperial Chemical Industries, Ltd.

[318] Brit. 588,475, May 22, 1947, E. I. duPont de Nemours and Co.

[319] U. S. 2,422,392, June 17, 1947, Brubaker, M. M., Roland, J. R., and Peterson, M. D. (E. I. duPont de Nemours and Co.).

[320] Brit. 589,577, June 24, 1947, E. I. duPont de Nemours and Co.

[321] Brit. 590,055, July 7, 1947, E. I. duPont de Nemours and Co.

[322] Brit. 590,816, July 29, 1947, E. I. duPont de Nemours and Co.

[323] U. S. 2,425,638, Aug. 12, 1947, Peterson, M. D. (E. I. duPont de Nemours and Co.).

[324] Brit. 591,335, Aug. 14, 1947, E. I. duPont de Nemours and Co.

[325] Brit. 592,335, Sept. 15, 1947, Imperial Chemical Industries, Ltd.

[326] Brit. 592,486, Sept. 19, 1947, E. I. duPont de Nemours and Co.

[327] Brit. 592,487, Sept. 19, 1947, E. I. duPont de Nemours and Co.

[328] Brit. 592,517, Sept. 19, 1947, E. I. duPont de Nemours and Co.

[329] U. S. 2,429,861, Oct. 28, 1947, Woodbridge, R. G. (E. I. duPont de Nemours and Co.).

[330] U. S. 2,431,042, Nov. 18, 1947, Ingersoll, H. G. (E. I. duPont de Nemours and Co.).

[331] Brit. 594,891, Nov. 21, 1947, Western Electric Co.

[332] U. S. 2,432,287, Dec. 9, 1947, Cramer, R. D. (E. I. duPont de Nemours and Co.).

[333] Brit. 595,689, Dec. 12, 1947, E. I. duPont de Nemours and Co.

[334] U. S. 2,433,045, Dec. 23, 1947, Hamilton, J. P. (Carbide and Carbon Chemicals Corp.).

[335] Alexander, E., Jr., Small, W., and Campbell, J. B., *Ann. Surg.*, 127 (8), 1212–1216 (1948).

[336] Blake, J. T., *India Rubber World*, 118, 216–218 (1948).

[337] Bludworth, J. E., *Oil Gas J.*, 46 (35), 48–51 (1948).

[338] Bridgman, P. W., *Proc. Am. Acad. Arts. Sci.*, 76, 71–87 (1948).

[339] Clagett, O. T., Grindlay, J. H., and Hoersch, H. J., *Arch. Surg.*, 57 (2), 253–266 (1948).

[340] Eastwood, S. C., and Potas, A. E., *Petroleum Processing*, 27, 837–840 (1948).

[341] Elliott, I. A., Ambrose, E. J., and Temple, R. B., *J. Chem. Phys.*, 16, 877–886 (1948).

[342] Ferris, D. O., and Grindlay, J. H., *Proc. Staff Meetings Mayo Clinic*, 23 (17), 385–390 (1948).

[343] Grindlay, J. H., and Mann, F. C., *Arch. Surg.*, 56, 794–812 (1948).

[343a] Heering, H., Puell, H., and Drewitz, I., *Kunststoffe*, 38, 49 (1948).

[344] Heller, G. W., and Oppenheimer, H., *J. Colloid Science*, 3, 33–43 (1948).

[345] Hurwitt, E. S., *Surg. Gynec. and Obst.*, 87 (3), 313–316 (1948).

[346] Ingraham, F. D., Matson, D. D., and Alexander, E., Jr., *Surgery* 23 (2), 252–268 (1948).

[347] Jessup, R. S., *J. Chem. Physics*, **16**, 661 (1948).

[347a] Kay, W. B., *Ind. Eng. Chem.*, **40**, 1459 (1948).

[348] Moll, H. W., and LeFevre, W. J., *Ind. Eng. Chem.*, **40**, 2172–2179 (1948).

[349] Natta, G., and Baccaredda, M., *J. Polymer Sci.*, **3**, 829–833 (1948).

[350] Seymour, R. B., *Ind. Eng. Chem.*, **40**, 524–527 (1948).

[351] Tani, H., and Sato, C., *Chem. High Polymers (Japan)*, **5**, 57–73 (1948).

[352] Thompson, W., *Lancet*, **2** (5), 182 (1948).

[353] Tuell, S. W., Martin, W. B., and Laufman, H., *Quart. Bull. Northwestern Univ. Med. School*, **22**, 353–355 (1948).

[354] Vogel, A., *Textbook of Practical Organic Chemistry*, Longmans Greene and Company, Ltd., London, 1948.

[355] Wall, L. A., *J. Research Natl. Bur. Standards*, **41**, 315–322 (1948).

[355a] Wenzel, B. M., *Psychological Bull.*, **45**, 231–247 (1948).

[356] Yeager, G. H., and Cowley, R. A., *Ann. Surg.*, **128**, 509–520 (1948).

[357] U. S. 2,434,179, Jan. 6, 1948, Sharkey, W. H. (E. I. duPont de Nemours and Co.).

[358] U. S. 2,434,662, Jan. 20, 1948, Latham, G. H., and Strain, E. D. (E. I. duPont de Nemours and Co.).

[359] U. S. 2,435,245, Feb. 3, 1948, Strain, E. D. (E. I. duPont de Nemours and Co.).

[360] Brit. 597,833, Feb. 4, 1948, E. I. duPont de Nemours and Co.

[361] U. S. 2,436,080, Feb. 17, 1948, Smith, A. F. (E. I. duPont de Nemours and Co.).

[362] U. S. 2,435,256, Feb. 17, 1948, Hanford, W. E., and Salzberg, P. L. (E. I. duPont de Nemours and Co.).

[363] U. S. 2,439,528, April 13, 1948, Roedel, M. J. (E. I. duPont de Nemours and Co.).

[364] U. S. 2,440,800, May 4, 1948, Hanford, W. E., and Joyce, R. M. (E. I. duPont de Nemours and Co.).

[365] U. S. 2,441,209, May 11, 1948, Rose, H. E. (All-American Aviation, Inc.).

[366] Brit. 604,580, July 6, 1948, E. I. duPont de Nemours and Co.

[367] Brit. 607,103, Aug. 25, 1948, Rigby, G. W., and E. I. duPont de Nemours and Co.

[368] Brit. 607,888, Sept. 7, 1948, Hammond, R., and Imperial Chemical Industries, Ltd.

[369] Brit. 607,911, Sept. 7, 1948, E. I. duPont de Nemours and Co.

[370] U. S. 2,448,666, Sept. 7, 1948, Fletcher, D. A., and Renfrew, M. M. (E. I. duPont de Nemours and Co.).

[371] U. S. 2,448,799, Sept. 7, 1948, Happoldt, W. B., and Stockfleth, A. (E. I. duPont de Nemours and Co.).

[372] U. S. 2,448,946, Sept. 7, 1948, Alderson, W. L., Jr. (E. I. duPont de Nemours and Co.).

[373] U. S. 2,449,489, Sept. 14, 1948, Larson, A. T. (E. I. duPont de Nemours and Co.).

[374] U. S. 2,450,451, Oct. 5, 1948, Schmerling, L. (Universal Oil Products Co.).

[375] U. S. 2,451,743, Oct. 19, 1948, Jarrett, K. B. (Imperial Chemical Industries, Ltd.).

[376] U. S. 2,451,963, Oct. 19, 1948, Loder, D. J. (E. I. duPont de Nemours and Co.).

[377] Brit. 612,056, Nov. 8, 1948, Downing, J., and Wilcox, M. H. (British Celanese, Ltd.).

[378] Brit. 612,266, Nov. 10, 1948, E. I. duPont de Nemours and Co.

[379] U. S. 2,456,265, Dec. 14, 1948, Frolich, P. K. (Jasco, Inc.).

[380] U. S. 2,455,910, Dec. 14, 1948, Alderson, W. L., Jr. (E. I. duPont de Nemours and Co.).

[381] U. S. 2,457,229, Dec. 28, 1948, Hanford, W. E., and Roland, J. R. (E. I. duPont de Nemours and Co.).

[382] U. S. 2,457,238, Dec. 28, 1948, Hunter, E., and Richards, R. B. (Imperial Chemical Industries, Ltd.).

[383] Bellamy, L. J., and Watt, C. H., *Chemistry & Industry*, 19–21 (1949).

[384] Blake, J. T., and Kitchin, D. W., *Ind. Eng. Chem.*, **41**, 1633–1641 (1949).

[384a] Borroff, E. E., and Wake, W. C., *Trans. Inst. Rubber Ind.*, **25**, 190–198 (1949).

[385] Brown, Alexander, J., *J. Applied Phys.*, **20**, 552–558 (1949).

[386] Condon, W. B., and Harper, F. R., *Arch. Surg.*, **59** (3), 705–709 (1949).

[387] Cooper, F. W., Jr., Robertson, R. L., Shea, P. C., Jr., and Whitehead, D. E. W., *Surgery*, **25** (2), 184–190 (1949).

[388] DeLong, W. B., and Peterson, E. V., *Chem. Eng.*, **56** (6), 123–125 (1949).

[389] Desreux, R. C., *Rec. trav. chim.*, **68**, 789–806 (1949).

[390] Donovan, T. J., *Amer. Surg.*, **130** (6), 1024–1043 (1949).

[391] Gohn, G. R., Cummings, J. D., and Ellis, W. C., *Proc. ASTM*, **49**, 1139-1151, discussion, 1152–1157 (1949).

[392] Grindlay, J. H., Clagett, O. T., and Bulbulian, A. H., *Proc. Staff Meetings Mayo Clinic*, **24** (13), 346–350 (1949).

[393] Hammond, G. L., and Moakes, R. C. W., *Trans. Inst. Rubber Ind.*, **25**, 172 (1949).

[394] Hawkins, S. W., and Richards, R. B., *J. Polymer Sci.*, **4**, 515–522 (1949).

[395] Herdman, J. P., *Brit. J. Surg.*, **37** (145), 105–106 (1949).

[396] Kellner, L., *Nature*, **163**, 877 (1949).

[397] King, G. W., Hainer, R. M., and McMahon, H. O., *J. Appl. Phys.*, **20**, 559–563 (1949).

[398] Kitson, R. E., and Mitchell, J., Jr., *Anal. Chem.*, **21**, 401 (1949).

[399] Kitson, R. E., Oemler, A. N., and Mitchell, J., Jr., *Anal. Chem.*, **21**, 404 (1949).

[400] Korshak, V. V., *Invest. Akad. Nauk S.S.S.R., Otdel Khim. Nauk*, 269–273 (1949).

[401] Korshak, V. V., *Invest. Akad. Nauk S.S.S.R., Otdel Khim. Nauk*, 487–492 (1949).

[402] Le Veen, H. H., and Barberio, J. R., *Am. Surg.*, **129** (1), 74–84 (1949).

[403] Madorsky, S. L., Straus, S., Thompson, D., and Williamson, L., *J. Research Natl. Bur. Standards*, **42**, 499–514 (1949).

[404] Matthews, J. L., Peiser, H. S., and Richards, R. B., *Acta Cryst.*, **2**, 85–90 (1949).

[405] Meissner, H. P., and Merrill, E. W., *Modern Plastics*, **26** (8), 104, 106, 108, 158, 160, 162, 166 (1949).

[406] Milas, N. A., Stahl, L. E., and Dayton, B. B., *J. Am. Chem. Soc.*, **71**, 1448–1450 (1949).

[406a] Morawetz, H., *Ind. Eng. Chem.*, **41**, 1442 (1949).

[407] Muthana, M. S., and Mark, H., *J. Polymer Sci.*, **4**, 527–529 (1949).

[408] Natta, G., and Baccaredda, M., *Makromol. Chem.*, **4**, 134–155 (1949).

[409] Natta, G., and Baccaredda, M., *Gazz. chim. ital.*, **79**, 364–378 (1949).

[410] Oakes, W. G., *Proc. Inst. Elect. Engrs.*, **96**, 37–43 (1949).

[411] Oakes, W. G., and Richards, R. B., *J. Chem. Soc.*, **1949**, 2929–2935.

[412] Parks, G. S., and Mosley, J. R., *J. Chem. Phys.*, **17**, 691–694 (1949).

[413] Parks, W., and Richards, R. B., *Trans. Faraday Soc.*, **45**, 203–211 (1949).

[414] Persak, K. J., *India Rubber World*, **121**, 315–316 (1949).

[415] Rall, F. A., and Danby, C. J., *J. Chem. Soc.*, **1949**, 2219–2222.

[416] Richards, C. E., and Bull, R. L., *J. Soc. Chem. Ind. (London)*, **68**, 19–22 (1949).

[417] Rocca, M., *Materie plastiche*, **15**, 119–125 (1949).

[418] Rochow, R. G. and Rowe, F. G., *Anal. Chem.*, **21**, 461–466 (1949).

[419] Ryan, W., *Modern Packaging*, **22** (12), 133 (1949).

[420] Seddon, H. J., and Scales, J. T., *Lancet*, **2** (18), 795–796 (1949).

[421] Shooter, K. V., and Thomas, P. H., *Research (London)*, **2**, 533–535 (1949).

[422] Southworth, J. L., *Am. Surg.*, **129** (1), 85–89 (1949).

[423] Teplitsky, D., and Rubin, L. R., *Plastic and Reconstructive Surg.*, **4** (3), 274–275 (1949).

[424] Victoreen, J. A., *J. Appl. Phys.*, **20**, 1141–1147 (1949).

[425] Wood, J. N., *Surveyor*, **108**, 349–350 (1949).

[426] Ziegler, K., *Brennstoff-Chem.*, **30**, 181–184 (1949).

[427] U. S. 2,462,331, Feb. 22, 1949, Myers, C. S. (Bakelite Corp.).

[428] U. S. 2,462,390, Feb. 22, 1949, Harmon, J. (E. I. duPont de Nemours and Co.).

[429] U. S. 2,462,678, Feb. 22, 1949, Roedel, M. J. (E. I. duPont de Nemours and Co.).

[430] U. S. 2,462,680, Feb. 22, 1949, Sargent, D. E. (E. I. duPont de Nemours and Co.).

[431] Brit. 619,905, March 16, 1949, E. I. duPont de Nemours and Co.

[432] Brit. 620,963, April 1, 1949, E. I. duPont de Nemours and Co.

[433] U. S. 2,466,038, April 5, 1949, Midwinter, E. L., and Richards, R. B. (Imperial Chemical Industries, Ltd.).

[434] U. S. 2,466,694, April 12, 1949, Freed, Wm. V. (E. I. duPont de Nemours and Co.).

[435] U. S. 2,467,196, April 12, 1949, Dietrich, M. A. (E. I. duPont de Nemours and Co.).

[436] U. S. 2,467,231, April 12, 1949, Richards, L. M. (E. I. duPont de Nemours and Co.).

[437] U. S. 2,467,234, April 12, 1949, Sargent, D. E., and Hanford, W. E. (E. I. duPont de Nemours and Co.).

[438] U. S. 2,467,245, April 12, 1949, Whitman, G. M., and Scott, S. L. (E. I. duPont de Nemours and Co.).

[439] U. S. 2,467,550, April 19, 1949, Fletcher, D. A., and Taylor, R. S. (E. I. duPont de Nemours & Co.).

[440] U. S. 2,467,774, April 19, 1949, Plambeck, L., Jr. (E. I. duPont de Nemours and Co.).

[441] U. S. 2,468,054, April 26, 1949, Ford, T. A. (E. I. duPont de Nemours and Co.).

[442] U. S. 2,468,111, April 26, 1949, Robertson, J. A. (E. I. duPont de Nemours and Co.).

[443] U. S. 2,470,166, May 17, 1949, Hetzel, S. J., and Kennedy, R. B. (Sun Oil Co.).

[444] U. S. 2,470,190, May 17, 1949, Schmerling, L. (Universal Oil Products Co.).

[445] Brit. 623,705, May 20, 1949, E. I. duPont de Nemours and Co.

[446] Can. 456,913, May 24, 1949, Loasby, G. (Canadian Industries, Ltd., to Imperial Chemical Industries, Ltd.)

[447] Can. 456,914, May 24, 1949, Richards, R. B. (Canadian Industries, Ltd., to Imperial Chemical Industries, Ltd.).

[448] U. S. 2,471,959, May 31, 1949, Hunt, M. (E. I. duPont de Nemours and Co.).

[449] U. S. 2,473,996, June 21, 1949, Hanford, W., Roland, J. R., Mochel, W. E. (E. I. duPont de Nemours and Co.).

[450] U. S. 2,474,612, June 28, 1949, Barney, A. L. (E. I. duPont de Nemours and Co.).

[451] U. S. 2,475,520, July 5, 1949, Roedel, M. J. (E. I. duPont de Nemours and Co.).

[452] Brit. 627,376, Aug. 8, 1949, E. I. duPont de Nemours and Co.

[453] U. S. 2,478,390, Aug. 9, 1949, Hanford, W. E., and Joyce, R. M., Jr. (E. I. duPont de Nemours and Co.).

[454] U. S. 2,480,296, Aug. 30, 1949, Burk, R. E. (E. I. duPont de Nemours and Co.).

[454a] U. S. 2,480,297, Aug. 30, 1949, Goldrick, R. M., and Marks, B. M. (E. I. duPont de Nemours and Co.)

[454b] U. S. 2,480,298, Aug. 30, 1949, Happoldt, W. B., Jr. (E. I. duPont de Nemours and Co.).

[455] U. S. 2,480,615, Aug. 30, 1949, Strain, D. E., and Osgood, W. V. (E. I. duPont de Nemours and Co.).

[456] U. S. 2,482,877, Sept. 27, 1949, Schmerling, L. (Universal Oil Products Co.).

[457] U. S. 2,484,530, Oct. 11, 1949, Schroede r, H. E. (E. I. duPont de Nemours and Co.).

[458] U. S. 2,485,796, Oct. 25, 1949, White, J .O. (E. I. duPont de Nemours and Co.).

[459] Dutch 64,982, Dec. 15, 1949, N. V. de Bataafsche Petroleum Maatschappij (Willem L. J. de Nie, inventor).

[460] Arnett, L. M., Meibohm, E. P. H., and Smith, A. F., *J. Polymer Sci.*, **5**, 737–738 (1950).

[461] Blake, J. N., *Iva*, **21**, 27–35 (1950).

[462] Bostwick, R., and Carey, R. H., *Ind. Eng. Chem.*, **42**, 848–849 (1950).

[463] Bryant, W. M. D., Tordella, J. P., and Pierce, R. H. H., paper presented at the 118th meeting, American Chemical Society, Chicago, Ill., Sept. 3–8, 1950.

[464] Buckley, G. D., Cross, L. H., and Ray, N. H., *J. Chem. Soc.*, **1950**, 2714–2718.

[464a] Carey, R. H., *ASTM Bull. No. 167*, July, 1950.

[465] Carey, R. H., Schulz, E. F., and Dienes, G. J., *Ind. Eng. Chem.*, **42**, 842–847 (1950).

[466] Cross, L. H., Richards, R. B., and Willis, H. A., *Discussions Faraday Soc.*, **1950** (9), 235–245.

[467] Dannenberg, E. M., Jordan, M. E., and Stokes, C. A., *India Rubber World*, **122**, 663–671 (1950).

[468] Desreux, V., and Spiegels, M. C., *Bull. soc. chim. Belges*, **59**, 476–489 (1950).

[469] Grindlay, J. H., Clagett, O., and Rydell, J. R., *J. Thoracic Surg.*, **19** (3), 391–398 (1950).

[470] Hancock, D. C., *Brit. Plastics*, 115 (Oct., 1950).

[471] Hermans, P. H., and Weidinger, A., *J. Polymer Sci.*, **5**, 269–281 (1950).

[472] Hopff, H., Goebel, S., and Kern, R., *Makromol. Chem.*, **4**, 240–261 (1950).

[473] Hopkins, I. L., Baker, W. O., and Howard, J. B., *J. Applied Phys.*, **21**, 206–213 (1950).

[474] Houwink, R., *Elastomers and Plastomers*, Vol. I, Elsevier Publishing Co., Inc., Houston, Tex., 1950.

[475] Lane, G., *Australian Plastics*, **6** (64), 35–36 (1950).

[475a] Keller, A., and Sandeman, J., *J. Polymer Sci.*, **15**, 133 (1950).

[476] Kodama, S., and Taniguchi, I., *J. Chem. Soc. Japan, Ind. Chem. Sect.*, **53**, 385–387 (1950).

[477] Kodama, S., Taniguchi, I., and Zenbutso, T., *Bull. Inst. Chem. Research, Kyoto Univ.*, **23**, 77 (1950).

[478] Leitch, L. C., Gagnon, P. E., and Cambron, A., *Can. J. Research*, **B28**, 256 (1950).

[479] Lehrer, E., and Eblinghaus, E., *Angew. Chem.*, **2**, 20 (1950).

[480] Madorsky, S. L., *Science*, **111**, 360–361 (1950).

[481] Mark, H., and Tobolsky, A. V., *Physical Chemistry of High Polymeric Systems*, Interscience Publishers, Inc., New York, 1950.

[481a] Maxwell, J. B., *Data Book on Hydrocarbons*, van Nostrand, New York, 1950.

[482] McCubbin, T. K., Jr., and Sinton, W. M., *J. Optical Soc. Am.*, **40**, 537–539 (1950).

[483] Neumann, J. A., *Modern Plastics*, **27** (10), 85–86, 88 (1950).

[484] Newton, R. G., and Wake, W. C., *J. Rubber Research*, **19**, 17 (1950).

[485] Pross, A. W., and Black, R. M., *J. Soc. Chem. Ind. (London)*, **69**, 113–116 (1950).

[486] Simha, R., Wall, L. A., and Blatz, P. J., *J. Polymer Sci.*, **5**, 615–632 (1950).

[486a] Stoeckhert, K., *Chem.-Ing.-Tech.*, **22**, 131 (1950).

[487] Timmermans, J., *Physico-Chemical Constants of Pure Organic Compounds*, Elsevier Publishing Company, Inc., New York, 1950.

[488] Trillat, J. J., *Compt. rend.*, **230**, 1522–1524 (1950).

[489] Trillat, J. J., Barbezat, S., and Delalande, A., *Compt. rend.*, **231**, 835 (1950).

[490] Trillat, J. J., Barbezat, S., and Delalande, A., *J. chim. phys.*, **47**, 877–882 (1950).

[490a] Vieweg, R., and Moll, J., *Kunststoffe*, **40**, 317 (1950).

[491] Wallder, V. T., Clarke, W. J., DeCoste, J. B., and Howard, J. B., *Ind. Eng. Chem.*, **42**, 2320–2325 (1950).

[492] Winogradoff, N. N., *Nature*, **165**, 123 (1950).

[493] Zettlemoyer, A. C., Chand, A., and Gamble, E., *J. Am. Chem. Soc.*, **72**, 2752–2757 (1950).

[494] Ziegler, K., and Gellert, H. G., *Ann.*, **567**, 195 (1950).

[495] U. S. 2,495,282, Jan. 24, 1950, Pinkney, P. S. (E. I. duPont de Nemours and Co.).

[496] U. S. 2,495,283, Jan. 24, 1950, Werntz, J. H. (E. I. duPont de Nemours and Co.).

[497] U. S. 2,495,284, Jan. 24, 1950, Pinkney, P. S. (E. I. duPont de Nemours and Co.).

[498] U. S. 2,495,285, Jan. 24, 1950, Hoehn, H. H. (E. I. duPont de Nemours and Co.).

[499] U. S. 2,495,286, Jan. 24, 1950, Brubaker, M. M. (E. I. duPont de Nemours and Co.).

[500] U. S. 2,495,292, Jan. 24, 1950, Scott, S. L. (E. I. duPont de Nemours and Co.).

[501] U. S. 2,495,293, Jan. 24, 1950, Scott, S. L. (E. I. duPont de Nemours and Co.).

[501a] U. S. 2,497,291, Feb. 14, 1950, Brubaker, M. M., Roland, J. R., and Peterson, M. D. (E. I. duPont de Nemours and Co.).

[502] U. S. 2,497,323, Feb. 14, 1950, Roedel, M. J. (E. I. duPont de Nemours and Co.).

[503] U. S. 2,499,486, Mar. 7, 1950, Fuller, E. D. (Visking Corp.).

[504] U. S. 2,499,756, Mar. 7, 1950, Jacobson, R. A. (E. I. duPont de Nemours and Co.).

[505] Brit. 634,140, Mar. 15, 1950, Imperial Chemical Industries, Ltd.

[506] U. S. 2,503,252, Apr. 11, 1950, Ernsberger, M. L. (E. I. duPont de Nemours and Co.).

[507] U. S. 2,508,893, May 23, 1950, Sadowski, E. M., and Miller, W. P. (Radio Corp. of America).

[508] U. S. 2,511,480, June 13, 1950, Roedel, M. J. (E. I. duPont de Nemours and Co.).

[509] U. S. 2,512,472, June 20, 1950, White, J. O. (E. I. duPont de Nemours and Co.).

[510] U. S. 2,516,960, Aug. 1, 1950, Coffman, D. D. (E. I. duPont de Nemours and Co.).

[511] U. S. 2,516,980, Aug. 1, 1950, Gray, H. W., and Latham, G. H. (E. I. duPont de Nemours and Co.).

[511a] U. S. 2,518,462, Aug. 15, 1950, Gowing, D. M., Langdon, D. R., and Selby, R. L. (E. I. duPont de Nemours and Co.).

[512] U. S. 2,519,013, Aug. 15, 1950, Banigan, T. F. (E. I. duPont de Nemours and Co.).

[513] U. S. 2,519,755, Aug. 22, 1950, Gribbins, M. F. (E. I. duPont de Nemours and Co.).

[514] U. S. 2,520,173, Aug. 29, 1950, Sanders, P. F. (E. I. duPont de Nemours and Co.).

[515] U. S. 2,520,338, Aug. 29, 1950, Robertson, J. A. (E. I. duPont de Nemours and Co.).

[516] U. S. 2,520,737, Aug. 29, 1950, Romeyn, H., Jr., and Ferrell, W. (United States Rubber Co.).

[517] Swiss 269,269, Oct. 2, 1950, Schaerer, A.

[518] Fr. 966,283, Oct. 5, 1950, Société nouvelle de métallisation.

[519] U. S. 2,525,691, Oct. 10, 1950, Lee, G. P., and MacLeod, N. D. (Imperial Chemical Industries, Ltd.).

[520] U. S. 2,526,773, Oct. 24, 1950, Richards, R. B., Myles, J. R., and Whittaker, D. (Imperial Chemical Industries, Ltd.).

[521] U. S. 2,528,523, Nov. 7, 1950, Kent, R. E. (E. I. duPont de Nemours and Co.).

[522] U. S. 2,533,207, Dec. 12, 1950, Dickey, J. B., and Coover, H. W., Jr. (Eastman Kodak Co.).

[523] U. S. 2,534,079, Dec. 12, 1950, Strain, D. E., and Peterson, H. (E. I. duPont de Nemours and Co.).

[524] U. S. 2,535,373, Dec. 26, 1950, Shearer, H. E., and Martin, A. R. (American Viscose Corp.).

[525] Ger. 801,165, Dec. 28, 1950, Badische Anilin- u. Soda-Fabrik (I. G. Farbenindustrie Akt.-Ges., "In Auflösung"), Alfred Kirsch, inventor.

[527] Biggs, B. S., *Bell System Tech. J.*, **30**, 1078–1101; *Bell Telephone System Tech. Pubs.*, Monograph No. 1913, 1951.

[528] Brown, H. P., and Harrison, J. H., *J. Urol.*, **66**, 85–93 (1951).

[529] Bryant, W. M. D., *J. Polymer Sci.*, **6**, 359–370 (1951).

[530] Cremer, E., and Prior, F., *Z. Elektrochem.*, **55**, 66 (1951).

[531] Cremer, E., and Müller, R., *Z. Elektrochem.*, **55**, 217 (1951).

[532] Cutler, J. A., Kaplan, E., McLaren, A. D., and Mark, H., *Tappi*, **34**, 404–407 (1951).

[533] DeCoste, J. B., Malm, F. S., and Wallder, V. T., *Ind. Eng. Chem.*, **43**, 117–121 (1951).

[534] Ellis, W. C., and Cummings, J. D., *ASTM Bull.* **178**, 47–50 (1951).

[535] Flory, P. J., and Fox, T. G., Jr., *J. Am. Chem. Soc.*, **73**, 1904 (1951).

[536] Fox, T. G., Jr., and Flory, P. J., *J. Am. Chem. Soc.*, **73**, 1909 (1951).

[537] Fox, T. G., Jr., and Flory, P. J., *J. Am. Chem. Soc.*, **73**, 1915 (1951).

[538] Gemmer, E., *Werkstoffe u. Korrosion*, **2**, 369–371 (1951).

[539] Goldberg, B., *Corrosion*, **7**, 47–50 (1951).

[540] Hermans, P. H., *Kolloid-Z.*, **120**, 3–9, discussion 9–24 (1951).

[541] Hillier, K. W., *Proc. Phys. Soc. (London)*, **64B**, 998–1005 (1951).

[542] Hoff, E. A. W., *Kunststoffe*, **41**, 413–414 (1951).

[543] Horsley, R. A., and Nancarrow, H. A., *Brit. J. Applied Phys.*, **2**, 345–351 (1951).

[544] Kellner, L., *Proc. Phys. Soc. (London)*, **64A**, 521–535 (1951).

[545] Kirchof, A. C., and Boals, D. C., *Current Res. Anesth.*, **30** (1), 41–46 (1951).

[546] Koizumi, M., *Chem. Researches (Japan)*, **9**, 1–51 (1951).

[547] Koppius, O. G., *Anal. Chem.*, **23**, 554 (1951).

[548] Kraus, G., and Manson, J. E., *J. Polymer Sci.*, **6**, 625–631 (1951).

[549] Krimm, S., and Tobolsky, A. V., *J. Polymer Sci.*, **7** (1), 57–76 (1951).

[550] Krimm, S., and Tobolsky, A. V., *Textile Research J.*, **21**, 805–822 (1951).

[551] Küchler, L., *Polymerisations-Kinetik*, Springer-Verlag, Berlin, 1951.

[552] Lenoir, J. M., and Comings, E. W., *Chem. Eng. Progress*, **47**, 223–231 (1951).

[553] Mackenzie, E. F. W., *J. Inst. Water Engrs.*, **5**, 596–604 (1951).

[554] Marks, L. S., *Mechanical Engineers' Handbook*, 5th ed., McGraw-Hill Book Co., New York, 1951.

[555] Meibohm, E. P. H., and Smith, A. F., *J. Polymer Sci.*, **7**, 449–456 (1951).

[556] Miller, W. J., *Modern Plastics*, **28** (5), 74 (Jan. 1951).

[557] Morawetz, H., *J. Polymer Sci.*, **6**, 117–121 (1951).

[558] Mund, W., and Coekelbergs, R., *Ann. soc. sci. Bruxelles, Ser. I*, **65**, 149–187 (1951).

[559] Neuman, P. H., and Scales, J. T., *J. Bone Jt. Surg.*, **33B** (3), 392–398 (1951).

[560] Nielsen, L. E., *Rev. Sci. Instr.*, **22**, 690 (1951).

[561] Peukert, H., *Z. Ver. deut. Ing.*, **93**, 1097 (1951).

[561a] Price, F. P., *J. Chem. Phys.*, **19**, 973 (1951).

[562] Renfrew, A., *Plastics Inst. (London) Trans.*, **19** (35), 5–19 (1951).

[563] Richards, R. B., *J. Applied Chem. (London)*, **1**, 370–376 (1951).

[564] Richards, R. B., *J. Polymer Sci.*, **6**, 397–402 (1951).

[565] Rubin, L. R., *Plastic and Reconstructive Surg.*, **7**, 131–142 (1951).

[566] Sherwood, P. W., *Petroleum Refiner*, **30** (11), 157–160 (1951).

[566a] Sisman, O., and Bopp, C. D., *ORNL*, 928 (A.E.C., June 29, 1951).

[567] Storch, H. H., Columbic, M., and Anderson, R. B., *The Fischer-Tropsch and Related Syntheses*, John Wiley and Sons, Inc., New York, 1951.

[568] Union Carbide and Carbon Corp., *Technical Data: Bakelite Polyethylene for Paper Coatings*, New York, 1951.

[569] Weir, C. E., *J. Research Natl. Bur. Standards*, **46**, 207–212 (1951).

[570] Wilson, H. F., *Brit. Plastics*, **24**, 309–313 (1951).

[571] U. S. Pat. Appl. 691,180 (1951), Bryant, W. M. D. (E. I. duPont de Nemours and Co.).

[572] U. S. 2,542,783, Feb. 20, 1951, Seed, L. (Imperial Chemical Industries, Ltd.).

[573] U. S. 2,543,329, Feb. 27, 1951, Myers, C. S. (Union Carbide and Carbon Corp.).

[573a] Brit. 652,669, April 25, 1951, Rugar, G. F. (Diamond Alkali Co.).

[574] Brit. 652,730, May 2, 1951, Buckles, C. W., and Williams, C. F. (Pirelli-General Cable Works, Ltd.).

[575] Ger. Pat. Appl. B-199, May 2, 1951, Badische Anilin u. Soda Fabrik A.-G.

[576] U. S. 2,551,591, May 8, 1951, Foord, S. G. (International Electric Corp.).

[577] U. S. 2,556,158, June 12, 1951, West, J. P. (Universal Oil Products).

[578] U. S. 2,559,649, July 10, 1951, Little, J. W.

[579] U. S. 2,563,631, Aug. 7, 1951, Young, D. W., and Smyers, W. H. (Standard Oil Development Co.).

[580] Ger. 811,506, Aug. 20, 1951, Norvin Kunststoff-G.m.b.H. (Franz Meixner and Robert Loch, inventors).

[581] U. S. 2,566,218, Aug. 28, 1951, Wayne, W. J. (E. I. duPont de Nemours and Co.).

[582] U. S. 2,566,244, Aug. 28, 1951, Pickney, R. S. (E. I. duPont de Nemours and Co.).

[583] U. S. 2,566,537, Sept. 4, 1951, Schmerling, L. (Universal Oil Products Co.).

[584] U. S. 2,566,538, Sept. 4, 1951, Schmerling, L. (Universal Oil Products Co.).

[585] U. S. 2,568,902, Sept. 25, 1951, Thompson, R. B., and Schmerling, L. (Universal Oil Products Co.).

[586] Brit. 658,893, Oct. 17, 1951, E. I., duPont de Nemours and Co.

[586a] Brit. 659,958, Oct. 31, 1951, E. I. duPont de Nemours and Co.

[587] *Modern Packaging*, **25**, 216 (May, 1952).

[588] Baker, W. O., Mason, W. P., and Heiss, J. H., *J. Polymer Sci.*, **8**, 129–155 (1952).

[589] Beaman, R. G., *J. Polymer Sci.*, **9**, 470–472 (1952).

[590] Bradbury, E. J., McNulty, D., Savage, R. L., and McSweeney, E. E., *Ind. Eng. Chem.*, **44**, 211–212 (1952).

[591] Bretton, R. H., *Progress Rept. IV*, (NYO-3311), Yale University (October, 1952).

[592] Brubaker, D. W., and Kammermeyer, K., *Ind. Eng. Chem.*, **44**, 1465–1474 (1952).

[593] Brubaker, M. M., Coffman, D. D., and Hoehn, H. H., *J. Am. Chem. Soc.*, **74,** 1509 (1952).

[594] Brusca, R., *Ingegneria chim.*, 1 (2), 7–9 (1952).

[595] Buckley, G. D., and Ray, N. H., *J. Chem. Soc.*, **1952,** 3701.

[596] Bunn, H., *Ind. Eng. Chem.*, **44,** 2128–2133 (1952).

[597] Charlesby, A., *Proc. Roy. Soc. (London)*, **215A,** 187–214 (1952).

[598] Cover, G. W., *J. Inst. Water Engrs.*, **6,** 110–144 (1952).

[599] Dole, M., Hettinger, W. P., Jr., Larson, N. R., and Wethington, J. A., Jr., *J. Chem. Phys.*, **20,** 781–790 (1952).

[600] E. I. duPont de Nemours and Co., Polychemicals Department, *Bulletin X-37,* Wilmington, Del. 1952.

[601] Eifflaender, K., *Chem.-Ing.-Tech.*, **24,** 555–563 (1952).

[602] Foulke, D. G., *Proc. Am. Electroplaters' Soc.*, **39,** 127–140 (1952).

[603] Frank, C. E., Blackham, A. V., and Swarts, D. E., *Natl. Advisory Comm. Aeronaut., Tech. Note 2848,* 1952.

[604] Haine, W. A., and Land, W. M., *Modern Plastics*, **29** (6), 109–110, 112, 116, 118, 120, 196–197 (1952).

[605] Haine, W. A., Smith, E. F., and Smith, N. R., *Elec. Eng.*, **71,** 113–117 (1952).

[606] Harris, I., *J. Polymer Sci.*, **8,** 353–364 (1952).

[607] Heering, H., *Kautschuk u. Gummi,* **5,** 36–38 (1952).

[608] Hoff, E. A. W., *J. Polymer Sci.*, **9,** 41–52 (1952).

[609] Hopff, H., *Kunststoffe,* **42,** 423–426 (1952).

[610] Hultzsch, K., *Mitt. chem. Forsch.-Inst. Wirtsch. Österr,* **6,** 1–4 (1952).

[611] Keller, A., *Nature,* 169, 913 (1952).

[612] King, C. C., and Warburton, J., *Oil Gas J.*, **51** (31), 92–94, 97 (1952).

[613] Kiyama, R., and Kinoshita, H., *Rev. Phys. Chem. Japan,* **22,** 1–3 (1952).

[614] Krimm, S., *J. Appl. Phys.*, **23,** 287 (1952).

[615] Low, B. W., and Richards, F. M., *J. Am. Chem. Soc.*, **74,** 1660 (1952).

[616] Madorsky, S. L., *J. Polymer Sci.*, **9,** 133–156 (1952).

[617] Mayburg, S., and Lawrence, W. L., *J. Appl. Phys.*, **23,** 1006–1011 (1952).

[618] McGeer, P. L., and Duus, H. C., *J. Chem. Phys.*, **20,** 1813–1814 (1952).

[619] Meybeck, J., and Iwanow, N., *Bull. inst. textile France,* No. 36, 7–26 (1952).

[620] Myers, C. S., *Ind. Eng. Chem.*, **44,** 1095–1098 (1952).

[621] Oppenheimer, B. S., Oppenheimer, E. T., and Stout, A. R., *Proc. Soc. Exptl. Biol. Med.*, **79,** 366–369 (1952).

[622] Peffer, R. J., and Dunbar, R. E., *Proc. N. Dakota Acad. Sci.*, **6,** 45–49 (1952).

[623] Pierce, R. H., Jr., Tordella, J. A., and Bryant, W. M. D., *J. Am. Chem. Soc.*, **74,** 282 (1952).

[623a] Pinner, S. H., and Stabin, J. V., *J. Polymer Sci.*, **9,** 575–579 (1952).

[624] Rabinowicz, E., and Shooter, K. V., *Proc. Phys. Soc. (London)*, **65B,** 671–673 (1952).

[625] Ray, N. H., *Trans. Faraday Soc.*, **48,** 809–812 (1952).

[626] Renfrew, A., *Trans. Plastics Inst. (London)*, **20** (41), 57–67 (1952).

[627] Rugg, F. M., Smith, J. J., and Atkinson, J. V., *J. Polymer Sci.*, **9,** 579–581 (1952).

[628] Schildknecht, C. E., *Vinyl and Related Polymers,* John Wiley and Sons, Inc., New York, 1952.

[629] Schmieder, R., and Wolf, K., *Kolloid-Z.*, **127,** 65 (1952).

[630] Shearon, W. H., Jr., *Chem. Eng. News,* **30,** 316–321 (1952).

[631] Shooter, K. F., and Tabor, D., *Proc. Phys. Soc. (London)*, **65B**, 661–671 (1952).

[632] Simonds, H. R., Weith, A. J., and Schock, W., *Extrusion of Plastics, Rubber and Metals*, Reinhold Publishing Corp., New York, 1952.

[633] Simonim, G. D. G., *Revêtement et protect.*, **5**, 5, 7, 9–15 (1952).

[633a] Staudinger, H., *Angew. Chem.*, **64**, 155 (1952).

[634] Thinius, K., *Analytische Chemie der Plaste (Kunststoff-Analyse)*, Springer-Verlag, Berlin, 1952.

[635] Tompa, H., *Monatsh.*, **83**, 1356–1368 (1952).

[636] Ubbelohde, A. R., and Woodward, I., *Trans. Faraday Soc.*, **48**, 113–121 (1952).

[637] Ueberreiter, K., and Orthmann, H. J., *Kolloid-Z.*, **126**, 140–149 (1952).

[638] Ueberreiter, K., and Orthmann, H. J., *Kolloid-Z.*, **128**, 125–136 (1952).

[639] Ueberreiter, K., Orthmann, H. J., and Sorge, G., *Makromol. Chem.*, **8**, 21–40 (1952).

[639a] Umminger, O., *Kunststoffe*, **42**, 169 (1952).

[640] Umstaetter, H., *Einfuehrung in die Viskosimetrie und Rheometrie*, Springer-Verlag, Berlin, 1952.

[641] Villabona, J., *Rev. plasticos (Madrid)*, **3**, 304–306 (1952).

[642] Vol'kenshtein, M. V., and Ptitsyn, O. B., *Doklady Akad. Nauk S.S.S.R.*, **86**, 677–680 (1952).

[643] Wallder, V. T., *Elect. Eng.*, **77**, 59–64 (1952).

[644] Ziegler, K., *Angew. Chem.*, **64**, 323 (1952).

[645] Ziegler, K., *Brennstoff-Chem.*, **33**, 193 (1952).

[646] U. S. 2,581,088, Jan. 1, 1952, Etherington, L. D., and Scheeline, H. W. (Standard Oil Development Co.).

[647] U. S. 2,582,327, Jan. 15, 1952, Haine, W. A. (Union Carbide and Carbon Corp.).

[648] U. S. 2,584,126, Feb. 5, 1952, Hanford, W. E. (E. I. duPont de Nemours and Co.).

[649] U. S. 2,585,537, Feb. 12, 1952, Coffman, D. D. (E. I. duPont de Nemours and Co.).

[650] U. S. 2,586,322, Feb. 19, 1952, Franta, W. A. (E. I. duPont de Nemours and Co.).

[651] U. S. 2,586,820, Feb. 26, 1952, Hemperly, W. F., and Smith, N. R. (Union Carbide and Carbon Corp.).

[652] U. S. 2,587,680, March 4, 1952, Box, E. O., Jr. (Phillips Petroleum Co.).

[653] U. S. 2,589,189, March 11, 1952, Ciapetta, F. G., and Buck, W. H. (Atlantic Refining Co.).

[654] U. S. 2,590,322, March 25, 1952, Imhoff, D. H., and Berg, C. H. O. (Union Oil Co. of California).

[654a] Brit. 669,771, April 19, 1952, Buckley, G. D., Ray, N. H., and Imperial Chemical Industries, Ltd.

[655] U. S. 2,592,526, April 15, 1952, Seed, L. (Imperial Chemical Industries, Ltd.).

[665a] Brit. 678,896, Sept. 10, 1952, Felten und Guilleaume Carlswerk A.-G.

[656] U. S. 2,592,763, April 15, 1952, Taylor, R. S. (E. I. duPont de Nemours and Co.).

[657] U. S. 2,595,400, May 6, 1952, Maynard, J. T. (E. I. duPont de Nemours and Co.).

[658] Ger. Pat. Application Z 1118 (May 8, 1952), Ziegler, K.

[659] U. S. 2,599,123, June 3, 1952, Pinkney, P. S., Pratt, B. C., and Wayne, W. J. (E. I. duPont de Nemours and Co.).

[660] U. S. 2,599,249, June 3, 1952, Friedman, B. S. (Sinclair Refining Co.).

[661] U. S. 2,599,501, June 3, 1952, Upson, R. W. (E. I. duPont de Nemours and Co.).

[662] Austrian 171,701, June 25, 1952, Asboth, K.

[662a] Ger. 844,348, July 21, 1952, Kreidl, W.

[663] U. S. 2,606,179, Aug. 5, 1952, Boyd, T. (Monsanto Chemical Co.).

[664] U. S. 2,609,150, Sept. 2, 1952, Bludeau, R. E. (Union Carbide and Carbon Co.).

[665] U. S. 2,609,545, Sept. 9, 1952, Bing, J. H. (Aktieselskabet "Ferrosan").

[665a] Brit. 678,896, Sept. 10, 1952, Felten und Guilleaume Carlswerk A-G.

[666] U. S. 2,612,480, Sept. 30, 1952, May, M. R. (Sun Chemical Corp.).

[667] U. S. 2,612,966, Oct. 7, 1952, Nicol, W. H. (Wingfoot Corp.).

[668] U. S. 2,615,857, Oct. 28, 1952, Clarke, W. J. (Bell Telephone Laboratories, Inc.).

[669] U. S. 2,615,955, Oct. 28, 1952, McLean, D. A. (Bell Telephone Laboratories, Inc.).

[670] Brit. 682,420, Nov. 12, 1952, E. I. duPont de Nemours and Co.

[671] U. S. 2,618,574, Nov. 18, 1952, Pavlic, A. A. (E. I. duPont de Nemours and Co.).

[672] U. S. 2,619,443, Nov. 25, 1952, Robinson, P. (Sprague Electric Co.).

[673] U. S. 2,619,479, Nov. 25, 1962, McQueen, D. M. (E. I. duPont de Nemours and Co.).

[674] U. S. 2,620,325, Dec. 2, 1952, Langkammerer, C. M. (E. I. duPont de Nemours and Co.).

[675] U. S. 2,622,024, Dec. 16, 1952, Gurnick, R. S., and Joy, R. T. (Thompson Products, Inc.).

[676] U. S. 2,622,056, Dec. 16, 1952, De Coudres, R. A., and Myers, C. S. (Union Carbide and Carbon Corp.).

[677] American Petroleum Institute, *Project 44: Selected Values of Physical and Thermodynamic Properties of Hydrocarbons and Related Compounds*, Carnegie Press, Pittsburgh, Penna., 1953.

[678] *Bakelite Rev.*, **25** (3), 22–23 (1953).

[679] *Brit. Plastics*, **26** (286), 79–81 (1953).

[680] *Brit. Plastics*, **26** (293), 357–360 (1953).

[681] *Can. Chem. Proc.*, **37**, 108 (Oct., 1953).

[682] *Can. Chem. Proc.*, **37** (12), 28 (1953).

[683] *Chem. Eng.*, **60** (10), 114 (1953).

[684] *Chem. Week*, **73** (9), 62, 64 (1953).

[685] *Chem. Week*, **73** (19), 22 (1953).

[686] *Chem. Week*, **73** (22), 16 (1953).

[687] *Chem. Week*, **73** (23), 68 (1953).

[688] *Inst. Petroleum Rev.*, **7** (84), 419 (1953).

[689] *Modern Packaging*, **26**, 142–143, 294 (April, 1953).

[690] *Modern Packaging*, **26**, 133–135 (Oct., 1953).

[691] *Modern Plastics*, **30** (5), 113 (1953).

[692] *Modern Plastics*, **31** (2), 236 (1953).

[693] *Modern Plastics*, **31** (3), 230 (1953).

[694] *Modern Plastics*, **31** (4), 185 (1953).

[695] *Petroleum Ref.*, **32** (11), 130–189 (1953).

[696] *Plastics (British)*, **18** (195), 331 (1953).

[697] *Plastics News Letter*, **13** (47), 1 (1953).

[698] *Plastics News Letter*, **13** (47), 2 (1953).

[699] *Plastics News Letter*, **13** (47), 3 (1953).

[700] *Rubber Age*, **73** (6), 798 (1953).

[701] Atkinson, T. E., and Owen, D. G., *Trans. Plastics Inst. (London)*, **21** (44), 40–60 (1953).

[702] BASF, *Lupolen H—A Thermoplastic Resin*, Badische Anilin- und Soda-Fabrik, A.-G. Ludwigshafen am Rhein, Germany, August, 1953.

[703] Barb, W. G., *J. Am. Chem. Soc.*, **75**, 224–226 (1953).

[704] Beasley, J. K., *J. Am. Chem. Soc.*, **75**, 6123–6127 (1953).

[705] Bell, R. E., and Graham, R. L., *Phys. Rev.*, **90**, 644–654 (1953).

[706] Biggs, B. S., *U. S. Natl. Bur. Standards Circ.*, **525**, 137–148 (1953).

[707] Biggs, B. S., and Hawkins, W. L., *Modern Plastics*, **31** (1), 121, 122, 124, 126, 203 (1953).

[708] Billmeyer, F. W., Jr., *J. Am. Chem. Soc.*, **75**, 6118–6122 (1953).

[708a] Bopp, C. D., and Sisman, O., *ORNL*, 1373 (A.E.C., July 23, 1953).

[709] Bowers, R. C., Clinton, W. C., and Zisman, W. A., *J. Appl. Phys.*, **24**, 1066–1067 (1953).

[710] Bowers, R. C., Clinton, W. C., and Zisman, W. A., *Lubrication Engineering*, 204–208, 218–222 (August, 1953).

[711] Bowers, R. C., Clinton, W. C., and Zisman, W. A., PB 111,185 (Naval Research Laboratory Report 4,167), May 19, 1953.

[712] Bowers, G., Roche, I. D., and Baker, R. C., *Rubber Age*, **73** (4), 505 (1953).

[712a] Breitenbach, J. W., and Forster, E. L., *Oesterr. Chem. Ztg.*, **54**, 346 (1953).

[713] Brit. Standards Inst. (London), *Brit. Standard*, **1972**, 1953.

[714] Brooks, R. E., Strain, D. E., and McAlevy, A., *India Rubber World*, **127** (6), 791–793 (1953).

[715] Brown, A., and Reding, F., *Phys. Rev.*, **91** (1), 226 (1953).

[715a] Brubaker, D. W., and Kammermeyer, K., *Ind. Eng. Chem.*, **45**, 1148 (1953).

[716] Bryant, W. M. D., and Voter, R. C., *J. Am. Chem. Soc.*, **75**, 6113–6118 (1953).

[717] Burgess, A. R., *U. S. Natl. Bur. Standards Circ. 525*, 149–158 (1953).

[718] Busse, W. F., and Smook, W. A., *India Rubber World*, **128**, 348–350, 353 (1953).

[719] Charlesby, A., *J. Polymer Sci.*, **10**, 201–211 (1953).

[719a] Charlesby, A., *J. Polymer Sci.*, **11**, 513 (1953).

[720] Charlesby, A., *Plastics (London)*, **18** (70), 142–145 (1953); *Nature* **171**, 167 (1953).

[721] Charlesby, A., and Hancock, N. H., *Proc. Roy. Soc. (London)*, **A218**, 245–255 (1953).

[722] Charlesby, A., and Ross, M., *Proc. Roy. Soc. (London)*, **A217**, 122–135 (1953).

[723] Clarke, E. G. C., *Proc. Roy. Soc. Med.*, **46**, 641–644 (1953).

[724] Cobbold, A., Daubney, R. deP., Deutsch, K., and Markey, P., *Nature*, **172**, 806 (1953).

[724a] Cooper, A. C., Keller, A., and Waring, J. R. D., *J. Polymer Sci.*, **11**, 215 (1953).

[724b] Cooke, E. I., *Brit. Plastics*, **26** (19), 36 (1953).

[725] Cutler, J. A., and McLaren, A. D., *Tappi*, **36**, 423–425 (1953).

[726] Diskant, E. M., *Chemist Analyst*, **42**, 46 (1953).

[727] Drogin, I., *India Rubber World*, **127**, 797–801 (1953).

[728] Erwin, P., Strickler, J. H., and Rice, C. O., *Arch. Surg.*, **66**, 673–678 (1953).

[729] Evans, V., *Chem. and Process Eng.*, **34** (10), 307–311 (1953).

[730] Farrelly, W. F., *American Paper Converter*, 18–20, 58, 60 (1953).

[730a] Fitzhugh, A. F., *Science*, **118**, 783 (1953).

[730b] Flory, P. J., *Principles of Polymer Chemistry*, Cornell University Press, 1953.

[731] Foster, F. L., Dewey, D. R., II, and Gale, A. J., *Nucleonics*, **11** (10), 14–17 (1953).

[732] Fowler, J. F., and Farmer, F. T., *Nature*, **171**, 1020 (1953).

[733] Hagenbach, W. P., and Comings, E. W., *Ind. Eng. Chem.*, **45**, 609 (1953).

[734] Hartshorn, L., *Proc. XIth Intern. Congr. Pure and Appl. Chem. (London)*, **5**, 563–574 (1947), pub. 1953.

735 Herdan, G., *J. Polymer Sci.*, **10**, 1–18 (1953).

736 Hinkel, R. D., and Raymond, R., *Anal. Chem.*, **25**, 470 (1953).

737 Jellinek, H. H. G., *J. Polymer Sci.*, **10**, 506–509 (1953).

738 Jolivet, P., *Rev. gén. élec.*, **62**, 267–275 (1953).

739 Junk, W. A., and Comings, E. W., *Chem. Eng. Progress*, **49**, 263–266 (1953).

740 Kantor, S. W., and Osthoff, R. C., *J. Am. Chem. Soc.*, **75**, 931–932 (1953).

741 Karas, S. A., *Am. Perfumer Essent. Oil Rev.*, **61**, 277–279 (1953).

742 Kargin, W. A., and Sogolova, T. I., *Doklady Akad. Nauk. U.S.S.R.*, **88**, 867–870 (1953).

743 Kaufman, H. S., *J. Am. Chem. Soc.*, **75**, 1477–1478 (1953).

744 Kaufman, H. S., and Solomon, E., *Ind. Eng. Chem.*, **45**, 1779–1781 (1953).

745 Keller, A., *J. Polymer Sci.*, **11**, 567–574 (1953).

746 Keller, A., *Nature*, **170**, 171 (1953).

747 Kerhoas, M., *Industrie Plastique Moderne (Paris)*, **6** (3), 30–31 (1953).

748 King, R. F., and Tabor, D., *Proc. Phys. Soc. (London)*, **66B**, 728–736 (1953).

749 Kirk, R. E., and Othmer, D. F., *Encyclopedia of Chemical Technology*, Vol. 10, Interscience Publishers, Inc., New York, 1953, pp. 938–957.

749a Kobe, K. A., and Lynn, R. E., Jr., *Chem. Rev.*, **52**, 117 (1953).

750 Kortsch, W., *Kolloid-Z.*, **133** (2/3), 91–96 (1953).

751 Krimm, S., *J. Phys. Chem.*, **57**, 22–25 (1953).

752 Lawton, E. J., Bueche, A. M., and Balwit, J. S., *Nature*, **172**, 76–77 (1953).

753 Le Montagner, S., and Le Bot, J., *Compt. rend.*, **236**, 593–594 (1953).

754 Madorsky, S., Hart, V., Straus, S., and Sedlak, V., *J. Research Natl. Bur. Standards*, **51** (6), 327–333 (1953).

755 Mandelkern, L., Hellmann, M., Brown, D. W., Roberts, D. E., and Quinn, F. A., Jr., *J. Am. Chem. Soc.*, **75**, 4093 (1953).

756 Manning, W. R. D., *Rubber Age and Synthetics*, **34**, 308–310 (1953).

756a Manowitz, N., *Nucleonics*, **11** (10), 18 (1953).

757 Nicolas, L., *Compt. rend.*, **236**, 809–810 (1953).

758 Oppenheimer, B. S., Oppenheimer, E. T., Stout, A. P., and Danishefsky, I., *Science*, **118**, 305–306 (1953).

759 Perrin, M. W., *Research*, **6**, 111 (1953).

760 Raine, H. C., *Kunststoffe*, **43** (12), 503–508 (1953).

761 Richardson, H. M., *Elec. Mfg.*, **51** (4), 114–118, 356, 358 (1953).

762 Roedel, M. J., *J. Am. Chem. Soc.*, **75** (24), 6110–6112 (1953).

763 Romanowski, A., *Kunststoffe*, **43** (4), 134–137 (1953).

763a Rugar, G. F., *Modern Plastics*, **31** (5), 148 (1953).

764 Rugg, F. M., Smith, J. J., and Wartman, L. H., *J. Polymer Sci.*, **11**, 1 (1953); *Ann. N. Y. Acad. Sci.*, **57**, 398–416 (1953).

765 Ryan, J. W., *Nucleonics*, **11** (8), 13–15 (1953).

766 Schmieder, K., and Wolf, K., *Kolloid-Z.*, **134**, 149 (1953).

767 Schuur, G., *J. Polymer Sci.*, **11** (5), 385–398 (1953).

768 Seymour, R. B., *Org. Finishing*, **14** (3), 9–15, 18 (1953).

769 Shultz, A. R., and Flory, P. J., *J. Am. Chem. Soc.*, **75**, 3888–3892 (1953).

770 Smook, M. A., Roche, J. D., Clark, W. B., and Youngquist, O. G., *India Rubber World*, **128**, 54–58 (1953).

771 Socha, M. K., Flentje, M. E., and Tiedeman, W. D., *J. Am. Water Works Assoc.*, **45**, 757–763 (1953).

[772] Sperati, C. A., Franta, W. A., and Starkweather, H. W., Jr., *J. Am. Chem. Soc.*, **75**, 6127–6133 (1953).

[773] Stein, R. S., and Sutherland, G. B. B. M., *J. Chem. Phys.*, **21**, 370–371 (1953).

[774] Tordella, J. P., and Jolly, R. E., *Modern Plastics*, **31** (2), 146, 148, 150, 229 (1953).

[775] Ueberreiter, K., and Orthmann, H., *Kolloid-Z.*, **132** (2/3), 1–75 (1953).

[776] *U. S. National Bureau of Standards Circ. 525* (Nov. 16, 1953).

[776a] Wilson, C. W., III, and Pake, G. E., *J. Polymer Sci.*, **10**, 503–505 (1953).

[777] Winding, C. C., and Wiegandt, H. F., *Ind. Eng. Chem.*, **45** (9), 2011–2022 (1953).

[778] Yarsley, V., *Times Review of Industry*, **7** (80), 64 (1953).

[779] U. S. 2,625,491, Jan. 13, 1953, Young, D. W., and Smith, P. V., Jr. (Standard Oil Development Co.).

[780] U. S. 2,627,938, Feb. 10, 1953, Frohmader. S. H., and Archer, V. C. (Research Products Corp.).

[781] U. S. 2,628,172, Feb. 10, 1953, Jenett, H. (Emhart Manufacturing Co.).

[782] U. S. 2,628,187, Feb. 10, 1953, Frohmader. S. H., and Shoemaker, M. J. (Research Products Corp.).

[783] U. S. 2,628,203, Feb. 10, 1953, Van Gilder, C. F., and Harney, W. C. (Standard Oil Development Co.).

[784] U. S. 2,628,205, Feb. 10, 1953, Shoemaker, M. J. (Research Products Corp.).

[785] U. S. 2,628,208, Feb. 10, 1953, Loukomsky, S. A.

[786] U. S. 2,630,425, March 3, 1953, Rodman, E. A. (E. I. duPont de Nemours and Co.).

[787] U. S. 2,631,954, March 17, 1953, Bright, W. M. (Kendall Co.).

[788] U. S. 2,632,014, March 17, 1953, Gresham. W. F. (E. I. duPont de Nemours and Co.).

[788a] U. S. 2,632,921, March 31, 1953, Kreidl, W. H.

[789] U. S. 2,634,254, April 7, 1953, Lipscomb, R. D. (E. I. duPont de Nemours and Co.).

[790] Ger. 874,215, April 20, 1953, Fischer, M. (Badische Anilin- u. Soda-Fabrik A.-G.).

[791] U. S. 2,635,709, April 21, 1953, Archibald, F. M., Konrad, W. A., and Haney, R. A. D. (Standard Oil Development Co.).

[792] U. S. 2,635,975, April 21, 1953, Peters, H. (Bell Telephone Laboratories, Inc.).

[793] U. S. 2,638,459, May 12, 1953, Bowman, J. R., Ridenour, W. P., and Whittaker, J. H. (Gulf Research and Development Co.).

[794] U. S. 2,639,275, May 19, 1953, Vickers, H. H., and Jaros, S. E. (Standard Oil Development Co.).

[795] U. S. 2,640,040, May 26, 1953, Lehman, R. L. (Brogdex Co.).

[795a] Ger. 878,560, June 5, 1953, Ziegler. K., and Gellert, H. G.

[795b] U. S. 2,640,048, May 26, 1953, Beekley, J. S. (E. I. duPont de Nemours and Co.).

[796] U. S. 2,642,344, June 16, 1953, Livingston, H. K. (E. I. duPont de Nemours and Co.).

[797] U. S. 2,642,366, June 16, 1953, Rumberger, G. C. (Marathon Corp.).

[798] U. S. 2,642,370, June 16, 1953, Parsons, G. B., and Depew, D. (Fairchild Engine and Airplane Corp.).

[798a] U. S. 2,643,955, June 30, 1953, Powers, J. B., and Bludeau, R. E. (Union Carbide and Carbon Corp.).

[799] U. S. 2,644,759, July 7, 1953, Schroeder, A. J., (Sterling Drug, Inc.).

[800] U. S. 2,644,760, July 7, 1953, Schroeder, A. J. (Sterling Drug, Inc.).

[800a] Brit. 694,271, July 15, 1953 (E. I. duPont de Nemours and Co.).

[800b] Brit. 694,870, July 29, 1953 (Plax Corporation).

[800c] Ger. 889,229, July 30, 1953, Ziegler, K.

[801] U. S. 2,650,913, Sept. 1, 1953, Boyd, T. (Monsanto Chemical Co.).

[801a] U. S. 2,655,489, Oct. 13, 1953, Lawson, W. O. (E. I. duPont de Nemours and Co.).

[802] U. S. 2,655,492, Oct. 13, 1953, Young, D. W., and Hardy, P. E., (Standard Oil Development Co.).

[803] U. S. 2,656,297, Oct. 20, 1953, Davis, H. G., Jr., Durette, W. L., and Johnson, E. C. (B. B. Chemical Co.).

[804] Fr. 1,042,310, Oct. 30, 1953, Scheermesser, W., and Spindler, W.

[805] U. S. 2,658,059, Nov. 3, 1953, Peters, E. F., and Evering, B. L. (Standard Oil Co.).

[806] U. S. 2,659,707, Nov. 17, 1953, Youngquist, O. G., Smook, M. A., and Brooks, R. E.

[806a] U. S. 2,663,652, Dec. 22, 1953, Railing, W. E. (E. I. duPont de Nemours and Co.).

[807] *Bakelite Rev.*, **25**, 12–14 (1954).

[808] *Brennstoffe-Chem.*, 104 (Dec. 15, 1954).

[809] *Brit. Plastics*, **27**, 487 (1954).

[810] *Canadian Chem. Processing*, **38** (3), 95 (1954).

[811] *Chem. Age*, 1235–1236 (1954).

[812] *Chem. Eng. News*, **32** (14), 1342 (1954).

[813] *Electrical Engineering*, 383–384 (April, 1954).

[814] *The Givaudanian*, 3 (Nov., 1954).

[815] *Modern Packaging*, 93 (April, 1954).

[816] *Modern Packaging*, 104–106 (May, 1954).

[818] *Modern Plastics*, **32** (2), 91–96 (1954); *Petroleum Processing*, **9**, 819 (1954).

[819] *Plastics News Letter*, **14** (5), 3 (1954).

[820] *Plastics Ind.*, **12** (12), 24–26 (1954).

[821] American Agile Corporation, *Properties and Applications of Agilene-HT*, 1954.

[822] American Society for Testing Materials, *ASTM Standards on Plastics*, Philadelphia, 1954.

[822a] Baccaredda, M., and Schiavinato, G., *International Symposium on Macromolecular Chemistry*, Milan and Turin, Italy, Sept. 26–Oct. 2, 1954.

[823] Baccaredda, M., and Schiavinato, G., *J. Polymer Sci.*, **12**, 155 (1954).

[823a] Ballantine, D. S., *Modern Plastics*, **32** (3), 131 (1954).

[823b] Ballantine, D. S., paper presented at the 1954 Annual Conference of the Society of the Plastics Industry, Inc., Cleveland, Ohio, June 8, 1954.

[823c] Ballantine, D. S., Dienes, G. J., Manowitz, B., Ander, P., and Mesrobian, R. B., *J. Polymer Sci.*, **13**, 410 (1954).

[823d] Baskett, A. C., *International Symposium on Macromolecular Chemistry*, Milan and Turin, Italy, Sept. 26–Oct. 2, 1954.

[824] Bawn, C. E., and Rhodes, T. B., *Trans. Faraday Soc.*, **50**, 934 (1954).

[825] Bernhardt, E. C., and McKelvey, J. M., *Rubber World*, **130** (4), 513–515 (1954).

[826] Bernhardt, E. C., and McKelvey, J. M., *Rubber World*, **130** (5), 655–658 (1954).

[827] Bockhoff, F. J., and Neumann, J. A., *Modern Plastics*, **32** (2), 150, 154, 240, 243 (1954).

[828] Bockhoff, F. J., and Neumann, J. A., *Soc. Plastics Engrs. J.*, **10** (5), 17–19 (1954).

[829] Booth, G. L., *Tappi*, **37** (10), 163A–170A (1954).

[830] Bosoni, A., *Materie Plastiche*, **5**, 361–367 (1954).

[831] Bowers, R. C., Clinton, W. C., and Zisman, W. A., *Modern Plastics*, **31** (6), 131–132, 135, 136, 138, 140, 142, 144, 210, 213, 220, 223, 225 (1954).

[832] Boyer, R. F., *J. Appl. Phys.*, **25** (7), 825–829 (1954).

[833] Bunn, C. W., *J. Appl. Phys.*, **25** (7), 820–825 (1954).

[834] Bunnell, F. H., *Gas Age*, **114** (Oct.), 58 (1954).

[835] Burnett, G. M., *Mechanism of Polymer Reactions*, Interscience Publishers, Inc., New York, 1954.

[836] Busse, W. F., and Billmeyer, F. W., Jr., *J. Polymer Sci.*, **12**, 599 (1954).

[837] Campbell, J., *Materials and Methods*, **40** (3), 91–95 (1954).

[838] Carey, R. H., *India Rubber World*, **130** (2), 215–220 (1954).

[838a] Carey, R. H., *Soc. Plastics Engrs. J.*, **10** (3), 16 (1954).

[838b] Charlesby, A., *International Symposium on Macromolecular Chemistry*, Milan and Turin, Italy, Sept. 26–Oct. 2, 1954.

[839] Charlesby, A., *J. Polymer Sci.*, **14**, 547 (1954).

[840] Charlesby, A., *Nucleonics*, **12** (6), 18–25 (1954).

[840a] Charlesby, A., *Proc. Roy. Soc. (London)*, **A222**, 542 (1954).

[840b] Dexter, F. D., *J. Appl. Phys.*, **25** (9), 1124 (1954).

[841] Dole, M., Keeling, C. D., and Rose, D. G., *J. Am. Chem. Soc.*, **76** (17), 4304–4311 (1954).

[842] Druckrey, H., and Schmähl, D., *Naturwissenschaften*, **22**, 534 (1954).

[843] Druckrey, H., and Schmähl, D., *Z. Naturforschung*, **9B**, 529–530 (1954).

[843a] E. I. duPont de Nemours and Co., *Alathon 10 and 14 Polyethylene Resin*, Bulletin, 1954.

[844] Durethene Corporation, *A Guide to the Application of Polyethylene Resins in Chemical Environments*, Nov., 1954.

[845] Eppler, W., *Modern Plastics*, **31** (9), 115–116, 118, 121–124, 201 (1954).

[846] Evans, V., *Corrosion Technol.*, 73–76 (May, 1954).

[847] Florin, R. E., Wall, L. A., Brown, D. W., Hymo, L. A., and Michaelsen, J. D., *J. Research Natl. Bur. Standards*, **53**, 121 (1954).

[847a] Formigoni, N., *International Symposium on Macromolecular Chemistry*, Milan and Turin, Italy, Sept. 26–Oct. 2, 1954.

[848] Fowler, J. F., and Farmer, F. T., *Nature*, **173**, 317 (1954).

[849] Freeman, A. J., Sheridan, L. W., and Renfrew, M. M., *Modern Packaging*, **27** (6), 147 (June, 1954).

[850] Gatos, H. C., *J. Chem. Education*, **31**, 533 (1954).

[851] General Electric Company, Chemical Division, *G. E. Irrathene 101*, April 27, 1954.

[852] Goodwin, W. J., *Modern Plastics*, **31** (12), 104–105, 196 (1954).

[853] Haim, G., and Neumann, J. A., *Manual for Plastic Welding. II Polyethylene*, Crosby, Lockwood and Sons, Ltd., London, 1954.

[854] Haskell, W. D., and Eliker, R., *Waxed Papers—Production Methods and Equipment*, presented at TAPPI Coating Conference, 1954 (in press).

[854b] Houwink, R., *Chem. u. Tech. Kunststoffe*, Akademische Verlagsgesellschaft, Liepzig, 1954.

[855] Kaufman, H. S., Kroncke, C. O., Jr., and Gianotta, C. R., *Modern Plastics*, **32** (2), 146 (1954).

[856] Keeley, F. W., and Roche, I. D., *Wire and Wire Products*, **29**, 636 (1954).

[857] Kilpatrick, M. O., Dean, L. E., Hall, D. S., and Seed, K. W., *Petroleum Processing*, **9**, 903–906 (1954).

[857a] Klug, H. P., and Alexander, L. E., *X-Ray Diffraction Procedures*, John Wiley and Sons, Inc., New York, N. Y., 1954.

[858] Kodama, S., Taniguchi, I., Yuasa, S., Ota, T., and Terada, Y., *J. Chem. Soc. Japan, Ind. Chem. Sect.*, **57**, 439 (1954). Translation by Engineering Societies Library, New York, N. Y.

[858a] Kortsch, W., *Kolloid-Z.*, **137**, 74 (1954).

[858b] Kovacs, A. J., *International Symposium on Macromolecular Chemistry*, Milan and Turin, Italy, Sept. 26–Oct. 2, 1954.

[859] Lawton, E. J., Balwit, J. S., and Bueche, A. M., *Ind. Eng. Chem.*, **46** (8), 1703 (1954).

[860] Lawton, E. J., Zemany, P. D., and Balwit, J. S., *J. Am. Chem. Soc.*, **76**, 3437 (1954).

[861] Lewis, J. G., Martin, J. J., and Anderson, L. C., *Chem. Eng. Progr.*, **50** (5), 249–255 (1954).

[862] Liberty, G., *Modern Plastics*, **32** (2), 137, 232 (1954).

[863] Madorsky, S. L., and Straus, S., *J. Research Natl. Bur. Standards*, **53**, 361 (1954).

[863a] Manowitz, B., *Chem. Eng. Prog.*, **50** (12), 201 (1954).

[864] Mark, H., *Chem. Eng. News*, **32** (32), 3122 (1954).

[865] Miller, A. A., Lawton, E. J., and Balwit, J. S., *J. Polymer Sci.*, **14**, 503 (1954).

[866] Morgan, L. B., *J. Appl. Chem.*, **4** (4), 160–172 (1954).

[866a] Münster, A., *International Symposium on Macromolecular Chemistry*, Milan and Turin, Italy, Sept. 26–Oct. 2, 1953.

[867] Myers, C. S., *J. Polymer Sci.*, **13**, 549–564 (1954).

[867a] Nasini, A., and Borello, E., *International Symposium on Macromolecular Chemistry*, Milan and Turin, Italy, Sept. 26–Oct. 2, 1954.

[868] Natta, G., and Corradini, P., *Angew. Chem.*, **66**, 505 (Sept. 7, 1954).

[868a] Natta, G., and Corradini, P., *International Symposium on Macromolecular Chemistry*, Milan and Turin, Italy, Sept. 26–Oct. 2, 1954.

[869] Natta, G., Pino, P., and Farina, M., *International Symposium on Macromolecular Chemistry*, Milan and Turin, Italy, Sept. 26–Oct. 2, 1954.

[870] Neumann, J. A., *Prod. Eng.*, **25** (4), 146 (1954).

[871] Nichols, J. B., *J. Appl. Phys.*, **25** (7), 840 (1954).

[872] Nielsen, L. E., *J. Applied Phys.*, **25**, 1209 (1954).

[873] Patton, C. W., *Paper, Film and Foil Converter*, **28** (1), 23–26 (1954).

[874] Pinsky, J., Nielsen, A. R., and Parliman, J. H., *Modern Packaging*, **27** (10), 145 (1954).

[875] Pledger, F., and Ryan, D. J., *Modern Plastics*, **31** (7), 112 (1954).

[876] Reding, F. P., and Brown, A., *Ind. Eng. Chem.*, **46** (9), 1962 (1954).

[877] Reding, F. P., and Brown, A., *J. Appl. Phys.*, **25** (7), 848 (1954).

[878] Reznikovskii, M. M., Yurovskaya, V. S., and Dogadkin, B. A., *Rubber Chem. Technol.*, **27** (2), 415–429 (1954).

[879] Ross, M., *A.E.R.E. Report M/R 1401 Department of Atomic Energy*, Harwell, Berks., England (Declassified, 1954).

[879a] Sharaswathi Devi, L., *Current Sci. (India)*, **23**, 409 (1954).

[880] Schaupp, F., *Kunststoffe*, **44** (8), 365 (1954).

[881] Schlicht, R., *Kautschuk und Gummi*, **7**, 232, 259 (1954).

[882] Schuur, G., *Rubber Chem. Technol.*, **27** (2), 374–384 (1954).

[883] Semet-Solvay Division, Allied Chemical and Dye Corp., *A-C Polyethylene*, New York, 1954.

[883a] Socci, M., and Lanzavecchia, G., *International Symposium on Macromolecular Chemistry*, Milan and Turin, Italy, Sept. 26–Oct. 2, 1954.

883b Stein, R. S., and Sutherland, G. B. B. M., *J. Chem. Phys.*, **22**, 1993 (1954).

884 Sun, K. H., *Modern Plastics*, **32** (1), 141–150, 229–233, 236–238 (1954).

885 Swallow, J., *Brit. Plastics*, **27** (9), 364–365 (1954).

886 Thor, C. J. B., and Goldman, M., *Modern Packaging*, **27** (9), 155 (1954).

887 United States Department of Commerce, *Commercial Standard CS 197-54, Dimensions and Tolerances for Flexible Standard Wall Polyethylene Pipe*, Oct. 15, 1954.

888 Wall, L. A., Madorsky, S. L., Brown, D. W., Straus, S., and Simha, R., *J. Am. Chem. Soc.*, **76** (13), 3430 (1954).

889 Walters, R. J., Tracht, J. H., Weinberger, E. B., and Rodgers, J. K., *Chem. Eng. Progress*, **50**, 511–514 (1954).

890 Wiese, R. A., *Modern Plastics*, **31** (6), 117–119, 122, 124 (1954).

890a Wilson, R. H., and McCormick, W. E., *Ind. Med. and Surg.*, **23**, 479 (1954).

891 Yustein, S. E., Winans, R. R., and Stark, H. J., "Three Years Outdoor Weather Aging of Plastics under Various Climatological Conditions," *ASTM Bull.*, **196**, 29–39 (1954).

892 Ziegler, K., Gellert, H. G., Martin, H., Nagel, K., and Schneider, J., *Ann.*, **589**, 191 (1954).

893 Ziegler, K., Gellert, H. G., Holzkamp, E. and Wilke, G., *Brennstoff-Chem.*, **35**, 321 (1954).

894 French 1,050,223, Jan. 6, 1954, Scheermesser, W., and Spindler, W.

895 U. S. 2,666,756, Jan. 19, 1954, Boyd, T., and Dickey, R. M. (Monsanto Chemical Co.).

895a U. S. 2,667,437, Jan. 26, 1954, Zoubek, C. M. (Swift & Co., Inc.).

895b U. S. 2,668,134, Feb. 2, 1954, Horton, P. V. (Plax Corp.).

896 French 1,055,561, Feb. 19, 1954, Spindler, W., and Scheermesser, W.

897 French 1,059,221, March 23, 1954, Spindler, W., and Scheermesser, W.

897a Belg. 527,736, March 30, 1954, Ziegler, K.

897b Brit. 706,412, March 31, 1954 (Imperial Chemical Industries, Ltd.).

898 U. S. 2,675,366, April 13, 1954, Pullman, J. C. (American Cyanamid).

899 U. S. 2,676,932, April 27, 1954, Deniston, G. L. (Commonwealth Engineering Company of Ohio).

900 French 1,063,919, May 10, 1954, Spindler, W., and Scheermesser, W.

901 Ger. 910,964, May 10, 1954, Scheermesser, W., and Spindler, W.

901a Can. 502,597, May 18, 1954, Larchar, A. W., and Pease, D. C. (E. I. duPont de Nemours and Co.), cf. 1133.

902 U. S. 2,679,469, May 25, 1954, Bedford, J. G. (Ciba Pharmaceutical Products, Inc.).

902a U. S. 2,680,763, June 8, 1954, Brubaker, M. M. (E. I. duPont de Nemours and Co.).

902b Brit. 710,523, June 16, 1954, Rudge, A. J. (Imperial Chemical Industries, Ltd.).

902c Ger. Pat. Appl. D 13 712, July 1, 1954, Deutsche Gold-und Silber-Scheideanstalt.

903 U. S. 2,683,141, July 6, 1954, Erchak, M., Jr. (Allied Chem. and Dye).

904 U. S. 2,685,575, Aug. 3, 1954, Heiligmann, R. G., and Benington, F. (Borden Co.).

905 U. S. 2,685,577, Aug. 3, 1954, Cerveny, W. J., Burney, D. E., and Weisemann, G. H. (Standard Oil Co. of Indiana).

906 Brit. 713,081, Aug. 4, 1954, Ziegler, K.

906a Brit. 713,634, Aug. 18, 1954, Brown, A. C., and Angel, T. H. (Vinesta, Ltd.).

906b Brit. 714,843, Sept. 1, 1954 (Imperial Chemical Industries, Ltd.).

[906c] Brit. 715,193, Sept. 8, 1954 (Dussek Brothers and Co., Ltd.).

[906d] Brit. 715,875, Sept. 22, 1954 (Mathieson Chemical Co.).

[906e] Austral. 3669/54, Oct. 7, 1954 (Imperial Chemical Industries, Ltd.).   Same as Brit. 744,875, Feb. 15, 1956, Burnett, J. D., and Huck, N. D. (Imperial Chemical Industries, Ltd.).

[906f] Brit. 713,174, Aug. 4, 1954 (Rome Cable Corp.).

[907] U. S. 2,691,647, Oct. 12, 1954, Field, E., and Feller, M. (Standard Oil Co. of Indiana).

[908] U. S. 2,691,668, Oct. 12, 1954, Ziegler, K., and Zosel, K.

[909] U. S. 2,692,257, Oct. 19, 1954, Zletz, A. (Standard Oil Co. of Indiana).

[910] U. S. 2,692,258, Oct. 19, 1954, Roebuck, A. E., and Zletz, A. (Standard Oil Co. of Indiana).

[910a] U. S. 2,692,259, Oct. 19, 1954, Peters, E. F. (Standard Oil Co. of Indiana).

[911] U. S. 2,692,258, Oct. 19, 1954, Peters, E. F., and Evering, B. L. (Standard Oil Co. of Indiana).

[911a] Austral. 4110/54, Oct. 25, 1954 (Monsanto Chemical Co.).

[912] Brit. 717,533, Oct. 27, 1954 (E. I. duPont de Nemours and Co.).

[912a] U. S. 2,693,459, Nov. 2, 1954, Fisk, C. F. (E. I. duPont de Nemours and Co.).

[912b] Span. 214,554, Nov. 22, 1954, Tausent, M.

[912c] Span. 214,555, Nov. 22, 1954, Tausent, M.

[913] U. S. 2,695,327, Nov. 23, 1954, Ziegler, K., and Gellert, H. G.

[913a] Brit. 718,815, Nov. 24, 1954, Scheermesser, W., and Spindler, W.

[914] U. S. 2,695,769, Nov. 30, 1954, Henning, G. E. (Western Electric Co.).

[915] U. S. 2,695,899, Nov. 30, 1954, Becker, W., and Bayer, O. (Farbenfabriken Bayer A-G.).

[916] U. S. 2,697,058, Dec. 14, 1954, Lasak, F. J. (General Electric Co., Inc.).

[917] U. S. 2,698,309, Dec. 28, 1954, Thwaites, H. L., and Hitchcox, H. F. (Standard Oil Development Co.).

[918] U. S. 2,698,317, Dec. 28, 1954, Ross, S. E., and Noether, H. D. (Celanese Corporation of America).

[919] Brit. 721,046, Dec. 29, 1954 (Standard Oil Co. of Indiana).

[919a] *Bakelite Rev.*, **27,** 8 (Oct. 1955).

[919b] *Brit. Plastics*, **28,** 440 (1955).

[919c] *Business Week*, 94, Dec. 10, 1955.

[920] *Chem. Eng.*, **62** (6), 103–104, 108 (1955).

[920a] *Chem. Eng.*, **62** (7), 104 (1955).

[921] *Chem. Eng. News*, **33,** 153 (1955).

[922] *Chem. Eng. News*, **33,** 1161 (1955).

[923] *Chem. Eng. News*, **33,** 3062 (1955).

[923a] *Chem. Eng. News*, **33,** 4226 (1955).

[923b] *Chem. Eng. News*, **33,** 5091 (1955).

[923c] *Chem. Eng. News*, **33,** 5412 (1955).

[923d] *Chem. Eng. News*, **33,** 5526 (1955).

[924] *Chem. Week*, **77,** 64 (May 7, 1955).

[925] *Chem. Week*, **77,** 46 (June 4, 1955).

[926] *Chem. Week*, **77,** 58 (June 4, 1955).

[926a] *Chem. Week*, **77,** 24 (June 25, 1955).

[926b] *Chem. Week*, **77,** 34 (July 9, 1955).

[926c] *Chem. Week,* **77,** 5 (July 23, 1955).

[926d] *Chem. Week,* **77,** 93 (Dec. 3, 1955).

[926e] *Ind. Eng. Chem.,* **47,** 11a (1955).

[927] *Journal Commerce* (Feb. 15, 1955).

[927a] *Modern Plastics,* **33** (1), 85 (1955).

[927b] *Modern Plastics,* **33** (2) ,100 (1955).

[927c] *Newsweek,* Dec. 15, 1955.

[928] *Plastics Industry,* **13** (2), 22–23 (1955).

[928a] *Plastics Industry,* **13** (8), 15 (1955).

[928b] *Plastics News Letter,* **15** (51), 1 (1955).

[929] *Plastics Technol.,* **1,** 175 (1955).

[929a] *Rubber and Plastics Age,* **36,** 349 (1955).

[929b] Aggarwal, S. L., and Tilley, G. P., *J. Polymer Sci.,* **18,** 17 (1955).

[929c] Alexander, L. E., Ohlberg, S., and Taylor, G. R., *J. Appl. Phys.,* **26,** 1068 (1955).

[930] BASF, Ger. Pat. Application, I 73,031.

[931] Becker, G. W., *Kolloid-Z.,* **140,** 1 (1955).

[932] Benzler, H., and von Koch, A., *Chem.-Ing.-Tech.,* **27** (2), 71–75 (1955).

[932a] Bloyer, S. F., *Modern Plastics,* **32** (11), 105 (1955).

[933] Bockhoff, F. J., and Neumann, J. A., *Modern Plastics,* **32** (7), 103 (1955).

[933a] Bockhoff, F. J., and Neumann, J. A., *Chem. Eng.,* **62,** 228 (1955).

[934] Bockhoff, F. J., and Roth, R. F., *Chem. Eng. Progr.,* **51,** 251 (1955).

[934a] Bosworth, H. R., *Modern Plastics,* **33** (2), 119 (1955).

[935] Boyd, R. C., *Rubber Age,* **77** (12), 882 (March, 1955).

[935a] Brandt, W., *Phys. Rev.* [2], **98,** 243 (1955).

[935b] Breitenbach, J. W., and Forster, E. L., *Oesterr. Chem. Ztg.,* **56,** 93 (1955).

[936] Bryant, W. M. D., Pierce, R. H. H., Jr., Lindegren, C. R., and Roberts, R., *J. Polymer Sci.,* **16,** 131 (1955).

[937] Bunn, C. W., *J. Polymer Sci.,* **16,** 323 (1955).

[938] Campbell, J. B., *Materials & Methods,* **42** (1), 88 (1955).

[939] Catsiff, E., and Tobolsky, A. V., *J. Colloid Sci.,* **10,** 375 (1955).

[940] Chapiro, A., *J. chim. phys.,* **52,** 216 (1955).

[941] Chapiro, A., Magat, M., Prévot-Bernas, A., Reinisel, M., and Seban, J., *Industrie plastiques mod.* (Paris), **7,** 44 (1955).

[942] Chapman, R. N., and Colombo, P., BNL 2431, Aug. 1955, Brookhaven National Laboratory, Upton, N. Y.

[943] Chapman, R. N., and Colombo, P., *Nucleonics,* **13** (10), 13 (1955).

[944] Charlesby, A., paper presented at the British Plastics Convention, London, England, 1955. See also Morgan, P., Editor, *Plastics Progress,* 1955, Iliffe & Sons, Ltd., London, England, 1955, or Philosophical Library, New York, N. Y., 1955.

[945] Clausen, D., *Progress thru Research,* **9** (4), 6 (1955).

[946] Claver, G. C., and Merz, E. H., paper presented at the 128th meeting of the American Chemical Society, Minneapolis, Minn., Sept. 11–16, 1955.

[947] Cole, Q. P., paper presented at the 127th meeting of the American Chemical Society, Cincinnati, Ohio, March 29–April 7, 1955.

[948] Courtaulds, Ltd., *"Courlene,"* Tech. Bulletin, 1955.

[949] Darrah, L. B., *Chem. Eng. News,* **33,** 5226 (1955).

[950] Dietz, K., and Lorentz, G., *Chem.-Ing.-Tech.,* **27** (10), 596 (1955).

[951] E. I. duPont de Nemours and Co., Report No. 55-5, *Hypalon* **20**, Smook, M. A., Fullam, P. V., and Remington, W. J., October 1955.

[952] Eastman Chemical Products, Inc., *Eastman's Polyethylene Waxes*, Kingsport, Tenn., 1955.

[953] Farbwerke Hoechst, A-G., *Preliminary Bulletin "Hostalen"*, April, 1955.

[954] Farnsworth, J. F., Manes, M., McGurl, G. V., and Bretz, G. M., *Ind. Eng. Chem.*, **47**, 1517 (1955).

[955] Feltzin, J., Restaino, A. J., and Mesrobian, R. B., *J. Am. Chem. Soc.*, **77**, 206 (1955).

[956] Fritz, J. C., *Flammspritzen von Stahl, Metallen und Kunststoffen*, Der Plastverarbeiter Verlagsgesellschaft mbH., Herxheim bei Landau i. d. Pfalz, Germany, 1955.

[957] Gemmer, E., *Chem.-Ing.-Tech.*, **27** (10), 599 (1955).

[958] Gemmer, E., *Plastverarbeiter*, **6** (3), 82 (1955).

[959] Goodwin, P. A., *Modern Plastics*, **32** (7), 102 (1955).

[960] Goodwin, P. A., and Wetzel, J. W., *Gen. Elec. Rev.*, **58**, 48 (1955).

[961] Grams, E., and Gaube, E., *Angew. Chem.*, **67**, 548 (1955).

[962] Grumer, J., Harris, M. E., and Schultz, H., *Ind. Eng. Chem.*, **47**, 1760 (1955).

[963] Hahn, W., and Müller, W., *Makromol. Chem.*, **16**, 71 (1955).

[964] Haim, W. G., *Can. Plastics*, **13**, (Aug.), 32 (1955).

[965] Harshaw Chemical Co., *Bulletin on "Harshaw Tetterette,"* 1955.

[966] Hawkins, S. W., paper presented at the British Plastics Convention, London, England 1955. See also Morgan, P., Editor, *Plastics Progress*, 1955, Iliffe & Sons, Ltd., London, England, 1955, Philosophical Library, New York, N. Y., 1955.

[967] Hayward, J. C., Jr., *Polymerization of Ethylene Initiated by Gamma Radiation*, doctoral dissertation presented to the Faculty of the Yale School of Engineering, Report No. NYO-3313, under Contract AT (30-1)-1173, New Haven, Conn., June 1955.

[968] Henderson, W. F., *Canadian Chem. Processing*, 70 (March, 1955).

[969] Higgins, W. T., *Soc. Plastics Engrs. J.*, **36**, 37 (1955).

[970] Irving, T., *Paper, Film and Foil Converter*, 28 (June, 1955).

[971] Irving, T., *Plastics World*, **13** (9), 1 (1955).

[972] Jellinek, H. H. G., *Degradation of Vinyl Polymers*, Academic Press, Inc., New York, 1955.

[973] Jones, S. T., *Canadian Plastics*, **13** (April), 32 (1955).

[974] Karam, H. J., Cleereman, K. J., and Williams, J. L., *Modern Plastics*, **32** (7), 129 (1955).

[975] Kargin, V. A., and Gatovskaya, T. V., *Doklady Akad. Nauk. S.S.S.R.*, **100**, 105 (1955).

[976] Keller, A., *J. Polymer Sci.*, **15**, 31 (1955).

[977] Keller, A. and Sandeman, I., *J. Polymer Sci.*, **15**, 133 (1955).

[978] Keller, A., *J. Polymer Sci.*, **17**, 291 (1955).

[979] Keller, A., *J. Polymer Sci.*, **17**, 351 (1955).

[980] Keller, A., *J. Polymer Sci.*, **17**, 447 (1955).

[981] Kennaway, A., *Brit. Plastics*, **28**, 18 (1955).

[982] Koppers Company, Inc., *Bulletin C-5-216, "Super Dylan,"* 1955.

[983] Koppers Co., Inc., *Bulletin C-5-225, Dylan Polyethylene for Injection Molding*, 1955.

[984] Koppers Co. Inc., *Bulletin C-5-224, Dylan Polyethylene for Pipe Extrusion*, 1955.

[985] Kortsch, W., *Kolloid-Z.*, **141**, 160 (1955).

[986] Kovacs, A. J., *Industrie plastiques mod. (Paris)*, **7**, 30 (1955).

[987] Krause, A., *Chemiker-Ztg.*, **79**, 657 (1955).

[988] Kreidl, W. H., and Hartmann, F., *Plastics Technology*, **1** (1), 31 (1955).

[989] Krupp, H., *Chem.-Ing.-Tech.*, **27**, 79 (1955).

[990] London, M., *Textile World*, **105** (9), 83 (1955).

[991] Madorsky, S. L., and Straus, S., paper presented at the 127th meeting of the American Chemical Society, Cincinnati, Ohio, March 29–April 7, 1955.

[992] Mark, H., lecture presented at meeting of the Akron Polymer Lecture Group, Akron, Ohio, Sept. 16, 1955.

[993] McCune, W., *Canadian Plastics*, **13** (Jan.), 42 (1955).

[994] McSweeney, E. E., and Kropa, E. L., *Chem. Eng. News*, **33**, 16 (1955).

[995] Meyer, R. A., and Boquet, F. L., *Physical Review*, **98**, 1531 (1955).

[996] Moore, L. D., Jr., Paper presented before the 127th meeting of the American Chemical Society, Cincinnati, Ohio, March 29–April 7, 1955. See also *J. Polymer Sci.*, **20**, 137 (1956).

[997] Müller, F. H., *Kolloid-Z.*, **142**, 165 (1955).

[998] Nakamura, M., and Skinner, S. M., *J. Polymer Sci.*, **18**, 423 (1955).

[999] Nakamura, M., and Skinner, S. M., *J. Polymer Sci.*, **18**, 583 (1955).

[1000] National Distillers Products Corp., U. S. Industrial Chemicals Co. Div., *Petrothene*, Bulletin, 1955.

[1001] Natta, G., *Atti accad. naz. Lincei. Mem.*, Serie VIII, Vol. IV, Sez. IIa, fasc. 4, p. 61 (1955).

[1002] Natta, G., *Makromol. Chem.*, **16**, 213 (1955).

[1003] Natta, G., and Corradini, P., *Atti accad. naz. Lincei. Mem.*, Serie VIII, Vol. IV, Sez. IIa, fasc. 5, p. 73 (1955).

[1004] Natta, G., Pino, P., Corradini, P., Danusso, F., Mantica, E., Mazzanti, G., and Moraglio, G., *J. Am. Chem. Soc.*, **77**, 1708 (1955).

[1005] Neumann, J. A., *Plastics Technol.*, **1**, 475; 498 (1955).

[1006] Neumann, J. A., and Bockhoff, F. J., *Modern Plastics*, **32** (12), 117 (1955).

[1007] Offenbach, J. A., doctoral dissertation presented to the Faculty of Princeton University, Princeton, N. J., 1955.

[1008] Oppenheimer, B. S., Oppenheimer, E. T., Danishefsky, F., Stout, A. P., and Eirich F. R., *Cancer Research*, **15**, 333 (1955).

[1009] Othmer, D. F. and Frolich, G. J., *Ind. Eng. Chem.* **47**, 1034 (1955).

[1010] Parker, M. E., *Petroleum Engineer*, D-28 (Jan., 1955).

[1011] Pepkowitz, L. P., *Anal. Chem.*, **27**, 245 (1955).

[1012] Phillips Petroleum Co., *Marlex-50*, Bulletin, 1955.

[1013] Pinsky, J., *Plastics Technol.*, **1**, 159 (1955).

[1014] Pollett, W. F. O., *Brit. J. Appl. Phys.*, **6**, 199 (1955).

[1015] Price, F. P., *J. Phys. Chem.*, **59**, 191 (1955).

[1016] Pruett, C. E., *Ind. Eng. Chem.*, **47**, 1196 (1955).

[1017] Reed, R. A., paper presented at the British Plastics Convention, London, England, 1955. See also Morgan, P., Editor, *Plastics Progress*, 1955, Iliffe & Sons, Ltd., London, England, 1955, Philosophical Library, New York, N. Y., 1955.

[1018] Reeves Brothers, Inc., *Technical Bulletin.* "Reevon," 1955.

[1019] Reis, T., *Chim. et ind.* (Supp. mensuel, Genie chim.) **73**, 63 (1955).

[1020] Rossmann, K., *J. Chem. Phys.*, **23**, 1355 (1955).

[1021] Ruhrchemie, A.-G., *RCH Hochmolekulare Polyäthylene*, Bulletin, 1955.

[1022] Saechtling, H., *Chem.-Ing.-Tech.*, **27** (10), 602 (1955).

[1023] Sauer, J. A., and Kline, D. E., *J. Polymer Sci.*, **18**, 491 (1955).

[1024] Schulz, G., and Mehnert, K., *Kunststoffe*, **45**, 410 (1955).

[1025] Schuur, G., *Some Aspects of the Crystallization of High Polymers*, Rubber-Stichting, Delft, The Netherlands, 1955, Communication No. 276.

[1026] Seymour, R. B., *Ind. Eng. Chem.*, **47**, 1338 (1955).

[1027] Seymour, R. B., *Corrosion*, **11** (7), 50 (1955).

[1027a] Smook, M. A., *Kautschuk u. Gummi*, **8**, WT314 (1955).

[1028] Sobolev, I., Meyer, J. A., Stannett, V., and Szwarc, M., *J. Polymer Sci.*, **17**, 417 (1955).

[1029] Sollenberger, G. H., *Plastics Ind.*, **13** (10), 16 (1955).

[1030] Stannett, V., and Szwarc, M., *J. Polymer Sci.*, **16**, 89 (1955).

[1031] Stein, R. S., and Keane, J. J., *J. Polymer Sci.*, **17**, 21 (1955).

[1032] Stein, R. S., Keane, J. J., and Norris, F. H., paper presented at the 128th meeting of the American Chemical Society, Minneapolis, Minn., Sept. 11–16, 1955.

[1033] Stoeckhert, K., *Kunststoffe*, **45**, 126 (1955).

[1034] Stuart, H. A., Editor, *Die Physik der Hochpolymeren, Vol. II, Das Makromolekül in Lösungen* (1953). *Vol. III. Ordnungszustände und Umwandlungserscheinungen in Festen Hochpolymeren Stoffen* (1955), Springer-Verlag, Berlin-Göttingen-Heidelburg.

[1035] Szwarc, M., Stannett, V. T., Meyer, J. A., and Rogers, C. E., *Annual Rept. State Univ. New York to TAPPI, 1953–1954*, Jan. 28, 1955.

[1036] Thompson, J. B., Turrell, G. C., and Sandt, B. W., *Soc. Plastics Engrs. J.*, **11** (4), 13 (1955).

[1037] Todd, D. B., and Elgin, J. C., *Am. Inst. Chem. Engrs. J.*, **1**, 20 (1955).

[1038] Tung, L. H., and Taylor, W. C., *J. Polymer Sci.*, **17**, 441 (1955).

[1039] Voigt, W., *Kunststoffe*, **45**, 238 (1955).

[1040] Waack, R., Alex, N. H., Frisch, H. L., Stannett, V., and Szwarc, M., *Ind. Eng. Chem.*, **47**, 2524 (1955).

[1041] Wall, L. A., *Chem. Eng. News*, **33**, 3390 (1955).

[1042] Wilkinson, P. G., and Mulliken, R. S., *J. Chem. Phys.*, **23**, 1895 (1955).

[1043] Wilson, J. E., *Ind. Eng. Chem.*, **47**, 2201 (1955).

[1044] Ziegler, K., *Kunststoffe*, **45**, 506 (1955).

[1045] Ziegler, K., Holzkamp, E., Breil, H., and Martin, H., *Angew. Chem.*, **67**, 426 (1955).

[1046] Ziegler, K., Holzkamp, E., Breil, H., and Martin, H., *Angew. Chem.*, **67**, 541 (1955).

[1047] U. S. 2,698,463, Jan. 4, 1955, Conwell, Y., Busse, W. F., and Caracciolo, V. P. (E. I. duPont de Nemours and Co.).

[1048] U. S. 2,699,457, Jan. 11, 1955, Ziegler, K., and Gellert, H. G.

[1049] Belg. 534,792, Jan. 11, 1955, Ziegler, K.

[1050] Brit. 721,678, Jan. 12, 1955, E. I. duPont de Nemours and Co.

[1051] Belg. 534,888, Jan. 14, 1955, Ziegler, K.

[1052] Austral. 6253/55, Jan. 18, 1955, Monsanto Chemical Co.

[1053] Austral. 6302/55, Jan. 19, 1955, Monsanto Chemical Co.

[1053a] Austral. 6303/55, Jan. 19, 1955, Monsanto Chemical Co.

[1054] Ger. 922,618, Jan. 20, 1955, Hopff, H., and Eilbracht, H. (Badische Anilin-u. Soda-Fabrik A.-G.).

[1055] Belg. 535,082, Jan. 22, 1955, Phillips Petroleum Co.

[1056] Belg. 530,617, Jan. 24, 1955, Phillips Chemical Co.

[1057] U. S. 2,700,663, Jan. 25, 1955, Peters, E. F. (Standard Oil Co. of Indiana).

[1058] Can. 509,678, Feb. 1, 1955, Pease, D. C. (E. I. duPont de Nemours and Co.).

[1059] Can. 510,145 (Feb. 15, 1955), Roedel, M. J. (E. I. duPont de Nemours and Co.).

[1060] U. S. 2,702,288, Feb. 15, 1955, Hoeksema, H., and Peters, E. F. (Standard Oil Co. of Indiana).

[1061] Austral. 6949/55, Feb. 16, 1955, British Cellophane, Ltd.

[1062] Austral. 7295/55, March 3, 1955, Imperial Chemical Industries, Ltd.

[1063] U. S. 2,703,792, March 8, 1955, Kropa, E. L., and Welcher, R. P. (American Cyanamid Co.).

[1064] U. S. 2,703,793, March 8, 1955, Naylor, M. A. (E. I. duPont de Nemours and Co.).

[1065] U. S. 2,703,794, March 8, 1955, Roedel, M. J. (E. I. duPont de Nemours and Co.).

[1066] Austral. 7788/55, March 23, 1955, British Cellophane, Ltd.

[1067] Austral. 7789/55, March 23, 1955, British Cellophane, Ltd.

[1068] Austral. 8094/55, April 4, 1955, Imperial Chemical Industries, Ltd.

[1069] U. S. 2,706,719, April 19, 1955, Newberg, R. G., Wilson, H. L., and Sayko, A. F. (Esso Research and Engineering Co.).

[1070] Brit. 728,551, April 20, 1955, Hopff, H., and Eilbracht, H. (Badische Anilin-u Soda-Fabrik A.-G.).

[1071] Belg. 533,362, May 16, 1955, Ziegler, K.

[1071a] Brit. 731,134, June 1, 1955, Land, W. M., and Meyer, W. T. (Union Carbide and Carbon Corp.). See also U. S. 2,737,502, March 6, 1956, Land, W. M., and Meyer, W. T. (Union Carbide and Carbon Corp.).

[1072] Belg. 538,782, June 6, 1955, Montecatini, and Ziegler, K.

[1073] U. S. 2,710,854, June 14, 1955, Seelig, H. S. (Standard Oil Co. of Indiana).

[1074] Brit. 731,728, June 15, 1955, Imperial Chemical Industries, Ltd.

[1075] Brit. 732,047, June 15, 1955, Charlesby, A. (United Kingdom Atomic Energy Authority).

[1076] U. S. 2,711,985, June 28, 1955, Olson, M. W. (United States Rubber Co.).

[1077] U. S. 2,711,986, June 28, 1955, Strain, D. E., and Crim, T. H. (E. I. duPont de Nemours and Co.).

[1078] U. S. 2,712,384, July 5, 1955, Corneil, E. R. (E. I. duPont de Nemours and Co.).

[1079] U. S. 2,713,044, July 12, 1955, McArthur, R. E., and Logan, J. S. (Olin Mathieson Chemical Corp.).

[1080] U. S. 2,713,071, July 12, 1955, Erchak, M. (Allied Chemical and Dye Corp.).

[1081] U. S. 2,714,557, Aug. 2, 1955, Mahaffy, R. A. (E. I. duPont de Nemours and Co.).

[1082] U. S. 2,714,571, Aug. 2, 1955, Irion, C. E., and Prindle, K. E. (The Dobeckmum Co.).

[1083] Ger. 931,216, Aug. 4, 1955, Gerlich H., (Badische Anilin-u. Soda-Fabrik A.-G.).

[1083a] Belg. 540,316, Aug. 4, 1955, Ruhrchemie A.-G.

[1083b] Belg. 540,362, Aug. 5, 1955, Montecatini.

[1084] U. S. 2,715,075, Aug. 9, 1955, Wolinski, L. E. (E. I. duPont de Nemours and Co.).

[1085] U. S. 2,715,076, Aug. 9, 1955, Wolinski, L. E. (E. I. duPont de Nemours and Co.).

[1086] U. S. 2,715,077, Aug. 9, 1955, Wolinski, L. E. (E. I. duPont de Nemours and Co.).

[1086a] Belg. 540,459, Aug. 9, 1955, Ziegler, K.

[1087] U. S. 2,715,363, Aug. 16, 1955, Hoover, K. S. (A. B. Dick Co.).

[1088] U. S. 2,716,075, Aug. 23, 1955, Wiese, R. A. (U. S. Atomic Energy Comm.).

[1089] Can. 516,510, Sept. 13, 1955, Brooks, R. E., and Smook, M. A. (E. I. duPont de Nemours and Co.).

[1090] U. S. 2,717,888, Sept. 13, 1955, Feller, M., and Field, E. (Standard Oil Co. of Indiana).

[1091] U. S. 2,717,889, Sept. 13, 1955, Feller, M., and Field, E. (Standard Oil Co. of Indiana).

[1092] U. S. 2,717,910, Sept. 13, 1955, Erchak, M. (Allied Chemical and Dye Corp.).

[1093] U. S. Re 24,062, Sept. 20, 1955, Horton, P. V. (Plax Corp.).

[1094] U. S. 2,718,473, Sept. 20, 1955, Powers, J. B. (Union Carbide and Carbon Corp.)

[1095] Ger. Pat. Appln. G 14015, Sept. 22, 1955, Osthoff, R. C., and Kantor, S. W. (General Electric Co.).

[1096] Ger. Pat. Appln. B 25064, Oct. 6, 1955 (Badische Anilin-u. Soda-Fabrik A.-G.).

[1097] U. S. 2,721,189, Oct. 18, 1955, Anderson, A. W., and Merckling, N. G. (E. I. duPont de Nemours and Co.).

[1098] Ger. Pat. Appln. B 30786, Oct. 20, 1955, Hirsekorn, B., and Fischer, H. (Badische Anilin-u. Soda-Fabrik A.-G.).

[1098a] U. S. 2,723,255, Nov. 8, 1955, Busse, W. F., and Smook, M. A. (E. I. duPont de Nemours and Co.).

[1099] U. S. 2,723,257, Nov. 8, 1955, McAlevy, A. (E. I. duPont de Nemours and Co.).

[1100] Brit. 740,054, Nov. 9, 1955, Montecatini.

[1101] Can. 518,479, Nov. 15, 1955, Heller, G. W. (E. I. duPont de Nemours and Co.).

[1102] Fr. 1,103,975, Nov. 15, 1955, Imperial Chemical Industries, Ltd.

[1103] U. S. 2,725,374, Nov. 29, 1955, Mosher, R. A. (Standard Oil Co. of Indiana).

[1104] U. S. 2,726,171, Dec. 6, 1955, Morf, M. (E. I. duPont de Nemours and Co.).

[1105] U. S. 2,726,204, Dec. 6, 1955, Park, H. F., and Bump, C. K. (Monsanto Chemical Co.).

[1105a] U. S. 2,726,218, Dec. 6, 1955, Arnold, H. R., and Herrick, E. C. (E. I. duPont de Nemours and Co.).

[1106] U. S. 2,726,231, Dec. 6, 1955, Field, E., and Feller, M. (Standard Oil Co. of Indiana).

[1107] U. S. 2,726,234, Dec. 6, 1955, Field, E., and Feller, M. (Standard Oil Co. of Indiana).

[1108] U. S. 2,727,023, Dec. 13, 1955, Evering, B. L., Roebuck, A. K., and Zletz, A. (Standard Oil Co. of Indiana).

[1110] U. S. 2,727,024, Dec. 13, 1955, Field, E., and Feller, M. (Standard Oil Co. of Indiana).

[1111] U. S. 2,727,879, Dec. 20, 1955, Vincent, J. R. (E. I. duPont de Nemours and Co.).

[1112] U. S. 2,728,752, Dec. 27, 1955, Brown, H. C. (Standard Oil Co. of Indiana).

[1113] U. S. 2,728,753, Dec. 27, 1955, Russum, L. W., Hatch, R. L., and Weisemann, G. H. (Standard Oil Co. of Indiana).

[1114] U. S. 2,728,754, Dec. 27, 1955, Evering, B. L., and Peters, E. F. (Standard Oil Co. of Indiana).

[1115] U. S. 2,728,755, Dec. 27, 1955, Weisemann, G. H. (Standard Oil Co. of Indiana).

[1116] U. S. 2,728,756, Dec. 27, 1955, Friedlander, H. N. (Standard Oil Co. of Indiana).

[1117] U. S. 2,728,757, Dec. 27, 1955, Field, E., and Feller, M. (Standard Oil Co. of Indiana).

[1118] U. S. 2,728,758, Dec. 27, 1955, Field, E., and Feller, M. (Standard Oil Co. of Indiana).

[1119] *Business Week*, 75, Feb. 4, 1956.

[1120] *Chem. Eng. News*, **34**, 1470 (1956).

[1120a] *Modern Plastics*, **33** (8), 39 (1956).

[1121] *Chem. Week*, **78**, 69 (Feb. 14, 1956).

[1121b] *Chem. Week*, **78**, 74 (March 24, 1956).

[1122] *Chem. Week*, **78**, 90 (Feb. 18, 1956).

[1122a] *Hercules Chemist*, No. 26, 4 (1956).

[1122b] *Ind. Laboratories*, **7** (4), 6 (1956).

[1123] *Plastics Ind.*, **14** (2), 8 (1956).

[1123a] *Plastics Ind.*, **14** (7), 34 (1956).

[1124] *Plastics News Letter*, **16** (5), 2 (1956).

[1124a] *Plastverarbeiter*, **7** (2), 71 (1956).

[1124b] *Plastics News Letter*, **16** (17), 1 (1956).

[1125] Arnold, J. W., *Soap and Chemical Specialties*, **32** (2), 121 (1956).

[1126] Ashby, G. E., Reitenour, J. S., and Hammer, C. F., paper presented at the 129th meeting of the American Chemical Society, Dallas, Tex., April 8–13, 1956.

[1127] Ballantine, D. S., Glines, A., Metz, D. J., Behr, I., Mesrobian, R. B., and Restaino, A. J., *J. Polymer Sci.*, **19**, 219 (1956).

[1128] Catsiff, E., Offenbach, J., and Tobolsky, A. V., *J. Colloid Sci.* **11**, 48 (1956).

[1128a] Clark, A., Hogan, J. P., Banks, R. L., and Lanning, W. C., paper presented at the 129th meeting of the American Chemical Society, Dallas, Tex., April 8–13, 1956.

[1129] Duch, E., and Küchler, L., *Z. Elektrochem.*, **60** (3), 218 (1953).

[1130] Edwards, D. C., *Rubber Age* (*N. Y.*), **78**, 550 (1956).

[1131] Goggin, W. C., Thayer, G. B., and Cheney, G. W., *Plastics Ind.*, **14** (1), 36 (1956).

[1132] Hercules Powder Co., *Hi-fax*, Bulletin, 1956.

[1133] Hines, R. A., Bryant, W. M. D., Larchar, A. W., and Pease, D. C., paper presented at the 129th meeting of the American Chemical Society, Dallas, Tex., April 8–13, 1956. See also references 901a and 1120a.

[1133a] Jones, R. V., and Boeke, P. J., paper presented at the 129th meeting of the American Chemical Society, Dallas, Tex., April 8-13, 1956.

[1134] Kaufman, H. S., and Kroncke, C. O., *Modern Plastics*, **33** (7), 167 (1956).

[1134a] Keane, J. J., Norris, F. H., and Stein, R. S., *J. Polymer Sci.*, **20**, 209 (1956).

[1135] Kovacs, A. J., *Industrie plastiques mod.* (*Paris*), **8**, 37 (1956).

[1135a] Miller, R. G. J., and Willis, H. A., *J. Polymer Sci.*, **19**, 485 (1956).

[1135b] Mills, J. M., *J. Polymer Sci.*, **19**, 585 (1956).

[1135c] Meikle, J. B., and Graham, B., *Electronics*, **29** (5), 147 (1956).

[1136] Muus, L. T., and Billmeyer, F. W., Jr., paper presented at the 129th meeting of the American Chemical Society, Dallas, Tex., April 8–13, 1956.

[1136a] Niven, C. D., *Can. J. Phys.*, **34** (4), 362 (1956).

[1137] Norris, F. H., and Stein, R. S., *Bull. Am. Phys. Soc.*, **1** (3), 109 (1956).

[1138] Peticolas, W. L., and Watkins, J. M., paper presented at the 129th meeting of the American Chemical Society, Dallas, Tex., April 8–13, 1956.

[1139] Rossmann, K., *J. Polymer Sci.*, **19**, 141 (1956).

[1140] Schildknecht, C. E., and Dunn, P. H., paper presented at the 129th meeting of the American Chemical Society, Dallas, Tex., April 8–13, 1956.

[1141] Slowinski, E. J., Jr., Walter, H., and Miller, R. L., *J. Polymer Sci.*, **19**, 353 (1956).

[1141a] Smith, D. C., paper presented at the 129th meeting at the American Chemical Society, Dallas, Tex., April 8–13, 1956.

[1141b] Supnik, R. H., and Adams, C. H., *Plastics Technol.*, **2**, 151 (1956).

[1141c] Szwarc, M., *J. Polymer Sci.*, **19**, 589 (1956).

[1141d] Tiedeman, W. D., *Modern Plastics*, **33** (8), 166 (1956).

[1142] Wilson, J. E., paper presented at the meeting of the North Jersey Section of the American Chemical Society, South Orange, N. J., Jan. 30, 1956.

[1142a] Wilton, P., and Marrow, F. D., *Plastics Technol.*, **2**, 158 (1956).

[1143] U. S. 2,729,608, Jan. 3, 1956, Strain, D. E. (E. I. duPont de Nemours and Co.).

[1144] Fr. 1,107,800, Jan. 5, 1956, Spécialitiés Alimentaires Bourguignonnes.

[1145] U. S. 2,731,452, Jan. 17, 1956, Field, E., and Feller, M. (Standard Oil Co. of Indiana).

[1146] U. S. 2,731,453, Jan. 17, 1956, Field, E., and Feller, M. (Standard Oil Co. of Indiana).

[1146a] U. S. 2,732,592, Jan. 31, 1956, Tunnicliff, E., and Barlow, R. (British Insulated Callender's Cables, Ltd.).

[1146b] Can. 521,294, Jan. 31, 1956, Hahn, O. M. (E. I. duPont de Nemours and Co.).

[1147] Fr. 1,109,864, Feb. 2, 1956, Jones, R. V., and Reynolds, W. B. (Phillips Petroleum Co.).

[1148] U. S. 2,734,039, Feb. 7, 1956, Peterson, L. C., and Batts, H. J. (United States Rubber Co.).

[1148a] Ger. Pat. Appln. R 13922, Feb. 9, 1956, Roelen, O., and Geiser, N.

[1148b] U. S. 2,737,461, March 6, 1956, Heisler, J. S., Heisler, A., and Starr, A. J.

[1149] U. S. 2,739,058, March 20, 1856, O'Flynn, D. J., and Pye, D. G. (E. I. duPont de Nemours and Co.).

[1150] Can. 522,921, March 20, 1956, Derksen, J. C., and Jacobs, F. M. (N. V. Philips' Gloeilampenfabrieken).

[1151] Can. 522,970, March 20, 1956, Zoubek, C. M. (Swift and Co.).

[1152] U. S. 2,739,975, March 27, 1956, Gearhart, W. M., and Crowley, J. D. (Eastman Kodak Co.).

AUTHOR INDEX

A

Acheson Industries, Inc., Acheson Dispersed Pigment Co., 402
Adams, C. H., 394
Adhesive Products Corp., 437
Aggarwal, S. L., 161
Aiken, W. H., 165
Alcock, T. C., 166
Alderson, W. L., Jr., 121, 136, 406
Alex, N. H., 280
Alexander, E., Jr., 468, 470, 471
Alexander, L. E., 161
Alfamine Corp., 417
All-American Aviation Corp., 419
Allen, P. C., 16
Allied Chemical and Dye Corp., 112, 237, 248–250, 355, 423, 460, 465, 483, 485
Alvarado, A. M., 423
Ambrose, E. J., 323
American Agile Corp., 356, 440, 485
American Cyanamid and Chemical Co., 81, 106
American Petroleum Institute, 21, 22
American Society for Testing Materials, 375, 381, 383, 387–389, 391, 392
American Viscose Company, 192, 415
Anchor Plastics Co., 485
Ander, P., 148
Anderson, A. W., 79
Anderson, L. C., 83, 85
Anderson, R. B., 4
Anfinsen, C., 381
Angel, T. H., 438
Arbeitsgemeinschaft für Olefinchemie, 16, 17
Archibald, F. M., 36
Armour Corp., 417
Arnett, L. M., 327
Arnold, H. R., 4, 126
Arnold, J. W., 286
Asboth, K., 36

Ashby, G. E., 188, 220, 229
Atkinson, J. V., 323
Atkinson, T. E., 410
Atlantic Refining Co., 68
Austen, A. E. W., 334, 335

B

Baccaredda, M., 255, 319, 321, 354, 355, 387
Bache, L. L., 415
Bacon, R. G. R., 63
Badische Anilin- und Soda-Fabrik A.-G., 54, 55, 60, 196, 356, 400, 408, 421, 441, 484, 485
Baird Associates, Inc., 37
Baird, W., 104
Baker, W. O., 184, 393
Baladin, A. A., 87
Ballantine, D. S., 86, 113, 138, 148, 153
Balwit, J. S., 143, 148
Bamberger, E., 1
Banigan, T. F., 440
Banks, R. L., 70, 71
Barb, W. G., 129
Barberio, J. R., 468
Barbezat, S., 175
Bardwell, D. C., 83, 85
Barker, E. F., 21
Barlow, R., 409
Barney, A. L., 126
Barrer, R. M., 269
Baskett, A. C., 153, 154, 201
N. V. de Bataafsche Petroleum Maatschappij, 57
Batts, H. J., 157
Bawn, C. E., 3
Bayer, O., 135
Baylis, J. R., 394
B. B. Chemical Co., 437
Beasley, J. K., 220, 229
Becker, G. W., 225

Freeth, F. A., 16, 434
Freund, E. H., 165
Frey, F. E., 85, 132
Friedlander, H. N., 63
Friedman, B. S., 118
Friedrich, M. E. P., 72
Frisch, H. L., 280
Frith, E. M., 306, 308
Fritz, J. C., 430
Fröhlich, H., 333
Frolich, G. J., 280
Frolich, P. K., 117
Frost, W., 39
Fuller, E. D., 416
Funahashi, H., 165
Fuoss, R. M., 191

G

Gagnon, P. E., 2, 228
Gale, A. J., 138
Gallaway, W. S., 21
Gamble, E., 269
Gatos, H. C., 237
Gatovskaya, T. V., 183
Gaube, E., 178, 233, 364, 368
Gearhart, W. M., 356
Gee, G., 39, 252
Geiser, N., 365
Geldermans, M., 21
Gellert, H. G., 37, 74–77
Gelsenkirchener Bergwerks A.-G., 17
Gemmer, E., 428, 430
General Aniline and Film Co., 57, 116, 117
General Electric Company, 3, 143, 357, 358, 438, 440, 485
General Mills Corp., 394
Gering Products, Inc., 485
Gerlich, H., 441
Gianotta, C. R., 382
Gibson, R. O., 6, 61, 411
van Gilder, C. F., 405
Gilmour, B. C., 401
Glines, A., 113
Glint, C. F., 426
Goebel, S., 55, 57, 116, 117
Goggin, W. C., 364
Gohn, G. R., 345
Goldberg, B., 430

Goldrick, R. M., 416
Gomm, A. S., 423
Goodrich-Gulf Co., 17
Goodwin, P. A., 356, 440
Goodwin, W. J., 407
Gowing, D. M., 464
Grace & Co.–Farbwerke Hoechst A.-G., 484
Graham, B., 441
Grams, E., 178, 233, 364, 368
Gray, H. W., 104
Great Britain
    Atomic Energy Authority, 357
    Atomic Energy Research Establishment
        Harwell, 138
Greenewalt, C. H., 36
Gribbins, M. F., 104
Griffiths, F. T., 409
Grindlay, J. H., 468, 470, 471
de Groot, S. R., 21
Grumer, M. E., 23

H

Habeeb, H., 82
Habgood, B. J., 402, 405
Hagenbach, W. P., 23
Hahn, F. C., 252, 298, 319, 328, 329, 341, 342
Hahn, O. M., 421
Hahn, W., 6
Haim, W. G., 397
Haine, W. A., 266, 399, 412, 413
Hainer, R. M., 323
Hall, D. S., 29
Hammer, C. F., 188, 220, 229
Hancock, D. C., 460
Hancock, N. H., 141, 150
Hancock, T., 401
Haney, R. A. D., 36
Hanford, W. E., 51, 52, 54, 63, 66, 72, 109–112, 116, 119, 122–125, 127, 130, 133
Happoldt, W. B., Jr., 155, 407
Hardy, P. E., 155
Harmon, J., 57
Harney, W. C., 405
Harper, F. R., 471
Harris, I., 3, 188, 190, 195, 196

Johnson, E. C., 437
Johnston, F. L., 421, 422
Jolivet, P., 86
Jolly, R. E., 383
Jones, A. V., 323
Jones, F. S. B., 134
Jones, R. V., 157, 364
Jones, S. T., 138
Jordan, M. E., 402
Joris, G. G., 82
Jovitschitsch, M. Z., 86
Joyce, R. M., Jr., 63, 96, 111, 112
Jungers, J. C., 82
Junk, W. A., 23

K

Kammermeyer, K., 281
Kantor, S. W., 3, 382
Kaplan, E., 283
Karam, H. J., 384
Kargin, V. A., 183
Kaufman, H. S., 176, 382
Keane, J. J., 388
Keeley, F. W., 362, 445
Keeling, C. D., 144, 147, 374
Keller, A., 169–171, 182, 388
Kellner, L., 323
Kellogg Co., M. W., 483
Kendall, Co., 416, 485
Kennaway, A., 401
Kennedy, R. B., 67
Kent, R. E., 137
Kerhoas, M., 434
Kern, K., 55
Kilpatrick, M. O., 29
King, G. W., 323
King, R. F., 354
Kinoshita, H., 95
Kirby, J. E., 4
Kirchof, A. C., 471
Kirk, R. E., 236
Kistiakowsky, G. B., 39
Kitchin, D. W., 266
Kitson, R. E., 186, 188
Kiyama, R., 95
Kein, J., 387
Klemm, J., 313, 384
Klevens, H. B., 324

Kline, D. E., 225
Klug, H. P., 161
Kobe, K. A., 19
Koch, H., 4
von Koch, A., 23
Kodama, S., 42, 44, 117
Kohle-Oel Chemie A.-G., 484
Koizumi, M., 67
Kolsky, H., 178
Konrad, W. A., 36
Koppers Company, Inc., 17, 364, 483, 485
Korschak, V. V., 39
Kortsch, W., 377
Kovacs, A. J., 177, 178, 306
Krase, N. W., 53, 64, 202, 203
Kratz, R. F., Jr., 366
Kraus, C. A., 72
Kraus, G., 351
Krause, A., 233, 364
Kreidl, W. H., 443, 444
Krimm, S., 181, 326
Kroncke, C. O., Jr., 382
Kropa, E. L., 16, 80, 81
Krupp, H., 38
Küchler, L., 193
Kume, T., 42

L

Laboratorie de Chimie Physique de la Faculté des Sciences de Paris, 113
Land, W. M., 412, 413
Lane, G., 441
Langdon, D. R., 464
Langkammerer, C. M., 130
Lanning, W. C., 70, 71
Lanz, H., 381
Lanzavecchia, G., 200
Larcher, A. W., 65, 234
Larson, A. T., 52, 53, 57, 64
Larson, N. R., 173, 304
Lasak, F. J., 438
Latham, G. H., 104, 404
Laufman, H., 468, 470
Lavers, C. G., 263, 379
Lawrence, W. L., 336
Lawson, W. D., 464
Lawton, E. J., 143, 148
Lee, G. P., 416

SUBJECT INDEX

A

Acetic acid, effect on physical properties of polyethylene, 238
  permeability of polyethylene, 282
Acetic anhydride, permeability of polyethylene, 282
  purification of ethylene with, 36
Acetone, effect on polyethylene, 251
  permeability of polyethylene, 282
  permeability of polyethylene versus vapor-pressure, 287
  polyethylene swelling index of, 239
Acetone–methylethyl ketone polyperoxide as catalyst for ethylene polymerization, 62
Acetophenone azine as catalyst for ethylene polymerization, 64
Acetyl chloride, permeability of polyethylene, 282
Acetylene, copolymerization with ethylene, 118
A-C Polyethylene, compatibility with various compounds, 249, 250
  resistance to liquid chemicals, 248
Acrylic esters, copolymerization with ethylene, 125
Acrylonitrile, copolymerization with ethylene, 116
  graft polymerization with polyethylene, 112–114
Activators in Ziegler catalysts, 76–77
Adhesion, effective, definition of term, 351–352
  of polyethylene, 351–352
  specific, definition of term, 351
Adhesives for bonding polyethylene, 437–438. See also *Bonding polyethylene to metals.*
Agilene, properties of (table), 356
Akroflex C as stabilizer for polyethylene, 98, 103–104

"Alfin" catalysts for ethylene polymerization, 71–72
Alkali metal-aluminum hydride–metal oxide as catalyst for ethylene polymerization, 70
Alkali metal borohydride–metal oxide as catalyst for ethylene polymerization, 70
Alkali metal hydride–metal oxide as catalyst for ethylene polymerization, 69–70
Alkali metal–metal oxide as catalyst for ethylene polymerization, 69
Alkaline earth metals as catalysts for ethylene polymerization, 68
Alkalis as catalysts for ethylene polymerization, 68
Alkathene HD, 234, 364, 485
Alkathenes, 102, 170, 234, 364, 460
Alkylene oxides, copolymerization with ethylene, 126
Alkyl hydroperoxides as catalysts for ethylene polymerization, 61
Alkyllithium compounds as catalysts for ethylene polymerization, 72
Alkyl radicals, polymerization of ethylene by, 82
Allyl alcohol, copolymerization with ethylene, 125
  permeability of polyethylene, 282
Allyl compounds, copolymerization with ethylene, 125
Alpha radiation, initiation of ethylene polymerization by, 83
Aluminum, effect on polymerization of ethylene, 66–67
Aluminum alkyls, reaction with ethylene, 74–76
Aluminum chloride as catalyst for ethylene polymerization, 60
Aluminum hydride, reactions with olefins, 74